Date Due

THIRST

Physiology of the Urge to Drink
and Problems of Water Lack

My strength is dried up like a potsherd; and my tongue cleaveth to my jaws; and thou hast brought me into the dust of death.

—P<small>SALMS</small>. XXII, 15

THIRST

Physiology of the Urge to Drink and Problems of Water Lack

By

A. V. WOLF, Ph.D.

Walter Reed Army Institute of Research
Walter Reed Army Medical Center
Washington, D. C.

CHARLES C THOMAS · PUBLISHER
Springfield · Illinois · U. S. A.

CHARLES C THOMAS • PUBLISHER
BANNERSTONE HOUSE
301–327 East Lawrence Avenue, Springfield, Illinois, U.S.A.

Published simultaneously in the British Commonwealth of Nations by
BLACKWELL SCIENTIFIC PUBLICATIONS, LTD., OXFORD, ENGLAND

Published simultaneously in Canada by
THE RYERSON PRESS, TORONTO

Library of Congress Catalog Card Number: 58-8437

Printed in the United States of America

PREFACE

A s ANYONE who attends to it soon finds out, the meaning of thirst shifts about. Clearly, a manifest urge to take water, which is sometimes referred to as thirst, may reflect something other than a sensation or percept. And problems which one thinks of as pertaining to thirst in man change gradually, as we go down the phyletic scale, becoming the different problems of drinking or more elementary kinds of water intake which are better described in terms of behavior, drive, or tropisms.

Definitions may be sharpened to fit the need, but it remains useful to regard thirst, drinking, and satiety as elements of a dipsologic triad, constituting by their sequence an iterative cycle of water metabolism. Our professed theme is thirst, but it is obviously neither possible nor desirable to refrain from considering the whole triad. Nor can we ignore the fact that in the realms of thirst lie the headwaters of the urine and the source of the extrarenal aqueous dissipations.

Although its roots lie deep in the most active issues of water metabolism, dipsology itself has been a neglected province of physiology and pathology. The purpose of this book (and its companion volume by J. H. Holmes, *Thirst: Clinical Pathology and Medical Aspects**) is to improve this situation by providing a store of physiologic and medical knowledge of thirst. Its pages necessarily treat of theory, experiment, observation, and lore, and of suffering, survival, and death. They consider practical problems of obtaining potable fluid from sea ice, fish, and cacti not less than the perplexing circumstances of Buridan's Ass. A few unorthodox matters, such as "volume regulation," have also seemed properly to merit inclusion in a comprehensive syntax. In all, I have tried to place a great many subjects in such order and deal with them in such ways as has seemed worthwhile.

It has been my good fortune to have had the indispensable aid

---

* To be published (Charles C Thomas, Publisher).

of interested individuals in the preparation of this monograph. I am grateful to Mrs. Phoebe G. Prentiss who deftly managed its bulks of bibliographic detail when she was not translating and paraphrasing some of the dusty but necessary Latin archives; to Mrs. Lillian G. Douglas for her careful help in checking the manuscript; to Mr. Edward M. Khouri who drew many of the figures for this work and translated some of the French quotations; and to Mrs. Donald E. Gregg for translating those works required from the Italian. I am indebted also to Captain R. A. Phillips, USN, who provided valuable information about persons and projects connected with the question of drinking sea water and to Dr. Stanley M. Levenson who refereed in certain matters of protein and energy metabolism. Not the least of my thanks is to Dr. John Lyman of the U. S. Navy Hydrographic Office for the scrupulosity of his advice about the intricacies of sea water composition, and for calling to my attention numerous and valuable narratives of the sea in which shipwreck survivors counted terrible thirst among their tribulations.

A. V. WOLF

Washington, D. C.

Contents

PART II

THIRST

Physiology of the Urge to Drink
and Problems of Water Lack

PART I

It is easy to obscure the relations among facts by translating them into imagery so alluring that fiction is taken for reality.

—EDWARD FREDERICK ADOLPH

CHAPTER I

SOME FUNDAMENTAL ASPECTS OF BODY FLUID

THE WATER content of mammals varies from 30% of the body weight, as in a fat pig (56), to over 95%, as in a human embryo (719). In general, young animals contain more water than old ones, and drying out with age can be represented by a curve (562, 572, Fig. 1). The lower percentage water content of the adult is related to the greater rigidity and tensile strength of mature tissues (6) as well as to a relative increase in the amount of body fat with age.

Gentle heating in air is the oldest practical method for determining water content. To this end, early investigators desiccated animals or cadavers, whole or in parts, in ovens. Bezold (94) found a human fetus to contain 87.5% water; Bischoff (102) measured 66.4% in a newborn girl. Other things being equal, the more fat in the body the less water percentagewise (612). This fact underlies the curious observation that some animals, e.g., rats, deprived of water or water and food (57, 626, 689, 869, 874), contain almost the same amount of water (expressed as a per cent of body weight) at death as do normal animals (p. 210). Water loss in rats is therefore approximately proportional to weight loss, and the "constant" of proportionality is the fraction of water in the body.

The composition of animals is often compared on a fat-free basis, being less variable thereby. On such a basis, a rat is about 72% water (64); an adult human being, 70 to 73% (525, 719). At "chemical maturity" the rate of change in water content and in

5

ash or protein suddenly decreases (Fig. 1), and nearly constant composition obtains thereafter. Nevertheless, in man, at least, water content continues to fall with age (219, 718). Mammals vary in composition at birth, those relatively mature physically having a low water content and those less physically mature having a high content. Chemical maturity is reached at different ages but these are a fairly constant relative part of the total life span (ca. 4.5%) according to Moulton (562).

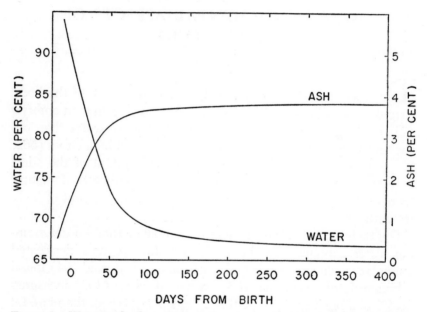

Figure 1. Water and ash content of the rat as a function of age. Chemical maturity is attained as curves level off. After Needham (572).

Newer techniques for determining body water employ dilution of administered loads of various materials such as heavy water, urea, antipyrine, or salt, as well as vacuum drying of the carcass (530, 680, 746, 747, 874). Subdivisions of the body water, i.e., extracellular, plasma, or intracellular water are also estimated by dilution techniques, using test substances with appropriate volumes of distribution. A full term infant contains 70 to 83% water (219, 230, 272, 719), 65% of which is extracellular (888).

The adult contains 50 to 60% water (558), of which perhaps 40% is extracellular. Thus, almost half of the infant's body weight is extracellular water, while only a fifth is so localized in the adult.

A considerable mass of water may be located within the lumen of the gut. In the rabbit, intraluminal fluid is 15% of the total body water; in the rat, 7%; guinea pig, 17 to 20%; and dog, 6 to 10% (171). An estimate of gastrointestinal water in post mortem man is 1.5%, but this may not represent the living state (300). Depending on the extent to which this transcellular water, along with that of cerebrospinal fluid, bile, synovial sacs, and glandular lumina (220), is available for the dilution of a test material used to determine a volume of distribution, the value assigned to the body water compartments will vary.[1]

Water is no less essential for growth than food (446, 447). Rats about one month old can be held at constant weight for several weeks by restricting the amount of liquid in a diet otherwise adequate for growth. The amount of food consumed under such conditions may exceed that required for maintenance when water is allowed ad libitum. Growth tendencies of various organs in

---

[1] Since most substances presently used to measure extracellular fluid by dilution do not readily enter transcellular water, the latter tends to be included in estimates of cellular water (by difference of total water and "extracellular" water). Confusion arises from the ineptness of the term "extracellular." When used in connection with the chloride or sodium space of a muscle (253) its meaning is reasonably definite; when applied to the body as a whole with its multifarious transcellular water pockets, and particularly in the presence of massive edema and/or ascites, its semantic deficiencies become apparent. The usual intent in measuring extracellular fluid is to measure interstitial (intercellular) fluid plus that of the circulatory and lymphatic systems. Although the plasma and cerebrospinal fluids are, by definition, equally "extracellular," they differ in that so-called extracellular "tracers" pass into the former freely; not so freely into the latter.

Transcellular fluid—and, to a degree, ascites—thus behaves in some ways as a dead space. If we define it operationally as that volume of (truly) extracellular fluid which, in effect, is not available to dilute our test material, then the remainder of the extracellular fluid might be called "ciscellular" (868). If transcellular corresponds to respiratory dead space, ciscellular corresponds to alveolar volume; extracellular to tidal volume.

Ciscellular fluid includes ideally only interstitial and plasma water, but includes practically any other noncellular fluid which, in effect, is a volume of distribution of an "extracellular" test substance. Some transcellular fluid tends to pass into ciscellular spaces in response to elevated effective osmotic pressures in the latter regions and, to this extent, behaves functionally as if it were cellular fluid.

such animals correspond in general to those found in rats of similar age during underfeeding.

Both basal oxygen consumption and intracellular (or total) water in adult man diminish with age but their ratio remains constant, suggesting that intracellular (or total) water may be an index of the amount of functioning protoplasm (718). However, although the water content of the brain generally falls with time from early life through most of the life span, a gradual percentual increase of brain water is observed in old age (366).

WATER INTAKE AND OUTPUT

When no factors shift the apparent water balance itself, the water content of the organism is maintained within narrow, characteristic limits. In man this amounts to ±0.22% of the body weight in 24 hour periods (9). Ordinarily, when a man or a dog loses water, about 0.5 and usually less than 1% of his body weight, he seeks to drink, thereby replacing at least part of his loss. Losses of water in urine and through lungs and skin go on continuously, unlike the gains by drinking which are interrupted. When a sufficient period of time is chosen, one may formulate for practical purposes the "balance" of water. Balance is defined either as intake minus output, gain minus loss, or rate of gain minus rate of loss. When the difference is zero (Table I), the organism is in zero water balance or, simply, in water balance; if gain exceeds loss, the balance is positive; if loss exceeds gain, the balance is negative (Fig. 4).

The ratio of gain to loss has been called the *economy quotient.* In water deficit, the economy quotient expresses a recovery response and is greater than 1; in water excess, it is less than 1. Its magnitude is a function of water load.

Water balance is not independent of other balances such as salts and nutrients, or heat. If a man drinks an excess of pure water steadily, but not too rapidly, his initial positive balance turns in a few hours into a negative one as urine flow gradually increases until it exceeds intake. This negative water balance leads to absolute dehydration (852, 853), a phenomenon apparently related to the loss from the body of urinary salts. A similar result obtains for individuals working in humid heat who lose water and salt in sweat. Ordinarily, and on a daily basis, water taken under the guidance of thirst provides a generous facultative margin (Table I) over obligatory water loss (278) but under these conditions, and in lesser time periods, men do not drink enough water voluntarily to replace their loss. Thirst does not appear until a considerable water deficit develops, and may fail completely as an index of need (80, 229).

TABLE I

A rounded off, 24 hour water balance statement for normal man at 15° C. and 40% relative humidity, based upon a particular 3000 Calorie diet and energy expenditure. The diet contained 98.8 grams of protein, 163.3 grams of fat, and 294.3 grams of carbohydrate, yielding 377.6 grams of oxidative and 755.6 grams of preformed water in "solid" food (1910.8 grams of preformed water if fluid foods such as orange juice, milk, etc., had been considered). The pulmonary water loss, based upon the assumptions that oxygen extraction in the lungs is 6%, that expired air is saturated at 35° C., and based upon those metabolic constants found on page 353, was 371 grams.

	Water Intake (grams)		Water Output (grams)		
	Obligatory	Facultative	Obligatory	Facultative	
Drink	650	1000	700	1000	Urine
Preformed	750		500		Skin
Oxidative	350		400		Lungs
			150		Feces
Subtotals	1750	1000	1750	1000	Subtotals
Total	2750		2750		Total

Actually, such *voluntary dehydration* (12, 18, 20, 386, Fig. 16, pp. 151, 224) is common. Rats, rabbits, mice, cats, guinea pigs, and men in dry heat, with water available ad libitum, do not drink as rapidly as they lose water. In men, voluntary dehydration becomes increasingly evident as water deficits exceed 2% of the body weight. Dogs maintain water balance more effectively but will not make up at one draft deficits exceeding 9% of the body weight (p. 160).

A man or dog deprived of water in a hot climate suffers "dehydration exhaustion," a condition thought to represent a circulation deficient from decrease of blood volume. The blood appears to lose, relatively, two to three times as much of its volume as the body as a whole. The dehydrated individual is intolerant of high ambient temperatures because of the failure of the circulation to carry heat to the surface for dissipation. Even in moderate dehydration of 2 to 4% of the body weight, the heart rate increases, especially in the standing man, deep body temperature usually rises, overbreathing may develop, and exhaustion is manifest by inability to work for prolonged periods, mental instability, and depression (13).

Relations of Water Intake and Output

By means of heterogonic analysis (p. 186), Adolph (9, 15) has generalized about water intake and output in mammals. Where i is water intake in grams per hour and B is body weight in grams, he finds

$$i = 0.010B^{0.88}.$$

Where u is urine flow in grams per hour,

$$u = 0.0064B^{0.82}.$$

A curious aspect of this relationship is the broad extent of its application to mammals ranging in size from mouse to elephant (Figs. 2 and 3). Adolph (9) concludes about mammalian species:

(1) Total intake is roughly proportional to $B^{0.9}$. (2) Maximal intake is nearly proportional to $B^{1.0}$. (3) Ordinary urinary output is proportional to $B^{0.8}$. (4) Maximal urinary output is nearly proportional to $B^{0.8}$. (5) The ratio of ordinary total intake (or equal output) to urinary output, ranges from 2 for small species to 5 for large ones. (6) The maximal urinary rates equal 20 to 32 times the ordinary rates, the augmentation ratio being less in small animals which have turnovers already large in proportion to body weight. (7) Maximal intakes after hypophyseal injuries, and maximal outputs after water ingestion are nearly equal. (8) Maximal intake rates equal 5 to 17 times the turnover rates (= augmentation ratios).

Heterogonic equations are frankly empirical. Yet they may be more exact than certain relations derived on theoretic or doctrinaire grounds. For example, there is the supposition that water

TABLE II

Water intake in several species of mammals. After (9).

Quantity Measured	Units	Rat	Rabbit	Dog	Man	Burro	Bovine	Elephant
Mean water intake	g./day	35	325	740	2,200	5,000	45,600	149,000
	% of body wt./day	15.7	11.0	4.6	3.1	5.1	6.1	4.0
Maximal water intake (hypophyseal injury)	g./day	232	...	9,200	35,600	...	...	...
	% of body wt./day	107	...	67	94	...	...	...
Augmentation ratio (Maximal/mean)	In hypophyseal injury	7	...	10	22	...	...	...
	After desiccation (1st hr.)	16	13	32	19	2.4	...	...
	In hot atmosphere (daily)	...	...	9	6	...	...	...
Frequency of drafts	Mean no./day	10	...	9	5	...	5	...
	Maximal no./day	...	...	15	8	...	11	...
Maximal draft	g./draft	2	103	1,800	1,200	12,200	27,000	86,500
	% of body wt./draft	1.0	3.5	10.3	1.8	12.6	3.6	2.4
	Minute/draft	2	2	3	2	5	...	7
Frequency of gulps	Maximal no./minute	190; 300–420*	160	190	60	...	...	12
Maximal gulp	g./gulp	.005–0.01	0.4	4.8	30	...	...	6,610
	% of body wt./minute	0.005	0.14	0.02	0.04	...	...	0.18
Maximal swallowing	g./minute	1.5–1.8	70	730	1,800	2,200	...	16,800
	% of body wt./minute	0.8	2.3	4.2	2.2	2.2	...	0.5
Absorption rate	g./minute	0.4	...	7.2	31	...	...	...
	% of body wt./minute	0.18	...	0.07	0.05	...	...	...

* Obtained by electronic recording of "lap rate" (163, 364, 763). Frequency is more variable between individuals than in single individuals, and is relatively independent of state of dehydration (364).

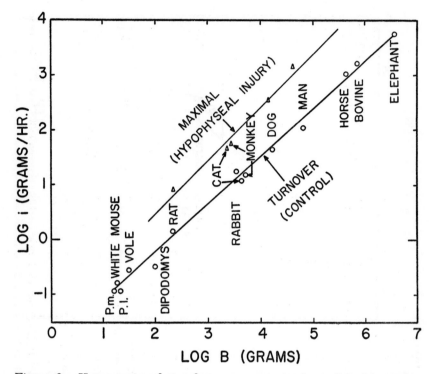

Figure 2.   Heterogonic relation between water intake and body weight. Log of total water intake, *i*, in relation to log of body weight, *B*, among diverse species of mammals.   Lower line, mean turnover rates in control condition, has heterogonic equation $i = 0.01B^{0.88}$; upper line, maximal rates after injuries of hypophysis, has equation $i = 0.033B^{0.97}$.   P. m. = *Peromyscus maniculatus*; P. l. = *Peromyscus leucopus*.   After Adolph (9).

loss through particular emunctories, or water intake, should be proportional to surface area or metabolic rate[2] (653, 781).   In the rat, water intake during fasting, unlike during free feeding, does not correlate significantly with either weight or skin area. No evidence supports a direct relation between water intake and weight or area; when either relation holds, it appears to depend upon food intake (723, 775).   Again, water and food intake measurements in rats made over 6 hour intervals for three days

---

[2] Adolph's convenient rule (6) that in mammals a liberal standard of total water intake is roughly 1 cc. per Calorie must be applied cautiously; thus, it does not hold for steers which generally consume relatively more water (470, Table II).

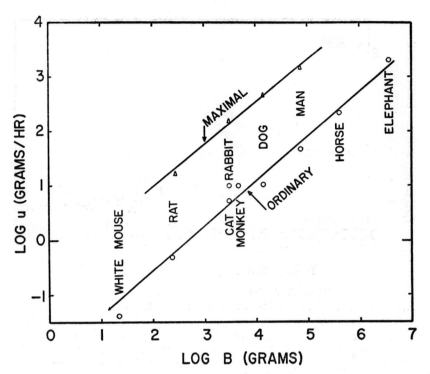

Figure 3. Heterogonic relation between urine flow and body weight. Log of urinary water output, *u*, in relation to log of body weight, *B*, among diverse species of mammals. "Ordinary" rates (lower line) are those of water balance; "maximal" rates (upper line) are those during continued forced administration of water by stomach. Heterogonic equations are $u = 0.0064B^{0.82}$ for ordinary rates and $u = 0.26B^{0.78}$ for maximal rates. After Adolph (9).

show that maximum intakes for both occur at night (in darkness); minima for both in the day (724, p. 125).

Another basic relation is that of water intake to water deficit. In general, the quantity of water drunk initially in response to water deficit increases with the size of the deficit (9, 722) although it may not be proportional to it (19). Use is made of such information to construct equilibration diagrams (Fig. 4) which describe water balance and characterize the forces activated under the stress of negative and positive water loads. However, newborn dog and rat pups do not drink in response to water deficit;

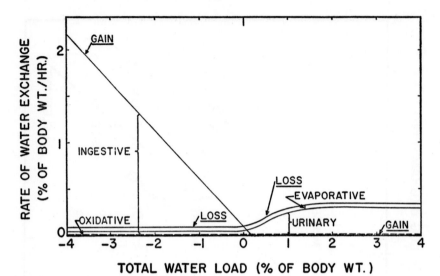

Figure 4.   Equilibration diagram for man.   Rate of water exchange in relation to water load during the first hour of recovery from water excesses or
deficits.   Total water loss equals urinary loss, plus 0.07% of the body weight
per hour as the mean evaporative + fecal loss at all positive loads, they
being taken as independent of water load.   Gain of oxidative water (0.02%
of body weight per hour) appears to be nearly independent of water load
whether positive or negative.   After Adolph (9).

the newborn will drink milk but regularly refuses water.   Ten
days later the thirst response is developing (17a).

As water intake under physiologic conditions correlates with
food intake (11, 135, 775, p. 110), so water output in the urine
correlates with metabolite (solute) output (107, 430).   Forbes
and Perley (264) presented a heterogonic analysis of the latter.
They showed that total sodium content of the body is proportional
to the 0.83 power of the body weight in infants and children, i.e.,
sodium content $= 0.281B^{0.83}$.   Since kidney weight happens also
to have the same power relation to body weight, i.e., kidney
weight $= 0.00892B^{0.83}$, it follows that the ratio, $0.281/0.00892 =$
31.5, is the number of milliequivalents of exchangeable sodium
(by isotopic dilution) supported by each gram of kidney tissue.
Nelson (574) observed that, of rats with free access to tap water
and 0.8% sodium chloride, the animals drinking the most salt had
the largest kidneys.

The output of water, of course, is highly correlated with its intake when water loads are positive. An excess of water taken by mouth, by rectum, or by vein leads to diuresis, a temporary increase in the urine flow, following a delay or latent period of 18 to 42 minutes. Adolph's rule (9) states that the time in hours, t, required to complete the diuretic response, is related to the water load, L_{H_2O} (in per cent of body weight), by the equation

$$t = 1.3 + L_{H_2O}$$

However, above 65° F. ("Corrected Effective Temperature") the duration of water diuresis decreases (412); and there is a decline in the magnitude of the diuresis. Above 93° F. there may be no increase in urine flow after ingestion of 1 liter of water. Moreover, very young animals and infants (522a) take longer to excrete test loads of water than do adults.

If fluid loads are eliminated more quickly than normal by the kidneys the condition is described as *tachyuria* (pp. 248, 456); if eliminated less quickly, it is called *bradyuria* (275, p. 267).

When water loads are negative, intake of water does not appreciably augment urine formation above the *obligatory urine volume,* that minimal volume compatible with the excretion of the solid material contained therein (857). This phenomenon provides the rationale for enjoining castaways with limited water supplies to refrain from drinking for the first 24 hours (where possible) lest water be wasted as *facultative urine* (p. 267, Table I). Curiously, there are indications that in extreme desiccation, even small (567), and certainly large (290) quantities of water drunk manifest themselves promptly in the urge to pass newly formed urine (655, 675).

FLUID TRANSLOCATION: OSMOTIC PRESSURE, TONICITY, FUGACITY

It is not possible to be wholly precise when defining terms in the area of osmotic pressure and related phenomena as there is not agreement between physical chemists and physiologists, and individuals in both groups have divergent opinions about proper usage.

A solution does not have any osmotic "pressure" in itself. What is called *the osmotic pressure denotes the hydrostatic pressure excess which would be produced in a solution if a semipermeable membrane (one permitting passage of solvent but not solute particles), rather than a permeable membrane, separated that solution in a manometric chamber of constant volume from its solvent, the latter at constant pressure.*

In this sense it is osmosis (or the tendency thereto) that produces the osmotic pressure (345), not osmotic pressure which produces osmosis (258). It may be undesirable, as some have maintained (169), to speak of the osmotic pressure of solutes or of solutions since such use implies that a property of solutes or of solutions is under consideration when, indeed, it is the properties of water (solvent) and the effects of dissolved substances on these properties of water which are under consideration. In practice, however, physiologists commonly reject the purist view and speak freely of the osmotic pressure of a solution. Bayliss (79) has elegantly described an attitude toward osmotic pressure becoming to a physiologist:

> It is, perhaps, well to make a few remarks with respect to the view held by some that osmotic pressure only exists in the presence of a semi-permeable membrane. If this is so, we are incorrect in speaking of the osmotic pressure of a solution under any circumstances except those in which it is separated from pure solvent by means of a membrane impermeable to solutes. When, therefore, that property of a solution which would cause it to show osmotic pressure under these special circumstances is determined by some other method, such as freezing point, another name must be used.
>
> It is clear that such a practice, although perhaps in agreement with the original meaning of osmosis as used by Dutrochet, would give rise to much inconvenience, and even confusion. We need a word to express the total concentration of a solution in such elements as act as molecules in the sense of Avogadro's law, since the molar concentration does not afford the information in the case of electrolytes and colloids. It seems to me that we are quite justified, even in theory, in speaking of the osmotic pressure of the blood, for example, without any reference, even in thought, to a semi-permeable membrane. We mean to express those properties conferred by the kinetic energy of the molecules, or elements equivalent

to them, of the solutes. In the presence of a semi-permeable membrane it would be shown as a definite pressure, capable of measurement by a manometer; but the phenomenon which causes this pressure is always there and leads to diffusion, amongst other things.

This denying of the existence of osmotic pressure except in relation to a membrane leads to the denial of its existence altogether, since we know of no perfect semi-permeable membrane.

No objection is made to the statement that the air in a vessel open to the atmosphere has a pressure of 760 mm. of mercury, although it is not to be detected unless the vessel is closed and provided with a manometer while the outer atmosphere is removed.

. . . . I shall continue to use the words "osmotic pressure," meaning thereby that property of solutions conferred upon them by the kinetic energy of the solutes.

The name "*tonicity*" is sometimes used, especially in reference to blood corpuscles and living cells in general, but it is not necessarily the same as osmotic pressure, unless we admit that the latter may vary according to the membrane used. For example, we say that a solution of sodium chloride is "isotonic" with mammalian blood corpuscles, because it produces no change in their volume. But we might add an equivalent amount of urea to this solution without making it less "isotonic" with the blood corpuscles, because their membrane is permeable to urea. On the other hand, its osmotic pressure is really doubled, as shown by vapour pressure measurements. The word "isotonic" can only be used when the nature of the particular membrane is specified, and refers only to those constituents of the solution to which the membrane is impermeable; osmotic pressure refers to the total concentration, assuming that the membrane is impermeable to all the solutes, permeable to the solvent.

Perhaps parts of Bayliss' account should now be modified (e.g., respecting the emphasis on the kinetic energy of the solutes (p. 19)), not only on technical and theoretic grounds but in the light of relatively recent experimental studies of "osmotic transients." Pappenheimer *et al.* (594) demonstrated that a substance like urea which penetrates certain biologic membranes relatively freely does not in fact do so as freely as water. An initial concentration gradient of urea across a membrane permeable to it tends to be dissipated exponentially. Nevertheless, whatever the gradient, urea manifests an effective osmotic pressure by governing the translocation of fluid, and the half-times of such osmotic transients for various substances are related inversely to their diffusion coefficients. In this sense, then, Bayliss' addition of urea to an isotonic saline *does* make it momentarily less isotonic, *viz.*, hypertonic, until no appreciable difference in urea concentration exists between cell water and ambient fluid. The brevity of the tonic effect of urea for many kinds of cells is one of its cardinal characteristics and constitutes a physiologic "invisibility" of the material which contrasts with its gross osmotic effects such as are detected in lowering of freezing point, etc.

There is less contrast between glucose and salt. Consider isosmotic solutions of glucose and sodium chloride (53 and 9.36 g./Kg. of water, respectively). If the glucose solution in a cellophane dialyzing bag, with attached manometer, is immersed in the saline, a passage of fluid into the bag is observed, i.e., the glucose, although isosmotic, behaves as if it were hypertonic (857). This osmotic system acts across a permeable, rather than a semipermeable, membrane which serves to stabilize the diffusion front and give expression to the different diffusion coefficients of the system. Salt diffuses into the bag more rapidly than glucose diffuses out,[3] producing an osmotic transient or temporary increase of total osmotic pressure within the bag. Eventually glucose and salt mix evenly on both sides of the cellophane and the osmotic and hydrostatic pressures become equal inside and outside of the bag.

It is of some importance to distinguish, at least for conventionally conceived "pore" membranes, two kinds of permeability which may be exemplified in terms of water. The osmotic flow discussed above is a flow in bulk in the same sense as filtration. On the other hand, a cellophane membrane might separate two water compartments, one of which had a high concentration of heavy water. At the same hydrostatic pressure, these fluids will not pass in bulk or by filtration across the membrane yet the heavy water will diffuse from where its concen-

---

[3] Indeed, chloride diffuses more rapidly than sodium, having a relative dialysance approximately one-third greater (876).

tration is high to where it is low, presumably exchanging almost molecule for molecule with ordinary water. Indeed, even if the hydrostatic pressure of the compartment with less concentrated heavy water were higher than the other so that filtration occurred into the one with the high concentration, heavy water could nevertheless pass against the bulk stream by diffusion.

The permeability of pore membranes to water is always greater for osmotic flow than for diffusion flow. Pappenheimer (593) treats this phenomenon by considering two membranes of the same thickness and the same cross-sectional pore area. In one membrane there is but a single pore; in the other, 10,000 pores. The rates of diffusion per unit activity gradient will be the same in the two cases. However, calculation shows that the membrane with the single pore will allow fluid to pass 10,000 times more rapidly per unit pressure difference than the one with 10,000 pores. In both cases hydrodynamic flow by a unit pressure difference will be over 1,000,000 times faster than flow by net diffusion. The equations of water transfer in both cases are identical in form but the numerical value of the permeability coefficients are different (793).

To the extent that mechanisms of osmosis and osmotic pressure are understood it may be stated that the cause of osmosis lies in the excess energy of the molecules of pure solvent over that of the solvent molecules in a solution (62). After osmosis has occurred so that a solution has become more dilute, the only way to return it to the original state is to add energy to the system either as heat to evaporate the solvent from the solution or as mechanical energy to filter off (squeeze out) the solvent (p 244). The energy causing entry of water into an osmometer is resident in the molecules of pure solvent, while the force represented in the hydrostatic or turgor pressure may be conceived as due to that energy of the solute particles transmitted to them from the entering solvent molecules. For arguments pertaining to the controversial "solvent" and "solute" pressure theories, the reader is referred to the monograph of Crafts, Currier, and Stocking (185) which offers a lucid, physiologically oriented account of osmotic pressure.

Osmotic pressure is a physicochemical concept. To the physical chemist it is merely a consequence of the tendency of two different liquid species, under the impulse of thermal agitation, to achieve a state of maximum disorder by any available path; it is thus related to entropy (361). Where it is possible to obtain a truly semipermeable membrane (as for large molecules) we may measure osmotic pressure in terms of the hydrostatic pressure developed in a suitable osmometer. For small particles such as crystalloids, this measurement cannot be precisely or simply effected because no truly semipermeable membranes for such particles are known (however, see p. 244); and the measurement of osmotic transients poses technical difficulties of its own.

Actually, osmotic pressure, where crystalloids are involved, is measured in terms of the so-called colligative properties of solutions, i.e., freezing point depression[4] or, less practically, vapor pressure lowering (solutions of the same vapor pressure are called *isopiestic*), and boiling point elevation. This fact is used by Chinard and Enns (170) to emphasize that osmotic pressure as experimentally determined is really a pressure difference, not an absolute pressure. However, except for didactic purposes, or in special fields such as capillary transudation or water movement and turgor in plants, where osmotic units are advantageously equated to those of hydrostatic pressure, the physiologist may have little use for osmotic pressure qua pressure. It is frequently more meaningful for him to employ the exactly proportional osmolality or even the osmosity (p. 342) which latter relates better to analytic concentrations of body fluid solutes.

In any case the physiologist is usually less concerned with osmotic pressure per se than with the *effective osmotic pressure*. The latter is for most (but not all) purposes approximated as a fraction of the total osmotic pressure, the fraction being the ratio of the number of dissolved particles unable to penetrate a membrane, to the total number of solute particles in a solution. The effective osmotic pressure or effective osmoticity is thus, for most purposes, synonymous with the physiologist's term *tonicity*, and is that part of the total osmotic pressure of a solution which governs

---

[4] Freezing point measurements offer a means of determining osmotic pressures at the freezing point. A singular characteristic of osmotic pressure among the other colligative properties is that *it is proportional to the absolute temperature* as well as to the number of dissolved particles. Accordingly it is corrected for temperature, when desired, as one might do for gas pressures following Boyle's law. Other kinds of temperature correction are given by Lewis (476).

the tendency of its solvent to pass across a boundary, usually a semipermeable membrane.

Whereas the physical chemist properly identifies and equates tonicity with total osmotic pressure, we have noted Bayliss' view that tonicity should not be discussed without reference to a given membrane. In this concept, accepted also by Heilbrunn (340), two solutions are isotonic only if, separated by a membrane, there is no net flow of fluid across the common boundary. If, through some metabolic process, a cell maintains an osmotic pressure difference between its fixed volume of contained fluid and its environment, the environment appears thereby to be isotonic while it may actually be hypo- or hyperosmotic. Solutions in which the volume of cells is maintained unchanged were once called isoplethechontic (621).

Heilbrunn discusses the sea urchin egg for which 0.53 M sodium chloride is isosmotic with its sea water environment and in which the egg volume remains the same as in sea water. Calcium chloride solution, 0.37 M, has almost the same freezing point as these solutions, but the egg shrinks when placed in it. Actually, 0.30 or 0.29 M calcium chloride is effectively isosmotic or isotonic with sea water, but the reason for this is not known.

Tonicity as a property of solutions with respect to membranes implies that the solutions in question are at the same hydrostatic pressure. We do not claim that plasma is hypo-, iso-, and also hypertonic to interstitial fluid merely because it may move in one direction or another through the endothelium, or not at all, at different places in the capillary as the blood pressure changes along the line of flow.

Again, in plant cells, where turgor pressure is more clearly a factor than in animal cells, osmotic pressure is the sum of the turgor pressure and the diffusion pressure deficit (185). The osmotic pressure excess of the cell contents at equilibrium with environing fluid is presumably equal to the turgor pressure. The addition of nonpermeating solute to the ambient fluid may result in a movement of fluid out of the cell (until turgor pressure fell appropriately) even though the osmotic pressure (freezing point depression) of the ambient fluid remains less than that of the cell

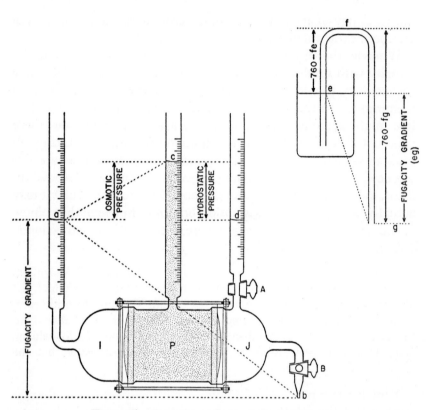

Figure 5.   Osmotic and atmospheric siphons.

Lower left: Osmometer-transfer cell has three chambers, I, P, and J. Solvent in I and J is separated from solution in P by semipermeable membranes which bulge outward because of the excess hydrostatic pressure in P. At equilibrium (stopcock A open, B closed), a and d are at the same level and the height of c above this measures the osmotic pressure of the solution.   Lowering the pressure in J by closing A and opening B upsets the balance between P and J so that fluid leaves P for J. This raises the concentration of solute and the osmotic pressure of P so that fluid enters P from I. Since level c remains higher than level a, the running of fluid "uphill" from I to P and "downhill" from P to J constitutes an osmotic siphon.   However, *although the hydrostatic pressure of P is greater than that of I, the fugacity of P is less than that of I.* Whatever may be the hydrostatic and osmotic pressures in this system, a fugacity gradient exists between *a* and *b*. In steady state, when fluid is added to I to replace loss, maintaining the level at a, it is seen how compartment P (plasma) may act as a conductor of fluid between two interstitia (I and J) at different fugacities (see Fig.

fluid, but the ambient fluid would be called hypertonic (not by the physical chemist) because it is associated with removal of cell fluid.

The least confusing path would be to accept, with the physical chemist, the identity of osmotic pressure and tonicity except that, physiologically speaking, we would not be advanced an iota in our description of fluid translocations across membranes. The effects of urea and salt on the volume of the cell may agree with theory when we correct for osmotic transients, but in practice the *rate* or time course of events is of the essence to the physiologist. *On the physiologist's usual time scale, urea behaves for many cells as if it contributed nothing to the osmotic pressure of solutions.*

A more comprehensive characterization of fluids in regard to their ability to cross membranes incorporates the effects of hydrostatic pressure and all other factors of fluid translocation. This is the *escaping tendency* (320) or the *fugacity* (134, 857), the tendency for fluid to leave a site.[5] Fluids, by definition, flow from regions of high fugacity to regions of low fugacity (Figs. 5, 6), and practical use has been made of this principle in various methods employed to relieve edema (857), including the "sump phenomenon" (678). An ambient solution (or the water therein) causing no net change in a cell's water content is called *isofugic;* if the cell loses fluid, the solution is hypofugic; if it gains, the solution is *hyperfugic.* Fugacity is thus identified operationally, and is clearly distinguished from osmoticity. Tonicity and its cognate,

---

[5] This definition, also, is at variance with that of the physical chemist.

---

6). Unlimited transfer of fluid may thus occur in steady states with no necessary or appreciable changes in the volume, osmotic pressure, or hydrostatic pressure of the plasma (857).

Upper right: In the atmospheric siphon fluid also runs "uphill" from *e* to *f* and "downhill" from *f* to *g*. The pressure pushing fluid from the reservoir, through the tube to the right, is atmospheric (760 mm. of mercury) less fe, i.e., 760 − fe; that pushing fluid through the tube to the left, toward the reservoir, is 760 − fg. Since fe is smaller than fg, 760 − fe is larger than 760 − fg and fluid leaves the reservoir along a fugacity gradient eg.

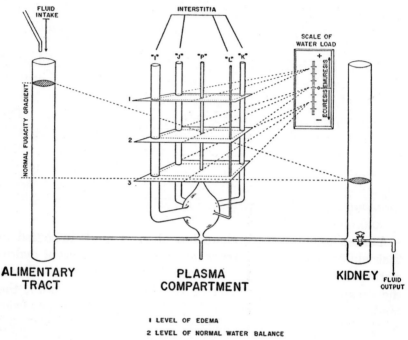

I LEVEL OF EDEMA
2 LEVEL OF NORMAL WATER BALANCE
3 LEVEL OF ABSOLUTE DEHYDRATION

Figure 6. Hydrodynamic model of fugacity in water balance. Where the
height of fluid symbolically measures fluid fugacity in a compartment (**alimentary tract, plasma, interstitia, kidney**), the diagram illustrates fugacity
gradients between gut and kidney. Water balance obtains whenever fluid
intake equals fluid output but this relation can exist at various water loads.
Zero water load (level 2) represents the normal water content of the body
or, more particularly here, of the plasma and the extracellular fluid. When,
in disease, the kidney reduces the normal rate of excretion of salt and water
(simulated by greater closure of the stopcock so that the level in **kidney**
rises), and when no substantial change of intake of these occurs, the fugacity gradient between gut and kidney becomes less than normal, the water
load becomes positive (emuresis), and a new water balance may be struck
at the level of edema (level 1).

If, as in diabetes insipidus, the fugacity of renal (preurinary) fluid falls
with respect to the plasma (simulated by opening the stopcock completely),
the fugacity gradient between gut and kidney is also increased and absolute
dehydration (negative water load, ecuresis) results (level 3) unless there
is compensatory increase in fluid intake. Reduction of fluid intake with no
change in stopcock also causes dehydration, but with diminution of fugacity gradients.

effective osmotic pressure, remain ambiguous except as they are defined in context.

For some purposes the *flux* is employed, a term defined as the amount of a substance which passes a unit area in unit time in a given direction (793). When the mode of penetration is unknown, the flux may be preferable to the permeability constant. Flux is one quantitative correlative of fugacity. There are others, one of which may be called a *transfer ratio*. It has been described how plasma acts as a conductor of fluid, between interstitial sites, at different fugacities (857, 858, 876). The transfer ratio is that of the volume of fluid translocated from or to a site through the plasma per unit time, to the volume of plasma (or blood) flowing through the site in question per unit time.

Glomerular filtration rate divided by plasma flow (i.e., the filtration fraction) is thus a transfer ratio. However, for the kidney as a whole, the transfer ratio is the ratio of the minute rate of urine flow to that of plasma flow which in a man might be $1/650 = 0.00153$. Similarly we may denote transfer ratios for saliva, sweat, bile, lymph, insensible perspiration, water of expired air, etc. If we take all water loss per day (e.g., three liters) and divide this by some average daily cardiac output, say, 10,000 liters per day, an over all transfer ratio might be 0.0003. Transfer ratios presumably have characteristic values in health and disease, and in altered physiologic states, and serve certain purposes of comparison.

PRESSURE-TENSION-RADIUS EQUILIBRIA

As we have noted, plant cells with heavy cellulose walls are capable of sustaining turgor pressures (from subatmospheric to 10 atmospheres) consistent with a substantial inequality of os-

---

The diagram suggests how interstitial fluid fugacities tend to equal that of the plasma at all levels of water balance. If fluid be introduced into any given interstitium, e.g., "I," raising the fugacity there, then fluid flows *through the plasma compartment*, "P," (see Fig. 5) until the fluid in all interstitia ("I," "J," "K," "L") and the plasma again have the same fugacity. This fugacity, now being greater than normal, causes an increased flow of fluid to the kidney. The final fugacity gradient between **kidney** (preurinary fluid) and **fluid output** (urine) is not considered here.

motic pressures inside and outside of the cell (185). With animal membranes it is commonly supposed from their delicate appearance that osmotic pressures inside and out are equal. The direct measurement of osmotic pressures of cellular fluids is technically difficult; and indirect methods such as determining the freezing points of tissue homogenates and correcting for the relative volumes of cellular and extracellular fluid (180), or analysis of osmotic volumes of distribution (866), may not be decisive. In general, it appears as if cell fluids of many tissues are, in vivo, isosmotic with their ambient fluid (207).

Rieser (656) has directly measured hydrostatic pressures within the unfertilized eggs of the sea urchin (*Arbacia punctulata*), the starfish (*Asterias vulgaris*), and the annelid worm (*Chætopterus pergamentaceous*). Microinjected with sea water, the maximum hydrostatic pressure tolerated by the eggs at rupture was only of the order of 1/100 of an atmosphere (11.9 mm. of mercury).

Harvey (334, 335) measured the "tension at the surface" of the eggs of *Chætopterus* by means of the microscope-centrifuge, finding a maximal value of 0.33 to 1.3 dynes/cm. This value is calculated with the aid of physical information about the specific gravity of the egg and its phases and of the medium as, in the centrifugal field, and at the moment of rupture, the heavier (yolk) and lighter (oil) poles of the cell are pulled apart. If the stalk at the moment of rupture is regarded as homogeneous material, its breaking strength, calculated on a cross-sectional basis, is 5900 dynes/cm.^{2} This, like the surface tension, is an extremely small value which contrasts with the breaking strength of rubber at about 100 million dynes/cm.^{2} Apparently there is no very firm pellicle around these eggs. If the tension at the surface were greater than 50 dynes/cm., a maximal value for liquid-water interfaces, this would argue for an elastic membrane and not true "surface tension." *Arbacia* eggs have a tension of less than 0.2 dynes/cm. but the membrane of the fertilized *Nereis* egg is considerably greater than 24 times that of *Chætopterus*. In any case, pressures (P) and surface tensions (T) at all times are interrelated through the magnitude of the radius of curvature (r) of spherical cells in accord with Laplace's formula (p. 180), $2T/r = P$.

It is instructive to examine the tension which might be expected in a cell wall if the hydrostatic pressure within were required exactly to counterbalance a 5% osmotic pressure difference between cellular and extracellular fluid. At an extracellular fluid osmolality of 0.3, we have an osmotic pressure at 37° C. of 579 cm. of mercury, 5% of which is ca. 29 cm. of mercury. If the cell were spherical, $T = Pr/2$. In dynes/cm.,[2] $P = hdg$, where h is cm. of mercury, d is density of mercury, and g is 980 cm./sec.[2] Thus $P = 29 \times 13.5 \times 980 = 3.8 \times 10^5$. If $r = 4 \times 10^{-4}$ cm., $T = 76$ dynes/cm. or 0.078 g./cm.

If we assume that for some cells, such as the fresh water *Ameba,* the cellular fluid is hyperosmotic to its ambient fluid, the tension in the wall need not be that calculable from the above formula. The contractile vacuole, whose contents are presumably nearly isosmotic with environing fluid, provides a means of drawing off the fluid entering the cell, obviating the necessity for a counterbalancing turgor pressure. Pressure-tension relations of the vacuole itself are discussed on page 183.

Burton (146) presents some interesting calculations on pressure-tension-radius relations in small blood vessels. For a capillary with a mean pressure of 30 mm. of mercury and a radius of 4μ, the tension (hoop stress) in the wall of the vessel is calculated to be 0.016 g./cm. He observes that the breaking strength of a strip of "kleenex" tissue, 1 cm. wide, will be found to be about 50 g. weight, i.e., over 3000 as great as the maintenance tension required in a capillary wall. It is thus not so difficult to realize how a fragile capillary is able to sustain pressures as high as arterial, which are attained when an occlusion cuff blocks venous return. Since in a cylinder, $T = Pr$, the tension in the wall at any given pressure is directly proportional to the radius and the tension required at moderate pressure is remarkably small at minute radii.

The importance of pressure-tension-radius relations in cells lies, among other considerations, in the meaning these have for the hypothesis that cellular and extracellular fluid are in osmotic equilibrium. While it is often supposed that most cells of the body are in such equilibrium, it is not necessarily wise, as we have shown, to base such conjecture on the "common sense" notion that cells of delicate appearance cannot sustain considerable turgor pressures. However, calculations to this end do not prove

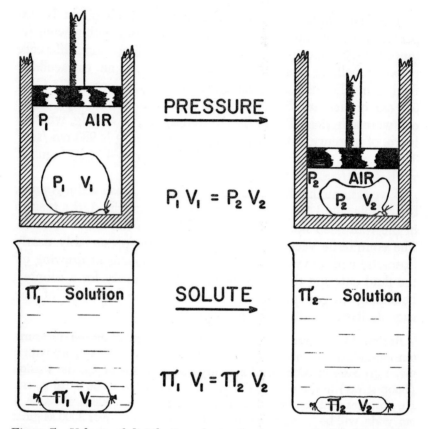

Figure 7. Volume of distribution of osmotic pressure. Boyle's law is illus-trated in the upper cylinder-piston diagrams. A flaccid balloon or bladder (which does not press appreciably on its contents) containing a volume of air, V_1, at pressure, P_1, is in a cylinder of air which, by Pascal's law, is also at P_1. Pushing the piston to halve the volume of the cylinder causes the air pressure to double, becoming P_2 within and without the balloon. The quan-tity of air in the balloon, proportional to P_1V_1, is unaffected by the pressure-volume change so that $P_1V_1 = P_2V_2$. Note that the *volume of distribution of pressure* is independent of the existence of the balloon which gained no air, i.e., P_2 is distributed evenly throughout the volume of the cylinder and would be the same were the balloon punctured or not even present.

The lower left beaker contains a solution of a single solute at an osmotic pressure, π_1. The concentration of this solute is equal within and without a semipermeable cellophane sac on the floor of the beaker so that osmotic equilibrium obtains with the sac at a volume V_1. The quantity of saccular solute is proportional to π_1V_1. By adding sufficient solute to the extrasaccular

that osmotic disequilibrium exists. The ameba with its contractile vacuole adumbrates a method, in theory, whereby cells could maintain hyperosmoticity and hypertonicity to their environment without turgor pressure.

The hypothesis of cellular hypertonicity with respect to extracellular fluid has been argued by Robinson (659–661). It holds that the cell fluid is actually hyperosmotic to extracellular fluid, that water continually enters the cell along the osmotic gradient, and that it is pumped out of the cell with an expenditure of aerobic metabolic energy. This, in a sense, invokes the operation of a semiinfinite number of semiinfinitesimal contractile vacuoles (p. 183).

There is a large literature on osmotic equilibrium which cannot be treated here. To sum it briefly, there is no decisive proof as to whether cells in the living animal are in osmotic equilibrium with extracellular fluid or in a steady state of water intake and output, or otherwise (866). For many practical purposes, however, the cells of the body in vivo behave as if they were osmometers, shrinking or expanding when subjected to appropriate osmotic stress. When they are studied in vitro, they may appear to behave differently (179, 180, 184, 207, 235, 324, 363, 530, 659, 660, 818, 849, 866, 873). It is also well to remember that cells which actually swell or shrink in strict obedience to osmotic stress may seem not to do so because of imperfect semipermeability of the cell membrane (134, 207).

Figure 7 illustrates one of the consequences of the osmometric behavior of body cells. When sodium chloride is taken into the

---

fluid we can bring about an osmotic shift of fluid from the sac until, at a new equilibrium, the osmotic pressure within and without doubles, becoming π_2; the saccular volume is halved to V_2 and $\pi_1 V_1 = \pi_2 V_2$. Note that the *volume of distribution of osmotic pressure* is independent of the existence of the cellophane sac which gained no solute, i.e., although solute did not enter the sac, π_2 is distributed evenly throughout the volume of fluid in the beaker and would be the same were the sac broken or not even present.

The volume of distribution of osmotic pressure, therefore, is equal to that of the total fluid of a perfect osmometric system and is given by the quotient of the osmotic load and the osmotic concentration increment. After Wolf (864).

body, it is confined substantially to the extracellular space. If the quantity administered is a radioactive microload, dividing the load by the concentration increment in plasma water yields a volume of distribution of sodium or chloride approximately equal to the extracellular fluid volume (25% of the body weight). With a macroload of ordinary salt, the concentration increment of sodium detectable by chemical analysis will, when divided into the load, yield a value approximating the total water of the body (60% of the body weight), i.e., the sodium behaves concentration-wise as if it were dissolved evenly throughout all the body water. The reason for the larger volume in the latter case is that water drawn osmotically from cells into the extracellular space dilutes not merely the loaded salt, but also the sodium and chloride initially present. Dilution of the extracellular sodium in this manner is largely responsible for decreasing the concentration increment of sodium so that the quotient of load to increment no longer has the magnitude of extracellular volume but rather that of total water. In the case of chloride, the quotient is perhaps 80% of total water (180, 530, 873). Basically, volumes of distribution of radioactive and ordinary sodium differ for this reason: there is so little radioactive sodium present initially that its contribution to the normal osmotic pressure of the body fluids is essentially zero; on the contrary, ordinary sodium (plus electroequivalent anion) contributes a high percentage of the effective osmotic pressure of the body fluid.

For reasons which are not entirely clear, the osmotic volume of distribution of sodium, whether determined by administering sodium chloride or sodium sulfate (530), appears closely to measure body water. To some extent empirically, therefore, it has been used as the basis for calculating or estimating by nomogram the volumes and concentrations of salt solutions required to erase sodium concentration deficits of the plasma (872).

The larger volumes of distribution which are calculated from macroloads and their concentration increments, where osmotic shifts of fluid from cells to extracellular space affect the results, are called "osmotic volumes of distribution" as opposed to "apparent volumes of distribution" found for radioactive or other tracer substances. If all of the sodium of the body were normally radio-active, the osmotic volume of distribution of even a tracer load of radioactive sodium would presumably equal total body water rather than extracellular or ciscellular fluid volume.

If one measures the osmotic pressure increment rather than the analytical (chemical) increment, when salt is administered, he does not in practice obtain total body water as theory would appear to indicate (Fig. 7) but, instead, a value perhaps 10% less called the "volume of distribution of osmotic pressure" of salt. This phenomenon has been attributed to idiogenic osmotic pressure supplied by the body cells in response to osmotic stress (530) but it could also reflect a hypertonicity of cellular fluid to extracellular fluid (866).

Some of the implications for thirst of subjects discussed in this chapter will be considered later; others must remain undeveloped in view of the paucity of relevant experimental studies.

> . . . . *it happens* . . . . *quite naturally that men who*
> *believe too firmly in their theories, do not believe enough*
> *in the theories of others.*
>
> —CLAUDE BERNARD

CHAPTER II

THIRST AND DRINKING

ALTHOUGH physiologic literature abounds with conjecture on the nature of thirst, relatively few accounts of the urge to drink can be considered thoroughly scientific. Nor is it surprising that the most influential ideas of the origin of thirst should have been of simple cast, colored introspectively. To some, a dry mouth and throat constituted a common denominator of the sensation— obviously; to others, thirst was clearly a general sensation. There are investigators who find no want of correlation between the intensity of thirst and the magnitude of cell water loss; but how, ask some, can thirst be anything but an expression of excitation in the central nervous system? Modern pluralistic physiologists never cease to remind us that thirst must reflect the interaction of multiple factors but they concatenate the factors according to their own lights and, combinatorial possibilities being what they are, no coherent theory of this kind has emerged.

FACTORS PREDISPOSING TO THIRST

To the extent they prove satisfactory, theories interrelate or clarify the significance of recognized factors in thirst or conditions predisposing to or enhancing the sensation. The following catalog includes most of the factors which have nominally taken the attention of writers on thirst in man. No significance beyond a measure of convenience attaches to their grouping.

I. Water Deprivation
   (a) Dryness of mouth and throat
   (b) Impoverishment of tissue water

II. Warmth (per se), Sweating

III. Nature of Food
   (a) Saltiness (55, 218, 780)
   (b) Sweetness (857)
   (c) Spiciness (218, 780)
   (d) Dryness (154)

IV. Air
   (a) Dryness, warmth
   (b) Talking, singing (154)
   (c) Smoking
   (d) Breathing through open mouth (sleeping or otherwise)

V. Activity or Occupation
   (a) Exertion
   (b) Pleasures of love (423, 673)

VI. Psychic Elements
   (a) Fear, anxiety (297, 780)
   (b) Suggestion[1] (auditory, visual, hypnotic (69))
   (c) Habit (154)
   (d) Dreams (673)

VII. State of Health or Disease
   (a) Constitution, idiosyncrasy, temperament (150, 206, 673, 780, 785)
   (b) Age, sex[2] (673, 780, 785)
   (c) Specific diseases (370a), e.g., diabetes, mushroom poisoning

---

[1] Reading about or listening to stories of the exigencies of thirst, or watching the play of clear, sparkling water induces in some individuals a desire to drink which would not otherwise have been manifest. It may be noted somewhat parenthetically that Achard and Ramond (3) coined the term "potomania" to emphasize the psychic factor in drinking and to distinguish such drinking from the "dipsomania" of diabetes insipidus.

[2] Thirst is less common in old age than in the young, being frequent in children, diminishing in adults, and becoming "rare" in old age. It has been alleged to be more frequent in women, perhaps because of habits (150, 206) but this is not confirmed (507).

VIII. Miscellaneous

(a) Bite of poisonous snakes[3] (55, 150) including true vipers (Viperidae) and pit vipers (Crotalidae)

(b) Strong alcoholic drinks

(c) Opium (216), atropine, epinephrine (208), metallic oxides, bitters, ethereal oils, drastic purgatives (150), diuretics

(d) X-irradiation (221, 582, 629, 732)

(e) Severe hemorrhage

(f) Alimentation (673)

(g) Lactation (154, 158, 176)

(h) Sorrows (780)

(i) ". . . . saltpeter and sulfur of the gunpowder getting into the mouth each time a man bites the cartridge." (748)

(j) Stimulation of the brain (thirst center)

(k) Inferior vena cava congestion

KINDS OF THEORIES OF THIRST

It is difficult to arrange historical conjectures about thirst in a fine taxonomic scheme. Few are distinct, sui generis. Basically similar conceptions may have had numerous expositors, in which case their tenets are likely to possess as many variants. Some writers have subscribed to more than one positive view; and some to none. It is easier to dispose of the latter. Magendie (508), who regarded hunger, thirst, a desire to urinate, respiration, and the venereal appetite as instinctive desires, remarked:

---

[3] Thirst is a recognized consequence of the bite of certain vipers or pit vipers. Aretæus, the Cappadocian (55), possibly contemporary with Galen, tells us of one of these, the serpent *dipsas*. "But if any one is bitten by the dipsas, the affection induced by the wound is of this nature; for the reptile, the dipsas, if it bite one, kindles up an unquenchable thirst. For they drink copiously, not as a remedy for the thirst, but so as to produce repletion of the bowels by the insatiable desire of drink. But if one be pained by the distension of the bowels and feel uncomfortable, and abstain from drink for a little, he again drinks copiously from thirst, and thus the evils alternate; for the thirst and the drink conspire together. Others do not pass urine, nor is there any relief from what is drank. Wherefore, what from insatiable thirst, an overflow of liquids, and distension of the belly, the patients have suddenly burst."

. . . . nor shall we presume to appoint to it [thirst] a place, either in the nerves of the pharynx, or in the sanguineous, or lymphatic vessels . . . . Thirst is an internal sensation, an instinctive sentiment, it is a result of organization, and does not admit of any explanation.

TABLE III

Range of average water requirement of children at different ages under ordinary conditions (719, 827).

Age	Average Body Weight (Kg.)	Total Water (cc./24 hours)	Total Water (cc./Kg./24 hours)
3 days	3.0	240–300	80–100
10 days	3.2	400–480	125–150
3 months	5.4	750–864	140–160
6 months	7.3	950–1,130	130–155
9 months	8.6	1,075–1,240	125–145
1 year	9.5	1,140–1,300	120–135
2 years	11.8	1,350–1,475	115–125
4 years	16.2	1,600–1,800	100–110
6 years	20.0	1,800–2,000	90–100
10 years	28.7	2,000–2,440	70–85
14 years	45.0	2,250–2,700	50–60
18 years	54.0	2,160–2,700	40–50

Coming from the 19th century pioneer in French experimental physiology, an early advocate of the mechanistic philosophy, this is an odd statement. It was not long in being challenged by Beaumont (81):

This sensation [thirst] is felt in the mouth and fauces. Like hunger, it is a kind provision of nature, designed to remind men and animals of the necessity, not of replenishing the wasting solids of the system, but of diluting the fluids that are carrying on these processes. Although Magendie has attempted to put a stop to all inquiries on this subject, in the remark, that "Thirst is an internal sensation, an instinctive sentiment"; "the result of organization, and does not admit of any explanation"; I apprehend a remote cause of this sensation may be found in the viscidity of the blood, which requires a liquid to render it more fluid, and more susceptible of introduction into the capillaries and secreting surfaces. The proximate cause may exist in an irritation, a kind of sub-inflammation of the mucous membranes of the mouth and fauces, the effect of the viscid state of the blood, and consequently impervious state of the secretory vessels of these membranes. The sensation of dryness, or thirst, is supposed to be the effect of evaporation, the mouth and throat being constantly exposed to the atmosphere. When there is sufficient fluidity of the blood, the secretion is so much more copious than the evaporation, that a constant moisture is preserved. The sensation of thirst resides in the tissues; and it is no more "an instinctive sentiment" than any other sensation of the economy. To say that it is the "result of organization," gives no explanation, amounts to nothing, and is certainly, to say the least, a very unsatisfactory way of disposing of the question.

In this chapter it is proposed first to remark the kinds of theories of thirst which have been proposed and then to consider further details. There are, of course, numerous general accounts which may serve similar purposes. Some are worthy for being rich in references to the less accessible literature, others as models of exposition of particular viewpoints, and still others simply as reviews. They include the following: Tancredi (780), Deneufbourg (206), Rullier (673), Callenfels (150), Tiedemann (785), Weber (811), Mayer (517), Wettendorff (823), Valenti (794, 795), Cannon (154, 155, 157, 158), Müller (563, 564, 565), Binet (97, 98), Bellows and Van Wagenen (85), Dill (208), Durig (218), Adolph and associates (18), Ladell (462), Strauss (771a), and Holmes (370a).

Adiposia, Oligoposia

There are sundry references in the literature (150, 494) to *adipsia* or a lack of thirst in man. E. Darwin wrote of it in his *Zoonomia* (201):

> Several of the inferior people, as farmers wives, have a habit of not drinking with their dinner at all, or only take a spoonful or two of ale after it.

And Magendie (508) stated:

> There are some persons who never perceive the sensation of thirst, who seem to drink merely to imitate others, but who are capable of living for a long time without thinking of it, or feeling any inconvenience from being deprived of it.

Bouffard (122) and Marchal (510) cited the case of a 22 year old girl who often went some months without drinking, and Blumenbach (111) repeats mention of the young woman who labored under:

> . . . . an anomalous nervous affection, and, excepting that on two occasions she swallowed some water, received no nourishment whatever for eight years.

Hutchinson (392) recounted the claims of a friend who, as a boy, was tormented by thirst but who, as an adult, had not known the sensation of thirst for 20 years. Of course, it was observed by the friend, he did drink coffee, wine, etc. for the effect of these beverages! As Darwin (201) noted, there are aberrations of thirst in that the desire may be diseased by indulgence in liquids grateful to the palate.

Fabre (247, 248) placed the matter in better perspective. He called people who rarely drink water as such, *oligopotes,* and the physiologic state, *oligopotism,* and recognized that these individuals get their water from food, soups, etc. His preference for terms using the root *pot* as against *dipsi* is well taken, since drinking rather than thirst is at issue. Reignier (643) cited the case of a woman given to a very dry diet who did not drink and who claimed the sensation of thirst was unknown to her. He described her, accordingly, as an *apote.*

The physician and naturalist, Erasmus Darwin, grandfather of Charles Darwin, had recognized evolution in animal forms. He held that transformations which they undergo are acquired partly by the individual's exertions in response to pleasures and pains, and are hereditary. And he saw thirst and hunger as pains or desires,[4] curiously connected by being situated at the upper and lower ends of the same canal (esophagus). The upper end of the gullet he supposed to become torpid and painful when there was a deficiency of aqueous fluid in the general system (201).

E. Darwin specified two kinds of thirst: *sitis calida* or warm thirst (due to loss of water in perspiration, fevers, evacuations, or to taking of salted foods); and *sitis frigida* or cold thirst (seen in dropsies and certain diseases such as diabetes).

---

[4] Cannon (156) also remarked how asphyxia of air hunger, discomfort of fatigue, and unpleasantness of confinement are all associated with an impulsive factor like hunger and thirst—a desire to get rid of a disturbing stimulus and to prolong or renew an agreeable one.

We may perceive in the foregoing as, indeed, in most concepts of thirst, significant and enriching threads of introspection and imagination. There is one orderly scientific account of the urge to drink, that of Boring (115), actually based on introspective analysis. He reported the personal reactions of a group of psychologists to their experiences with thirst (abstention from water for up to 50 hours), hunger, nausea, defecation, and urination, processes which, as he imagined, had their origin in the alimentary canal and urogenital system. Such accounts, he believed, were more reliable than the usual answers to a questionary for being written at the time of the experience by trained observers. From them he concluded that these organic processes were reducible under favorable conditions to various patterns of pressure and pain.

"Seat" and "Cause" of Thirst; Common Chemical Sense

A judiciously conceived duality in thirst is illustrated in the thesis of Deneufbourg (206) who cautioned against confusing the local sensation which urges us to drink with the general state which results from failure to drink. It is true, he stated, that these things ordinarily coincide in nature, but they are not necessarily related and the two may exist alone and independently. In disease, thirst may not exist as a sensation in the throat sufficient to care for the actual state of dehydration of the patient (pp. 9, 151, 224); and in some patients with polydipsia, there may be no reason to think that the general system is depleted of water. Deneufbourg held the "seat" of thirst to be in the back of the mouth yet he saw the "cause" in general depletion of body water. Not dissimilar positions about thirst have been taken by many writers, including Ludeman (494), Callenfels (150), Tiedemann (785), Weber (811), Schiff (679), Colin (176), Wettendorff (823), Cannon (154), Müller (564), Wolf (857), and Hamburger and Mathé (325).

Weber (811) extended the idea of the relation of dryness in pharyngeal and palatine membranes to thirst by supposing that were the conjunctivas not wet by lachrymal secretion, one might feel "thirst" in the eyes[5] as well. It is interesting to take this con-

---

[5] Even in severe dehydration lachrymation is still possible (p. 225).

ception together with that of the common chemical sense (552), which is restricted in man to the mouth and nasal cavities, the eyes, anus, reproductive openings, and any part where mucous membrane is exposed. A cut or scratch in the skin is similarly vulnerable to chemical irritant action. The feeling aroused by salt in wounds is not unlike the burning of certain kinds of thirst, and in another place (p. 84) we may note the case of a subject who, in a sense, became "thirsty" at both ends of his alimentary canal.

It cannot be suggested, however, even for lower animals, that thirst is simply a common chemical or osmotic sense. Against such an implication we may place the earthworm's negative de-hydrotropism (848), a turning away from surfaces which tend to dehydrate the epidermis. Perception of dehydrating surfaces in this animal, which some consider semi-aquatic, is quite dependent upon reception localized in the prostomium and not common to the rest of the worm's similarly exposed surface.

Esophageal Contractions

A somewhat unusual view of the origin of thirst was that of Müller (563, 564, 565). He proposed that that sensation was caused by a condition of tension of the deep pharyngeal and esophageal musculature, basing this contention on measurements which showed that the dog's esophagus contracts vigorously after 18 hours of water deprivation. Just as contractions of the stomach would indicate hunger so, he supposed, should the thirst sensation be caused by activity of the throat and esophagus.[6] He offered two further supporting considerations: his observation that young children, presumably unperplexed by scientific predicates, referred the thirst sensation to the region of the breastbone; and his suggestion of a logical co-adaptation of contractions at the both ends of the gastrointestinal tract, those of thirst at the one end, favoring intake, and those at the other which serve to evacuate excreta.

---

[6] The repetition of muscular movement in swallowing has also been considered a factor in satiety (p. 155).

Dill's objection (208) that Müller had not demonstrated the esophageal contractions to be primarily associated with thirst regardless of how it was produced, and that the latter's view could not otherwise be accepted, was sustained by Ladell (457) who measured esophageal activity in men during water privation. By means of small balloons placed in the esophagus and attached to pressure recording apparatus, Ladell found that in the normal state this organ was practically quiescent at the level of the arch of the aorta but was more active at each end, particularly near the diaphragm. In the aortic region there were occasional spontaneous contractions sometimes as powerful as in swallowing, but subjects were unconscious of these contractions. Records taken after 36 hours of water deprivation showed increased activity throughout the whole esophagus when the balloon was swallowed and for some time after. But this activity died out and the esophagus became quiescent after the subjects swallowed, dry or wet, a few times. These results appear to signify that the esophagus is irritable to the swallowing of the dry balloon, and irritability increased with the duration of water deprivation. Since quiescence always supervenes, Müller's belief that the esophagus is in continuous turbulent activity during thirst is not confirmed. Pressure changes and the speed of the wave of contraction accompanying swallowing are the same in both water debt and hydration.

Water of the Blood

Thirst has frequently been referred to a diminution of water in the blood. Dumas (216), whose experiments are cited in the older literature (206, 222, 673), introduced the conception that anything which deprives the blood of water thickens it and so produces thirst. He considered the paucity of the nutritive juices of the blood and their richness, or lack of water, as elements which, acting in the vascular system, provoked thirst by inflammatory irritation of the nervous system (brain). The cause of thirst lies, he stated, in the dominant action of the vascular system which, charged with heat and blood, produces some sort of inflammatory irritation manifested in redness of lips and tongue, dryness of throat, and fever. The cause of hunger, he held, lies in the lymphatics. After exhausting the nutritive materials, they exert on the very substance of the organs a sort of impotent suction, the stimulating effect of which, communicated to the nervous system, results in the sensation of hunger. Thus, hunger is determined by the lack of nutritive substances; thirst by their concentration.

Rullier (673) cites Orfila's toxicologic researches which necessitated the tying of the esophagus in dogs to prevent expulsion of administered poisons. Orfila discovered, by distilling the blood of such animals suffering prolonged abstinence from water, that the serous part was diminished, and he was led to appease the thirst in his dogs by injecting water into the jugular vein. Bichat (see 488, 673), in his course in physiology, had advanced the opinion, based on experiment, that intravenous water was as effective in relieving thirst as water by the usual route; and Dupuytren is said to have palliated thirst by injecting water, milk, skimmed milk, and diverse other liquids in this manner. Schiff (679) believed that thirst was a general sensation arising from a deficiency of water in the blood and remarked accordingly that Magendie relieved thirst in hydrophobia by injecting water intravenously. Bernard (89) appears to have been well acquainted with the antidipsic property of intravenous water (p. 59).

Ludwig (495) considered the thirst sensation to arise secondarily to a loss of water from the blood, when the per cent of water of the gums and throat membranes fell below a certain value. He, too, observed that water by vein or gut relieved thirst. Müller (564) also believed that a water-poor blood was a necessary condition for thirst. And Klippel (431) considered the thirst of Bright's disease to be *dyscrasic* or due to alteration in the blood, in distinction to compensatory, polyuric, or nervous classes of thirst.

Fiori-Ratti (260) attempted to correlate the gravimetrically determined percentage of water of the blood with the sensation of thirst arising in subjects at rest and eating dry and salty food. Except in one of his cases it could not be shown that a connection existed, nor could it be found that drinking 625 cc. of water had any significant effect on the water content of the blood. It should be remembered, however, that determination of the water content of whole blood is susceptible of considerably more technical error than the determination of the water content of the plasma. A diminution of plasma water in thirsting men has been reported by Rubini *et al.* (671).

A correlative measure of water in the blood is its osmotic pressure, and Mayer (515, 516, 517) showed that reduction of water intake resulted in an increased osmotic pressure (freezing point depression) of that fluid. However, he emphasized the primacy of elevated osmotic pressure, or hypertonicity, of the blood as the cause of thirst. Wettendorff (823) preferred to stress the concomitant hypertonicity of tissue fluids, but inevitably these ideas gave way to osmometric theories which emphasized the role of translocations of fluid, particularly cellular dehydration, in response to osmotic pressures, rather than osmotic pressure, per se.

Theories of Thirst: Classification

With Luciani (493) we can still classify theories of the origin of thirst in three broad categories: peripheral, general, and central. "Peripheral" denotes reference to local sensations arising in the mouth, throat, and neighboring parts, or perhaps in certain specified tissues or organs. It is distinguished from "general" which signifies an origin of sensation in unspecified deeper tissues, perhaps from all parts of the body (p. 46). As applied to sensation, general impulses would appear necessarily to originate at the periphery also, but the usage as indicated is not inconsistent historically. General theories have also been considered to represent combinations of peripheral and central theories—invoking afferent impulses from all parts of the body in conjunction with stimulation of the brain by the blood (161). Central theories place the origin of thirst in some part of the brain or central nervous system, perhaps as the result of direct stimulation of a thirst or drinking "center."

With due regard for its inherent limitations, and recognizing that it is not practical to hew closely to the outline, one may order theories of thirst as follows:

A. Instinctive Desire (Magendie)
B. Anhydremia
    1. Acting on mouth and throat (Beaumont, Ludwig, Colin, Luciani)

2. Acting on brain (Dumas, Müller)
3. Acting generally (Schiff)
C. Peripheral (Local) Origin
    1. "Dry mouth," etc. (Hippocrates, Tancredi, Haller, Deneuf-bourg, Luciani, Valenti, Cannon, Gregersen, Holmes)
    2. Esophageal contraction (Müller)
    3. Heart and lungs (Galen)
    4. Viscera (Aristotle)
D. General Origin
    1. General sensation
        a. Depletion of water (Schiff)
        b. Cellular dehydration (E. Bernard, Kerpel-Fronius, Gilman, Dill)
        c. Diffuse (Wettendorff, Luciani, Carlson)
    2. General need of water (Deneufbourg, C. Bernard, Longet, Meigs)
E. Elevated Osmotic Pressure of Blood (Mayer, Leschke, Nonnenbruch)
F. Osmometric
    1. Cellular dehydration (Wettendorff, Gilman, Dill)
    2. Central osmoreceptor (Wolf, Andersson)
G. Central
    1. Blood concentration (Dumas, Mayer, Leschke, Müller)
    2. Osmoreceptor (Wolf, Andersson)
    3. Association or conditioned reflex (Schiff, Wettendorff, Kourilsky, Wolf)
    4. Thirst hormones (Linazasoro, Adolph, Gilbert)
    5. Miscellaneous (Nothnagel, Voit, Bellows, Oehme, Kourilsky)
H. Multiple Factor (Bellows, Adolph, Stellar)

PERIPHERAL AND GENERAL THEORIES OF THIRST: LOCAL DRYNESS

In 1747[7] Haller (322) clearly stated what in recent times has come to be known as the "dry mouth" theory:

Thirst is seated in the tongue, fauces, oesophagus, and stomach. For whenever these very sensible parts, which are constantly and naturally moistened by mucous and salival juices, grow dry from

---

[7] See English translation (323) of 1779 and also Boring (116).

a deficiency of those or the like humours, or are irritated by a redundancy of muriatic or alkalescent salts here lodged, there arises a sense much more intolerable than the former [hunger], as thirst is more dangerous; whose uneasy sense continues until the proportion of diluting water in the blood, being recruited, restores the necessary moisture and free secretion required in the parts before mentioned. From hence we learn, why thirst attends labour, which exhales a greater proportion of the watery perspiration; and why it is a symptom of fevers where there is an obstruction of the exhaling vessels belonging to the tongue and fauces; why simple water is less efficacious in abating thirst, which yields nevertheless easily to some acid liquors, that not only moisten and render fluid, but also, by their mild irritation of the tongue and mouth, provoke forward the humours, and at the same time correct their putrid tendency.

It is difficult to say just how old the xerostomic conception must be (176). It was certainly held before Haller and is discussed in the *De Siti* of his contemporary, Jessen (400). Ludeman (494) attributed it to Hippocrates. After Haller, it is mentioned or supported by Bouffard (122), Fodéré (263), Blumenbach (111), Weber (811), Ludwig (495), Colin (176), Lepidi-Chioti and Fubini (472), Luciani (493), Valenti (794, 795), Cannon (153–158, 160, 310), Pack (589), Gregersen and co-workers (307, 308, 311, 373, 374) and others. Nevertheless the observation that thirst may exist when the mouth is wet is also old, and Ludeman in 1745 remarked that insatiable desire for drink, as in disease, should never be observed, as it is, considering how easy it is to moisten the fauces, by which act the desire for drink should be satisfied.

The specific "seat" of thirst is localized variably; and Callenfels (150) detailed various old arguments for assigning the seat of thirst to one region or another. Aristotle believed thirst to be kindled in the viscera, and Galen held it to be affected by the heart and lungs, according to Tancredi (780). Tancredi himself, Jessen (400), and Haller seated thirst in the tongue, fauces, esophagus, and stomach. Royer (669) cites P. Katz who emphasized the role of the tongue (p. 61). Weber (p. 38) considered even the conjunctiva as a potential thirst receptor. Ludwig (p. 41) specifically included the gums; Valenti (794), the esophagus and cardia; Aretæus (55) and Smith (733), the stomach; and Kanter (405) and Linazasoro *et al.* (482) have even tested the kidneys (p. 205). Generally, the mucous membranes of the mouth and throat are cited but, as Ladell (462) observes, thirst is an elusive sensation.

In 1821, before any considerable experimental evidence for various theories of thirst had been adduced, Rullier (673) had stated that the dry mouth theory and all other theories were unsatisfactory; and in 1947 Adolph and his associates (18) were compelled to observe in their *Physiology of Man in the Desert:*

> We have tried to make use of the current theories about the urge of thirst . . . . It can be concluded that in practice the theories regarding thirst have proven useless.

Oral Secretions: Salivary Glands

To the extent that thirst or its presumptive manifestation, drinking, is the reflection of an arid alimentary portal, it should be correlated with the activity of those glands in the mouth, particularly the salivary, which provide moistening. Early experiments are frequently noted in this regard. Thus, in 1852 Bidder and Schmidt (96) tied the salivary ducts in the dog, observing that only when the mouth was held closed were the mucous surfaces then kept moist. If a dog breathed through its mouth, drying of the membranes could hardly be prevented,[8] and they reported that the eagerness for water was thereby enormously increased so that the animal was always ready to drink. However, they gave no data on water intake. Against this report stands Fehr's (252), 10 years later, to the effect that extirpation of all salivary glands in the dog was without important consequences except that the animal takes somewhat more water, perhaps to make chewing and swallowing easier.

Austin and Steggerda (61) and Steggerda (759, 760) reported observations of thirst in a young man with congenital dysfunction of the salivary glands. Apparently this individual had been without salivary glands since earliest infancy; no ostia of Stensen's and Wharton's ducts could be found. The mucous membranes

---

[8] Breathing through the mouth ordinarily stimulates salivation reflexly (p. 50).

of his mouth were always dry although there was some mucinous secretion from gland cells along the inside of the cheeks and under the tongue. There was no amylolytic activity on starch paste from the mouth moisture and no iodide secretion, compared with controls (761). The record of this man's fluid intake over 18 days was not different from that of four normal subjects. Although he had learned to relieve his uncomfortable xerostomia by taking a few swallows of water (about 60 cc.) nearly every hour, he became "actually thirsty" about four times a day, taking then about 250 cc. Eating was made possible by drinking water throughout the meal and by avoiding dry foods. His taste thresholds for salt, sweet, acid (hydrochloric) and bitter (quinine) were essentially normal. Accordingly, the investigators concluded that salivary glands are not the sole factors governing thirst.

Zaus (891) reported the case of a 10 year old child with similar asialia in whom no excessive thirst was present.

Oral and Pharyngeal Anesthesia

Longet (488) maintained that thirst, like hunger, sex, sleep, and breathing, is a general need (for water) which is simply manifested by a special sensation.[9] He cut the glossopharyngeal and lingual nerves on both sides in dogs, and in some cases also the vagi, and found his animals to drink after meals as usual. Voit (800) observed that some branches of the vagus and the trigemini to the mouth and pharynx remained so that some sensation may have persisted, but he did not, as did Cannon (154), deny that Longet proved thirst to exist as a general feeling. Cannon argued that even if all of these nerves had been cut a dog might drink from the sight of fluid, or from habit, without the stimulation of a dry mouth, just as one may eat from the sight of food without the stimulus of hunger.

Actually, in dogs, Bellows and Van Wagenen (86) did com-

---

[9] See Magendie's view (508, p. 34). Meigs (541) has discoursed plainly about the general need. "Thirst does not mean that the mouth, or throat, or stomach, merely want water poured over or into them, but that the hand, the foot, the brain, the body and all its members, need water." Citing Bain, he noted that appetites are a select class of sensations defined as the uneasy feelings produced by the recurring wants of the organic system. Commonly recognized appetites are sleep, exercise, repose, thirst, hunger, and sex.

pletely cut the trigeminal nerves bilaterally in one animal with effect, it was believed, of abolishing all sensation except taste. In other animals, the gustatory sense was believed to have been abolished by bilateral section of the glossopharyngeals and chordae tympani. In still others, the olfactory sense was eliminated by division of the olfactory tracts. In no dogs was water drinking in normal amounts, or in the excessive amounts of diabetes insipidus, altered. They concluded that the urge to drink may not be identified with any one of the interrupted pathways or with any single one of the sensations they mediate.

As long ago as 1867, Schiff (679) had stated, in support of his view that thirst was a general sensation arising from a deficiency of water in the blood, that total pharyngeal anesthesia allows thirst to exist fully. As thirst is above all a general sensation, it is idle, he observed, to look for particular nerves which might mediate the sensation. He cited the lack of effect of cutting the glossopharyngeal and superior laryngeal nerves bilaterally in the cat, and also referred to Longet's dog studies in evidence. Pharyngeal sensation may thus be lacking, yet thirst be very lively.

However, Lepidi-Chioti and Fubini (472) studied a 17 year old boy with polyuria who, when prevented from drinking for several hours, was tormented by thirst referred to the back of his mouth and epigastrium. Brushing the back of his mouth with weak cocaine quickly eased the sensation for 15 to 35 minutes. If water instead of cocaine was used, thirst was relieved for 2 minutes only.

Valenti (794, 795) anesthetized the throat and upper esophagus in dogs with 6% cocaine and repeatedly observed their refusal to drink even after three to five days of water privation. He regarded it proved thereby that thirst had a local origin. From further experiments with cocainization of the isolated vagi, he concluded that the vagus was the pathway mediating thirst, although he supposed they might be replaced by other nerves (sympathetics) in a compensatory manner. Valenti called attention to the ancient observation that the chewing of coca leaves palliates hunger and thirst, and he ascribed this action to anesthesia in the digestive tract. He did not consider the direct effects of drug action on the central nervous system, however (p. 49).

Cannon (154) personally vouched for the thirst relieving property of a novocaine mouth rinse, but he was reporting an action
merely against the sensation arising in the mouth and throat from
atropinization (p. 62). Rowntree (667, 815) argued against
the local theory of thirst on the basis of his experience with a case
of diabetes insipidus in which local application of cocaine was
pushed to the point of constitutional toxicity and failed to decrease
water intake. Allison and Critchley (33) also found in two such
patients that painting the throat with 10% cocaine did not relieve
thirst. Moreover, Leschke (474) found novocainizing the throat
not to prevent the thirst resulting from hypertonic sodium chloride
given intravenously.

Since it is generally acknowledged that drinking is partially
dictated by sensations arising in the mouth, Adolph, Barker, and
Hoy (19) examined the effect of procainizing the mouths of dehydrated rats and offering them water, 0.4 osmolal sodium chloride, and 0.4 osmolal urea. In each case drinking followed the
same pattern as in unanesthetized animals. Although smaller
drinks were taken by anesthetized rats, especially in the initial
hour, these animals still differentiated among the three liquids.
If the same effects of cocaine and procaine obtain in rats as in
man, namely, that the tongue is anesthetized to pain and to bitter
taste but not to sweet, sour, or salt tastes, nor to heat, cold, or
pressure (367), differentiated drinking would be expected. In
any case, locally anesthetized rats did drink.

Drugs Affecting Salivary Flow and the Central Nervous System: Polypnea Secretion

Numerous studies of the local theory of thirst have been made
with drugs which affect salivary flow. Pack (589) reported that
while rabbits which had been deprived of it drank water when
offered, they did not do so if given 1% pilocarpine (0.5 cc./Kg.)
which stimulated salivation. Pilocarpine in rabbits causes increased hemoconcentration, even in dehydrated animals (792),
associated with profuse secretion of saliva and watery stools. Its
depressive side effects and the abdominal pain which it may produce in man (18) have been supposed to contribute to its apparent
antidipsic influence. Gregersen and Bloomberg obtained data re-

ported by Gregersen and Cannon (310), confirming Pack's experiment but they noted that rabbits injected with pilocarpine were more or less prostrated.

Early attempts to promote parasympathetic antidipticums (695, 846) such as cesol and others, failed to work out satisfactorily. Weir, Larson, and Rowntree (815) found pilocarpine to produce salivation[10] but no relief of thirst in patients with diabetes insipidus, but Allison and Critchley (33) reported allaying thirst by this means for 10 to 15 minutes and for 1 hour in two patients with this disease. Adolph *et al.* (18) discovered no consistent reduction in the desire for water or in the amount of water drunk by men suffering dehydration in the desert when pilocarpine was used to bring about increased salivation, although some men tested thought their thirst was lessened by the drug.

In rats, Adolph (14) observed as much salivation after 50 μg. of doryl (carbaminoylcholine) and after 0.5 mg. of pilocarpine, which did not inhibit drinking, as after larger doses of each that did suppress drinking. He regarded this as clear evidence that water intake is not diminished merely by having the throat flooded with saliva. And Kleitman (430) found subcutaneous pilocarpine in dogs to result usually in an increase in water intake on the day of injection. Aminophylline, caffeine, cortin (18), amphetamine (benzedrine) (18, 33), and olive oil (33) have been found not to be substantially antidipsic in man although cortin and amphetamine gave hints of beneficial action. Amphetamine, acting centrally, confers exhilaration without removing other signs of dehydration although some amelioration of thirst has been reported (243).[11] It may be helpful in sustaining one over the tiredness and irritability accompanying dehydration (240).

However, Andersson and Larsson (44) found in dogs that am-

---

[10] Pilocarpine, it should be noted, is not a true substitute for parasympathetic stimulation but merely possesses some of the properties of the parasympathetic chemical transmitter (65).

[11] Smoking is often recognized as contributing to thirst (218, 382a, 570, 786) but this is not necessarily so. So long as cigarettes lasted, according to Hedin (339), they had to some extent stilled the tortures of thirst in the bleak Taklamakan desert. Foster (267) spoke of circumstances among castaways in which smoking did not appear to increase thirst and was a factor in reviving spirits and giving comfort. Howard (382a) noted that most men queried about desert survival episodes said they were just too dry and cigarettes did not even seem desirable (p. 413).

phetamine does inhibit drinking following a potogenic intravenous injection of 20 cc. of 20% sodium chloride. This inhibitory effect is exerted or mediated at least in part from structures localized in the prefrontal areas of the cerebral cortex since it tends to be abolished after prefrontal lobotomy. Prefrontal lobotomy, per se, has no influence on the potogenic effect of sodium chloride, nor, primarily, on the ordinary water intake.

So-called antidipticums (adipsa) are numerous and varied (400). Camphor, spirits, ether, Hoffmann's anodyne, glycyrrhizin (peeled root of licorice), cocaine (chewing of coca leaves), and opium (754) (although Dumas (216) considered this to sharpen and increase thirst) are among the older drugs in this category.

Practices calculated to relieve thirst include placing in the mouth a pebble, twig (especially (168), a little peeled plug of the creosote or greasewood bush), coin, nail, button, or a piece of coal, gum, or hard candy ("lemon drops," lime "life-savers" (270)).

Hippocrates' four defenses against thirst (780): close mouth, keep silent, breathe cold air, take cold drinks.

M. F. Montgomery (555) extirpated all six salivary glands and two orbital glands of the dog and found no increase in daily average water intake. She concluded it improbable that the salivary glands play a major role in the thirst mechanism. However, the buccal mucosa remains in a healthy and remarkably moist condition in these animals. The quantity of secretion poured out by glands of buccal, pharyngeal, and nasal mucosa was measured in one dog with an esophageal fistula. Lying quietly, it produced 8.9 g. of extremely viscid mucous per hour; during sleep, 1 g. per hour. Pilocarpine (5 mg.) brought the level to 20 g. in the first half hour after injection. The responses of oral and pharyngeal mucous glands to pilocarpine, atropine, morphine, and epinephrine are, generally, similar to those of salivary glands (557) and related to a similar dual innervation of both groups of glands by cranial autonomic and sympathetic systems.

Montgomery (556) also found no substantial difference in water intake after pilocarpine between normal dogs and those deprived of salivary glands, again suggesting that whatever changes in water ingestion may occur after such drugs, they are caused by some other factor than drying or moistening of the mucous membranes of the mouth and pharynx by suppression of or increase in the salivary secretion. Repeated injections of small doses of atropine over a period of three days did not significantly alter the water intake of dogs with or without salivary glands, and large single doses (up to 20 mg.), similarly, did not affect the bi-hourly fluid intake of these animals.

Archdeacon *et al.* (53) injected dogs every other day with 0.3 mg. of atropine sulfate and, on alternate days, with isotonic sodium chloride. The atropine inhibited food ingestion. These experimenters suggested that salivary glands are not primary regulators of thirst because the ration of daily water drunk to dry food ingested in control intervals was disturbed but little by atropine (or by 1 mg. of pilocarpine).

Gregersen (306) examined quantitatively the reflex salivation in dogs which results from drying of the mouth. A warm atmosphere at constant temperature provides a uniform stimulation of salivary glands by inducing constant panting, constant drying of the mouth, and a constant flow of thin saliva which he called "polypnea secretion." In a room at 40° C., for example, on a normal water intake, polypnea secretion remains nearly the same from day to day, but after a dog has gone 24 hours without water it is often reduced to half the normal rate; after three days, to one-fifth the normal rate. To some extent, dehydrated dogs are reluctant to pant. Water deprivation actually raises the threshold of thermal stimulation of polypnea; so also does intravenous injection of hypertonic salt solution (212).

Considering the experiments of Montgomery above, purporting to show that salivary glands do not play a major role in thirst and that the membranes of her dogs' mouths were reasonably moist even without salivary secretion, Gregersen and Cannon (310) interpreted her results to indicate that conditions were not present to make the mouth dry and therefore the local dryness theory was, in fact, not properly tested. Utilizing the polypnea technique in dogs, they found that the amount of water taken during 1 or 2 hours of panting is increased after extirpation of the submaxillary, sublingual, and infraorbital glands, and tying of the parotid ducts.

They concluded that under conditions which actually make the mouth dry, a deficient salivary flow causes thirst and increased water intake even in the absence of bodily dehydration. Austin and Steggerda (61) raised the question whether these results may not have been due to the disturbing element of heat regulation. In the dog this depends in part on evaporation from mucous membranes of the mouth, and it is well known that significant interactions of heat and water regulating mechanisms exist (18, p. 170). On the other hand, Robinson and Adolph (658) found drinking in polypneic dogs not to be related to the rise of body temperature during heating.

Salivary glands are generally absent in aquatic amphibia, birds, and marine mammals such as whales;[12] but they are present in seals and their allies, and swifts produce a glandular secretion to hold the twigs of their nests together. In frogs and toads multicellular mucous glands appear in the mouth and posterior nasal passages. Many amphibians have an *intermaxillary gland* with a duct opening between the intermaxillary bones. Reptiles generally have *palatine, sublingual, premaxillary,* and *labial glands.* . . .

In mammals, three pairs of salivary glands are typically present. They are the *parotids, submaxillaries,* and *sublinguals.* Some mammals have *retrolinguals* near the base of the tongue, and ungulates have large *molar glands* which secrete a watery saliva which is mixed with forage before it is swallowed (59).

The Dry Mouth Theory

The question of aptyalia or xerostomia as the prime element of thirst always returns to deal with an abundance of subjective results. Cannon's plea for the dry mouth theory (154), detailed below, which has had more currency among dipsologists than the substance of its experimental support would warrant, was based quite largely on his personal experience with rather mild thirst and upon consonant testimony which he gleaned from the literature. At the time he first presented his dry mouth theory, in 1918, he had managed to find only the report of a single observer among

---

[12] The bottle-nose dolphin (*Tursiops truncatus*) produces a ropy saliva from glands of the "salivary" group which may contain chloride in higher concentration (120 to 170 mEq./L.) than in serum (256).

the group of psychologists studied by Boring (115, p. 38) to the effect that thirst was experienced while saliva flow was still copious. To reconcile it with his theory he was led to consider that this observation might have been in error. Although Schiff in 1867 had remarked that wetting of the throat does no more than momentarily relieve thirst (679), it is true that few observers up to 1918 had discoursed on this association of thirst and salivary flow. Subsequently, however, the situation altered radically, but Cannon's later writings did not reflect this; nor do those of Gregersen and Cizek (311) who argue for the xerostomic view of thirst.

In 1920 Müller (564) pointedly remarked, with Cannon's theory in mind, that thirst can arise when the mouth contains wet food. Rinsing the mouth, he said, relieves dryness but not thirst. He specifically stated that the effect of atropine is to cause dryness of the mouth which is distinguishable from thirst, a point which Leschke (474) and Allison and Critchley (33) also made. And Kunde (449) observed the buccal membrane to become very dry in a human subject after a few days of fasting, yet there was no thirst nor was the dryness relieved by taking water. In fact, the desire for water was almost nil. The dehydrated subjects of Hervey and McCance (352) complained of dry mouths but never of intolerable thirst; some of those of Rubini et al. (671) developed thirst although retaining an appreciable ability to produce saliva. Whittaker (831), co-pilot of the ill-fated Rickenbacker party (655, p. 417), noted that his own reaction to lack of water was, at times, not so much thirst as dryness.

Just as Wettendorff (823) earlier separated "true thirst" or tissue dehydration from "false thirst" or the sensation arising in the dry mouth, so Winsor (844), studying the effect of dehydration on parotid secretion, remarked that constant chewing during dehydration might keep the mouth moist but did not prevent "true thirst." Nor does the fact that cud-chewers, such as the goat and sheep (175), and cattle in hot countries in the summer (451), are always salivating prevent them from drinking. Drooling infants may avidly drink proffered water, and even extremely dehydrated dogs (869) and donkeys (208) often retain a considerable wetness of the mouth under presumably hyperdipsic conditions.

Smith (733) caused normal human adults to become thirsty by administering 30 to 100 cc. of saturated sodium chloride solution by stomach and observed that, while saliva flow diminished in some, it increased in others. Bruce (136), investigating the thirst drive in rats, found that moistening the mouth and throat of his animals did not satisfy it. And Andersson (43) observed that drinking in goats, precipitated by direct stimulation of the hypothalamus (p. 84), may be prolonged even though the mouth is bathed with water.

King's (422) account of desert thirst, given in full in Chapter VII, describes the behavior of men with access to water after rescue:

> . . . . the inclination to drink was irresistible; it seemed impossible to refrain from pouring down water, notwithstanding that their stomachs would not retain it. As they kept filling themselves with water, it was vomited up . . . .
>
> Although water was imbibed again and again, even to repletion of the stomach, it did not assuage their insatiable thirst, thus demonstrating that the sense of thirst is, like the sense of hunger, located in the general system, and that it could not be relieved until the remote tissues were supplied.

Carlson (162) described thirst as an uncomfortable sensation in the mouth and throat which, when more intense, consists in a feeling of tension and discomfort extending to the whole body[13] and causes one to become restless, and to feel feverish and dry. Of the local dryness aspect he stated, in contrast to Cannon (154, 156):

> But it is my experience that the feeling of dryness in the mouth and throat after taking atropine or after prolonged talking is not true thirst. I also feel that true thirst can be experienced (as after eating salt or very salty food) long before salivation is decreased or before the mouth and throat become dry. This thirst is a salty, tickling, burning sensation in the throat and gullet. It is mildly

---

[13] Luciani (493) made a similar point. At their inception, he says, hunger and thirst are local; only when intense are they diffuse, assuming the character of general sensations. He noted that people without stomachs get hungry but related this to the remnant portion of the cardia.

unpleasant but is not accompanied by any feeling of dryness in the mouth or throat. The feeling of dryness or stickiness in the mouth seems to come much later.

Jessen (400) early observed the following distinction:

> . . . . the saliva becomes viscid, so that the tongue often adheres to the sides of the mouth to a noticeable degree, occasionally becomes dry. At the same time a healthy man perceives something in the mouth and throat, which perception he is unable to express indeed by words and indicates its difference from other perceptions felt in the mouth and throat . . . . he himself distinguishes [it] well from all other perceptions felt in the mouth. It is overcome nevertheless in the same way . . . . unpleasant in itself, he calls [it] *thirst.*

Steggerda (759) reported of his subject devoid of any active salivary glands (p. 45) and of normal subjects, all made thirsty by administration of salt, that the resulting increased water intake showed thirst to be not necessarily related to a dry mouth. It was noted of this unique subject (61):

> Upon careful questioning, and after due consideration, the patient, a university student, stated that he differentiated between dry mouth and a sense of thirst. Sips of water which would moisten his mouth could still leave a sense of thirst, and thirst was not always experienced when his mouth was dry.

Cullumbine *et al.* (192) studied the effects of large doses of atropine sulfate upon healthy male subjects. They used 2, 3, and 5 mg. as opposed to the clinical doses of 1 mg. commonly used. Of these experiments, Cullumbine (191) writes:

> . . . . in our experience, following atropine, the sensation of dry mouth is distinguishable from that of thirst. No subject in our series ever complained of thirst but all complained of dry mouth after the administration of atropine.
>
> When water was freely available men would drink but almost immediately they discovered that the relief obtained was momentary. Some would continue to take small sips or to rinse the mouth but the majority found the relief obtained was so slight that such action was not considered worthwhile.

Critchley (190), who pointed out that atropine produces not thirst but only a dryness of the mouth such as can be promptly relieved by gargling, remarked:

> It would be erroneous to regard the feeling of thirst as synonymous with, and the expression of, a mere dryness of the mouth and pharynx. This is a mistake that has been made by certain physiologists, chief among them Cannon.

Arden (54) and Wolf (856) have also noted the dissociation between thirst and dryness of the mouth. The latter, studying men brought gradually to eudipsia and then to hyperdipsia by slow intravenous infusions of hypertonic sodium chloride, found that these subjects invariably reported a drying of the mouth considerably before any clear desire to drink set in. Conversely, when their thirst was being relieved by intravenous infusion of 5% glucose, the mouth moistened notably before the desire to drink abated.

Holmes and Gregersen (374) emphasized the admittedly high correlation between the reduction of salivary flow and thirst engendered by intravenous hypertonic sodium chloride, but these results do not negate the validity of the contrary observations. Actually, little attention has been given to the possible differences in the modality of the sensation of thirst as it is excited by different stimuli (dryness, spiciness, metallic taste, etc.) in the same individual. And it appears (p. 65) that the threshold to oral stimulation by any given stimulus varies widely among different individuals.

The salivary glands respond to chemical (acids, alkalis, salts, bitters) and osmotic stimuli (dry salt, hypertonic solutions) (65, 601). Pavlov (601) observed that canine salivary glands respond more to the dryness than to the mechanical stimulation of food. Winsor (844), also, has remarked on the reflex increase of salivary flow excited by drying of the mouth.

The parotid, a serous gland, continues to secrete a thin watery fluid even when the latter's volume may be diminished in certain stages of thirst, but the mucous glands deliver a viscid secretion. Crisler (189) studied the effect of withdrawal of water on the salivary conditioned reflex induced by morphine in dogs, finding the conditioned secretion of saliva to be practically abolished by three to five days of water deprivation. The unconditioned secretion caused by morphine or pilocarpine is also reduced by dehydration but less so. He supposed that while the peripheral mechanism[14] of secretion is little affected by dehydration, certain central processes are depressed, a view which is not generally considered. Gantt (282) cautioned against working with conditioned reflexes when thirst is present; however, Finch (257) has shown that the specific component, salivary gland response, is not a necessary prerequisite of salivary conditioning. The conditioning process can occur during the absence of the conditioned response in atropinized dogs.

Schneyer (696, 697), after developing a mandibular appliance or "segregator" for collecting separate submaxillary and sublingual salivas in man, ascertained that of the total salivary output under "resting" conditions (reduced exogenous stimulation) the submaxillary glands contribute 69%, the parotids 26%, and the sublinguals, 5%.

White et al. (826) give mean electrolyte concentrations for saliva in fasting man, after chewing paraffin for 15 to 20 minutes: sodium, 26.4; chloride, 29.0; potassium, 19.7 mEq./L. After 6 mg. of pilocarpine, sodium increased by 4.11 and potassium fell by 3.97 mEq./L. The saliva secretion in man is probably always hypotonic (362, p. 52). Burgen (143) reported the osmotic pressure of dog parotid secretion to vary from 82 mOs./L. at low flows to 232 mOs./L. at highest flows when the salivary output was varied by changing the rate of electrical stimulation of the auriculotemporal nerve.

Holmes and A. V. Montgomery (380) have studied the way in which different stimuli can significantly alter the volume and electrolyte concentration of the salivary secretion in man. In 10 normal subjects, with mouth breathing the salivary flow averaged 1 cc./min. and the sodium

---

[14] The peripheral mechanism of salivary secretion is presumably supported by a supply of water from the blood but the relationship is quantitatively undefined (p. 25). Gregersen and Bullock (309, 311) found in man that abstention from water for two or three days resulted in parallel falls of plasma volume and salivary secretion. They suggested that the secretion is reduced by decrease in blood volume. Holmes and Gregersen (374), however, found that in subjects made hyperdipsic by intravenous sodium chloride (5%), blood volume was augmented by 5 to 10% at the time salivary flow was reduced. On the other hand, salivary flow appears to be reduced when the body is depleted of salt, at least in the dog (200) if not in man (519). There is no reason to think the reflex mechanism of salivary secretion to be impaired in dehydration (311).

concentration 7.7 mEq./L.; with citric acid stimulation the flow was
1 cc./min. and the sodium concentration 17.1 mEq./L.; with paraffin
"gum" the flow was 2.8 cc./min. and the sodium concentration 31.2
mEq./L. Potassium concentration remained relatively constant, averaging 17 mEq./L. Following pilocarpine, flow increased 260%, and
potassium and chloride concentrations decreased 25%. Epinephrine
produced a 45% reduction in flow but no significant change in electrolyte concentrations. Pitressin produced a 60% decrease in volume, and
a 30% elevation in potassium concentration. In patients treated with
cortisone there were no significant changes in salivary electrolyte concentrations over a three week period (mouth breathing), though an
occasional patient did show a drop in sodium and chloride concentrations. Thiocyanate and radioactive iodine are excreted in saliva at
higher concentrations than in serum and the salivary thiocyanate clearance averaged 7.6 cc./min. and that for I^{131}, 7 cc./min., at low rates of
flow. At higher rates of salivary flow (above 0.5 cc./min.) the iodine
clearance ranged from 30 to 40 cc./min. and was not affected by
the type of stimulus, the rate of flow, or change in the chloride clearance.

A substantial argument against the dry mouth theory was advanced by Claude Bernard (89). First, he showed that a horse
with divided parotid ducts and parotid fistulas produced more
salivary secretion per unit weight of ingested food as that food
was the drier (fresh bread, bran, alfalfa, hay, respectively). He
also showed how a horse with such resected ducts took longer to
masticate straw, hay, or oats than a normal horse; and he stated
that, with the loss of saliva through the parotid fistulas, a horse
would drink appreciably more than a normal horse in a day.
Nevertheless, it is not necessary to believe, he said (p. 66), that
this exaggerated thirst after section of the ducts is engendered by
the greater dryness of the pharynx. Rather the thirst is an expression of a general need of water caused by loss of body fluid including that from the fistulas. He then cites his experiments on
a horse with esophagus divided. With every swallow the water
was forcibly ejected between the front legs. Thirst was not
calmed by wetting the throat in drinking; the animal drank until
fatigued and then recommenced to drink. He also describes his
repeated experiments on a dog with a gastric fistula. Again, thirst
was not appeased although the water traversed all the way to the

stomach and then to the outside. Such a dog was reduced to a sort of cistern of Danaïdes, drinking until stopped by fatigue; an instant after, when rested, it began again. If he stoppered the cannula, causing water to be absorbed, thirst was quickly satisfied just as when one injects water into the veins.

Voit (800) recognized two stages of thirst, the first of which could be relieved by moistening the mucous membranes of the mouth with water and the second representing such a large loss of water that it could not be so relieved. Still, he interpreted Bernard's results as due possibly to the nerves of the dry throat not getting enough water from the drink which flowed so quickly by. He cited Schoenborn who found that water introduced into a stomach fistula in man did not relieve thirst so promptly as water by mouth. Bellows (83, p. 152) studied dogs with esophageal fistulas and concluded with Bernard that the persistent sham drinking of dogs whose intake does not reach the stomach must wet the mouth just as in a normal dog and simply, therefore, the dry mouth theory per se cannot be valid.

Here is Cannon's view (154) of Bernard's (89) experiments:

. . . . The inference was drawn that thirst must be a general sensation, for the passage of water through the mouth and pharynx wet those surfaces, and yet the animal was not satisfied until the water was permitted to enter the intestine and be absorbed by the body. This evidence appears conclusive. The expressions "fatigued" and "rested," however, are interpretations of the observer, and not the testimony of the dog. Indeed, we may with equal reasonableness assume that the animal stopped drinking because he was not thirsty, and started again when he became thirsty. The only assumptions necessary for such an interpretation of the animal's behavior are that appreciable time is required to moisten the buccal and pharyngeal mucosa sufficiently to extinguish thirst—a point made by Voit—and that these regions become dried rapidly when there is absence of an adequate water-content in the body. This interpretation is consistent with the view that thirst is a sensation having a local source. Furthermore, this interpretation is not contradicted by the satisfaction manifested by the dog after the fistula was closed, for the water which is absorbed, like that injected into the veins, may quench thirst by altering local conditions. We cannot admit, therefore, that Bernard's experiment is proof that thirst is a general sensation.[15]

Because of its historical importance rather than because it represents the view of modern dipsologists, and particularly because it expounds and accredits the dry mouth theory so far as possible, we draw further on Cannon's 1918 Croonian Lecture (154). Compare portions of the following with Haller's account (p. 43):

> About six years ago I called attention to some graphic records of motions of the stomach in man which showed that the sensation of hunger is associated with powerful contractions of the empty or nearly empty organ. And because the hunger pang began to be experienced after the contraction had started, the conclusion was drawn that hunger is not a "general sensation," as was formerly held by physiologists and psychologists, but has its immediate origin in the stomach, and is the direct consequence of the strong contraction[16] . . . .

---

[15] Colin (176), whose anhydremia-dry mouth theory resembled Cannon's, used this argument before Cannon and had, moreover, seen horses with esophageal fistulas drink one or two pails of water and stop as if the water had reached the stomach; then they drank again, he stated, because their mouth membranes became dry.

While these objections are serious, there is the fact, as Dill (208) reminds us, that Bernard states the dog resumed drinking "un instant après." And it is difficult to believe, he continues, that such a keen observer and careful experimenter as Bernard could have been wholly misled by the behavior of the horse and dog.

[16] It was Cannon and Washburn (160) in 1912 who remarked that if hunger is a manifestation of general bodily need it is absurd to think the body is not in need after the third day when hunger disappears. It is perhaps natural that Cannon's philosophy which sprang from the apparent demonstration that hunger, a once widely credited "general sensation," is rather the result of local activity in the stomach, should attempt also to encompass thirst in local and not general terms. But an important analysis of the incompleteness and inadequacy of such a mechanical view of hunger has been given by Janowitz and Grossman (397); this also supplies cogent arguments against parallel "mechanical" theories of thirst. Grossman and Stein (315) detail the composite nature of the sensation-complex of hunger, indicating how vagotomy, in those in whom epigastric pangs of distress associated with individual gastric contractions are a part of the sensation-complex, abolishes this particular kind of sensation. The removal of this component is recognized by the subject, but it does not cause a significant change in the general affective response to hunger. Keys et al. (421), also, do not regard the concept of hunger as a gastric sensation to be tenable.

. . . . . .

There is a general agreement that thirst is a sensation referred to the mucous lining of the mouth and pharynx, and especially to the root of the tongue and to the palate . . . .

. . . . . .

The foregoing review of observations and theories has revealed that the attitude of physiologists with reference to thirst has been much as it was with reference to hunger. In each condition a general bodily need has arisen from a lack of essential bodily material and is signalled by a well-defined sensation. In each the testimony of ingenuous persons regarding their feelings has been carefully set down, and then explained away. Thus in the case of thirst the primary sensation is described universally as an experience of dryness and stickiness in the mouth and throat. Instead of attempting to account for the experience as such, however, attention has been paid to the bodily need which accompanies it; apparently, since the need is a general one, the sensation has been supposed to be general, and the thirst which everybody experiences and knows about has been classed as an associated secondary phenomenon or the peripheral reference of a central change. The really doubtful feature in this view of thirst, just as in the older conception of hunger, is the "general sensation." That even the early stages of a need of water may be accompanied by increased irritability, and a vague sense of weakness and limpness, is not denied. But the thirsty man does not complain of these general conditions. He is tormented by a parched and burning throat, and any explanation of the physiological mechanism for maintaining the water content of the body must take into account this prominent fact.

. . . . . .

. . . . The action of these organs [salivary glands] is to secrete a fluid which is normally more than 97 per cent., and may be more than 99 per cent., water. The theory of thirst, on which I wish to offer evidence, may now be stated. In brief, it is that the salivary glands have, among their functions, that of keeping moist the ancient watercourse; that they, like other tissues, suffer when water is lacking in the body—a lack especially important for them, however, because their secretion is almost wholly water, and that, when these glands fail to provide sufficient fluid to moisten the mouth and throat, the local discomfort and unpleasantness which result constitute the feeling of thirst.

. . . . . .

The question whether there is a relation between the existence of water-need in the body and diminished flow of saliva I have examined in two ways—by going without fluid for a considerable period and by profuse sweating, combined with measurements of salivary secretion under uniform stimulation . . . .

. . . . . .

The relation between the decrease of salivary flow in these experiments and the sensation of thirst was quite definite . . . .

The increased spontaneous activity of the tongue and the repeated swallowing motions as "thirst" became more marked are noteworthy. These movements are a slight stimulus to salivary secretion, and they have, furthermore, the obvious effect of spreading about any fluid that might be present. In the absence of sufficient fluid, however, they augment the disagreeableness of the condition by making prominent the friction due to lack of lubricant. The "lump in the throat," which is complained of by persons who suffer from extreme thirst, can be explained as due to the difficulty encountered when the epiglottis and root of the tongue are rubbed over the dry back wall of the pharynx in attempts to swallow.[17]

. . . . . .

Other evidence on the relation between absence of saliva and the presence of thirst as a sensation was obtained through checking salivary secretion by atropine . . . . After the full effect of the drug . . . . the amount fell . . . .. All the feelings that were noted in ordinary thirst—the sense of dry surfaces, the stickiness of the moving parts, the difficulties of speaking and swallowing—all were present. These disagreeable experiences, constituting the thirst sensation, disappeared as soon as the mouth and throat were washed out with a weak novocaine solution. The immediate effect

---

[17] *And every tongue, through utter drought,*
   Was withered at the root;
   We could not speak, no more than if
   We had been choked with soot.
               —SAMUEL TAYLOR COLERIDGE

in these circumstances was doubtless due to the water in the solution, but since the relief lasted much longer than when water was used, the anaesthetic was also a factor . . . . No water was drunk by me during the period of atropine effect, and yet when that effect disappeared, and the saliva flow was re-established, thirst also was abolished. The relation between thirst and such drug action has been noted before, but so strong has been the theory that thirst is a "general" sensation, that the drug has been supposed to produce its effect not by local action but by central changes and by alteration of the blood.

Similar in character to the thirst which results from the action of atropine is that which accompanies anxiety and fright. The effect of such emotional states in causing inhibition of salivary secretion is well known. It was the basis of the ancient "ordeal of rice" employed in India as a means of detecting the guilty one in a group of suspected persons . . . .

On the basis of the foregoing evidence I would explain thirst as due directly to what it seems to be due to—a relative drying of the mucosa of the mouth and pharynx. This may result either from excessive use of this passage for breathing, as in prolonged speaking or singing, or it may result from deficient salivary secretion . . . . The importance of this failure of action of the salivary glands, however, to the mechanism of the water supply of the body, lies in the strategic position of these glands in relation to a surface which tends to become dry by the passage of air over it. If this surface is not kept moist, discomfort arises and with it an impulse to seek well tried means of relief. Thus the diminishing activity of the salivary glands becomes a delicate indicator of the bodily demand for fluid.

. . . . . .

. . . . And the water supply is maintained because we avoid, or abolish, by taking water or aqueous fluid, the disagreeable sensations which arise and torment us with increasing torment if the salivary glands, because of a lowering of the water-content of the body, lack the water they need to function, and fail therefore to pour out their watery secretion in sufficient amount and in proper quality to keep moist the mouth and pharynx.

It is unnecessary, as we shall see, to dwell further on the apparent diversity of evidence and contradictions regarding the local dryness theory. The whole issue is less sharply drawn in the light of modern work and theories which reconcile previously conflicting observations. It suffices to state two overriding considerations which seriously weaken this purely siccative view of thirst. First, the basic premise of the dry mouth theory that thirst and a dry mouth are indissolubly colligated, and the corollary that thirst should not exist when the membranes are wet, are unquestionably at variance with observational facts. Secondly, the dry mouth theory does not possess within it, and has never been exploited for, those quantitative elements which would enable it to account for the variable magnitude of the drinking response to graded hyperdipsia and water deficit. Indeed, Moss (561) used the siccative view of thirst to explain the apparent miscalculation made by the body when men deficient in salt "overdrink" in hot, relatively dry atmospheres (p. 104). Clearly, the volume drunk, per se, has no necessary relation to the local moistening produced prior to absorption (e.g., a small volume of water held in the mouth and gargled, or sucking a piece of ice, should wet the throat more thoroughly than a large volume of water quickly swallowed; and, conversely, the prompt onset of thirst following rapid injection of concentrated salt solutions, before the mouth has a chance to dry (p. 80), argue to the same end. Even when ignoring the special problems of satiety, the mechanics of the dry mouth theory do not clarify the regulatory aspect of the water intake (559).

As Stellar (762) observed:

. . . . Cannon's theories were good in their day, but the new facts available on the physiological basis of motivation demand that we abandon the older conceptualizations . . . .

. . . . the local factors proposed by Cannon (e.g., stomach contractions or dryness of the throat) are not necessary conditions for the arousal of motivated behavior.

It is worthy of remark that Cannon's idea, unlike the cognate ideas of others (150, 206) is singular in positing the closest propinquity of the "seat" and the "cause" of thirst (p. 38). Allison and Critchley (33) remark that it would appear that though dryness of the mouth is a cardinal symptom of thirst, its importance ends as such.

Of some interest is the tabulation of results of the following questionnaire submitted to men and women with no instruction save not to discuss it with any one before answering (869).

1. Do you promptly become thirsty (that is, desire to drink water) upon chewing or eating sweet chocolate?

	Yes	(55%)
(60 replies)	No	(45%)

2. Are your own thirst sensations associated with a dry mouth or throat?

	Always	(2%)
(60 replies)	Generally	(43%)
	Occasionally	(47%)
	Never	(8%)

3. Do you ever become thirsty while your mouth and throat are moist?

	Always	(0%)
(57 replies)	Generally	(26%)
	Occasionally	(70%)
	Never	(4%)

Whatever allowance need be made for imperfections or inconsistencies in this means of evaluating subjective aspects of thirst, several points are outstanding. Thus, local stimulation even in the wet mouth can excite thirst promptly in half of those queried (this suggests the thirst threshold to oral stimulation by a given stimulus varies widely among different individuals); thirst sensations are by no means always associated with a dry mouth and, indeed, some individuals "never" recognize such a relation; most individuals generally or occasionally become thirsty while the mouth is moist or wet. Few comments were offered in a space provided on the questionnaire; these were trivial and are therefore not recorded.

GENERAL AND OSMOTIC THEORIES

Distinctions drawn here among theories of thirst are nominal rather than substantive by reason of their extensive overlapping. In the previous section we remarked on various aspects of the "general" theory of thirst, culminating with Bernard's view. But it is sometimes difficult to determine just what certain writers have intended to signify by "general" sensations. Cannon (154) did not lessen confusion when he attacked Bernard (89) (and Longest (p. 46)) for holding thirst to be a general sensation when, in fact, Bernard specifically stated that thirst is the expression of a general need, quite a different idea:

> *Il ne faudrait pas croire, messieurs, que cette soif exagérée après la section des conduits parotidiens vient de ce qu'il y a une sécheresse plus grande du pharynx qui donne lieu au sentiment de la soif. Ce sentiment est bien l'expression du besoin général causé par la diminution de quantité des liquides du corps.*

No one acquainted with the fierce "determinism" of Bernard (90, 91) will imagine that his failing to study and elucidate further the intimate mechanism of thirst reflected in the slightest degree an abdication of faith that further research would specify aspects which then to him appeared generic. Indeed, it is difficult to see how a more satisfactory distillation of the knowledge of thirst in Bernard's time could have been made; and a perusal of Cannon's own paper (154) reviewing evidence before and since Bernard can have the unsettling effect of leading a distinterested reader to draw conclusions quite opposed to Cannon's.

We gather that the expression "general," as applied to thirst theories, is as indefinite as the supposititious areas from which thirst stimuli were considered to arise. Such theories are scarcely susceptible of pointed attack. Much that has been argued against general theories appears merely to have been directed to such of their elements as are dissident to some less general theory, usually a dry mouth or a central theory. In a sense, the views of Mayer (515, 516, 517) and Wettendorff (823) form a bridge between the older, vague, general theories and the more modern osmotic, osmometric, and central theories.

In 1900 Mayer (515, 516) showed that when dogs were deprived of liquid, the osmotic pressure of the blood serum, determined cryoscopically, rose. He observed also that when hypertonic solutions were placed in the stomach of a curarized dog, there followed a lowering of the freezing point of the venous blood of the stomach; and he postulated that thirst is produced by hypertonicity of the blood. Mayer elaborated this view the following year in an extended essay on the cause and mechanism of thirst (517).

There is, he remarked, a modification of molecular state (osmotic pressure) in the cells of the organism, in the milieu intérieur, and in the blood. The change in the latter excites the walls of blood vessels, which excitation is transmitted to bulbar centers.[18] The response of the centers tends to re-establish equilibrium by bringing about drinking which reverses the osmotic pressure change. Mayer, interestingly, gave more attention to the regulatory aspect of drinking for the water balance than had others until then. He thought that hypertonic loads in the body fluids gave rise to vascular and systemic effects such as local vasodilatation and elevated blood pressure, and that renal excretion was thereby stimulated, a phenomenon which also protected the body against hypertonicity. Progressive intensification of osmotic stimulation ultimately excited the mouth and throat, bringing the thirst impulse to the conscious level.

Every elevation of osmotic pressure of the internal environment leads to thirst, he said; and the blood in thirst is a steady convulsive excitant to the nervous system. He supposed by the logic of propinquity that the bulb was the critical nervous center, containing as it does the vasomotor centers which were assumed to be affected by hypertonicity. His theory held thirst to be the last of a series of regulatory mechanisms tending to preserve the normal tonicity of body fluids.

Wettendorff (823) confirmed Mayer's cryoscopic finding of a rise in osmotic pressure of the blood of dogs in water deprivation, but detected no change in the first day or so.[19] He interpreted this to mean that the tissues ceded water to the blood to preserve it osmotically; but that, rather than from changes in the blood itself, thirst originated diffusely in the general tissue dehydration and was exteriorized to the mouth and throat by association (p. 94). He regarded the stimulus from general tissue dehydration as something independent or apart from stimulation set up in or localized in the central nervous system. Thus Wettendorff did not propose a strictly "central" theory but held rather that the central

---

[18] See Dumas' theory, page 40.

[19] In man, also, Lifson (479) found no change in osmotic activity of serum (= heparinized plasma activity) before 24 hours. After 40 hours of food and water deprivation in an environmental temperature range of 18° to 29° C. (relative humidity, 47 to 94%) osmotic activity rose 0.84%; after 48 hours it rose 1.6% above control values. However, see page 102.

nervous system is a coordinator of thirst, taking stimuli from general tissue receptors. A charge made by Cannon (154) against theories like Luciani's (493), which supposed that sensory nerves of the buccal and pharyngeal mucosa are particularly sensitive to a diminution of the water content of the circulating fluid of the body, was that no special end organs were known to subserve this function; and in some respects this charge may be also considered relevant to Wettendorff's theory.

We are no longer constrained to argue at length the question of which fluid—blood, interstitial fluid, or cellular fluid—suffers the crucial alteration of osmotic pressure. To most practical purposes body fluids appear to sustain equal increments of osmotic pressure at equilibrium (530, 873, p. 29). In essence Wettendorff proposed that the effect of increased osmotic pressure is diffused throughout the body tissues; accordingly, cellular dehydration may be imputed to his theory although there is no specific clarification of this point. The organs (and their cells) are reservoirs of fluid, he said, charged at the time of repast, yielding liquid to the organism when need arises.

Nonnenbruch (583) emphasized the dependence of thirst rather on increased osmotic concentrations of body fluids than upon water deprivation since on a salt-poor diet it may be observed that there is little thirst, and water and salt are being lost simultaneously.

The important observations in man of Arden (54) are frequently mentioned. He showed that when 20 g. of sodium chloride were taken in 200 cc. of water, the sensation of thirst began to be felt after 30 minutes. At the end of an hour the mouth was becoming dry; at 2 hours the secretion of saliva had entirely ceased, the mouth was parched, and thirst was excessive. This state lasted for some time and passed off gradually, almost disappearing by 7 hours. At this time there was still an excess of salt in the body, but it is not stated whether concentrations of sodium or the osmotic pressure of the plasma had returned to normal. Sodium bicarbonate solutions produced almost as much thirst as sodium chloride but, significantly, potassium salts did not cause thirst.

TABLE IV

Dog deprived of water and food.   Initial (control) body weight, day 0: 9.07 Kg. (626, 871).

Day	Weight Loss (%)	Milli-osmosity*	Sodium (mEq./L.)	Chloride (mEq./L.)	Potassium (mEq./L.)	NPN (mg. %)	Water (g./100 g. plasma)	Protein (%)	Hematocrit	Average Volume (L./day)	Sodium (mEq./L.)	Chloride (mEq./L.)	Potassium (mEq./L.)
				Plasma						Urine			
0	0.0	160.9	149.3	117.2	4.40	42.8	92.58	7.17	.523	.164	81.4	86.8	177.6
4	10.6	162.1	150.0	119.5	3.58	49.0	91.76	7.07	.567	.044	183.6	123.8	178.0
9	19.4	163.3	158.2	126.2	4.16	33.0	92.06	6.98	.590	.043	79.0	75.5	229.6
14	25.9	169.4	152.8	127.6	4.23	29.1	92.14	6.35	.605	.041	33.6	40.6	180.8
18	30.9	174.3	160.6	127.6	3.94	33.2	91.83	6.86	.590	.032	32.4	34.7	203.4
22	34.7	180.4	157.6	131.3	4.23	34.9	91.36	6.81	.582	.024	25.2	20.0	199.2
25	38.1	182.5	160.4	136.2	3.94	32.3	91.59	7.55	.550	.020	16.3	16.3	199.2
29	42.2	188.8	164.6	137.4	3.87	44.2	90.81	7.16	.511	.021	12.4	10.6	234.0
33	45.9	201.5	166.8	140.0	4.48	82.0	90.16	8.33	.469	.018‡	9.2	...	192.0
37†	49.7	259.4	177.8	132.4	6.33	277.0	88.29	6.08	.380	.015‡	22.4	...	208.0

* Millimolarity of a sodium chloride solution having the same freezing point as plasma.   See page 342.
† Moribund.
‡ Lipuria.

Arden's observations were supplemented for the dog and rabbit by Janssen (398) who found that while sodium chloride solutions led to drinking, equimolar (essentially isosmotic) potassium chloride did not. Janssen observed how, in the latter case, the adjustment of the electrolyte imbalance was largely achieved by means of augmented renal excretion, while with sodium loads, regulation of osmotic pressure of body fluids is accomplished more quickly by drinking water. Kanter (405) has discussed this physiologic phenomenon in his studies of maximal and minimal internal regulators (p. 205). As Starling (755) tersely stated the problem:

> It is a familiar circumstance that the ingestion of an excessive quantity of salt provokes thirst rather than diuresis.

Elkinton and Taffel (232) and Wolf and Eddy (871) studied urinary and plasma electrolytes in dogs deprived of water until moribundity or death (Table IV); Prentiss *et al.* (626) did the same with cats. It was found that urinary excretion of sodium and chloride diminished to the vanishing point as urinary concentration of those ions fell to low values. This occurred despite a concurrent rise in plasma sodium and chloride, reflecting an increased threshold of retention (857) of these ions. At the same time potassium excretion was maintained while, because of the diminution of urine volume, its concentration rose in the urine as high as 500 mEq./L. Whatever meaning these results have for osmometric theories of thirst, it is not to be concluded therefrom that thirst is specifically dependent upon, or governed simply by, the level of sodium or chloride in the plasma. Holmes and Gregersen (377) showed, for example, that hypertonic (50%) sorbitol solution was quite as effective in stimulating thirst as sodium chloride even though the administration of the former results in a fall in plasma sodium and chloride concentrations.

CELLULAR DEHYDRATION AND OSMOMETRIC THEORIES

Kerpel-Fronius (413, 414) was the first clearly to distinguish two different forms of experimental water loss: a form of exsiccation characterized by thirst, in which water loss relatively exceeds salt loss, causing hypertonicity of remaining body fluids;

and a form characterized by salt loss which, depending on whether the loss is sodium or potassium, leads to loss of interstitial or intracellular water. The water loss in thirst was considered to derive from both extracellular and intracellular phases, although plasma volume might be conserved (415).

Nadal, Pedersen, and Maddock (568) supported this outlook, specifying that simple water deprivation is characterized by thirst and oliguria, no impairment of circulation, and is relieved by water. Dehydration associated with abnormal salt loss was recognized to lead to loss of extracellular fluid volume and plasma volume, increased hematocrit and plasma protein concentration, disturbances in circulation (weakness, fainting, low blood pressure, peripheral failure), no necessary change in urine volume, and no thirst. The latter form of dehydration was not relieved by water but by saline.

A more comprehensive analysis of salt water states (857) defines nine possible and verifiable combinations of absolute and relative dehydration, euhydration, and hydration (= overhydration), and illustrates how thirst is characteristic not simply of water loss alone but also of water excesses, provided salt excess is relatively greater (Fig. 8). Such analysis is rooted in earlier ideas about the distributions of water and salts. Gamble, Ross, and Tisdall (281) were the first to regard fixed base (except calcium) as entirely in solution at a uniform concentration in body water (the role of other bone minerals has yet to be ordered precisely in this scheme). Extended by Hill (363), Lavietes *et al.* (466), and many others, this concept embraces that of the totality of body cells behaving as an osmometer such that fluid moves in or out of cells in response to gradients of osmotic pressure (p. 15).

In this climate of physiologic theory and doctrine, Gilman (292) reported that in dogs, despite equal increments in osmotic pressure produced from injections of sodium chloride or urea, drinking was significantly less after urea than after salt. From this he concluded that it was not simply increased osmotic pressure of cellular fluid which was the stimulus of true thirst but rather the condition of cellular dehydration. It was known that urea distributes itself almost evenly throughout all of the body water and has little effective osmotic pressure which could act to with-

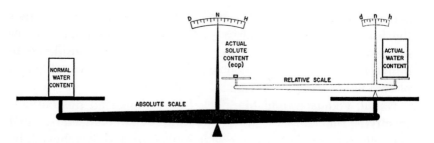

Figure 8.   Diagram illustrating nine salt-water states in hydration, normalcy, and dehydration.   Absolute water contents are determined by the larger **absolute scale** and relative water contents by the smaller **relative scale**.   The latter points up the balance or imbalance of actual water content and actual solute content responsible for effective osmotic pressure (*eop*).   When the ratio of actual solute to actual water in the body is normal (relative euhydration, *n*), the *eop* is normal.   When the ratio of solute to water content is greater than normal the effective osmotic pressure of body fluids is elevated and the condition is one of relative dehydration (*d*).   This may obtain because solute is in excess or water in deficit, or because both are elevated or depressed but in different degrees.   When, conversely, actual water is proportionately greater than solute, relative hydration (*h*) obtains.   The three relative states *d*, *n*, and *h* are seen to be independent of states of absolute water content measured by the **absolute scale**.   Considering the **relative scale** to be itself weightless and the weight of solute as negligible, we ascertain by the **absolute scale** whether the water content of the body is less than normal (absolute dehydration, *D*), equal to normal (absolute euhydration, *N*), or greater than normal (absolute hydration, *H*).*   Since the three absolute states *D*, *N*, and *H* exist independently of the relative states, nine combinations are possible, viz., *Dd, Dn, Dh, Nd, Nn, Nh, Hd, Hn,* and *Hh,* all of which are known.   *Dd* is the state most commonly supposed to be found in thirst although any *-d* state, providing the thirst threshold is exceeded, is consistent with thirst.   Actually, thirst is known to exist in other states as well.   After Wolf (857).

---

* Commonly the term "overhydration" is used to designate what we call here absolute hydration, in which case "normal hydration" denotes what we call normalcy, normal water content, or absolute euhydration.   When it is desired to place emphasis on deviations from euhydration in specific water compartments, as in the blood, such terms as anhydremia and hydremia or hydremic plethora are used primarily for the states of relative dehydration and hydration (although they have been used to include absolute states).   Hypovolemia and hypervolemia denote the respective absolute states; normovolemia or euvolemia are the normal states.   It is suggested, by way of extending this terminology to other compartments, that the terms hypovolia, euvolia, and hypervolia be used.   Thus salt deficiency might lead to extracellular hypovolia and cellular hypervolia.

draw cell water osmotically;[20] and it was also known that sodium chloride has a largely extracellular distribution signifying that its osmotic pressure increment would be effective. This shift in emphasis from osmotic pressure, per se, to cellular dehydration, sui generis, marked an important turning point in interpretations of the dipsogenic mechanism.[21]

Nevertheless, as Dill (208) indicated in his review of thirst, other reasons were at hand which would support the same conclusion. For example, Darrow and Yannet (200) had found that dogs depleted of salt relative to water, and with presumably lowered effective osmotic pressure of body fluids, showed no thirst although they had dry mouths which might have been expected to stimulate drinking; and Dill himself reported how the loss of equal amounts of water as sweat could be differently provocative of thirst in the man in the desert. Less thirst resulted when the sweat was almost as concentrated osmotically as plasma (in unacclimated men) as when it was only one-third so concentrated (in acclimated men). Thirst, in Dill's view, depends on diminished water content[22] and possibly increased osmotic pressure of body cells.

Gilman's (292) work led him to remark on that of Gamble et al. (279, 280). The latter had studied the "optimal" water requirement in renal function by measuring water drinking and urinary volumes and concentrations in rats. In their experiments water was allowed ad libitum and the animals were offered basal diets whose composition was modified by addition of urea and/or a salt (sodium chloride, potassium chloride, etc.) among other ways. A diet might contain a certain maximum quantity of added urea and almost no salt; stepwise, this would be modified by decreasing the urea and substituting for the urea decrement an equal increment of a salt. In this way a diet was finally provided in

---

[20] In evidence, Gilman also showed by rough calculation from his vapor pressure measurements that the volume of distribution of osmotic pressure of urea was essentially identical with the volume of distribution of urea itself. This relationship has been confirmed and its theoretical significance examined (530, 866).

[21] Wettendorff (823), as noted in the previous section, considered that the tissues and extravascular fluids ceded water to the blood. In a sense his theory is also osmometric but is not stated precisely in terms of cellular dehydration.

[22] In fasting, loss of body protein is accompanied by removal of cell water (277) but this in itself does not appear necessarily to cause thirst (p. 108).

which the salt was a maximum and the urea was zero. But in each diet of such a series the sum of the ingested osmols of urea and of the salt was kept essentially constant. Instead of urea, some other salt or non-electrolyte such as galactose might be employed. When two salts were thus complementarily varied, the urinary osmotic concentration tended to remain at a relatively stable "maximum," as that term was defined (280, p. 343).

It was found that the water requirements established for the individual substances remained additive when mixtures of them entered the urine, except when urea was a component of the mixture. In the presence of urea, water expenditure was found to be less than the sum of the requirements for urea and the accompanying substances as separately determined.

Gilman pointed out that the urine output of these rats varied with the ad libitum water intake, that is, with the magnitude of the thirst. This, in turn, appeared to depend more on the intake of salt than of urea. Thus, it seemed that water economy, in the sense of a minimizing of water intake, derived not by virtue of any property of urea but merely from the fact that as urea intake increased, that of salt decreased.

While the apparently equal dipsogenicity of sodium and potassium salts in these experiments is not thereby precisely accounted (pp. 68, 131), neither does this dipsic hypothesis explain the main finding that only when appreciable amounts of urea were replaced by salt in the urine, and vice versa, did the kidneys achieve minimal excretion of water per osmol of urinary solute, i.e., achieve a maximal urinary osmotic concentration as determined, not merely by summing analytical concentrations of urea and of the ingested ions which appeared in the urine, but by cryoscopy. These findings have not been further elucidated.

The cellular dehydration theory blocked out by Dill had a measure of quantitative backing, e.g., Gilman's studies, but was largely qualitative. One of the difficulties in working with this concept was the fact that, while experimental studies could be performed on animals made extremely hyperdipsic by doses of salt which caused large, measurable increases in plasma electrolyte concentration, it was not feasible to study eudipsic or mildly hyperdipsic animals because the quantities of salt required might be too small to augment the plasma electrolyte level sufficiently for accurate detection. This proves troublesome to investigators who wish to define functional relations between these variables. Indirect methods for determining cellular water are inadequate for assessing minute changes in its volume. The measurement of cellular water by difference of total and "extracellular" water is subject to errors in excess of some of the changes predicted by theory (less than 1%) which might suffice to cause thirst. To estimate differences of cellular water between normal and thirsting states is to compound experimental errors to a degree which precludes testing the theory by this means.

Osmometric Thirst Threshold

To circumvent this difficulty Wolf (856) used an osmometric equation (855) permitting reasonably valid calculations of the quantity of water lost by cells generally for any combination of loads of water and sodium chloride. Assuming body cells, collectively, to behave as a perfect osmometer, we may employ the osmometric equation,

$$V'_e = \frac{(W + L_{H_2O})(V_e A_{eop} + L_{eop})}{W A_{eop} + L_{eop}}$$

where V'_e is the final extracellular fluid volume after equilibration of a load of osmotically effective material, V_e is the initial extracellular volume (e.g., 20% of the body weight), W is the initial water content of the body (e.g., 60% of the body weight), L_{HO_2} is the net load of water (difference between administered load and water excreted), A_{eop} is the initial effective osmotic concentration of the plasma or extracellular fluid, and L_{eop} is the net effective osmotic load (difference between administered effective osmotic load and effective osmotic material excreted). The detailed use of this equation is described in several places (405, 530, 855–857, 866, 873).

By means of slow intravenous salt-water infusions, various degrees of hypertonicity of body fluids and of thirst were produced in dog and man. It was thus possible to measure a *thirst threshold* (Fig. 9) in terms of a calculated relative decrease in the cellular water content, this value being called τ. The value 100τ is theoretically the percentual decrement in cellular water

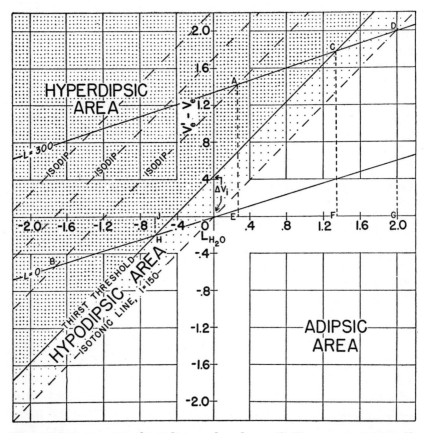

Figure 9. Osmometric thirst diagram based on a 70 Kg. man containing 49 liters of total body water and 14 liters of extracellular fluid.*

Ordinate: change in extracellular volume in liters $(V'_e - V'_e$).
Abscissa: load of water in liters (L_{H_2O}). The thirst threshold, separating the hyperdipsic area (densely stippled) from the hypodipsic area (sparsely stippled) is the heavy line, parallel to the isotonic line, which intersects the ordinate at ΔV_i (= loss of cellular water). The value for ΔV_i was obtained by using the average τ value (0.0123) found in human experiments. Thus, where the cellular water in a 70 Kg. man is 35 liters, $\Delta V_i = 0.0123 \times 35.000 = 0.431$ liters.

An isodip (isodipsic) is a line (e.g., *AB*) which is the locus of all points of equal thirst corresponding to all combinations of loads of sodium (L) and of water (L_{H_2O}) which result in a given water requirement to restore isotonicity (or the state of the thirst threshold). For a hyperdipsic point, *A*, one measures the degree of thirst by passing a salt load line (in this case $L = 300$ mEq. of sodium) from *A* to the thirst threshold at *C* or to the content at the thirst threshold. In man, 100τ averaged 1.23% and, since the dipsic end point was determined at the time the subject receiving a steady infusion of hypertonic salt stated unequivocally that he had become thirsty, this figure was thought to represent an upper limit of the true thirst threshold.

This threshold, of the order of 1 to 2% shrinkage of cell volume, was based conceptually upon the assumption that cells behaved as if they were perfect osmometers (hence "osmometric"). It had a value remarkably similar to the osmotic threshold calculated by Verney (798), by entirely independent methods, to exist for stimulation of osmoreceptors of the antidiuretic hormone system (293). Accordingly it was suggested that osmoreceptors, probably in the central nervous system and similar to, if not the same as, those postulated by Verney, lie on the afferent side of a thirst reflex (p. 94).

When a man loses about 0.8% of his body weight as water alone, he ordinarily seeks drink (9, 18, 865). A dog drinks when it loses 0.5% (658, 856). These figures are "thresholds of thirst" in much the same way as percentual cellular dehydration. With the assumption that the cells of the body behave as an osmometer, these two osmometric thresholds are related. Thus, where V_i is the volume of cellular water, W is the volume of total body water, and Δ signifies "change of," $\Delta V_i/V_i =$

---

isotonic line at D. The projections EF and EG measure, respectively, the volume of water required to move from the given hyperdipsia to hypodipsia, and from the given hyperdipsia to adipsia. The "adipsic area" is relatively unexplored and uncharted; parts of it may actually correspond to antidipsia, paradipsia, pseudodipsia, even hyperdipsia, or a state of salt hunger. Quantities of water required to relieve true hyperdipsia (hypertonicity) may be determined directly from equations of thirst (p. 165).

From the intersection of the thirst threshold and the salt load line $L = 0$, at H, the perpendicular to J may be erected. The abscissal distance from J to the origin represents the absolute water deficit, with no salt loss, which should just provoke thirst, according to the cellular dehydration or osmometer theory. The value obtained here, viz., -0.60 liters, represents a deficit of 0.86% of the body weight. Algebraically, this latter value is equal to 70τ (total body water as percentage of body weight, multiplied by 0.0123).

From Wolf (856).

* At the time of this study, it was commonly supposed that the body contained 70% water (p. 78).

$\Delta W/W = \tau$. Therefore, $\tau W = \Delta W$ or, expressed as per cent of body weight, B, $\tau(100W)/B = 100\Delta W/B$, i.e., the water loss in per cent of body weight at the thirst threshold is the product of the thirst threshold, τ, and the percentual water content of the body. For a water content of 70% (perhaps high, but originally used as the basis for estimating $\tau = 0.0123$), one predicts that a man should lose an amount of water, 0.0123×70 or 0.86% of body weight at his threshold. This compares favorably with the observed value noted above (Fig. 9).

Obviously one could define a thirst threshold in terms of the calculated per cent increment of osmotic pressure of body fluids which exists rather than in terms of cellular hypovolia and, in a perfect osmometer, the two are inversely related. But the volumetric analysis is more instructive and heuristic as may be seen from a study of Fig. 9.

Administration of concentrated solutions other than sodium chloride can also induce drinking. Holmes and Gregersen (376) found similar effects in dogs of sodium sulfate and sodium acetate. Among the nonelectrolytes, glucose, sucrose, sorbitol, isomannide, and urea were tested. Isomannide and urea have little disturbing effect on the serum concentration of protein or chloride presumably because of their large volumes of distribution; neither do they cause such large drinking responses. However, although none of their dogs drank immediately after injections of urea, some did begin lapping water after a delay of 5 to 10 minutes (Bellows (83) reported sham drinking following 40% urea to begin after 10 to 15 minutes); others took no water, and the variation was thought to be related to the individual drinking habits of the animals inasmuch as some dogs that responded best to urea were also the ones that drank the largest amounts after sodium chloride. The injected solutions of urea and salt tested were mutually isosmotic but, as discussed previously (pp. 15ff., 71), their tonicities for cells may have differed.

Adolph, Barker, and Hoy (19) observed in rats that administration of sodium chloride induced approximately twice as much drinking as equiosmolal urea solutions, i.e., salt, particle for particle activitywise, was twice as potogenic as urea. Beyond the labored interpretation which might be proposed in terms of osmotic transients,[23] the analysis of drinking following urea is not now well made through the cellular dehydration or osmometric theory; it may demand consideration of other physiologic effects, and possibly psychologic ones. It has been remarked (856) how dogs may fail as suitable subjects for "thirst" experiments; and it is always necessary to remember that drinking responses are a function not merely of dipsogenic stimuli but also of the antidipsic influences associated with satiety and nimiety, taste, etc. Obviously the magnitude of the thirst sensation cannot be decided by observations of drinking in animals; only man can report this.

Leschke (474, p. 80) has reported thirst to set in rather promptly in man following intravenous urea (see footnote 23). This suggests that some component of the thirst arises other than secondarily to urea diuresis which might be supposed to cause concentration of the salts of body fluids. Platt (618) took 30 to 45 g. of urea per day for 16 days during which period his blood urea was 50 to 54 mg.% on waking and 70 to 90 mg.% during most of the day. He suffered from lethargy, headache, dry mouth, and thirst. Yet there was no elevation of serum sodium level to reflect an ecuretic concentration of residual salts of the blood. Nevertheless, a potogenic response to urea ingestion, as has also been demonstrated in rats by Gamble et al. (280), may still be meaningfully related to an augmented obligatory urine volume.

That urea may actually activate osmoreceptors transiently and perhaps otherwise is suggested in the results of Zuidema, Clarke, and Minton (893). Their experimental program, similar to that of Verney's (798) but slightly modified, essentially confirmed the latter's results with this difference: whereas Verney found urea to be inadequate to excite the antidiuretic osmorecep-

---

[23] It is well to remember that, in classic osmometric theory, an effect of urea on drinking ought to be prompt, before too much of it diffuses into osmoreceptors. If a load of urea is insufficiently large or not administered rapidly enough, little effect on thirst is to be expected; or, it may be missed. Sodium chloride, however, is effective primarily through its elevating the body fluid tonicity, and its dipsogenic and potogenic influence is less a function of time except as renal excretion of salt, or even adaptive response, may come into play.

tor system, they obtained definite activation with urea, as with sodium chloride and sodium sulfate.

CENTRAL THEORIES

We have seen how inextricably various theories of thirst have been combined: dry mouth and central; general and central; etc. Theories which could be called primarily "central" are, however, relatively modern. Already noted are the ideas of Mayer and of Wettendorff. Dumas (216) and Callenfels (150) had earlier discussed the role of the brain in the perception of thirst, but merely in the way it might mediate sensations other than thirst as well.

Bonnier (114) suggested the existence of a "hygrostatic" regulatory center. He placed it in the olfactory lobe, using in evidence his observations that edema disappeared following nasal cautery.

Leschke (474) believed that an increase in blood concentration of crystalloids acted on the cerebral cortex to produce thirst. He observed that patients reported severe thirst almost the instant they were injected with 10 to 20 cc. of 20 to 25% sodium chloride intravenously, and that they required large quantities of water. He reported similar but lesser effects of calcium chloride and urea. On the other hand, brushing the mouth or throat with strong salt gave an unpleasant taste but no true thirst sensation (p. 95). Thus he concluded that the salt had no peripheral effect, such as on taste nerve endings, which would cause thirst. The suddenness of the response to injection may be taken to argue that the source of thirst could not be the dry mouth which might secondarily be caused by intravenous salt and, as noted previously, Leschke specifically stated that dryness of the mouth following atropine seemed essentially different from true thirst.

Brunn (141) took issue with Leschke, being unable to confirm the latter's findings when salt solutions were given orally or intravenously. Brunn proposed, somewhat as had Wettendorff (823), that the important factor was a shift of water from tissues to blood, and that not all tissues were equally important. He thought that the mucous membranes of the mouth and esophagus played the main role, with nerves reporting to a vegetative center for thirst.

Müller (564) stressed the diminished water content of the blood, rather than raised osmotic pressure of that fluid, as the stimulus for the diencephalon which in turn released contractions in the pharyngeal and esophageal musculature. These contractions supposedly gave rise to a sensation identical with the thirst sensation (p. 39). Because of its relation to diabetes insipidus, the hypothalamus seemed a likely place to find a thirst center, and was therefore proposed as its site.

Oehme (585) proposed a central nervous system integration, involving the cortex, diencephalon, and sensory vagus nuclei of the medulla, to combine the local dryness theory and a general theory of thirst, the latter based upon chemical changes in body fluids, such as increased salt concentration.

Carlson (162) considered that the brain must be normal or nearly so for the thirst sensation to be perceived, which may not be the case in sickness or, obviously, when one is unconscious. The fever which may be induced by water deprivation[24] (111, 176), however, he regarded as possibly due to stimulation of the thalamus (temperature regulating site) by concentrated blood. Voit (800) ascribed the lack of thirst in many sick people to a paralysis of a central nervous thirst mechanism and alleged that direct stimulation of this central organ will induce thirst even when membranes of the mouth are wet.

No one doubts that the cortex must be involved ultimately in the sensation of thirst but it has not previously been remarked that cortical activity might primarily engender thirst. Cannon (158) drew attention to a dramatic experience of Dr. H. J. Howard who thought he was going to be shot by Chinese bandits, using it

---

[24] So-called "thirst" or "inanition" fever (512) as in infants, has been attributed to failure of heat dissipating mechanisms for lack of fluid. However, maintenance of normal body temperature in cats is not affected by dehydration from water deprivation (149); and body temperature drops with hydropenia in mice, dogs (Table V), guinea pigs, and rabbits (99). If exposed to heat, men show a rise in rectal temperature, by as much as 2° C. even when sitting, at a 6% water deficit (18, pp. 10, 217).

in support of his dry mouth theory. It might possibly be used to support a central theory. Howard (382) wrote:

> So I was going to be shot like a dog! My tongue began to swell, and my mouth to get dry. This thirst rapidly became worse until my tongue clove to the roof of my mouth, and I could scarcely get my breath. The thirst was choking me. I felt dizzy. I looked towards our destination and realized that it was only two minutes away. I was in a terrible state of fear; I was going to die like a coward. That thought . . . . was more than I could bear . . . . I had strength enough left to pray . . . .
>   . . . . Instantly my thirst began to disappear. In less than a minute it was entirely gone, and by the time we had reached the gate, I felt perfectly calm and unafraid.

One may inquire here whether thirst followed from a dry mouth or the dry mouth was part of a syndrome which includes thirst centrally excited.[25] The remarkable rapidity of the dipsic and antidipsic responses somewhat suggests the latter possibility. One may be reluctant to entertain this view after introspective analysis of his own experiences with the pseudodipsia of fear; nevertheless, we have a conceptual parallel in the observation that injected salt can lead to thirst promptly, followed by drying of the mouth. This could signify stimulation of a thirst center by the salt (in lieu of stimulation of the thirst center by the cortex) with concomitant depression of salivary secretion and delayed drying of the mouth. The role of the cortex in mediating the inhibition of drinking by amphetamine has already been noted (p. 49).

Welt *et al.* (819) have referred to an observation of Stevenson *et al.* that a monkey developed primary hyperdipsia after a prefrontal lobotomy, but this does not occur in dogs (44), and specific information concerning the role of the forebrain as the site of a thirst center or a regulator of body fluid tonicity is inconclusive (18, 34, 51, 236, 434, 478, 496, 500, 779). Polyposia following certain central lesions which produce hyperphagia

---

[25] The ancient legal custom, ordeal by rice, was based on this reflex. One who could not swallow rice because of the dryness of his mouth was recognized to be fearful—and guilty (p. 63).

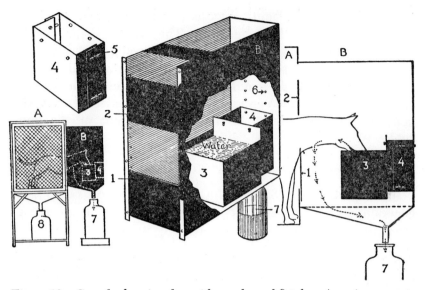

Figure 10. Cage for housing dog with esophageal fistula. A, main compartment from which urine may be collected. B, auxiliary compartment from which "water of thirst" may be collected. 1 and 2, adjustable plates which reduce opening between the two compartments to appropriate size and height, depending upon the size of the dog. 3, container for water. 4, adjustable hanger for holding water container. 5, slots by means of which hanger may be adjusted to hold water container at suitable distance from main compartment. 6, holes upon which hanger may be suspended at suitable height. 7, container for collecting "water of thirst." 8, container for collecting urine.

The dog is confined to main compartment. The auxiliary compartment admits only the head and neck of the animal. The adjustable parts are so fixed that in order to reach the water container the manubrium sterni of the dog will be pressed against the edge of plate 1 and the neck will be horizontal. Thus the superior esophageal fistula will be above the intervening space between plate 1 and container 3 and the discharged "water of thirst" will escape to the bottom of the auxiliary compartment. From Bellows and Van Wagenen (85).

(p. 117) is generally regarded as secondary to the increased intake of food (36, 135, 765, 766, 775).

Bellows and Van Wagenen (85) concluded from a detailed study (p. 98) of experimental diabetes insipidus in dogs with and without esophageal fistulas (Fig. 10), that the production of a persistent "unjustified" thirst, or primary polyposia, by an injury in the hypothalamus suggests that this region of the brain is the center of the thirst function. They regarded diabetes insipidus as a fundamental disturbance of water metabolism in which the thirst function is an integral component. In their view, therefore, normal thirst may logically be regarded as the activity of a mechanism in the central nervous system affected by variations in either the water or the solute content of the body fluids.

The Osmoreceptor Theory

In the postulation (856, p. 77) that osmoreceptors rather than general body tissues were receptors in a thirst reflex, it was recognized that these receptors were probably in the central nervous system and similar to or the same as those envisaged by Verney (798) to regulate the antidiuretic hormone of the posterior pituitary. During osmometric studies of thirst in human volunteers made sufficiently hyperdipsic to report a severe burning sensation in the throat, one subject announced such a sensation first in the arm above the point where the intravenous injection was entered, then in the throat, the back, and the perineum, in that order. These paresthesias were rapidly relieved by intravenous glucose solution (5%), and their widespread distribution was regarded as indicative of a central origin.

"Thirst" or "Drinking" Centers: Stimulation and Ablation. Highly suggestive support for an osmoreceptor theory of thirst was subsequently presented by Andersson (39, 40, 41, 46). He arranged at first to inject directly into the anterior hypothalamus of unanesthetized goats a small quantity (0.1 cc.) of 1.5 to 2% sodium chloride. In about half of the experiments the response of the animals was to drink 500 to 2500 cc. of water after a latent period of one-half to one and one-half minutes. In several experiments the effect could be repeated three or four times with a half hour between injections. Positive results were obtained with injections medially in the anterior hypothalamus, not in front of the optic chiasma nor in the posterior and lateral parts of the hypothalamus; the most obvious effect was obtained with the injection in the middle hypothalamic region near the paraventricular

nucleus. Injection of iso- and hypotonic saline had no effect.[26] Injections into the supraoptic regions or lateral hypothalamus did not provoke thirst as those into the medial hypothalamus near the third ventricle. On the other hand, stimulation of the lateral anterior hypothalamus (38) led to some autonomic functional activity such as licking movements, salivation, rumination.

These studies are far-reaching. Not only do they help reify speculations about central mechanisms of thirst, but they suggest the level of integration of related functions such as salivary flow, lip-smacking (798), etc. Andersson (41) also showed how an injection of 4% sodium chloride into the rostral part of the median eminence (with possible spread into the supraoptic region) resulted in an oliguresis, increased urine concentration, and no polyposia. He believes his results resolve the polemic of "primary" polydipsia versus "primary" polyuria (85, 857, p. 97) in that both seem to exist.

Andersson and McCann (46) later located the drinking area of the hypothalamus more exactly (Figs. 11, 12) by microinjection of 0.003 to 0.01 cc. of 2 to 3% sodium chloride in goats. They induced drinking of two to eight liters of water, on some occasions repeatedly. Drinking began 30 to 60 seconds after injection and continued for 2 to 5 minutes.

Euler (246) has added to the osmoreceptor picture by recording in chloralosed cats slow potential changes from the supraoptic region in response to the rapid injection of 2% sodium chloride into the common carotid. While 10% glucose solutions gave similar responses, tap water evoked a potential of opposite polarity to hypertonic solutions. Sawyer and Gernandt (676) found characteristic changes in electroencephalograms of the anesthetized rabbit, associated particularly with intracarotid injections of hypertonic sodium chloride or glucose, but not with urea.

---

[26] Indeed, Miller et al. (550) cite a report indicating that in moderately thirsty cats, minute injections of water into the third ventricle will reduce drinking. Miller (548a, 549) found also that the volume drunk after an injection of 0.15 cc. of isotonic saline was approximately the same as that after a mock injection. Apparently the minute volume, per se, had little effect. An injection of 0.15 cc. of 2% sodium chloride reliably increased water consumption. Thus, minute injections of hypo- and hypertonic solutions have opposite effects on drinking. And they affect concordantly the rate at which animals will work at a learned response to secure water.

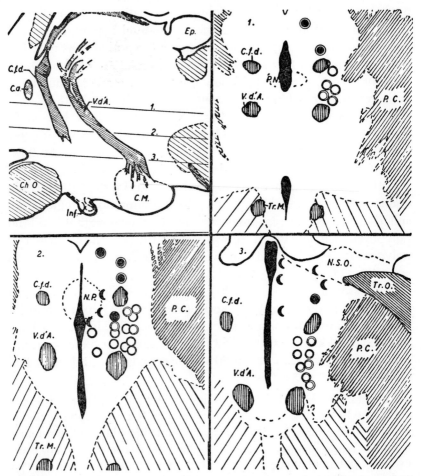

Figure 11. Points in the hypothalamus where electrical stimulation evoked drinking, antidiuresis, and milk ejection in the goat. Diagrams of a sagittal section and, corresponding to the lines labelled 1, 2, and 3, three horizontal sections (1, 2, and 3) through the hypothalamus. Black circles: points where electrical stimulation caused drinking, inhibition of water diuresis, and milk ejection. Open circles: points where drinking was obtained in the absence of antidiuresis and milk ejection. Black half moons: points where stimulation gave inhibition of water diuresis and milk ejection, but no drinking. C. A., Commissura anterior; C. f. d., Columna fornicis descendens; C. M., Corpus mammillare; Ch. O., Chiasma opticum; Ep., Epiphysis; Inf., Infundibulum; N. P., Nucleus paraventricularis; N. S. O., Nucleus supraopticus; P. C., Pedunculus cerebri; Tr. M., Tractus Meynert; V. d'A., Tractus Vicq d'Azyr. From Andersson and McCann (47).

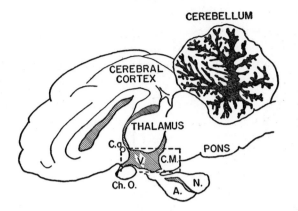

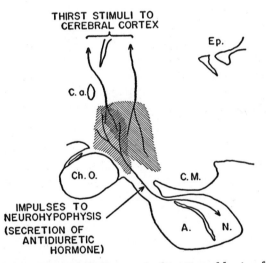

Figure 12. *Upper:* Midline sagittal section of brain of the goat. The rectangle indicated by the broken lines approximates the extent of the hypothalamus. Key below.

Lower: Hypothalamus and hypophysis of the goat, illustrating overlap of the "thirst center" (hatched area to the right) and the probable center of regulation of the antidiuretic hormone of the neurohypophysis (hatched area to the left). A., Adenohypophysis; *C. a.*, Commissura anterior; *C. M.*, Corpus mammillare; *Ch. O.*, Chiasma opticum; *Ep.* Epiphysis; *N.*, Neurohypophysis; *V*, third ventricle. After Andersson (42).

Of interest also is Hillarp's (365) observation of chromatolytic reaction (indicative of increased cellular activity) in the nerve cells of the supraoptic nucleus and the magnocellular portion of the paraventricular nucleus when the body fluids of rats are made hypertonic by administration of sodium chloride.

Andersson and McCann (46) not only induced osmometric drinking in the manner indicated but also, and more consistently, obtained similar results in goats by electrical stimulation of the same regions (Figs. 11, 12). In contrast to injections, electrical stimulation could be repeated frequently without failing to cause a drinking response when it was applied in a discrete region lying between the Columna fornicis descendens and the Tractus Vicq d'Azyr at the horizontal level of the middle of the hypothalamus. "Electrical" drinking began 10 to 30 seconds after onset of stimulus and stopped two to three seconds after discontinuing the current. Overhydration up to 40% of the body weight, with hemodilution and polyuria, could be induced. Even uriposia was observed. In one experiment stimulation at the same point where polyposia was evoked led to an antidiuresis of neurohypophyseal type, suggesting the close propinquity of the central loci of water intake and output faculties.

Andersson and McCann (47) have further confirmed their basic findings on electrical stimulation (Fig. 11). As for the presumptive osmoreceptors, they consider various hypotheses. Thus, such osmoreceptors might have a dual function in regulation of water intake and output. Both drinking and inhibition of water diuresis are found when stimulating the rostral portion of the "drinking area"; and this may be the site thereof. Then the caudal portion of the "drinking area" where no antidiuresis was found might represent fibers from the receptors to the cortex or other effector areas in a similar manner as the paraventricular and supraoptic nuclei may represent effectors concerned in antidiuretic hormone release, since no drinking was obtained from stimulation in or close to these nuclei. A second explanation is that there are osmoreceptors of two kinds in the hypothalamus, one group concerned with water conservation by the kidneys and the other with water intake. The two groups would then be localized to two areas which overlap (Fig. 12) in the region where both drinking and antidiuresis are obtained from stimulation. Again, the inhibition of water diuresis which was obtained in the region where drinking could also be evoked may have been due to stimulation of fibers running from the paraventricular to the supraoptic nuclei and/or the neurohypophysis since stimulations in or adjacent to the paraventricular nucleus evoked inhibition of water diuresis. The data are not considered to permit of a decision among these or other possible explanations; indeed it cannot be ruled out that hyperposia after hypothalamic injections of hypertonic saline is due to a nonspecific effect (43).

Notable side effects seen during the stimulations included temporary increase of urine flow (stimulation in the posterior part of the drinking area), licking, panting (stimulation in a small region in the anterior and dorsal hypothalamus), and a strange behavioral pattern, which normally may be related to a sexual smell in the goat.

Electrical stimulation of the anterior portion of the drinking area in the goat causes inhibition of water diuresis and milk ejection simultaneously with the drinking of water. Stimulation of the paraventricular nuclei or adjacent sites causes inhibition of water diuresis and milk ejection, but no drinking of water (43).

Independently, an important experiment concerning a possible "drinking" center[27] was performed by Greer (304, 305) in the

---

[27] Hess (354) remarks, "It is a burning problem to arrive at a clear concept of the structure of a so-called center. Center is a word in universal usage. However, it is very difficult to find out what notion a person has of the functioning of a center. It is clear that a system of synapses must be involved here. This provides the coordinated connections between definite reflexogenous areas, or patterns of cortical association, and definite effectors. The nervous apparatus mediating the coordination of the effectors is the central representation of a definite performance or, in brief, its center as a physiologic concept. As this paraphrase indicates, the physiologist does not connect a topographic focal but a topologic notion with the term center. . . .

"A brain nucleus quite certainly is not identical with a center. A nucleus probably has, in the first place, trophic functions. To illustrate the problem of a center, a phase of the regulation of motor activity in the trout can serve as an example. The retina, that is, the optical impression, has its representation on the *surface* of the tectum opticum. In the lower portion of the tectum are located the end organs of proprioceptivity and of other sensory systems. When the fish goes into action, this action is the sequence of an integration of different afferent impulses. It is quite certain that it is not a simple superposition. The first and activating stimulus is the optical impression. Proprioceptivity plays a decisive role in providing the adequate combination of muscles . . .

". . . . It is to be kept in mind that the observed symptoms [in electrical stimulation of the brain] are caused to a large extent, if not predominantly, by stimulation of fiber tracts. . . ."

And Stellar (762) writes, " 'Center' is a useful and convenient term, but it is also a dangerous one, for it may carry with it the implication of strict localization of function within isolated anatomical entities."

course of stimulating the central nervous system of rats by radio-frequency activation of a subcutaneously buried unit. Two plati-num-iridium electrodes were placed in the hypothalamus of a female rat with a stereotaxic instrument. On later sectioning it was found that the tips of the electrodes were situated immedi-ately behind the level of the paraventricular nuclei, at the lateral edge of the dorso-median nuclei and in the sulcus between the dorsomedian and ventromedian nuclei. The needle tracks were easily visible, there was no obvious reaction around the electrodes, and the remainder of the hypothalamus did not appear abnormal. Both the paraventricular and supraoptic nuclei appeared intact and contained a normal complement of the typical large nuclei.

The exact current flow across the electrodes could not be de-termined, but it was estimated that the animal began to react when 0.5 to 1 volt (60 cycle square wave direct current pulse of two milliseconds duration) was developed across the electrodes, and showed convulsions at five to eight volts. Greer made most of his observations on drinking in a single animal, having been unable fully to duplicate the unique experiment described in the following account:

Stimulation of the animal began 24 hours after the electrodes were implanted. It was immediately apparent that the animal was under great compulsion to perform violent "licking" activity when a current was passed between the hypothalamic electrodes. In response to stimulation, it would stand on its hind legs and run vigorously around the glass enclosed circular cage, licking wildly at the glass wall. This behavior would cease immediately upon shutting off the current. If the voltage were slowly in-creased, licking would gradually become more vigorous.

With stimulation continuing by timer control, the reaction of the animal changed during the first night. The water bottle con-taining 200 ml. was found completely empty at 9 a. m. even though it had been filled at 6 p.m. the previous evening. It was now found that stimulation would result in violent drinking activity. The nonspecific licking response had been lost. As soon as the current was turned on, the animal would jump for the water bottle and continue to drink avidly until the switch was turned off. If the water bottle were removed and the current then turned on, the rat would go back to its "licking" behavior of the previous day, but would immediately transfer it to drinking behavior when the water bottle was replaced.

If the voltage were slowly turned up, the animal would gradually lose its drinking behavior and become hyperactive and squeal, but it would still transform part of this stimulation into drinking. When the tap water in the drinking bottle was replaced with 5% saline, the rat would begin by drinking as vigorously as before, but it was obvious that the saline was quite distasteful. She would push at the water spout with her forepaws and would finally be able to force herself away from the bottle for a few seconds, then the compulsion to drink would again become too great and she would be forced back to lapping at the saline. It was possible by changing the strength of the current to produce a response that would range from only partial drinking activity when tap water was used, through violent and sustained drinking activity, to hyperreactivity, jumping and convulsions. During this period of marked drinking behavior the rat drank in excess of 400 ml. tap water daily. It was being chronically stimulated five minutes every half hour.

By the fourth day of stimulation, the rat had begun to lose its response to stimulation. It would still respond by drinking, but the voltage of the transmitter had to be turned much higher than previously. During the fourth day its water consumption fell to about 50 ml. On the fifth day the animal no longer responded to stimulation, even though the transmitter was operating at maximum strength. It was then killed and autopsied.

Andersson and McCann (47) have considered how, if a drinking area exists, it should be possible to abolish drinking by its ablation. They cited the report of Stevenson *et al.* (766) on oligoposia concurrent with dehydration in rats with lesions in the ventromedian nuclei (p. 119); and the findings of Witt *et al.* (847) that if the lesions of dogs with diabetes insipidus are extended dorsally and laterally in the hypothalamus, drinking may be abolished. Moreover, Andersson and McCann (45, 48) have shown that partial or complete loss of "thirst" can be produced in dogs by electrocoagulations in the drinking area, and the animals may show no transient or permanent diabetes insipidus. There may be no associated disturbance of sodium chloride metabolism. A load of water produced no water diuresis in oligoposic, hypertonic animals, suggesting the satisfactory operation of the Verney antidiuretic system. Dogs ate and drank milk and broth readily (43, p. 149) but might otherwise be oligoposic. The degree of oligoposy is roughly proportional to the extent of destruction of the area which on electrical stimulation evokes drinking in the goat. In rats, bilateral, complete destruction of the paraventricular nuclei does not seem to cause any marked disturbance in water balance (585a). Gilbert (291, 291a) has shown that electrocoagulative destruction of the subcommissural area in rats results in a sustained drop in water consumption which in a few days may lead to death by dehydration. Morrison and Mayer (560a, 560b) have described localized electrolytic lesions in the lateral subthalamic area of rats which produce a high success rate of aphagia accompanied by aposia. It is believed that these lesions produce both effects directly but that the aphagia and aposia are separate responses; neither complete food deprivation nor complete water deprivation in sham-operated animals is capable of simulating the pattern of exchange of materials found in the operated animals. responses; neither complete food deprivation nor complete water made bilaterally in and around the area in the hypothalamus where electrolytic lesions produced aphagia and aposia. Sham operations might produce hypophagia and oligoposia, the magnitudes of which appear to bear a linear relation to the distance of the insertion from the area of maximum (aphagic, aposic) effect. Aposia accompanying aphagia produced by electrolytic lesions in the diencephalon of chickens has also been reported (252a).

Gilbert (291) has postulated that the subcommissural organ (or, as he suggests it be called, "gland") of the rat, perhaps regulated by the osmotic pressure of the blood or cerebrospinal fluid, secretes a hormone which, acting on end organs presumably neural in nature, alters water consumption. The functioning gland he conceives as facilitative to drinking. With its electrocoagulative ablation, as noted, there results a sustained drop in water consumption. Injection of extracts of this organ (taken from rats) into normal rats leads to a transient drop in drinking succeeded by a return to normal. This phenomenon is interpreted in terms of overcompensation by the recipient's own subcommissural gland, antagonizing the tendency of the injected subcommissural area material to increase water consumption. No report is given of the effect of the extract in rats with ablated gland, and the findings generally call for amplification.

Aqueous extracts of beef subcommissural area into rats had qualitatively similar effects (291a). When such extracts were injected into either adrenalectomized or hypophysectomized rats, water intake fell to about half on the first day. If recovery occurred, it was a gradual process. Extracts of cerebrum had no effect on water consumption.

Kourilsky *et al.* (437, 443) have cited a significant clinical case bearing on the central origin of thirst. A 22 year old girl with traumatic diabetes insipidus came to surgery because of visual complications. An arachnoid cyst at the base of the brain, sunken toward the cisterna chiasmatis, had raised the hypothalamus and stretched the hypophyseal stem. Incision of the cyst caused an outward flow of fluid decompressing hypothalamico-hypophyseal connections, whereupon the patient who had been complaining of thirst and asking to drink every 5 minutes during the operation suddenly said she experienced no more thirst, exclaiming, "What are you doing? I am no longer thirsty" (436). In the following days her water intake and, secondarily, her urine flow returned to normal. Kourilsky (436) remarks further of neurosurgeons who, conversely, noted the sudden appearance of thirst without any preliminary polyuria.

It is possible that thirst in certain forms of disease has an important central component. In reporting on hemorrhagic fever as observed in Korea, Barbero *et al.* (70) noted marked thirst in 97% of the patients starting at the time of chills and fever and lasting into the second week. Powell (624) recorded thirst in 72% of his cases, remarking that the excessive desire for water became a major complaint during the period of protracted vomiting. Some hemorrhagic fever patients, questioned about the onset of their thirst (869), remarked that it was one of the first symptoms of the disease and seemed to be unsatisfied by drinking water. Coupled with the fact that plasma electrolyte concentrations in this disease are not simply consistent with thirst on an osmometric basis, it may be that this is a hyperdipsia of central origin, a part of the developing pathologic processes. Kennedy (410) has described his personal experience with hemorrhagic fever, but the thirst he described may only have been due to the regimen of fluid restriction practiced at the time of his illness in a hot July in Korea.

The Conditioned Thirst Reflex

Carlson (162) remarked that central stimulation (as by osmotic pressure) theories had difficulty in explaining how the thirst sensation was referred to the mouth but this is not, in fact, a serious physiologic objection any more than arises in accounting for the projection of the sensation of a phantom limb. Much earlier, Schiff (679) had argued against the local theory of thirst (p. 47), observing that the dry sensation of the throat which accompanies thirst has only the value of a secondary phenomenon analogous to the heaviness of the eyelids announcing sleep. Indeed, local sensation might be lacking and yet thirst be very lively, he said. Although Schiff regarded thirst as a general sensation arising from a deficiency of water in the blood, his view nevertheless contains the germ of a central theory of thirst in its concept of "association" (this term not being used by him), i.e., the dry sensation being a secondary phenomenon.

Wettendorff (823) elaborated on this. "True" thirst, he said, stems from tissue dehydration and is related to bodily need of water. "False" thirst is the painful sensation of dryness of the mucous membranes of the mouth and throat.[28] However, the central nervous system is a coordinator taking stimuli from the general tissues, and the sensation in the throat is exteriorized by association, from experience. In the evolution of our own being, we have acquired the habit of localizing our impressions in the region where they originate or disappear. When dryness of the periphery occurs, it is merely an expression of general dehydration of the tissues.

Having conjectured that the sensation of thirst originates in osmoreceptors (856), Wolf (857, 862) further extended these inchoate views. He considered that the dehydration of such receptors would parallel that of general body tissues, including membranes of the oral cavity. Few physiologic associations would seem to have better opportunity to be locked into condi-

---

[28] Presumably also it is the sensation associated with a desire to drink water as a lubricant or a rinse.

tioned reflex. Where local dryness of the mouth and throat (facilitated by diminished salivary flow, however caused) or osmotic or chemical stimulation of their membranes appears to elicit thirst directly (218), a conditioned stimulus may be at work. This conceivably acts through sensory nerves from the mouth and throat which join a primitive thirst reflex whose primary afferents (attached to osmoreceptors) lie in the central nervous system.[29] Strictly, a thirst reflex terminates in effectors which cause water to be drunk;[30] but in man, alone, the sensation of thirst provides an index of the excitation of this reflex useful in physiologic experimentation.

When the sensation of thirst arising directly from stimulation of the membranes of the mouth and throat is considered as part of a conditioned rather than a primary thirst reflex, many of the difficulties which have remained refractory to unilateral theories of thirst are resolved, at least in part. The rapid induction of thirst caused, for example, by eating salted anchovies or sweet chocolate, when the mouth is quite wet, is inexplicable in terms either of general tissue dehydration or of local dryness (p. 65). Such thirst may be taken as a manifestation of a conditioned thirst reflex where the conditioned stimulus is activity (perhaps osmotic) in the membranes of the mouth and throat and the unconditioned stimulus, which is here dispensed with, is the usually associated, parallel dehydration of osmoreceptors. The rapid disappearance of such thirst when the material leaves the mouth, without the taking of water, and where only small quantities of salt or sugar have been ingested, indicates the "local" aspect of the stimula-

---

[29] No one distinguishes clearly between thirst receptors (e.g., osmoreceptors) which may lie in the central nervous system, and the thirst center, per se (p. 89). It is conceivable that osmoreceptors actually constitute the thirst center or, in another way, that thirst center neurons are capable directly of responding osmometrically as other cells (676), obviating the need for an afferent limb of the thirst reflex. This would not substantially modify the sense of conditioned reflex or other central theories.

[30] It is of interest to quote one of Boring's (115) subjects analyzing thirst introspectively (p. 38). "Thirst began to show itself by dryness of the lips. I did not clearly realize that I was thirsty, but found myself at intervals going to the water cooler. All along I was being reminded that I had certain sensations in my mouth that indicated thirst by finding the motor habit of securing a drink set off."

tion.[31] The exteriorization of thirst to the mouth and throat when central osmoreceptors have been primarily stimulated (such as following hypertonic salt injections) could be accounted for on a basis of "local sign" and convergence-projection, somewhat as in the case of referred pain. However, exteriorization of a thirst sensation to the mouth or throat need not occur at all in the execution of a thirst reflex and no particular local sensation need be manifest. There may be present simply, but definitely, an urge to drink, hard to describe but not vague, perhaps not unlike an urge to eat a sour pickle.

A type of conditioning may be illustrated in the account of Bellows and Van Wagenen (85) concerning postprandial thirst (p. 202). They observed during the first few weeks after esophagostomy in dogs that thirst was apparent a few hours after tube feeding. In spite of giving the normal requirement of ingested water with the food, this was not enough for the temporary needs of the digestive glands. Consequently additional quantities of water were given 1 to 3 hours postprandially in order to prevent thirst, and the thirst of one of the dogs was controlled in this way. Some of this additional water was required as compensation for salivary loss through the esophageal fistula. The remainder constituted a real excess. After several weeks the supplementary quantities of ingested water were incorporated with the regular feedings. After a day or two of postprandial thirst the animal adjusted itself to the new regimen and rarely showed thirst again.

The conditioned reflex theory of thirst integrates basic tenets of local and central theories, along with those of osmometric analysis. It is flexible and fairly comprehensive, but by no means completely satisfactory. For one thing, it deals primarily with the initiation of thirst. It fails to encompass the manifold problems of drinking and satiety, although perhaps the antidipsia or disgust for water at positive water loads is explicably subsumed. How far one can go with a such a view predictively and operationally, and how amenable it will prove to amalgamation with new experimental evidence remain to be seen.

---

[31] The local aspect of stimulation may be no simple thing. The burning irritation in the throat in colds, coughs, or in response to allergens is not usually misconstrued as thirst; and water provides no relief. Kourilsky (436) considers the persistence of thirst in certain polydipsias of pituitary origin to depend upon conditioned reflexes.

While the conditioned reflex theory of thirst leans heavily on a specificity of primary stimulus (osmometric), which may not be warranted, it does not stand or fall on this principle alone. Janowitz and Grossman (397) have discussed a type of conditioned reflex theory of hunger in which it appears necessary to consider multiple stimuli on the afferent limb. Hunger behavior and hunger sensation are two manifestations of the hunger state, the physiologic state resulting from privation of food. They stress that hunger behavior is an unconditioned, unlearned primitive response, and this may hold true for the hunger sensation, considered solely as the psychic concomitant of the hunger state in the intact individual. However, and as Carlson (161) said of appetite, these hunger sensations acquire meaning for the organism through its experience. Thus the newborn mammal manifests restlessness and an inherited sucking reflex during the hunger state which leads to the ingestion of milk which, in turn, induces repose. The frequent repetition of the cycle establishes a conditioned state in which the animal finally learns that the ingestion of food leads to abolition of the tensions accompanying the hunger state.

Diabetes Insipidus

Characterized by the cardinal signs of polydipsia (or polyposia), polyuria, and hydruria, diabetes insipidus has been the object of innumerable clinical and laboratory researches. We consider it here chiefly in relation to theories of thirst and drinking.

One of the most curious, long standing polemics in physiologic literature concerns the question of the primacy of polydipsia or polyuria in the experimental and clinical forms of this disease. Some of the arguments in the case (85), reviewed from an osmometric point of view (857), will not be represented further. So long as it is supposed that polyuria and polyposia in the disease depend on the salt:water intake (and balance) ratios, emphasis is removed from the question of primacy and shifted to the importance of the relative dehydration of body fluids and the hydruria or watery character of the urine as dipsogenic influences.

It has often been held, from our understanding of the antidiuretic nature of posterior pituitary hormone, of the polyuria which proceeds from its lack, of the oliguresis which follows its administration in excess, and of the control which it often exerts in diabetes insipidus (375), that the mechanism of this disease is settled. But evidence for involvement of the thirst mechanism in the disease, aside from an association of the sensation with a dry mouth, independently of the kidney and its hormonal control, continues to mount.

There is no want of instances reported in which, at the onset of diabetes insipidus, polyposia appeared before polyuria[32] (84, 85, 194, 435–437, 439, 441, 444, 584, 857). No doubt some of the clinical reports of the temporal relations of polydipsia and polyuria are of little value (511); and the evidence for such extreme dissociations between polyuria and polydipsia as have been alleged (442) is not wholly convincing thus far. Nevertheless the following observations used to support the primacy of polydipsia are of interest.

Bellows and Van Wagenen (85) found that in dogs with diabetes insipidus the manifest thirst was similar whether the animals possessed an esophageal fistula or not. Fistulous dogs received normal amounts of water by stomach tube. However, the polyposia of the fistulous dog had the unmodified form and duration of that of the nonfistulous dog regardless of the marked difference in the respective amounts of their water ingestion. The fistulous dog was deprived ingestion of its "water of thirst" (Fig. 10), whereas the nonfistulous dog ingested the water which it was provoked by thirst to drink. This was interpreted to mean that the thirst was excessive and unjustified, that is, "primary," since the fistulous dog appeared to suffer no ill effects of deprivation. The excess ingested by nonfistulous dogs gave rise to polyuria. Dogs with diabetes insipidus when deprived of water, unlike some human subjects so afflicted, excrete urine almost as slowly as do normal dogs so deprived (475). They can be maintained on less than one-half the quantity of drinking water taken spontaneously, with no symptoms of dehydration distress. Rats also tolerate

---

[32] The earliest premise of so-called primary polydipsia appears to be that of Nothnagel (584) in 1881. He cited the case of a man, dragged and kicked by a horse, who did not lose consciousness and was observed to become polydipsic, taking 3 liters of water within half an hour of his fall. Urine was not voided for 3 hours. Nothnagel supposed the existence of a thirst center in the brain (medulla, possibly pons), like a respiratory center, with which nerves from the mouth connected.

similar mild dehydration indefinitely (135).[33]

Another argument advanced by Bellows (82) was derived from an experiment in which a loose ligature was placed around each renal artery of a dog. After diabetes insipidus was produced the ligatures were tightened without anesthesia, producing sudden anuria. The dog continued to drink water four to five times in excess of the prediabetic intake until its body weight was appreciably increased. Thereafter its water intake fell until death.

Barker, Adolph, and Keller (74) identified, in dogs with experimental neurohypophyseal lesions, an abnormality of drinking that was independent of the processes of urinary excretion. While normal dogs drank back an amount of water equal to a water deficit induced by panting, dogs with lesions consistently overdrank in response to water deficit. Pitressin affected operated dogs differently than control dogs. The former overdrank in recovering from water deficit and no larger drink was taken under the influence of pitressin than without it. Pitressin by itself did not produce any urge to drink in normal dogs in water balance but, in conjunction with water deficit, it might, in moderate doses (0.1 U./Kg.), augment drinking by 70%. Larger doses (0.5 U./Kg.) did not enhance drinking, nor did pitressin modify drinking in dogs with salt loads as contrasted with hydropenic dogs.

Levkoff, Demunbrun, and Keller (475) also placed in evidence a pathologic thirst factor in some degree independent of renal defect in diabetic dogs of the same group used by Barker, Adolph, and Keller. Since the spontaneous water intake of diabetic dogs was far more than enough to excrete the daily urinary solute, and a reduction of water intake to one-half the spontaneous ad libitum intake did not engender any dehydration symptomatology, they considered thirst to be to some extent primary.

This type of argument applies to the situation in normal man also. It makes use of the phenomena of the obligatory and facultative urine volumes (35), the former being the minimal volume

---

[33] However, dehydration may not be a patently distressful experience in dogs and cats (626, 871) or rats (874) as it is in man. Deprived of food and water until death, these animals may appear relatively normal to the observer except that they waste away and become lethargic terminally. Some white rats may become more prone viciously to bite at objects thrust at them.

of urine compatible with the excretion of the solid material contained therein, and the latter being any excess above the obligatory volume, determined by ingestion, and supposedly independent of physiologic requirement. Thus, any facultative urine volume reflects some measure of primary thirst. In these terms, diabetes insipidus is a disease which (in addition to its effect on the obligatory water turnover) augments the facultative water intake and its closely associated facultative urine volume (857), more so in the dog than in man.

Levkoff et al. (475) artificially create a condition of primary polyuria in the permanent phase of diabetes insipidus in the dog as follows: subcutaneous administration of 5 U. of pitressin in oil is given to restrict the urinary excretion of water for a period of four or five days. During this period, 500 cc. of dilute milk is given daily to the animal in addition to the routine meat and dry pellet diet; the animal avidly drinks the milk though not interested in water per se. A mild positive water balance is thus accumulated, evidenced by progressive increase in body weight. It is rapidly adjusted by an appropriate polyuria at the end of the four or five day period when the pitressin in the oil depot disappears. Correction of this positive water balance (polyuria) precedes the reappearance of polydipsia.

Pasqualini and Avogadro (597, 598) suspected the polydipsia of diabetes insipidus of being more than a phenomenon secondary to polyuria from their observations of two patients with the disease who were deprived of water for 22 hours. Each was injected with 1 cc. of pitressin in oil (5 U.) intramuscularly at a time when thirst was intense. In about 20 minutes these individuals were no longer very thirsty, and not suffering; in one case there was a diminution of thirst within 10 minutes although after 20 minutes the throat and tongue still appeared dry. The investigators discussed the possibility that, here, polydipsia might be primary, but they considered the primacy of polyuria too firmly established for such a hypothesis. Accordingly, they postulated a dual action of pitressin on the renal tubules and on central nervous system receptors. They also claimed to have seen a small number of cases in which pitressin reduced even normal thirst. Holmes (370) failed to observe any effect of pitressin on either the polyuria or thirst of two renal cases (one of 7 to 10 liters, the other of 13 to 15 liters of urine daily).

Pasqualini and Avogadro suggested that thirst in diabetes insipidus might be different from ordinary thirst because diabetic patients may, unlike ordinary individuals, enjoy drinking urine. But it must be said that the urine of such individuals is, by definition, relatively insipid and quite different from ordinary urine, not to mention the difference in the intensity of thirst. The drinking of concentrated urine by hyperdipsic but otherwise normal individuals is, of course, well known and is noted in other parts of this book.

Kourilsky (436) states that when thirst is associated with "true polyuria," posterior lobe extract works instantaneously on the polyuria and only after a measurable delay of 5 to 7 minutes on thirst. Although he continues to say that if true polyuria is not present the extract is without noticeable influence on the thirst, the short time interval noted may still serve as some support for the thesis of Pasqualini and Avogadro. It is of interest to note that mercurial diuretics are reported to have an antipolyuric effect in diabetes insipidus, possibly related to the desalinating effect of these drugs with consequent lessening of thirst stimuli (440).

Rowntree (666) observed that in some patients with diabetes insipidus drinking did not bring relief, but others derived infinite satisfaction from long drafts of one or two liters. He quotes one of his patients subsequent to treatment with pituitrin, "water tastes differently, it is flat and has no snap to it." On the other hand, he mentions patients with this disease, subsequent to taking pituitary extract, who continued to take water in the amounts to which they had become accustomed, precipitating water intoxication within a few hours (668).

None of the foreging arguments concludes a case for assigning a larger role to the primacy of thirst in diabetes insipidus than has often been supposed. Those of which the skeptic does not question the veracity or preciseness of the supporting evidence may still appear susceptible of contrary interpretation. However, taken in conjunction with repeated presumptive demonstrations of "centers" of thirst and drinking, the primacy of thirst becomes increasingly credible.

In the absence of a new approach to the solution of the problem, a more convincing evaluation of the relative importance of polydipsia and polyuria looks to the discovery of more precise detail on the behavior of the effective osmotic pressure of the plasma as the course of the disease is modified experimentally.

Although Wettendorff (823) detected no rise in osmotic pressure of the plasma of normal dogs going one or a few days without water, or without water or food, Wolf and Eddy (626, 871) in the course of their studies observed elevations in osmotic pressure after one day of deprivation. Rubini *et al.* (671, Table XVII) found the same in man; in ordinary dehydration thirst occurred in association with hypertonia and hypersalemia. Lifson (479) observed changes in plasma osmotic pressure not in 24 hours but in 48 hours of total fasting.

It is difficult to decide primacy of intake or output without reference to the question, "What is zero water balance?" The question has no easy answer. Perhaps the salivary flow test as used by Holmes (369) and Holmes and Montgomery (381) to distinguish diabetes insipidus from other polyposias will provide some anchor for various hypotheses.

The possibility ought not be neglected that even in a primary polydipsiac there may ensue a "disuse atrophy" (p. 131) of the generative mechanism for antidiuretic hormone (453). If such were the case, tests to reveal psychogenic drinking in excess would break down in the presence of the superimposed, true diabetes insipidus. A reversible, functional hyposthenuria, probably secondary to chronic polydipsia has actually been described (243, 429).

Barker, Adolph, and Keller (74) concluded from their tests in dogs that either polyuria or polydipsia, or both, may be primary (p. 85). They found that certain lesions of the neurohypophysis produce abnormalities of drinking without any unusual feature of water excretion and remark that thus a specific neural and hormonal basis of thirst can be identified.

Kourilsky *et al.* (438) think there may be evidence for an infundibular lesion causing abnormal extrarenal elimination of water. Futcher (275) cited Dickinson's patient with diabetes insipidus who, between acts of micturition (and with no food or water taken in the interval), gained 15.5 ounces in 3 hours and 19.8 ounces in 5 hours and was supposed to have absorbed water from the air!

HYPOSALEMIA AND HYPOTONIA

The formalism of osmometric theory and the manner in which it lends itself to quantitative analysis of thirst are desirable aspects which, however, should not be regarded uncritically. The theory has also been misinterpreted. A high correlation between the intensity of thirst and the degree of hypertonia or increased effective osmotic pressure of body fluids is significant beyond cavil. By extension, the correlation between thirst and the diminished water content of general body cells and/or osmoreceptors is equally remarkable. And osmometric theory is further supported by evidence of a converse sort.

Thus, Darrow and Yannet (200) lowered the electrolyte concentrations of body fluids in the dog by the following technique. They placed a volume of *isosmotic* glucose (5%) in the peritoneal cavity, allowed equilibration (temporary increase of fluid volume in the cavity as electrolytes moved into the *hypertonic* glucose (p. 18)) followed by absorption of peritoneal fluid, and withdrew after 4 to 6 hours a volume approximately the same as that injected. Although the water content of the body was thus kept rather constant, signs of mild to severe "dehydration" developed. The tongue and mucous membranes of the mouth were dry. There was a loss of skin turgor and the animals looked sick. Plasma sodium and chloride concentrations fell; protein rose. There was, however, no manifest thirst. Such observations appear to accord with deductions from osmometric theory: if cellular dehydration in hypersalemia or hypertonia is associated with thirst, we should expect no thirst (either adipsia or antidipsia) in hyposalemia where cells are swollen and extracellular fluid is correspondingly diminished. Negative correlation between intake of fluid and cellular water content was also affirmed by Remington, Parkins, and Hays (645).

McCance (519–521) studied salt deficiency in man in a series of important experiments. By combining a low salt diet and sweating in a radiant heat bath, he induced hyposalemia in his subjects with a corresponding reduction of 28 to 38% of extracellular fluid volume. The results of these studies suggest possible inconsistencies in the osmometric theory. One of the characteristic symptoms of salt deficiency as McCance observed it in himself and his subjects was an aberration of the sense of flavor and taste. One of his subjects interpreted this as thirst[34] (519):

. . . . She complained of it constantly and drank freely but without obtaining any relief. R. A. M. recognized the feeling as distinct from thirst. His mouth was not unduly dry but food was tasteless, even highly flavoured food, and this was the more noticeable because such foods were eagerly sought to make the meals more appetizing. Chewing fried onions, for example, evoked only a sensation of greasy sweetness which was extremely nauseating. The distaste, however, was not confined to meals and was a feature of every waking hour . . . . R. B. N. was not so much troubled by this symptom but felt it from time to time. He noted once that he was "Thirsty all morning—drank a lot but water seems to make little difference" and on another day reported that he had a "funny feeling in the mouth. " . . . .

Recovery was quite dramatic. Half an hour after eating 15 gm. of NaCl with bread, butter, and an egg E's sense of flavour and taste had returned, although no fluid had been taken. This she spoke of as a quenching of her thirst. Genuine and almost unbearable thirst supervened later and was only satisfied by copious draughts of water.

McCance remarks again (520):

. . . . All food seems to be tasteless, even fruit, which contains no salt and is normally eaten without any. I found that cigarettes had lost all their flavour. At the same time an apple would never be mistaken for a pear. The characteristic flavours are there, but they are blunted . . . . I tried the effect of washing out my mouth with salt and water and found it very refreshing, and thought my sense of flavour was thereby restored . . . . it is quite possible that the "thirst" so often complained of by patients with intestinal obstruction may really be this curious loss of taste brought about by

---

[34] Kuno (451), reaffirming an observation in the first edition of his monograph, remarks, "We sometimes experience in extremely hot environments that severe thirst due to copious sweating cannot be satisfied by taking water, and that we feel more thirsty the more water we take." Kunstmann (452), also, has clearly recognized and discussed this phenomenon. A reduction in fluid intake by a miner taking supplemental salt has been noted by Moss (561). See page 263.

salt deficiency. At all events Mr. J. B. Hunter has informed me that a patient's "thirst" is often relieved by hypertonic saline in amounts too small to relieve the general dehydration.

Similarly, in describing the syndrome of salt depletion[85] induced by a regimen of sodium restriction and forced natriuresis, Soloff and Zatuchni (749), Schroeder (700), and others (197, 231, 751, 771a, 878) have remarked on the thirst, not relieved by plain water, which might set in. Nelson *et al.* (577) and Nelson (576), as indicated (p. 204), assert that it is not hyponatremia alone but reduction in effective extracellular volume which underlies this phenomenon. However, McCance (519), judging from the rapid restoration of flavor sense in salt depleted subjects who take salt, regarded the loss of that sense as an effect of hyponatremia or hypochloremia, not connected with anhydremia.

Severely undernourished persons hunger for salt and drink excessive quantities of water despite hydremia (421); and fasting dogs with free access to water may gradually augment their drinking in spite of a fall in plasma osmosity (626, 871). Goodyer *et al.* (298) infused hypertonic saline into cirrhotics with untapped ascites and hyponatremia, sufficient to bring the serum sodium level to, but not above, normal range. When their patients were subsequently allowed water ad libitum, they unerringly drank enough to lower the serum sodium to its previous hyponatremic level (p. 202).

In addition to these suggestions of inconsistency in osmometric theory (i.e., that thirst is augmented not only in cellular dehydration but also, paradoxically, in cellular hydration) are experiments of Holmes and Cizek (372) and Cizek *et al.* (172). They reported that dogs depleted of sodium chloride, by peritoneal extraction technique and low salt diet combined, show increased daily water intake which drops to control values after sodium chloride is restored to the diet. Thirst as measured by drinking response could occur at values as low as 125 mEq./L. for plasma sodium and 75 mEq./L. for plasma chloride. Since the weight

---

[85] Hyponatremia is the term preferred by Danowski *et al.* (197) over "low salt syndrome." They classify hyponatremias on the basis of association with decreased, intact, or increased total stores of sodium. See also Wynn (878, 879) on the hypotonic syndromes.

of an animal remained essentially constant and the thiocyanate space decreased in the procedure, it may be presumed that there was cellular hypervolia. These findings were considered not to support the concept that drinking is regulated by the state of cellular dehydration. Gregersen and Cizek (311) point out that the immediate effect of rapid salt depletion by the peritoneal dialysis technique is a profound depression in which the animal is apathetic and listless and therefore, it is supposed, aposic. This state is soon succeeded by recovery and drinking.

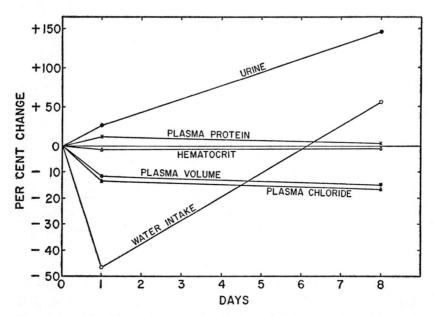

Figure 13. Physiologic changes after peritoneal dialysis of the rabbit with 5% glucose. Average of four experiments. After Huang (385).

Thirst in hyposalemia seems at first a negation of the cellular dehydration or osmometric theory, but this is not necessarily the case. Strictly, osmometric theory rests on the correlation between cellular dehydration and thirst; and this still appears to be incontrovertible. It is a limited theory which does not tell us that drinking or thirst cannot coexist with cellular hydration, and does not rule out the play of multiple factors. The regulatory process appears to be quite complex, varying among different species (p.

159). In the rat, this is revealed by drinking responses which contrast to those of the dog, being related more to the quantity of chloride-free diet taken than anything else (713, p. 117). Huang (385) has shown that in the rabbit, as in other animals, acute depletion of chloride causes transient depression and reduced water intake. The latter rises above normal in eight days (Fig. 13). In any case it is undeniably evident that, under certain conditions (including, of course, ordinary small positive water loads), cellular hydration is indeed associated with adipsia or even antidipsia (200, 208, 568).

No generally satisfactory explanations of hyposalemic or hypotonic thirst have been given; certainly none in terms of a wholly consistent theory. Elkinton and Squires (231) suggested that the development of thirst in hyponatremic cardiac patients reflects an altered response of cellular (osmo-) receptors which sets the total electrolyte concentration of body fluids at a new low level, and that changes in osmotic activity of cellular solutes might produce such a result. This has elements in common with Verney's (798) "accommodation" of osmoreceptors wherein such receptors were supposed to acquire a different osmotic setting if they sustained prolonged hypotonia. The latter concept was introduced by Verney to account for the fact that hyponatremic states are not necessarily accompanied by polyuria, which might be supposed to be the case if the situation were otherwise governed strictly according to his theory of water diuresis.

One difficulty with the accommodation hypothesis as noted by Wolf (857) is that one should expect, not uncommonly, to find accommodation in hypersalemia, e.g., adipsia in the presence of hypertonia. But the desert habitué calls for his water at pretty much the normal physiologic threshold, and no success attends training with an eye to getting along with large deficits of body water (18, 862). There is reason to believe, however, that accommodation, or at least a lack of hyperdipsia in hypersalemia, may be characteristic of disease (238, 434, p. 119).

Another possibility is that idiogenic cellular increments or decrements in osmotic pressure (530) might permit cell hydration actually to remain relatively "normal" even in hypertonia or hypotonia. If so, volume-osmometric analysis rather than pressure-osmometric analysis might be the more valid.

The finding that serum sodium and chloride levels may fall in fasting where water intake is sufficiently limited to cause thirst (177, p. 216) is not inconsistent with this view; nor is the finding that thirst sensations are less intense during exercise (18, p. 137), at which time some (e.g., muscle) cells may take up extracellular fluid (530, 849) (central inhibition of the thirst sensation is not precluded here). Loss of cell volume, whether through glycogen loss (281), through osmometric dehydration, water loss with potassium loss and/or with protein breakdown, or in association with an initial hydropenia in which osmotic pressure of body fluids may not change (823, p. 67), may be more generally correlated with thirst than osmometric dehydration sui generis. And in this may lie a means of deciding whether osmoreceptors behave as if their fluids are "cellular" or "extracellular." It has been conjectured (106, p. 133) that thirst in cellular dehydration may occur only if intracellular osmotic pressure is at the same time elevated.

The phenomenon of accommodation is suggested more particularly in regard to "water" diuresis and renal concentrating ability. Adolph (4) first observed that when water was taken in an amount to make a previously administered hypertonic load of sodium chloride isotonic, the result, far from the expected inhibition of diuresis, was the immediate excretion of a large quantity of water. Baldes and Smirk (67) and Birchard *et al.* (100) noted a similar response. The latter authors inferred that an influence other than tonicity of body fluids is a determinant of water excretion (p. 191), while the former considered that the *change* in osmotic pressure is of greater importance than the absolute value in determining diuresis. It appeared to them that, given time, the kidney (we might now say the pituitary osmoreceptor system) is able to adjust itself to a limited change in its environment, and it may be that it resembles the thermal receptors in the skin which indicate a rise or fall in skin temperature more accurately than the actual temperature. With respect to sodium, rather than water, excretion, Green and Farah (303) have also emphasized the rate of change of cell water loss (= rate of change of effective osmotic pressure?), rather than absolute values, as the determining influence in sodium excretion.

Epstein *et al.* (243) suggested that the renal concentrating process is conditioned to an important degree by the state of hydration of body fluids. Preliminary water deprivation in man, and forced drinking, respectively increased and decreased the maximum urinary concentration achieved under the influence of pitressin.

Wolf (862) suggested another possible mechanism for hypotonic thirst. Assuming the existence of osmoreceptors for thirst that excite afferent nerves when, ordinarily, they shrink in response to hypertonicity, it is conceivable that these receptors, swollen in hypotonicity, also stimulate the same afferents. By Johannes Müller's old Doctrine of Specific Nerve Energies, we may take it that no matter how stimulated, whether by shrinking or excessive swelling of osmoreceptors, those same afferents of the thirst reflex mediate one basic sensation, *viz.*, thirst. This would account for the observation that hyposalemic thirst is unassuageable by water, since its administration does not relieve the swelling of the osmoreceptors; salt, which can shrink the osmoreceptors toward normal does, "logically," relieve thirst.

Hyposalemic thirst, therefore, may not be "real" thirst where, unlike ordinary thirst, it is not satiated by water. How far satiety can be used crucially to define thirst is an open question. The possibilities that thirst is a "release" phenomenon, or that there is a "satiety center" have not yet been investigated. Apparent paradoxes such as of hypotonic thirst might be resolved in unsuspected ways if such mechanisms operated.

Epstein (240) describes the following case: A 45 year old alcoholic had taken about 200 cc. of carbon tetrachloride and had become anuric for about four days before he arrived at the hospital. The striking thing about him was his intense thirst, associated with a dry mouth, despite a serum sodium concentration of 109 mEq./L. He had gained about 2 Kg. over his usual weight (drinking water and vomiting intermittently at home), and had a slight pitting edema. He had developed hypertension and mild congestive failure. His thirst did not abate when he was given hypertonic saline which raised his serum sodium to 130 mEq./L.; neither did it get much worse. It did not disappear until the third day of his diuresis, when his hypertension and signs of heart failure disappeared. At this time his serum sodium was still 130 mEq./L. and he had lost 8 Kg.—chiefly water—of his body weight from the time of admission.

Epstein further observed other patients with acute renal failure who had moderate to rather intense thirst in association with a serum sodium of 120 to 130 mEq./L. and an absolute hydration evidenced either by obvious edema or by considerable and rapid weight loss during a subsequent diuretic phase. It was thought that the thirst might be a symptom of occult heart failure but it was not strikingly altered by digitalization, nor were other signs of congestive failure unequivocal. Infusing hypertonic saline and raising the serum sodium did not ameliorate thirst and, in some instances, worsened it. The patients were not in shock nor more than mildly anemic. The nonprotein nitrogen in each was over 150 mg.%. When diuresis supervened, thirst disappeared as total body fluid diminished, serum sodium rose, and nonprotein nitrogen fell.

The foregoing hypotheses taken together—accommodation, Doctrine of Specific Nerve Energies—channelize our interpretation of such hypotonic thirst. But we still lack knowledge of the actual state of hydration or dehydration of body cells in general and of osmoreceptors in particular in such complex metabolic dipsoses.

FOOD-WATER RELATIONS

Hunger and thirst are not confused in man except perhaps in the infant (150, 494, 673, 785, p. 14). Distinct on the level of sensation, they are nevertheless interrelated.

Men and some animals ordinarily require less water when deprived of food (152, 308, 658). Deprived of water, they take less food (18, 57, 99, 183, 285, 430, 473, 632, Table V); and when water is again available, appetite for food returns. It has been noted how, with the relief of thirst, men who have been without food and water discover an accentuation of hunger (18, 327, 671, p. 246). While the rat, rabbit, dog, and man are said to exhibit such dehydration anorexia, there is actually a spectrum of variable response among different species. The camel and donkey, when deprived of water, continue to eat "dry" dates and hay (p. 116). However, they lose weight, and when desiccation becomes severe (20 to 25% of body weight), they gradually lose appetite (686). Most of their weight loss is water and, with renewed access to it, they drink at one time enough to restore original body weight.

Loss of appetite apparently signals relative as well as absolute dehydration, although it is difficult to decide whether one of these is a primary anoretic influence. Cort (183) has suggested that some property of ingested food which is related to its "potential"

TABLE V

A dog deprived of water (604).

	Day	Body Weight (Kg.)	Urinary Volume (cc./24 hrs.)	Urinary Specific Gravity	Urinary Urea (g./L.)	Food Eaten (g./24 hrs.)	Body Temperature (°C.)
Before water deprivation	..	6.700	265	1.020	19.65	350	39
Water deprivation	1	6.600	150	1.038	18.3	156	40
	2	6.450	70	1.036	16.7	70	39
	3	6.325	65	1.041	20.2	85	39
	4	6.200	60	1.041	14.8	70	38
	5	5.875	60	1.041	18.4	15	38
	6	5.900	70	1.041	17.9	15	38
	7	5.700	30	...	17.6	25	37
	8	5.550	27	...	18.7	50	38
	9	5.400	20	...	20.1	0	38
	10	5.200	30	...	17.6	0	37
	11	5.075	25	...	16.5	0	37
Death	12						

osmolality seems to act as a check on food intake. Such an inhibitory factor may be independent of that physical disability of swallowing attending dryness of mouth and throat.

When food as well as water is denied to a rat, its loss of weight proceeds at much the same rates as when food is allowed because the small food intakes which occur in the absence of water add essentially nothing to the net content of the body (10). A rat deprived of food alone survives no longer than one deprived of food and water and loses just as much weight; this contrasts with larger animals in which food stores outlast "water stores" (p. 359). Barker and Adolph (73) have found rats to die sooner (8.5 days) when denied food only than when denied water only (13 days), a relationship confirmed by Wolf and Meroney (874). There is a record (384) of a dog maintained in good spirits on water and no food for 117 days, sustaining a weight loss of 63%. Withholding water and food, however, has been found to result in death within 38 days, with a loss of 50% of body weight (626, 871, Table IV). Forcing water in inanition does not alter survival time in the rat (471). Thirst and hunger drives in this animal do not appear significantly different (259).

When food is being eaten, thirst sensations are stimulated; man tends to drink the water his body lacks more avidly at mealtimes than at other times (18). In dogs, increasing the water content of comparatively dry pulverized food facilitates ingestion, yet ingestion of the food without addition of water does not affect appreciably the urge to drink (52). Bing and Mendel (99) considered that the white mouse, which takes about 1.1 to 1.3 cc. of water per gram of dried food without much correlation to food composition, drinks (in the laboratory) in order to moisten food and render it capable of being ingested. The weight of water so used for lubrication is slightly greater than that of the dried food provided this water exceeds that required to excrete metabolites. There is no evidence that the white mouse can thrive in the absence of water, as has been alleged of the wild or house mouse (p. 357). Some of the complex relations of food and water intake in farm animals have been discussed by Leitch and Thomson (470).

Kleitman (430) studied the effect of starvation on the daily consumption of water. He found the fasting dog to drink about one-half the quantity of water taken during alimentation, but its total water intake (350 to 450 cc. ordinarily from food) was only about one-fifth to one-third of normal. Robinson and Adolph (658) observed dogs to drink one-tenth to one-third as much water on days when food was withheld as otherwise; and Meyer *et al.* (547) found water intake of dehydrated sheep to be regulated by food intake. Kleitman suggested that the decrease in total metabolism (lessened excretion of urinary nitrogen and therefore of obligated water) might be the reason for decreased water intake but he left open the question whether this could explain the 65 to 80% reduction in total water intake.[36] Gregersen (308) disagreed that this accounts for it because water is taken so promptly after a meal (p. 202). Dogs drink when they have eaten, rarely before the meal is finished, taking water from time to time 2 to 5 hours after the meal. Holmes and Behan (371)

---

[36] Kleitman's dogs generally drank surprisingly little on Sunday, the day on which they were not fed. He was constrained to remark, "What is very hard to account for is that even during continuous fasting the dogs often drank less water on Sunday than on either Saturday or Monday." (!)

showed that dogs on 16 to 80 grains of thyroid per day responded with increased fluid intake with maxima five to eight times that of control periods.

It would appear, in fasting, that an animal actually uses its own body water in lieu of exogenous drink or preformed water of food, and that this is a factor in the reduction in drinking (p. 118). Elkinton and Taffel (232) and others (626, 871) have shown that when dogs are deprived of food and water, up to three-quarters of their weight loss reflects water loss. If a dog with access to water but not food maintained approximately the same percentage of water in its body as it had before fasting, its water loss in starvation would still be of the order of 60% of the weight loss. Thus, a starving animal, with or without access to drinking water, would tend to be absolutely dehydrated. Because there is no coexisting relative dehydration in the case of a dog with access to water, one may not consider such an animal to be hydropenic. Hamilton and Schwartz (326) observed:

> We do not, however, speak of dehydration in such cases where the loss of weight is due to insufficient intake of food . . . . nor do we then observe the characteristic symptoms of dehydration. When we speak of dehydration, it indicates our belief that in some cases the loss of water plays a specially important part in producing the clinical symptoms observed.

Lepkovsky et al. (473) have proposed a novel view about gastrointestinal regulation of water and its effect upon food intake. They studied rats, trained to eat their daily food requirement in 2 hours, with and without access to water. Before and after feeding, samples of stomach and intestinal contents were analyzed for water. Although rats without water ate considerably less food than those receiving water, all groups maintained a fairly constant water to food ratio in the stomach (about 50% water) and in the intestinal tract (about 76% water). They considered that water regulates food intake such that food is eaten only in amounts which enable the rats to maintain this ratio of food to water in the stomach which is considered the site of regulation. The source of the water, whether mobilized from the tissues of the animal (and possibly acting as a factor causing "satiety" and cessation of eating) or taken by mouth, appears to make little difference. When water is supplied ad libitum, food is ingested along with water until some other satiety mechanism gets the animal to stop

TABLE VI

Prolonged fasting in man (87). This study on A. Levanzin was begun April 10, 1912 with four control days preceding the start of his 31 day fast; it terminated after three post-fast days on May 18th. The amounts of water in urine for the first 16 days were obtained by means of computed amounts of total solids, using a Haeser-type coefficient of 3.2 (not 2.33), determined in the last 16 days of the fast. It is assumed that the amount of water from fatty tissue (column M) is equal to 10% of the fat catabolized. It is assumed for column N that 4 grams of water are lost per gram of protein as flesh disintegrates so that grams of nitrogen $\times$ 6.0 $\times$ 4 is the preformed water loss from flesh.

Day	Water Consumed (g.) (A)	Volume of Urine (cc.) (B)	Weight of Urine (g.) (C)	Water in Urine (g.) (D)	(D)/(A) (E)	Specific Gravity (F)	Total Solids in Urine (g.) (G)	Loss of Body Weight (g.) (H)	Body Weight (End of Day) (Kg.) (I)	Insensible Perspiration Per 24 Hrs. H + A − C. (g.) (J)	Water Vaporized (calc.) (g.) (K)	Loss of Preformed Water Total (g.) (L)	From Fat (g.) (M)	From Flesh (g.) (N)	From Other L − W + N (g.) (O)	Daily Excretion Urea N (g.) (P)	Na (g.) (Q)	K (g.) (R)
Pre-fast 1		1,485				...			60.13							17.02		
2		1,521				1.0184			60.53							15.92		
3		1,528				1.0186			60.95							14.48		
4		1,441				1.0159			60.64							11.54		
Begin fast 1	720	660	673.7	630.2	.875	1.0206	43.51	1040	59.60	1086	859	769	14	170	585	5.68	2.070	1.630
2	750	468	482.0	436.6	.582	1.0303	45.38	920	58.68	1188	977	664	14	202	448	6.69	0.926*	1.368*
3	750	565	581.2	530.6	.707	1.028	50.62	890	57.79	1059	854	635	13	272	350	9.11	"	"
4	750	713	730.5	674.4	.899	1.0246	56.13	760	57.03	779	600	524	14	285	225	9.03	"	"
5	750	667	682.6	633.5	.845	1.023	49.09	660	56.37	727	545	429	13	250	166	7.58	0.276	"
6	750	610	623.9	577.8	.770	1.0236	46.07	480	55.89	606	440	268	13	244	11	7.36	"	1.1445

Day	(A)	(B)	(C)	(D)	(E)	(F)	(G)	(H)	(I)	(J)	(K)	(L)	(M)	(N)	(O)	(P)	(Q)	(R)
7	750	524	536.5	495.9	.661	1.0242	40.58	390	55.50	603	437	183	13	235	−65	7.02	0.154	0.883
8	750	587	601.0	556.9	.743	1.0235	44.14	420	55.08	569	405	212	13	246	−47	7.45	"	"
9	750	607	622.1	575.3	.767	1.0241	46.81	450	54.63	578	411	236	12	258	−34	7.83	"	"
10	750	565	577.8	535.3	.714	1.0235	42.49	500	54.13	672	516	301	12	241	48	7.44	0.100	1.006
11	900	564	577.2	535.1	.595	1.0233	42.05	250	53.88	573	421	56	12	246	−202	7.66	"	"
12	900	517	529.1	489.9	.544	1.0237	39.21	320	53.56	691	537	127	12	243	−128	7.43	"	:
13	900	561	574.3	532.3	.591	1.0234	42.01	110	53.45	436	288	−80	11	248	−339	7.69	"	..
14	900	647	659.9	619.3	.688	1.0196	40.58	300	53.15	540	389	108	12	250	−154	7.69	0.109	0.814
15	900	758	768.3	735.8	.818	1.0134	32.50	310	52.84	442	299	135	12	203	−80	6.18	"	"
16	900	889	902.3	861.2	.957	1.0154	41.12	580	52.26	578	435	396	11	230	155	6.71	"	..
17	900	848	860.9	821.4	.913	1.0153	39.51	470	51.79	509	369	290	11	212	67	5.95	"	:
18	900	657	668.8	633.3	.704	1.0177	35.47	290	51.50	521	385	118	11	198	−91	5.70	0.051	0.676
19	900	728	739.6	705.0	.783	1.0153	34.59	390	51.11	550	414	219	11	201	7	5.58	"	"
20	900	699	708.7	678.6	.754	1.0143	30.06	180	50.93	371	236	15	11	184	−180	5.36	0.066	0.644
21	900	708	717.2	685.3	.761	1.013	31.88	440	50.49	623	485	270	11	190	69	5.54	"	"
22	900	785	794.6	763.4	.848	1.0127	31.18	360	50.13	465	332	195	11	186	−2	5.60	0.083	0.643
23	900	556	565.8	536.5	.596	1.0176	29.30	170	49.96	504	371	8	11	176	−179	5.01	"	"
24	900	750	759.5	727.5	.808	1.013	32.01	340	49.62	480	345	173	11	196	−34	5.92	0.065	0.787
25	900	713	722.1	691.8	.769	1.0135	30.32	290	49.33	468	334	126	11	188	−73	5.43	"	"
26	900	728	737.1	706.1	.785	1.0129	31.04	310	49.02	473	339	145	11	189	−55	5.62	0.055	0.656
27	900	653	662.7	631.2	.701	1.0147	31.52	320	48.70	557	422	153	11	194	−52	5.90	"	"
28	900	655	663.4	634.3	.705	1.0134	29.06	240	48.46	477	338	72	11	183	−122	5.46	0.036	0.585
29	900	697	705.8	676.2	.751	1.0129	29.64	360	48.10	554	420	196	11	181	4	5.55	"	"
30	900	771	780.3	750.7	.834	1.0119	29.58	410	47.69	530	397	248	11	188	49	5.53	0.053	0.606
31	900	566	574.5	547.4	.608	1.0150	27.07	300	47.39	625	488	135	12	166	−43	4.84	"	"
End fast																		
Post-fast 1		414				1.0203	24.73		47.05							3.21	0.054	0.430
2		1,262				1.002	14.55		47.12							2.69	"	"
3		241				1.017	16.35		48.17							1.54	0.046	0.116
		(22 hrs.)					(22 hrs.)									(22 hrs.)	(22 hrs.)	(22 hrs.)

* Figures in these columns represent averages for two to three day periods.

eating, but the food to water ratio in the stomach is no different from that in rats ingesting food without access to water. The regulation of water and solids in the intestinal lumen is taken to indicate that the lumen is part of the internal environment. However, as shown in the rabbit (285) and the camel (686, p. 358), the feces have less water when water intake relative to food falls.

Studies of prolonged fasting in man are of interest for their bearing on water metabolism. Benedict's (87) famous subject (A. Levanzin), in the longest scientifically controlled fast, went 31 days without food. No noteworthy observations on thirst were made except that there seemed to be no serious aberration in this department. The subject took a controlled amount of distilled water, 750 g. for the first 10 days and 900 g. for the last 21 days (Table VI). On some days the quantity of water seemed sufficient, at other times insufficient. The importance of this observation is that it defines roughly the minimal water requirement of a man (p. 288) under these conditions.

Keys *et al.* (421) remark that severely undernourished persons have a greatly increased hunger for salt and consume excessive quantities of water in spite of persistent hydremia and perfectly adequate kidneys. In the rabbit, also, fasting produces chronic chloride depletion and gives rise to polyposia and polyuria (385, p. 107). In the same time period, by comparison, the fasting dog shows reduced water turnover.

It is often said that an outstanding difference between hunger and thirst is that the former sensation disappears after a few days, while the latter grows ever more intense.[37] However, Keys *et al.* note important differences between total abstinence from food and caloric deficiency. In total fasting the hunger sensation disappears after a few days; but in semistarvation there is no diminution of hunger. In a limited way a parallel exists in that certain (but not all) episodes of acute dehydration in unacclimated men, as may occur in the desert (p. 73), give rise to little thirst, but

---

[37] There is a version of "Buridan's Ass," recounted by de Morgan (205), among others, which unaccountably persists. It seems a donkey found itself between a bundle of hay and a pail of water and was pressed equally by hunger and thirst. Some say that no such balance could exist; others that the creature died of indecision. If this is a physiologic sophism it is easily resolved, at least in theory (p. 110).

when dehydration is developed chronically, worse subjective features of thirst develop.

Central Nervous Regulation

Brobeck, Tepperman, and Long (128) showed that lesions, necessarily bilateral, along the ventrolateral border of the ventromedial hypothalamic nuclei produce hyperphagia in the rat. The water intake of such rats which become obese, and of normal rats, has been supposed to be secondary to the food intake. Thus, Strominger (775) observed the ratio between food and water intake to remain about the same in hyperphage as in normal rats. In normal animals restriction of water intake caused depression of food intake and restriction of food intake produced depression of water intake, maintaining much the same water:food ratio. However, animals receiving no food drank some water and animals with no water ate some food.

Stevenson (765) and Stevenson *et. al.* (766) did not find the actual water intake to vary much between control and hyperphage rats and discovered therefore a lowered water:food intake ratio in the latter (183). Bruce and Kennedy (135) pointed out that the correlation between the food eaten and water drunk by normal and hyperphage rats is valid only in the particular case of a diet of constant composition. Varying the composition shows that water intake depends neither on weight of food eaten nor on its caloric value. However, increasing the nitrogen content of the diet increases water intake (57) secondarily to augmenting the urinary excretion of water. Since an animal eating a general diet of constant composition changes its intake of water with change in nitrogen intake, food and water consumption are correlated.

One gram of completely metabolized protein yields 0.396 g. of oxidative water and 0.343 g. of urea (p. 353ff.). In potential, this is as if 0.653 cc. of a 52.5% solution of urea (g./100 cc. of solution) had been added in lieu of that protein. To excrete the 0.343 g. of urea contained therein at a maximum urinary concentration of 5.0% (man), 6.9 cc. of urine would be obligated; or 6.9 cc./g. of protein metabolized. The urinary water obligated would be only slightly less than this. At the presumably smaller, limiting isorrheic concentration of urea (851), possibly as much as 10 cc. of urine would be obligated (741), even without consideration of the water obligated to the removal of sulfate and phosphate derived from the protein.

Each gram of body protein holds in physical combination over 3 g. of preformed water so that destruction of body protein in starvation yields a total quantity of water greatly in excess of oxidative water alone. However, while over 3 g. of water per gram of tissue protein is derived thus in starvation, little, if any, of this can be considered "free" (p. 163). Presumably preformed water is released as a solution of tissue substance, rich in potassium and other electrolytes, and at least isosmotic with other body fluids. Also, in effect a solution of approximately 28 g. of protein per 100 g. of water, this obligates in man a volume of urinary water greater than the water which was preformed. Even in the dog and cat (p. 327ff.) and other animals which withstand the water deprivation of total inanition relatively well, despite the greater nitrogen concentrating capacity of their kidneys, the steady increase of body fluid hypertonia in total inanition (626, 871, Table IV) proves that they suffer a steadily increasing relative deficit of water; however, this is rather with respect to salt than to nonprotein nitrogen of the plasma.

Oxidative water from fat may be important during hibernation (p. 211) and otherwise in the severe economy imposed by total deprivation of exogenous water and food, but its own metabolites obligate variable quantities of urinary water, and considerable quantities of body fat, nevertheless, often remain in the carcasses of cats and dogs after death from total inanition (626).

We do not know how nonosmometric cellular dehydration, such as may follow tissue protein breakdown, may be associated with thirst (p. 108).

Anand and Brobeck (36) localized a small area in the extreme lateral part of the lateral hypothalamus of rats, in the rostrocaudal plane corresponding to the central part of the ventromedial nucleus. Bilateral (not unilateral) destruction of this area leads to complete cessation of eating (aphagia). If an animal is made obese by medial lesions, eating ceases when the lateral areas are destroyed bilaterally. The lateral area is therefore called a "feeding center" and is considered responsible for the urge to eat or central hunger reaction, while the ventromedial nucleus or some structure in its neighborhood is taken to exert inhibitory control over the feeding center through fibers which run laterally into the lateral hypothalamic area. Anand, Dua, and Shoenberg (37) have extended these findings to the cat and monkey. Bilateral destruction of the lateral "feeding center" leads to aphagia; bilateral destruction of the medial "satiety center," alone, leads to hyperphagia; but destruction of both lateral and medial centers leads to aphagia.

It has been suggested that amphetamine may inhibit the urge to eat by exciting the satiety center (127), but where this drug inhibits the urge to drink, its action depends at least partly on structures in the prefrontal area of the cortex (44, p. 50).

Although hyperphagia is not well expressed in terms of single causation but rather as the interaction of constitutional, traumatic, and environmental factors (518), the neurologic findings above, relative to hunger, may have counterparts for thirst. No one has yet explored the analysis of thirst in terms of such a "release" phenomenon. In some individuals, strong alcoholic drinks appear to excite thirst shortly, and in a different manner from the well-known delayed effect (p. 125). Does this phenomenon represent an inhibition of an inhibitory or satiety center for thirst?

Bruce and Kennedy (135) remarked that if the thirst center were closely associated with the supraoptic nuclei, its destruction in the same lesions as damage the nuclei would be likely, with the production of chronic dehydration without a thirst response; at the time of their writing they knew of no evidence that this ever occurred, either clinically or experimentally. However, it seems likely that some, if not complete, neutralization of the thirst center occurs in diseases where the thirst sensation is depressed (p. 81). Stevenson, Welt, and Orloff (766), for example, noted that in hyperphagic rats with lesions of the ventromedian region, the mean plasma sodium concentration is higher than in control animals, when food and water are freely available or when food and water are deprived for 16 hours. This and the lowered water: food intake ratios observed by them were taken to imply a deficit in neural mechanism responsible for thirst. More recent studies suggest that the "drinking center" can, indeed, be destroyed with resulting aposia or oligoposia (p. 91).

If food (milk solids) is diluted with water, the total bulk eaten of most mixtures may exceed considerably the bulk of concentrated food consumed in control periods. Adolph (11) induced ingestions of water in rats in this way up to 125% of the body weight per day; in one instance, urine was collected in the amount of 240% of the body weight in a day. The amounts of liquid taken by the animals increased progressively with dilution, less food was taken, and with tap water alone the ingestion was small. Patterns of ingestion and excretion of diluted milk show coordination among several factors of turnover; water ingestion is tempered to excretory capacities and to food ingestion (11, 23).

Ordinarily the urge to eat appears to be governed largely in accordance with the potential energy of adequate food. Bruce and Kennedy (135) examined this phenomenon in their studies of central nervous control of food and water intake. They showed that in rats with diabetes insipidus, when food and water were given together as milk, the intake was still governed by calorie content[38] even though in severe cases the associated fluid was inadequate to prevent dehydration. If the lesion producing diabetes insipidus was extended to damage the center inhibiting food intake, limitation of milk intake did not occur and there was no dehydration. The cause of dehydration in milk feeding lies in the experimental interdependence created between food and water intake; intake is governed by the "calorimetric" center and thirst has little effect in raising it. When the rat is allowed to control its fluid and solid intake independently, no reduction of food intake or alteration of its composition results in dehydration. Food and water intake, then, do not appear to be coordinated at the hypothalamic level; correlation of food and water intake does not imply it. Thirst and feeding centers appear to be independent and sensitive to different stimuli. Siegal and Talantis (725) have also argued for a "pure" thirst function which may be affected by, but which is basically independent of, food intake.

These studies place in a different light the older ideas (150, 494, 673, 785) that thirst in the infant is a substitute for hunger and presides over alimenation until, in time, the sensations become distinct.

Self-Regulation

The apparent simplicity of an osmometric theory of thirst is no longer an asset when we look beyond those special instances in which certain relationships of salt and water loads may be pre-

---

[38] Richter (652) has shown that rats which could slake their thirst only with 8, 16, or 24% alcohol reduced their other food intake to keep the total caloric intake constant.

dicted to be conducive to drinking. It is too simple and does not penetrate far into immediate questions of drinking and satiety, and interdependence of water and other nutrients. For example, thirsty rats may actually show some preference for slightly salty solutions, such as 0.2% sodium chloride, tap water, or mineral water over distilled water (424); men also show preference for dilute saline over plain water at times (p. 201); and the factor of potential osmolality of food has already been mentioned (p. 110).

Richter (652) examined the total self-regulatory function in rats, finding that adrenalectomized animals take enough salt solution to keep alive and free from symptoms when they choose between plain water and 3% sodium chloride solutions. Parathyroidectomized rats, given access to calcium solutions take enough to be free of tetany, and have a reduced appetite for phosphorus compounds. Study of numerous aspects of this problem led Richter to consider that, while the question might not be settled, taste played an important part in it. Thus, section of taste nerves (glossopharyngeal, chorda tympani, and lingual) abolishes the ability of the animals to make beneficial selection; and it was found that the animals' choices depended on the chosen materials being offered at concentrations above their taste thresholds. Possibly the ingestions of certain solutions might exert their effects by making the animal feel better or worse, but it was noted also that adrenalectomized animals appeared to have a lower taste threshold and enhanced discrimination for salt (651, p. 122). The importance of taste threshold was also seen in the sudden preference evinced for water over proffered mercuric chloride solution, and in the fact that they preferred salt even in amounts which did not benefit them (651). Adolph (11) found that it seems difficult to fool a rat into accepting non-nutrients by means of flavoring but, admittedly, more impelling flavors than those tested may be found, and species may vary in this respect.

Richter's idea that appetite leads rats to ingest food for their needs and so carry out homeostasis is opposed by the view that rats take what they like. Young (883, 885, 886) found that when a rat reached satiation upon one food it might still continue eating another. He supposed this was because food constituents or derivatives entered the blood and reached body cells, including taste cells, whose internal constitution regulates the responsiveness to substances needed by the body. He thought of this as a "peripheral" theory and pointed to the difficulties in the idea of separate, partial hungers. Although animals may select foods which they like rather than foods which they need nutritionally, they do to a considerable extent, nevertheless, like what they need (397).

Epstein and Stellar (239) showed that taste was less important than the level of salt available to the internal environment in adrenalectomized rats. Under the influence of ion-exchange resin, rats tasted and swallowed one concentration (3%) of salt, but they absorbed only half of the salt. Operated animals increased their salt intake under the influence of the resin, thus responding to the salt they were (or were not) absorbing rather than to taste stimulation, it was supposed.

Young (885) designated the characteristics of food (concentration, temperature, kind, texture, etc.) that excite head receptors as *palatability* determinants of acceptance-rejection; the conditions within the organism (produced by deprivation, satiation, glandular secretions, etc.) as *appetitive* conditions. He defined three critical concentrations: (1) *preferential threshold*, the lowest concentration at which an animal (rat) distinguishes preferentially between a test solution and distilled water (= taste threshold);[39] (2) *optimal concentration*, the concentration

---

[39] Preference thresholds differ from absolute taste (sensory) thresholds (599, 600, 611, 884). If a rat discriminates between two solutions one can assume that sensory discrimination between them is possible. If it fails to discriminate, we are uninformed concerning the sensory threshold. The fact that normal rats do not prefer very weak salt solutions to water may only mean that motivation to discriminate is insufficient. Salt depletion in adrenalectomy, however, may provide sufficient motivation for finer discrimination, just as hunger drives an animal to finer discrimination when food is the reward.

Pfaffmann and Bare (611) determined the sensory threshold of the white rat from gustatory afferent nerve discharges in the chorda tympani following application of sodium chloride solutions to the tongue. They concluded that taste thresholds of normal and adrenalectomized (salt deficient) rats were similar and that salt deficiency does not alter the sensitivity of taste receptors. In normal animals the sensory threshold is considerably lower than the preference threshold whereas in adrenalectomized ones the two more nearly coincide. It is as if normal rats taste weak concentrations but do not prefer them to water; the animals in a condition of increased need for sodium chloride prefer salt to water as soon as it is tasted.

best liked by the animal as shown by tests of food acceptance and preference; and (3) *indifference concentration*, the concentration above the optimum at which no preference exists between a test solution and distilled water. For sucrose, these three concentrations are, respectively, 0.5, 8.5, and 80%. For sodium chloride these are 0.01 to 0.05, 0.5 to 0.7, and 0.9 to 2.4%.

Rats do not take a constant quantity of sodium chloride each day. The amount varies with the concentration and thus rats seem to take what they like rather than what they need; they may take more than they need if they like a food. Young and Chaplin (886) stated that adrenalectomized rats do not like their solutions any more or less salty than normals; the optimal concentration is not changed by adrenalectomy, but the quantity of salt taken is greater in the adrenalectomized animals and, as seen, in adrenalectomized rats the preference threshold for sodium chloride falls (72, 651). There is a direct relation between salt and water intake for all rats. Although adrenalectomy may affect salt intake (appetite), it does not affect the relative acceptability of different concentrations (palatability) when a choice is offered.

It is also found by others that in preference or free choice situations, normal white rats ingest more sodium chloride solution than tap water (72, 574, 638, 654, 814), presumably more than they need. However, Randoin *et al.* (638) noted that the young rat first chooses 1% salt over water but after three to four weeks the consumption of water increases progressively and that of saline falls. Often the behavior is reversed. Disagreeing somewhat with Richter's theory that the choice expresses a need, they proposed two ideas: (1) that the initial choice is based on appetite until experience teaches the inconvenience of excessive saline,

It may be necessary at times to distinguish a preference situation defined by the relative ingestion of one of two or more fluids freely and simultaneously available ("free choice"), and a preference situation defined by the relative intakes of different fluids available freely but singly. Thus, an animal taking greater quantities of a salt solution than of water or of some other saline, when only one of these fluids is available at a time, may not thereby indicate a preference for that salt solution (in the sense that it is more desirable) over the other fluids. Relative ingestion rate may be related to the amount of free water available from a given solution (p. 163) rather than a preference (desire) such as would be expressed in a free choice situation; or it may be a matter of taste, including whatever way, if any, this is related to bodily need.

and (2) that preference is linked to the great activity of young rats, diminishing with age. Richter used adult rats.

Scott *et al.* (703–708) found that while appetite for salts and for calories does seem to be related to need, appetite for certain purified components of diets shows no apparent relation to physiologic or nutritional need. Rats do or do not like casein. If they do, they eat an average of 3 g./day and grow well; if they do not, they eat less than 0.1 g./day and die shortly. They differ in liking sucrose; only a few rats eat large amounts. As a species, rats do not attach much importance to the flavor of food. No appetite for nor avoidance of flavors of diacetyl, anise, monosodium glutamate, or butyric acid could be demonstrated, although they appear to avoid trimethylamine (fishy) flavor in food. There is no appetite for protein in the general sense; appetite for various proteins, found in some animals, is apparently based on simple preference, although it may possibly be a learned appetite. Appetites for various carbohydrates are independent; lactose is avoided, but sucrose, starch, and dextrin are accepted to various degrees. Appetites for thiamine, riboflavin, and pyridoxine shown by rats previously fed diets deficient in these, are learned, probably as a result of beneficial experience.

McCay and Eaton (528) found that rats fed an adequate stock diet drink about 12 cc. of water or 24 cc. of 10% sucrose solution per day per 100 g. of live weight; they prefer 0.3% saccharin to water (887).

We have noted that increasing the nitrogen content of the diet increases the water intake, presumably secondarily to the augmentation of urine flow (pp. 117, 328). Increasing the salt content of the diet also increases water intake, although this response may be in part primary insofar as the thirst mechanism is directly stimulated.[40] The relative roles of the intake and excretory regulations

---

[40] A curious case of halophagia was reported by Darley and Doan (198) in a 20 year old girl with signs and symptoms of obstruction of the lesser circulation since early childhood. During most of her life she had an abnormal appetite for and ingested excessively large quantities of sodium chloride, allegedly up to several hundred times as much as normal subjects and up to 3 pounds in one week. Her fluid intake and output were stated not to be materially disturbed by variations in salt intake, but the supporting records and data are not compelling in this regard. Her taste threshold for salt was unusually low.

differ (398, 405) not only among species but within a species. Richter and Mosier (654) found that domesticated rats are able to handle large amounts of salt, 15 to 20 g./Kg./day, if allowed to ingest sufficient water. They need 50 to 60 cc. of water per gram of salt to maintain good health. When given access to water, rats freely take diets containing up to 35% salt and will eat fair amounts of a diet of 50 to 70% salt. Salt does not produce as much drinking in domesticated rats as in wild ones of the same species (Norway), possibly on a hormonal basis. When forced to eat salt mixed in the diet in order to get calories, rats did not appear to regard it as a poison such as strychnine or morphine which leads these animals to choose self-starvation. The daily water intake of domesticated rats per unit surface area was found to increase with the salt content of the diet, being about 620 cc./m.^{2} on a low salt diet (ca. 0% salt), 800 cc./m.^{2} on a 1% salt diet, and 5500 cc./m.^{2} on a 25% salt diet. In no case was edema, ascites, or diarrhea observed.

Holmes and Behan (371) have observed that dogs whose fluid intake was augmented by thyroid feeding drank somewhat more fluid when 0.9% sodium chloride was offered than was the case with plain water (p. 162).

Generally, rats do most of their drinking at night, or in the dark, when they are most active (364, 763, 887). Calvin and Behan (152), however, found that rats deprived of water and food for 24 hours before a test situation showed no difference of water intake between night and day.

MISCELLANEOUS DIPSOGENS

Ethyl Alcohol

Jessen (400) wrote in 1751 that dryness in the mouth and throat occurs even to the point of thirst if beer is drunk in abundance. Not only the following night and early morning of another day but also at the time of drinking may thirst be manifest, he stated. His explanation of this phenomenon can no longer be presented in terms meaningful for present day physiology, nor can we profitably discourse on it; but he did not attribute it to the spirituous character of the beverage.

Rullier (673) and Tiedemann (785), however, clearly indicted strong alcoholic drinks as dipsogenic. Tiedemann attributed the effect to immediate stimulation of gut nerves and stated that this could be relieved by moistening the mucous membranes of the gut. He did not consider thirst following alcohol to be in the category of anhydremic thirst where water loss affects all organs and the brain especially, and which cannot be relieved merely by wetting local surfaces as in the mouth. This distinction is of interest because in recent years emphasis has shifted to the secondary effects of alcohol on water and electrolyte metabolism. There is, of course, no scientific basis for the old view that alcohol "dehydrates" the body by virtue of its affinity for water (486). Indeed, 99% of alcohol ingested may be oxidized, each gram (ca. 1.26 cc.) yielding 1.17 grams (ca. 1.17 cc.) of water.

Nicholson and Taylor (580, 581) studied the effect of alcohol ingestion in man and found that it was followed by a retention of sodium, chloride, potassium, and nitrogen, and that there was some rise in plasma sodium concentration. The urinary concentration of sodium, chloride, and potassium fell as diuresis developed, much as in water diuresis. There was some evidence in men and dogs that alcohol administered in quantities sufficient for intoxication led to an increase in plasma volume, the maximum increase occurring 4 hours after ingestion in man and 24 hours after in dogs. It was supposed that fluid drawn from interstitial and intracellular stores made this possible.

Lolli, Rubin, and Greenberg (486) pointed out that thirst is one of the features of acute alcoholic intoxication as well as of the "hang-over" period (to which latter, loss of fluid by vomiting and all other emunctories contributes). Diuresis, they said, is not responsible because it is moderate and occurs only in the period of rising alcohol concentration in the blood; and the thirst is not relieved by taking water in amounts even greater than that lost by diuresis. Using rats, they found the thiocyanate space to be augmented at the expense of intracellular fluid in animals getting alcohol as compared with controls. The augmentation was even greater in those animals receiving food and water than those fasting, if alcohol was given by stomach. There was no difference between the fed and fasting groups when alcohol was administered intravenously. They concluded that alcoholic "dehydration" is cellular rather than of the body as a whole and, although they did not study drinking responses, they believed that such cellular dehydration underlay the thirst following alcohol.

Strauss, Rosenbaum, and Nelson (774) examined the renal excretion of water and electrolytes in man following ingestion of whiskey and found that the diuresis promoted thereby differed from water diuresis. Water diuresis leaves the body fluid isotonic while water-alcohol diuresis leaves it hypertonic. They found little change in the urinary excretion of sodium with alcohol, but the increased urine flow, making for elimination of a larger volume of more hypotonic fluid is consistent with the onset of thirst on an osmometric basis.

While the physiologic picture following alcohol suggests that this drug leads to or favors a state of cellular and/or osmometric dehydration, the pattern is not remarkable either quantitatively or temporally. Strauss *et al.* concluded that, following alcohol, the supraopticohypophyseal system continues to respond to the stimulus of hypotonicity following ingestion of water, but the resulting urinary water loss is excessive, suggesting some altered reactivity.

There is no reason to rule out an effect of alcohol on thirst through its action on the central nervous system. Ethanol in normal subjects inhibits transiently the release of antidiuretic hormone regardless of provocation by antidiuretic stimuli; and the site of this action appears to be in the supraopticohypophyseal system (463). Considering the nature of alcohol as an inhibitor, it is an interesting question whether a "release" phenomenon is involved (p. 119).

Can "alcohol" be used to alleviate dehydration and thirst? This depends upon its concentration in a beverage, the quantity consumed, and the circumstances of the individual. Beer can be used in relatively large quantities, even on the desert. Wines are of varying alcohol content but those containing perhaps 10% are widely used, as in France, in lieu of water. However, where water requirements are great, such wines must be diluted to avoid profound intoxication. The absolute intake of alcohol and the corresponding degree of intoxication produced determine the tolerable limits of consumption of alcoholic beverages (however, see pp. 120, 229, 404). The fact that ethyl alcohol yields almost its own volume of water of oxidation, or whether the metabolic rate (and with it the insensible water loss) is raised or lowered, or whether the urinary water loss is more or less, while conceivably important, are secondary matters. So also for the carbohydrate, fat, and protein sparing actions of alcohol.

Actually, the uncontrolled consumption of wine has had serious consequences for castaways short of water (p. 247); indeed, it has been alleged that even the smallest sips of wine produce intoxication in persons weakened by dehydration and starvation. Desert troops have been forbidden to drink alcoholic beverages because of the belief that they increase dehydration and the feeling of dryness, thus increasing the desire for water (804).

Voluntary Polyposia: Hyperposic Polydipsia

In 1916 Regnier (640) described some of the effects of sustaining a sharply increased water ingestion. For 11 days he drank 6 liters of water daily (taking also about 750 cc. preformed in food), incurring in consequence an extremely pressing sensation of thirst. This procedure (796, 797) was said to result in a decreased water content of the blood after an initial brief increase, with a rise in the serum's refractive index, chloride, and protein. There was also an increased freezing point depression and a net removal of salt from the body as well as an augmented urine output. All of the changes outlasted the period of forced drinking. Body weight was maintained.

Strauss (771) was unable substantially to confirm these findings. His results on two students, one drinking an average of 6 liters per day for 10 to 11 days, the other 7 liters per day for eight days showed no hemoconcentration, but rather hemodilution; no thirst, but rather antidipsia, or an aversion to the large fluid intake; and no fundamental similarity of the artificial steady state with diabetes insipidus. Epstein *et al.* (243) observed no continued thirst in subjects who had taken 5 to 6 liters per day for three days.

Kunstmann (452), however, under the impression that something like "addiction" to water existed, undertook voluntary polyposia to an average level of 10 liters of water daily for 127 days, reaching intakes as high as 18 liters per day. The taking of large amounts of fluid was difficult during the first days, and on the first day headache and slight nausea were observed:

. . . . If a large amount of fluid was taken rapidly in short intervals there always occurred even during the later period a numb feeling in the head which lasted for some minutes. After a few days there was noticed a clearcut adaptation, and after eight days there occurred a strong feeling of thirst which caused waking to drink at night. The greatest nuisance was the necessity to urinate so frequently that it was hardly possible to leave the house. The body weight remained between 79.8 and 80.2 Kg. with only very minor variations which indicated that the water balance did not undergo any striking change.

Kunstmann reported striking losses of chloride from the body, but neither these nor his values for concentrations in the serum can be given much credence. The total net loss of sodium chloride alleged to have occurred during his entire experiment, *viz.*, 195.8 g., represents approximately the normal total salt (chloride) content of an individual of his weight. In any case, he stated the salt content of serum increased during the drinking period (503); and the most striking phenomenon was the marked depression of the freezing point which went from 0.56° to 0.68° C., paralleling findings of Regnier (640) and Veil (796, 797). The abnormal depression of freezing point was still demonstrable several months after the end of his first drinking period, although thirst and other subjective symptoms were no longer present. He recounted:

It was particularly remarkable that the thirst occurred also at a time when the body still contained large amounts of fluid. If, for example, 4 liters had been taken rather rapidly until noon, an increasing sensation of thirst would start at 1 p. m. which sometimes was stronger than before the intake of the fluid. The mouth and especially the lips would become quite dry and sticky, and a sensation of heat would occur over the entire body. The amount of urine excreted at that time was about 1.8 liters; the absolute water content of the body was, therefore, greater than in the morning. Sometimes it really felt as if the passage of water through the organism would cause the thirst . . . .

During the last weeks of the first drinking period striking symptoms of fatigue occurred as a physical and mental limpness. It was difficult not to fall asleep during the daytime while sitting at the desk. Particularly annoying proved a marked lack of ability to make decisions . . . . It was not possible during that time, for example, to make the decision to have the stomach siphoned in order to determine the value for acid. After the thirst subsided these symptoms also gradually disappeared, but much more slowly.

The craving for sodium chloride during the second half of the first drinking period also was remarkable. During the period of large fluid intake and a low salt diet the thirst remained the same but the disturbance of the general condition was much more severe.

Kuntsmann's investigations were heroic. They included water deprivation studies and excisions of pieces of his pectoral muscle and skin for tissue analysis. It is unfortunate that the results are in certain details inconsistent or presently incredible but, until others extend his work, it remains the most significant of its kind for the effect of forced water drinking on thirst.

Holmes and Montgomery (378) performed parallel experiments in hyperposia. A device was employed to administer water continuously by gastric fistula to dogs for up to 14 days, or even longer. Throughout each 24 hour period 8 to 14 liters were given and during this period urine volumes approximated intakes. Specific gravity of the urine ranged from 1.001 to 1.005. Urinary chloride concentration dropped to 5 or 10 mEq./L. representing, despite its low value, a considerable loss of chloride daily. Correspondingly, serum chloride concentrations of 90 mEq./L. were found and a rise in blood pH from 7.45 to 7.65. On intakes less than 10 to 14 liters there was no evidence of fluid retention, i.e., no weight increase or change in serum protein concentration or hematocrit. When the intake exceeded this amount, water intoxication occurred. While it was not concluded that hyperposia or polyposia could be induced by this regimen, one animal was reported which, after four periods of forcing fluid, attained a voluntary daily intake of more than 3 liters. This compared with a control period of less than 1 liter.

It is difficult to interpret these various reports. Where serum chloride falls one is tempted to consider such experiments in the category of hyposalemic thirst although, considering the rise in pH (bicarbonate?), it is not proved that hyposmoticity or hypotonicity existed. Kunstmann (452) felt his thirst was engendered largely by salt loss, and he does note (above) the existence of salt hunger. There is some agreement on the matter of salt loss during enforced polyposia but evidence on plasma concentrations of chloride is conflicting. It has been suggested (862) that Kunstmann's findings are consistent with a state of real but temporary diabetes insipidus, perhaps caused by some transient "disuse atrophy" of the posterior pituitary system in the face of steady water loading (p. 102); and adaptive responses in renal concentrating power have been considered to occur (243, p. 108). Some effect of conditioning has also been suggested (857). Rowntree (668) noted patients with diabetes insipidus, taking pituitary extract, who continued to take water in their customary large amounts, leading to water intoxication. And Wynn and Rob (878) also speak of the effect of the "habit" of a large water intake which is possibly not easily broken even when dangerous hypotonicity exists. Many water intoxicated patients are said to complain of thirst (879). Neither the experimental and clinical facts nor their interpretation are wholly clear at this time.

Potassium Deficiency

Sodium and potassium can replace each other to some extent in the tissues and either of these ions is displaced from the plasma into the urine by a load of the other (857). Considering this reciprocity of sodium and potassium and the high correlation between loads of sodium salts and thirst, it is perhaps not unexpectedly observed that deficiency of potassium is associated with thirst.

Smith and Lasater (744) reported that dogs deprived of potassium developed a striking increase in fluid exchange, approximately doubling their intake of water. The increase usually started within 24 hours after an animal was placed on a potassium deficient diet; a peak was reached after three to seven weeks, and drinking gradually returned to normal in 10 to 11 weeks. Paralysis from potassium deficiency was not observed until well after the polyposic-polyuric tendency had spent itself and fluid exchange had returned to normal.

Brokaw (133) confirmed this phenomenon in rats, moreover observing that water turnover was augmented even further by removal of sodium from the potassium deficient diet. If the animals were offered 0.9% sodium chloride to drink instead of water, much less turnover was observed in potassium deficiency than with plain water as drinking fluid (p. 163), although drinking in either case was greater than in rats with a sufficiency of potassium. Potassium deficiency also caused renal hypertrophy, and both the hypertrophy and polyposia were readily reversed by the administration of potassium. In potassium deficiency, also, muscle cell potassium was replaced by sodium, as had been found by Heppel (346), but plasma sodium concentration was not altered significantly.

Brokaw's measurements of fluid compartments (using chloride space as a measure of extracellular fluid) and fluid concentrations suggested to her that if increased water turnover were to be accounted for in terms of a single fluid compartment, it would have to be related to the reduction in extracellular fluid. Little change in the volume of intracellular fluid was found and, in any case, potassium deficient rats drinking saline had the smaller (more dehydrated) cellular compartments as well as the smaller turnovers. In view of the associated negative chloride balance of potassium deficient animals, it was conjectured that the polyposia arose from a deficiency of extracellular electrolyte and was of a hyposalemic type (pp. 103, 203). Actually no striking change in plasma chloride or sodium was noted although the former was somewhat depressed in some animals.

Polyposia and polyuria result from administration of desoxycorticosterone to dogs for several weeks (448, 637, 857). Superficially this condition resembles diabetes insipidus but pituitrin is relatively ineffective against the polyuria and fluid restriction does not lead rapidly to dehydration. Thirst has been considered the "primary" feature of this syndrome, related to the high plasma sodium which follows from the response of the kidney to the steroid, among other things. However, the low potassium also present may be looked upon in the light of the more recent work on hypokalic polyposia mentioned above. In Brokaw's studies, plasma sodium was not high as in the case of desoxycorticosterone experiments; nor was it depressed.

Black and Milne (106) examined experimental potassium depletion in two men; on a low potassium diet (less than 10 mEq./day) plasma potassium fell to 3.1 and 2.6 mEq./L., respectively. Intracellular fluid was estimated to have shrunk 2 to 7%, but no thirst was reported. It was supposed that thirst might be associated with cellular dehydration only when there is a concomitant rise in intracellular osmotic pressure. Fourman (268) brought about hypokalia and hypokalemia in man by means of a low potassium diet and the use of cation-exchange resins. However, in his study, although plasma potassium fell only to about 3 mEq./L., important symptoms appeared when the potassium loss exceeded 15% of the total exchangeable potassium (76 mEq./L. of body water). Only slight changes in cellular volume were estimated to have occurred but subjects became weak, apathetic, irritable, unduly sensitive to cold, and anoretic. While taking the resin, they were thirsty and this thirst was not relieved by drinking water.

A significant distinction between the conditions of Black and Milne and of Fourman is that in the former, sodium was available while the potassium deficiency was being induced; in the latter, the resin removed potassium and prevented the retention of sodium in its place. This suggests a parallel to Brokaw's (133) finding that polyposia was augmented by the removal of sodium from potassium deficient diets, and may account in part for the polydipsia observed by Fourman and its absence according to Black and Milne. Moreover, Fourman's experiments entailed considerably greater deficits of potassium.

Mahler and Stanbury (509) discussed the severe thirst, unrelieved by drinking water, of the patient with potassium-losing renal disease. This dipsosis may exist when the serum sodium (and presumably tonicity) is not elevated (136 to 138 mEq./L.); it is alleviated when the potassium deficit is made good.

The degree of inaccuracy in present methods for determining quantities of intracellular fluid makes purely volumetric analysis of hypokalic polyposia questionable. If we assume that in potassium deficiency there is a tendency toward cellular dehydration (631) we have some basis for interpreting hypokalic thirst accordingly. Where the thirst may be potentiated by sodium deficiency, an added element of hyposalemic thirst, not to be sated by water, may be present. However, cells which have lost large quantities of potassium and behave thus as an imperfect osmometer (530) would not necessarily be hypervolic in extracellular

hyposmoticity; in this case thirst would arise under conditions
other than those of so-called hyposalemic thirst in which cells are
presumably excessively hydrated (p. 103ff.).

It may be added that there are symptomatic resemblances
between sodium deficiency and potassium deficiency (268), and
between the dipsoses of these states and of hyperposic polydipsia
(p. 128); and it should not be forgotten that the eudipsia of
relative dehydration and hypernatremia may also be accompanied
by some deficit of cell potassium (233).

For the dipsologist, resolution of the problems of thirst and
satiety in this area, perhaps with the aid of hemodialytic techniques, would be highly desirable.

Hemorrhage

It is commonly supposed that hemorrhage exerts a dipsogenic
influence (494), a view which appears to derive in some measure
from the anciently known association of hemorrhage and thirst
with extensive trauma. Thus Cannon (159) speaks of the "universal call for water" of the wounded man. Actually, there is no
extensive information on, and some doubt about, the putative
dipsogeny of hemorrhage. Dumas (216) held that small bleed-
ings, well managed, appease thirst and make the body less
sensitive to deprivation of drink.

E. Bernard (92) stated that thirst follows hemorrhage constantly in nonedematous individuals but not constantly in edematous ones. This contention followed the idea that after hemorrhage in the former, fluid leaves cells to enter the blood
compensatorily and so thirst appears. In edematous states, it was
supposed, the connective tissue and extracellular fluid stores serve
to reestablish this fluid equilibrium and thirst does not appear.
Delaunay (204) considered that the posthemorrhagic drainage
of intercellular liquid leads to a dehydration of the tissues which
is translated into thirst.

Brocq-Rousseu and Roussel (131) compared drinking in horses
on ordinary days and on days when they had been bled six liters
of blood, in order to ascertain the effect of simple hemorrhage
uncomplicated by trauma. In 72 horses, the average of the

reported figures for daily water intake was 23.43 liters[41] for control days; on the day of bleeding, it was 25.06 liters, a statistically significant difference. They checked these results by studies of individual horses. In general, their animals drank more than usual after bleeding, but not always.

Holmes and Montgomery (379, 381) sought a relation of hemorrhage to thirst in 50 blood bank donors, each giving up to 500 cc. or 5 to 10% of his blood volume. These subjects showed neither consistent reduction in salivary flow nor thirst, although there is other evidence of relationship between hemorrhage and salivary flow (311). Dogs which they bled to the extent of 10, 20, 30, and 40% of their blood volume showed no drinking response. Various tests to examine whether fluid shifts following hemorrhage served as a subthreshold stimulus which could enhance drinking induced by other methods were negative except that the administration of epinephrine along with 20% hemorrhage induced drinking in 25% of their experiments. They concluded that thirst occurs after hemorrhage only when associated with the more complicated metabolic and circulatory phenomena of shock.

Whatever the extent to which thirst may actually supervene in pure hemorrhage, at least two interpretations may be noted therefor. First, such thirst may reflect the operation of volustatic mechanisms as discussed in Chapter IV. Second, it may have the character of hypokalic thirst, the desire for water which sets in during potassium deficiency, and in which case no definitive explanation is at hand (p. 133).

Stewart and Rourke (767) bled unanesthetized female dogs to the extent of 2 to 3.5% of the body weight in 5 to 20 minutes. They observed an increased urinary excretion of potassium which appeared to come from cells along with cellular water. There was no increased nitrogen excretion and, regardless of whether water was drunk, a fall in plasma sodium, potassium, and protein concentration was found.

Borst (117) studied the effects of massive hemorrhage from peptic ulcer and observed that as long as posthemorrhagic blood dilution exists the kidneys excrete practically no sodium or chloride and increase potassium excretion; if sodium chloride is given, the plasma concentrations of sodium and chloride rise above normal. His thesis (118) is that the retention of sodium and chloride along with water and the

---

[41] Not 23.58 as reported.

excretion of potassium in these circumstances is part of a regulating mechanism established to restore normal filling of the arterial system by way of increasing blood volume and the extracellular space. Rapid transfusion of blood so as to increase blood volume results in increased chloride and water excretion the effect of which tends to minimize the possible increase in blood volume.

A possibly germane correlative was noted by Prudden *et al.* (631). In acute hemodialytic depletion of potassium in dogs, largely cellular, consequent cellular dehydration and increased plasma volume apparently associated with hypotension was observed. However, extracellular volume showed little net change.

These general findings may be consistent with the view that thirst, when it occurs in hemorrhage, is associated with, and has some basis in, cellular dehydration.

Trauma and Battle Stress

We have noted that while hemorrhage may induce some degree of thirst, the sensation seems rather to derive from related conditions of shock, trauma, etc. Traumatic hyperdipsia is a widely recognized phenomenon. Summers (776) stated that the intense thirst experienced by the wounded man is not always due to loss of blood but is the direct effect of the suffering which he undergoes. Cannon (159) had observed how the wounded man in shock calls for water but may eject it promptly after swallowing, as part of his torment.

As in hemorrhage, potassium leaves cells in trauma. The loss of potassium may be astonishingly great and rapid but it is to a considerable extent associated with devitalization of tissue (546) and, with renal insufficiency frequently concurrent, the reduced excretion of this ion is reflected in inordinately high plasma concentrations. Unfortunately, no studies show whether traumatic thirst is fundamentally like that of potassium deficiency; cellular hypokalia in the presumably uninjured tissue has not been demonstrated under such conditions.

Restriction of fluid for the prevention of clinical overhydration in severely wounded men is managed with difficulty because of the exigencies of thirst. Meroney and Herndon (546) wrote of their experience with war casualties in Korea:

. . . . Patients so restricted often suffer a cruel thirst, yet their thirst is not an accurate gauge of their needs. If allowed to drink freely, they will literally drown themselves. When denied fluids they develop great craftiness in prevailing on compassionate neighbors and attendants for small sips of any fluid or for pieces of ice, a bountiful and easily overlooked source of water. When unobserved they will quaff heartily from flower vases, emesis basins, or urinals[42] with great stealth and cunning.

The thirst of the battlefield is legend. Dr. Russell Scott, Jr., a medical officer of the United States Army during the Korean War, has kindly communicated his impressions and experiences with this problem (710). He considered four aspects:

(1) *Dehydration during combat.* There is good reason for dehydration during combat. Combat requires real exertion and soldiers . . . . "sweat." Water is often not available prior to and during combat. The clothing, fox hole, etc. are conducive to overheating and excessive perspiration. During the stress of combat, most men are not thinking about drinking and will go for long periods of time without realizing that they need water. I know during combat I might go most of the day without realizing that I had not taken food or water and find myself fiercely hungry and thirsty.

(2) *Latent period for development of thirst after wounding.* I know there was thirst on the field of battle within a short period of time after injury. I remember specifically thirst developing within 30 minutes on two occasions. This does not mean it did not develop much more rapidly in other situations, but I was not familiar with these. I know that aidmen in attendance with the wounded at the front line had to be continually warned not to give men with abdominal injuries water by mouth, for the wounded would certainly ask for it at this early time. In discussing this problem with the aidmen who were in attendance with the men in the forward area, I remember specifically that the aidmen commented that casualties quite often asked for water shortly after being wounded. In relation to the specific experiences of these aidment, I cannot

---

[42] That is, they would drink vomitus and urine (545). Trousseau (790) wrote of a polydipsic man subjected to severe restriction of fluid who suffered so cruelly from it that one day "he seized the chamber-pot, and drank the contents to the last drop!"

comment on the state of dehydration or the previous battle experience that these particular casualties had gone through.

(3) *How long thirst persisted.* Thirst was also observed at the Battalion Aid Station and at the Mobile Army Surgical Hospital level. It was difficult to say when thirst subsided because as soon as operation was contemplated the casualty was told he could not have water and therefore the casualty often but by no means routinely stopped asking for water. Therefore, by recollection it would be impossible to know when thirst disappeared during the process of resuscitation. An organized program of questioning the casualties during the process of resuscitation might well have revealed that thirst did disappear at a specific time with therapy, or did continue on until anesthesia was started. I have no recollection one way or the other whether thirst was present after operation. As a matter of fact, I do not remember a casualty asking for water following surgery . . . .

(4) *Type of wound accompanied by thirst.* I have no definite impression as to which types of wounds were always accompanied by thirst or whether the man in shock is always thirsty. I do remember that some casualties with peripheral wounds and some casualties with abdominal wounds had thirst, in the absence of and in the presence of shock. I remember casualties with all combinations asking for water . . . . Of course, I was not familiar with the state of hydration in any of the given casualties before they were injured. I have no specific recollections about head wounds.

Renal Ischemia; X-irradiation; Heavy Water

Rats made hypertensive by renal ischemia show a mild polyposia and polyuria (2, 587, 787). The presence of a normal kidney exerts a compensatory influence which may mask either hypertension or polyuria, or both. The appearance or exacerbation of the changes upon removal of the normal kidney, and the elimination or mitigation of symptoms upon removal of the ischemic kidney has suggested that the changes observed were not due to passive elimination of kidney tissue by ischemia but to active renal malfunction. The polyuria has been considered a primary sequel of ischemia rather than secondary to intra- and extrarenal effects of hypertension. When offered free choice of 0.17 M sodium chloride and sodium bicarbonate, hypertensives elected only one-third to one-half as much of the salt as normal animals.

The reduced salt intake of these animals was shown not to depend on the adrenals or on an increased fluid intake, but more likely on an abnormal renal function (787).

X-irradiation affects water exchange. Water intake may be reduced in rabbits and, to a lesser extent, in dogs. In the rabbit urine flow is temporarily raised, favoring dehydration (629).

In rats there is a transient polyposia (582) and polyuria associated with a significant decrease in antidiuretic activity in the serum (221). Adrenalectomy abolishes the polyposia which directly follows irradiation (732).

Rats receiving 10 to 50 mg. of heavy water per day for two months grow and develop normally. Young rats (ca. 27 days and 37 g.), given 20 to 50% deuterium oxide in ordinary water, corresponding to 1.1 to 2.7 cc. of heavy water per rat per day for eight days, showed no abnormality except unusual thirst and a smaller daily weight gain. Heavy water dosing, stopped on the ninth day, permitted weight gain to return to normal, but abnormal drinking persisted for five to six days after pure water was again started (694).

CHAPTER III

SATIETY

ON DEFINITIONS

IT MAY BE conceded that no formal definition of "thirst" was essential to previous discussions largely because its meaning is generally and ostensively clear. As Darwin remarked of "instinct" in his *Origin of Species*, "I will not attempt any definition . . . every one knows what is meant. . . ." Nevertheless there are diverse physiologic usages of the term thirst (116, 865, Glossary) which will now bear scrutiny.

Adolph *et al.* (18) list three. (1) *Sensations* are interpreted as need for water and are known by the experiences and reports of people. They are undetectable by any other means. It is usually assumed that when an animal drinks it is responding to such sensations. (2) *Urges to drink* are impelling motives which lead an animal to the act of ingesting water. Thirst then denotes the whole complex of factors which lead to the response. (3) *Deficit of water* in the body, or lack or need of water, is also described by the word thirst, and subjection of a man to thirst refers to the shortage of water that is created in his body. This meaning is readily avoided by using other terms such as water deficit, negative water load, or dehydrated state. Thirst may also refer to a *type of behavior* such as motor activity in seeking water, or restlessness. These four concepts, applied to food, parallel "hunger sensation," "appetite," "hunger state," and "hunger behavior," respectively (397).

"Thirst drive" has been defined by Warner (806) as the tendency of animals to approach water under certain conditions. He measured drive in white rats in terms of the number of times a rat would cross an electrical grid used as an obstruction to available water. While the least drive was found immediately after the animal was removed from a cage where water was easily obtained, the greatest drive was evidenced after one day of water deprivation. From this point on, the drive diminished constantly until death. Thirst drive appeared stronger than hunger drive.

However, Brady (126) indicates that in experiments involving the training of laboratory albino rats to perform some simple instrumental act such as pressing a bar to receive a drop of water, it is possible to generate stable response rates over relatively long periods of time by arranging the reward contingencies so that the lever press produces the water only aperiodically (at irregular intervals). Since every bar press is not reward and there is no way for the animal to tell when the response will be reinforced, thirsty animals develop stable rates of lever pressing for such an aperiodic water reward and there are clear indications that these response rates are quite sensitive to deprivation level. When, for example, an animal is deprived of water for 48 hours, the lever pressing rate is reliably higher than when the animal has been deprived for only 24 hours, even though the reward schedule produces the same number of water reinforcements under both conditions. Beyond the 48 hour deprivation point, however, the rate seems to level off until the animal has been deprived so long that the rate is adversely affected by debilitation.

Thirst drive measured in terms of activity was found by Finger and Reid (259) to increase for at least three days of water deprivation in the rat.

It is in part the variable sense of the term thirst which makes difficult the interpretation of satiety. Janowitz and Grossman (397) in their definitive paper on hunger and appetite identify satiety with physiologic anorexia, a state of lack of desire to eat conceived as a total phenomenon, i.e., satiety is the absence of appetite, the desire to eat (p. 46). However, these authors also consider that satiety for food is measured by an animal's refusal to continue eating it. Consequently, their "satiety" admits no distinction between lack of "sensations" and lack of "urges." More specifically, it does not distinguish between absence of that "desire" which can be expressed or verbalized singularly by man and absence of "desire" which is inferred from animal behavior.

It is understood, of course, that eating is not necessarily a criterion of hunger (161), nor is drinking of thirst.

Drawing a parallel with the concept of Janowitz and Grossman, we may define satiety for water as a physiologic adipsia or aposia, recognizing that, in its strictest sense, adipsia can only apply to man (but loosely to animals generally); aposia to man and animals. And neither adipsia nor aposia, in itself, is synonymous with satiety. Evidence from intragastric and intravenous alimentation in man and animal indicates that these procedures do not lead to satiety which, for food, may be distinct from repletion of the hunger state; however, hydration by these routes can lead to satiety for water.

Physiologic adipsia, then, is satiety directly consequent either to normal drinking or to such administration of aqueous fluid as will remove the thirst sensation in man; physiologic aposia is the corresponding satiety inferred from the disappearance of the urge to drink in man or hydrodipsic animal. We do not, therefore, consider the adipsias and aposias of diseased states necessarily as states of satiety. Where certain unphysiologic agencies produce adipsia or aposia, it would seem proper to qualify the states according to be means whereby they are produced. Thus, a transient "pilocarpine adipsia" would not qualify as a state of satiety.

The meaning of satiety, as employed by physiologists for food and water, is frequently at variance with the literal sense of that term, *viz.*, as synonymous with surfeit or gratification beyond desire; it has been rather closer to the term satisfaction, implying just that gratification of desire which gives contentment, and it is in this latter sense that we use satiety with respect to water. For that degree of repletion with water which would elicit not adipsia but antidipsia, we reserve the term *nimiety*.

Grossman (314) has enlarged on this matter of definition and appears to favor, at least for food, the literal sense of satiety. We note in context his statements:

> *Hunger* is the complex of sensations evoked by depletion of body nutrient stores.
>
> Appetite has been variously defined as sensation and as desire. For the present discussion, I shall define *appetite* as the desire for food, an affective state.

For lack of a better term, I have selected *fullness* to designate the complex of sensations associated with repletion of body nutrient stores. *Satiety* is the corresponding affective state in repletion signifying a lack of desire to eat or, more precisely, a desire not to eat. . . . It is reasonable to assume that, between the sensations of hunger and fullness and between the affective states of appetite and satiety, there must lie a neutral zone in which the psychic correlatives of energy balance are absent. A corollary of this view is that fullness and satiety are positive psychic states and do not represent merely the absence of hunger and appetite.

The triad of thirst, drinking, and satiety constitutes a repeating temporal cycle of water metabolism. However intimately satiety seems an integral part of the thirst process (sensation or urge to drink, specifically), it remains an entity which can be studied to some degree independently of thirst, just as thirst can be studied (in man) independently of the drinking process, and drinking (in animals) can be studied independently of the presumptive thirst sensation. It has been said that the accuracy with which dehydrated animals such as dogs replace their water deficits in one draft argues strongly against cellular dehydration as the activating stimulus for drinking (333). But this confounds drinking and satiety and takes no cognizance of species differences in this regard (p. 159).

THE PLEASURES IN ATTAINING SATIETY

The tortures of thirst have been endlessly recounted by writers and sufferers. Yet few have sought equally to depict the reciprocal delectations and joy attending access to water after severe deprivation.[1] Among these latter was the explorer Sven Hedin (339). After a frightful journey across the western Taklamakan desert,

---

[1] Meigs (541) subscribed to psychologist Bain's view of thirst as an appetite (p. 46). Its operation is twofold: "the massive uneasiness of privation, and the equally massive pleasure of gratification, whose combined motive power makes the strength of the volition or appetite."

Skattebol (727) describes the behavior of dehydrated castaways at sea who came into possession of ample quantities of rain water. A few stuck fingers in their throats to cause vomiting—to be able to relish again the sensation of liberal quantities of water pouring down their gullets.

during which camels and men of his caravan succumbed for lack of water, he finally reached a forest and struggled to safety:

> ... I stood on the brink of a little pool filled with fresh, cool water—beautiful water! ...

It would be vain for me to try to describe the feelings which now overpowered me. They may be imagined; they cannot be described. Before drinking I counted my pulse: it was forty-nine. Then I took the tin box out of my pocket, filled it, and drank. How sweet that water tasted! Nobody can conceive it who has not been within an ace of dying of thirst. I lifted the tin to my lips, calmly, slowly, deliberately, and drank, drank, drank, time after time. How delicious! what exquisite pleasure! The noblest wine pressed out of the grape, the divinest nectar ever made, was never half so sweet. My hopes had not deceived me. The star of my fortunes shone as brightly as ever it did.

I do not think I at all exaggerate, if I say that during the first ten minutes I drank between five and six pints. The tin box held not quite an ordinary tumblerful, and I emptied it quite a score of times. At that moment it never entered my head that, after such a long fast, it might be dangerous to drink in such quantity. But I experienced not the slightest ill effects from it. On the contrary I felt how that cold, clear, delicious water infused new energy into me. Every blood-vessel and tissue of my body sucked up the life-giving liquid like a sponge. My pulse, which had been so feeble, now beat strong again. At the end of a few minutes it was already fifty-six. My blood, which had lately been so sluggish and so slow, that it was scarce able to creep through the capillaries, now coursed easily through every blood-vessel. My hands, which had been dry, parched, and hard as wood, swelled out again. My skin, which had been like parchment, turned moist and elastic. And soon afterwards an active perspiration broke out upon my brow.[2] In a word, I felt my whole body was imbibing fresh life and fresh strength. It was a solemn, an awe-inspiring moment.

Rapid Drinking

It is an old idea (400) that it is dangerous to drink rapidly to repletion in severe thirst (pp. 401, 415, 456). There is some foundation for this (561) in that acute hyposalemia or water intoxica-

---

[2] Possibly the common, so-called sudomotor reflex of deglutition (18, 461) which has been noted after recovery from moderate dehydration (671).

tion, or heat cramp, not to mention diarrhea (272a), may follow rapid drinking after a relatively rapid onset of negative water and salt loads in exercise. As for dehydrations and hyperdipsias which have developed more gradually, there appears to be little basis in fact for this belief, whether applied to man, dog, or cat.

However, it is another question, according to Kuno (451), whether, in early stages of dehydration, a restoration of the water debt is good for the activity of man.

It is customary in all kinds of sports in Japan, to avoid drinking at recess even when sportsmen are suffering from intense thirst on account of a considerable loss of body water during preceding exercises. It is traditionally believed that intake of water in this case hastens fatigue. During exercise or in hot environments, the blood vessels of the skin and muscles undergo dilatation and a compensating vasoconstriction takes place in the splanchnic vascular beds. The latter may be more intense under a dehydrated condition. It may be interpreted that the vasoconstriction in the abdominal organs is of significance not only for keeping the unused organs at rest, but also for restraining the heat production of the liver, other glands and intestines at the minimum rate.

Abrahams (1) noted that the original precepts of training included as a sine qua non the reduction of liquids to an extreme degree, to the limit of endurance and certainly beyond the limits of comfort. He conceived that the idea arose from the salutary reduction of alcoholic beverages when professionals started to train for competitions; and from this arose, in his view, the misconception that liquids of any kind, and even moist food, in some way detracted from feats of strength and endurance.

That rapid drinking of cold water is deleterious may be another matter (620). The occurrence of abdominal cramps or other distressful symptoms as a result, although not to be gainsaid, is apparently less widespread than the belief in these sequelae. Rausse (639) claimed that cooling of the body through cold water drinking never produces sickness in a healthy person. However, Tancredi (780) tells us water should not be ice cold; Durig (218) that cold water closes sphincters of the stomach, preventing water absorption; Johnson (401) that water should not be ice cold and should not be taken in amounts large enough to interfere with work by sloshing about in the stomach (to the extent that more cold water may be drunk under certain conditions than water not cold, this observation is relevant); and Smiley and Gould (730) that it is not generally wise to gulp down large quantities of cold water when one is overheated, and that ice water should always be sipped. But little scientific information exists beyond such statements.

Adolph (17) has opined:

> My impression is that a large quantity of water produces discomfort in a number of people. . . . I repeatedly observed in the desert that men who had been hiking without water for some hours would gratefully down two litres of ice water on one draught. In the desert situation there seems to be no danger of water intoxication, but that may have been because we did not sample enough individuals and all our subjects were receiving high salt intake. So far as I am concerned, such a belief should be subjected to some sort of critical experiment and in more than one environment.

MULTIPLE FACTORS

Most so-called "theories of thirst" discussed in the previous chapter deal with the origin or incipience of the sensation of thirst or the urge to drink as a function of one or two physiologic variables (dryness of mouth, cellular dehydration, etc.). But there have been attempts to point up "multiple factors" in thirst just as in hunger (19, 397, 762). Purporting to designate the factors that determine the amount of drinking, such studies have been concerned at once with the concepts of sensation, urge, drinking, and satiety, all mingled, and called "thirst." It is well to recognize that the argument attributing inadequacy to monistic as opposed to pluralistic theories, when no distinction is drawn among these conceptual elements, has this particular semantic orientation. This is not to say that a multiple factor theory will not prove most useful to dipsologists, but no one has yet proposed a sequacious theory along these lines solvent of all the crucial problems of thirst.

Adolph, Barker, and Hoy (19) regard the multiple factor prob-

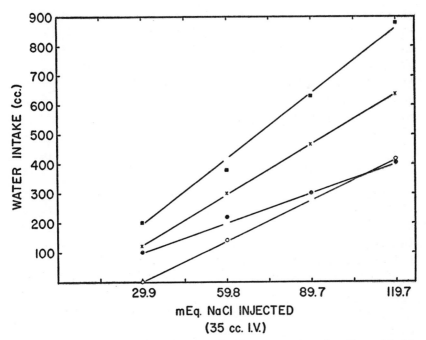

Figure 14. Linear relation of water drunk to quantity of sodium chloride (5, 10, 15, and 20% solution) injected into four normal dogs. Note variation in drinking response to same amount of salt. After Holmes and Gregersen (376).

lem somewhat as follows. Drinking is a response to circumstances, the quantitation of which will describe its operating controls. One circumstance is that drinking occurs only in the presence of a factor termed a stimulus, which (in their experiments) is either a deficit of body water or an excess of a solute. Within limits, drinking appears to be proportional to the strength of stimulus.[3] A second circumstance is that the amount of drinking is modified by other factors called *modulators*. Of these, inhibi-

[3] If drinking is proportional to strength of stimulus, a point made also by Holmes and Gregersen (376, Fig. 14), the same has not been said of thirst. No one has assessed the "psychophysical" law for thirst, but it may be doubted that the sensation of thirst simply varies with the logarithm of the intensity of stimulus (water deficit, cellular dehydration, etc.) if we may judge from the steep exacerbation of thirst in man as hypertonic salt is steadily administered. On the other hand, in the desert, thirst is noticeable very early, but does not increase much in intensity as the water deficit continues to increase (18), at least within limits.

tors are most common (in rats): severe restraint, gastric distention, solutes concentrated in drinking fluid, cocainization of the
mouth, large doses of pitressin (83, 376), and warm air (31° C.).
Only two enhancers of drinking were noted for rats: dilute solutions of diverse substances (e.g., sodium chloride, urea) as drinking fluid, and experimental diabetes insipidus following neurohypophyseal lesions. It was considered unlikely that all drinking
should represent a response to one trigger (e.g., osmoreceptors).

The satiations of drinking, they say further, appear to be volume effects, i.e., the volume drunk is what matters. The dog with
esophageal fistula meters a volume equal to twice its deficit
through the pharynx before ceasing to drink; the dog fills its
stomach with an amount equal to the deficit through the mouth.
But a dog with stomach experimentally filled with a volume equal
to its water deficit is only partly inhibited.

Another enhancer of drinking in rats is found in operant-conditioning (837). When it is arranged that by licking fluid at the end of a
tube a rat can postpone an electric shock through the grid floor of its
cage, abnormally large quantities of water may be taken. In addition,
by this technique, it is possible to force ingestion of fluids normally refused and, using a liquid nutrient, to produce obesity in normal rats.

In man, occasionally one may observe a partly compulsive, partly
conditioned enhancement of drinking. Thus, the contents of a glass of
water may be drained completely even though satiety be attained with
a lesser intake.

Stellar (762) has taken the multifactor approach not only to
thirst but generally to motivated behavior. The basic assumption
is that the amount of motivated behavior is a function of the
amount of activity in certain excitatory centers of the hypothalamus. The level of activity of the critical hypothalamic
centers, in turn, is governed by the operation of four factors: (1)
inhibitory centers in the hypothalamus directly depress the activity of the excitatory centers and may be responsible for the
production of satiation; (2) sensory stimuli (e.g., from the mouth
and throat in the case of thirst) set up afferent impulses which
naturally contribute to the excitability of the hypothalamus or
come to do so through a process of learning; (3) changes in the
internal environment (e.g., tonicity in the case of thirst) exert both

excitatory and inhibitory effects on the hypothalamus; and (4) cortical and thalamic influences increase and decrease the excitability of hypothalamic centers.

SATIETY AND INHIBITION

Satiety and thirst cannot, by definition, coexist. But also, by our definition, the terms are not antonymous. Since some adipsias are not satieties, and since diverse mechanisms appear to underlie satiety and thirst, the terms satiety and thirst imply a degree of, but not an absolute, reciprocal inhibition in the neurophysiologic sense. Inhibition and satiety are allied concepts, but inhibition is the more general phenomenon and, unlike satiety, has greater and lesser degrees.

There is evidence that the "drinking center" of the hypothalamus can be ablated with loss of thirst drive (p. 92), and we may suppose neither thirst nor satiety then to exist. Witt *et al.* (847) have found in dogs so made adipsic that the absence of thirst is evidenced by a complete lack of interest in water even to the point of critical dehydration. Yet, when water is baited slightly with milk or meat juice, the animal drinks it ravenously, apparently as food but not as water. Aposia continues in the presence of physiologic stability maintained by therapy (administration of pituitrin and appropriate forced hydration).

We have previously noted Wettendorff's (823) distinction between "true" and "false" thirst (p. 94), the former depending on bodily need of water, the latter merely on the sensation of a dry mouth not associated with concurrent systemic dehydration. Wettendorff stated that even in true thirst the sensation can be obtunded merely by moistening the pharyngeal mucous membranes with water. The consequence, however, is only false satisfaction, again based on individual experience with actual ingestion which ordinarily relieves systemic dehydration. Thus, moistening the membranes, we may say, only causes thirst to be inhibited, not satiated.

A relevant situation is seen in the man with no deficit of water who, after eating highly spiced food, becomes inordinately thirsty (pseudodipsic), getting little relief from water which is "excess."

In this category also may be placed the observation of Remington (644) who described the occasion of his accidentally taking a mouthful of 0.1 N silver nitrate solution which deadened all but a metallic taste, left a sensation of dryness with no reflex salivation, and left him "thirsty" for hours. We cannot say from such information whether an unremitting stimulation in the mouth is too powerful to be inhibited by the ordinary mechanism of satiety, whether satiety mechanisms are somehow reciprocally inhibited by the oral stimulation, or whether, as Remington considers, the desire for water may be prompted by a craving to flush strange material from the mouth.

Wolf (851) has described behavior in dogs made extremely hyperdipsic (the act of turning on the water faucet within sight of the animal was sufficient to excite it violently) with hypertonic salt loads. Such animals drank water or their urine greedily until they were forced to vomit, whereupon they drank further.[4] Clearly the hypersalemic animal has not, at the time of first vomiting, assuaged the osmometric stimulus to thirst and there is no reason to assume that satiety mechanisms were not in operation. These mechanisms, ordinarily activated as by distention of the stomach with fluid drunk, would rather seem impotent to neutralize the effects of a powerful dipsogenic stimulus. If so, we may conclude that, however appropriately balanced and reciprocal the satiety and thirst mechanisms may be under ordinary conditions, thirst is potentially the more puissant at least in man and dog.

---

[4] King (422, p. 379) told of the related situation in men suffering from desert thirst. Skattebol (727) described dehydrated castaways who, when ample rain water became available, overloaded their stomachs, some vomiting. On the other hand, a dog deprived of food and water until 39% of its body weight was lost was observed to drink water amounting to 6.7% of its initial body weight (735 cc.) in one hour and 20 minutes, regurgitating nothing. Then, with free access to 5% dextrose, it drank no more until dilute milk was offered the next day (871).

Bean (80) has noted that when men worked at the top limit of physical endurance at a temperature of 150° F. dry bulb with no moisture in the air, or at 95° with air saturated, the quantity of water they took or tried to take was sometimes beyond the capacity of the stomach. During a morning's work sometimes as much as 12 or 14 liters would be taken and almost all of it was lost as sweat. In many subjects there was a phase of vomiting; once past that, they could drink and retain large quantities of water.

One of Futcher's (275) patients with diabetes insipidus became ravenous for food. He would stop eating, not because his hunger was stopped, but because he "felt he could not hold any more." However, in some individuals hunger sensations may become so strong that nausea predominates and actually leads to loss of appetite (397). In extreme thirst, also, the least attempt to swallow may produce violent nausea (632).

Inhibition or modulation of thirst presumably occurs at various levels, not necessarily through any one mechanism of satiety but through the action of diverse central and afferent impulses. Thirst sensations are less intense during exercise (18); at the same water deficit and in the same environment, the man at work and sweating rapidly is more content without drink than the man at rest and sweating slowly (we have already noted (p. 137) the inhibition of thirst of men in combat). As soon as the exertion stops, the man makes up with alacrity, but only in part, for his delayed drinking. Such a remaining deficit, reflecting *voluntary dehydration* (pp. 9, 224), may amount to 4 or 5% of the body weight. In man, at least, with his relatively poor powers of urinary concentration, this type of ingestion is unsuited to precarious water supplies (20, Table XX). When men who had been severely dehydrated were given all the water they wanted to drink, copious amounts were usually ingested. Some drank as much as 2 liters in less than 10 minutes; but in half an hour only 50 to 80% of the deficit had been replaced (18).

Peripheral inhibition has long been alleged to be provoked characteristically by acidulous fruit juices, vinegar (122, 322, 780), lemon (309), etc. in a manner aside from the direct moistening effects these might have on the throat. One of their virtues was supposed to lie in the greater ease with which such fluids might cause to dissolve thick or encrusted mucus in the dry mouth, compared with water. The specific effect of vinegar, however, has been denied (33). Possibly, in addition, some central inhibition may flow from the peculiarly "refreshing" qualities of certain beverages, but this could even be said of nonpotable sea water or urine under certain circumstances.

The "regulation pebble" (168), button, nail, or piece of vegetation held in the mouth (p. 50) by the experienced desert traveler short of water—or some drug—may excite some peripheral activity (saliva flow) or sensation but its effect is largely psychological, especially in preserving morale for some individuals (18). They may, in other words, actually engender some central inhibition of thirst and to this extent be physiologic. Otherwise, these putative antidipticums have no noteworthy effect[5] and, generally, because of the associated water deficit, it appears worthless to aim merely at relieving the thirst sensation alone.

Holding ice-cold water in the mouth may be refreshing but does not quench thirst. However, slow sipping of limited rations of water can provide some direct relief of a parched throat which would not be gained simply by swallowing it quickly and taking it into the system (727). The relief afforded by ice in the mouth has been attributed to the cooling of the inspired air (780); and the inhibition of drinking in man which may be engendered by oral menthol is possibly a related effect insofar as nerve endings for cold are stimulated by that drug.

The intensity of thirst in men exposed to the elements has been intimately related to the course of the sun and the heat of the day, increasing as the sun rises above the horizon and declining toward the end of the day (339). These modulations are described for desert thirst particularly by Pujo (632) whose account is given on page 409. The phenomenon has been attested by others (190, 483, 675, 786) for thirst at sea. And Bombard (112) has stated that a good remedy for thirst at sea, especially when one's face is in the sun, is to cover it with a towel or piece of cloth soaked in sea water.

Bellows (83) has shown that there are at least two factors which inhibit thirst and which may be elucidated from the study of the esophagostomized dog. From the fact that sham drinking does not remain continuous during a constant water deficit,[6]

---

[5] Adolph *et al.* (18) state, "None of these methods is very effective, although they give the man something to do to divert his attention. In experiments, when given water, the man with the pebble or the drug drank just as much as he who had done nothing to quell his thirst sensations." It may also be remarked that smoking, sometimes dipsogenic, does not sensibly alter man's fluid requirements; nor does atropine in the dog (p. 51).

[6] See Bernard's experiment (p. 58) and that of Towbin (p. 155).

where swallowed water leaves the fistula without entering the stomach, he concluded that there is one factor which acts, immediately, above the fistula; a second factor acts below the fistula, after a delay. These can be called the pharyngeal and subpharyngeal (subfistulous) factors, respectively, or the pharyngeal and gastric (647). The subpharyngeal factor may consist of one or

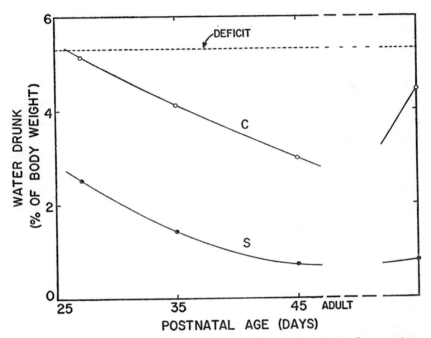

Figure 15. Water drunk after water deficit of 5.3% of body weight at various ages of weanling rats and adult rats. Each point is the mean of thirty measurements. *C*, control drink; *S*, drink after placing a quantity of water equal to 5.3% of body weight in stomach; both within fifteen minutes. The difference between *C* and *S* is the inhibition due to filling the stomach. After Adolph, Barker, and Hoy (19).

more processes. The entrance of water, to the amount of the deficit, below the pharynx inhibits the repetitive act of drinking to the actual amount of the deficit. This also leads to a more permanent satisfaction after a delay of 10 to 15 minutes, which is a shorter period than the absorption time for water of 36 minutes (432). It may be noted in this connection, however, that unabsorbed water in the gut can take up systemic salt, possibly relieving thirst on an osmometric basis quite as if water had been absorbed; and small amounts of water absorbed or introduced into the system have a high satiety value (Table VIII).

Bellows and Van Wagenen (85) distinguished the *water of thirst*, or the water which an animal drinks presumably because of dipsia or polydipsia from the *ingested water* or the water which reaches the stomach for having been placed there by the experimenter through a tube. Water of thirst can be eliminated by proper adjustment of the ingested water.

A specific relation of drinking to age has been determined in rats by Adolph, Barker, and Hoy (19). Replacement of a deficit is most complete at an early age (Fig. 15); is less three weeks later; and is partially regained in the adult. (See pp. 13, 33 and Table III).

Drinking activity may be independent of time until the cessation of activity. Smith and Smith (743) observed that drinking (of milk) activity in the cat is not a function of a gradually changing physiologic state but is controlled by factors which maintain

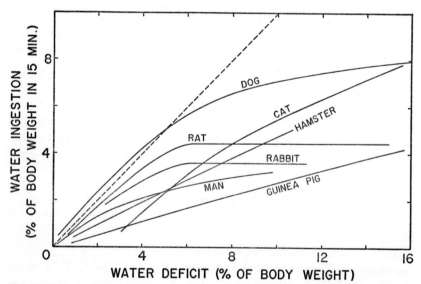

Figure 16.   Relation between initial water ingestion and water deficit in seven species. Note varying degrees of voluntary dehydration. With high probability, each of the curves is different. After Adolph (16).

constant "strength" until drinking is discontinued. Electronically determined "sip" or "lap" rates in rats accord with this (163, 364, 763), as well as some observations of the "suck" rate of the human infant (869), and numerous observations of drinking behavior (9, Table II), including sham drinking in the dog (8).[7] However, the rate of drinking tends to be proportional to the water deficit at the start of drinking (Figs. 4, 16) when computed in terms of the quantity of water taken in some initial period in which at least a transient satiety is attained.

GASTRIC INHIBITION

Sham Drinking

Following Bellows' (83) identification in dogs of different factors in satiety above and below an esophageal fistula, Towbin (788) studied quantitative relations between real and sham drinking, and the role of the filling of the stomach. Thirsty dogs with esophagostomy were placed in a stock and allowed to drink. Most drank steadily, then stopped and left the water pail, giving a clear end-point to the drinking. The water that poured out of the fistula was caught and measured. Satiation from such sham drinking is short-lived, lasting only a few minutes.[8] After establishing a control level for sham drinking, a volume of water, expressed as a percentage of control sham drinks was put into the stomach. After an hour, adequate time for absorption, the dog was again allowed to drink. Such experiments indicated that absorption of approximately 40% of the amount of water sham drunk in the control tests was adequate to slake thirst completely,

---

[7] Aspects of drinking such as rate, frequency of gulps, etc. are sometimes studied by instruments such as the potometer (308) and drinkometer (364).

[8] Bellows (83) has suggested that the repetition of muscular movement in swallowing is a possible factor by which satisfaction is secured, as satisfaction is said to be obtained in many instinctive desires by muscular movement. The drinking of fluid constitutes the only condition in which swallowing may be rapidly repeated. Contrast this view with Müller's (p. 39), in which esophageal activity was thought dipsogenic.

Adolph (7) showed that a fistulous dog in extreme desiccation could take 71 liters of water in 24 hours; 6.9 liters in one draft. One fistulous dog at 4% deficit habitually drank 0.3 to 1.0 liter about every 3 minutes. Occasionally, 20% of the time was spent in drinking.

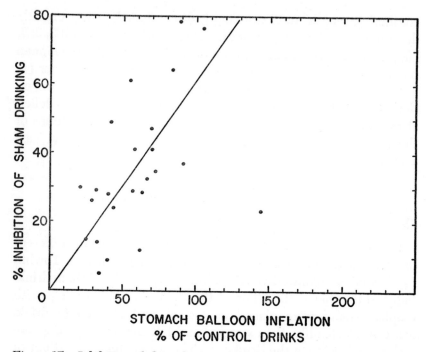

Figure 17.   Inhibition of sham drinking by inflation of stomach balloon (10 dogs, 24 experiments).   See text.   After Towbin (788).

i.e., it might be said that the dog sham-drinks about 250% of what Towbin designates as the real deficit.[9]   It was concluded that when swallowed water is short-circuited through a fistula and does not reach the stomach, the animal's ability to judge accurately the volume drunk is seriously impaired.

A balloon attached to a length of soft rubber tubing and passed into the stomach through the gastric stoma of the esophagostomy could be filled with air or with water to various percentages of the quantity of the control sham drink taken as 100%. When the stomach was filled to the extent of 100% of the control sham drink, then drinking of proffered water was only one-third as great as the

---

[9] "Real deficit" is here ambiguous. To "slake thirst completely" is not necessarily to produce repletion from water deficit but rather any degree of satiety including that of hypodipsia or hypoposia. Osmometrically, thirst may be slaked when the thirst threshold is recrossed, i.e., osmoreceptors are no longer dehydrated sufficiently to excite thirst (Fig. 9, p. 75ff.).

control drinks, a 65% inhibition.. It made no difference if the water were in contact with the stomach or were within a balloon. Towbin found an essentially linear relation between the per cent inhibition of sham drinking and the extent of stomach balloon inflation (Fig. 17).

Gastric Distention: Taste

The distention cue is only a part of the complex that enables a dog to judge the volume of water drunk for, even when deprived of this cue in sham drinking, the dog does stop drinking. Without the distention cue the other components of temporary satiation appear to overwork before drinking is inhibited, resulting in over-drinking. Mechanical factors account for the major effect of stomach filling on inhibition. There was some evidence that, following vagotomy, distention of the stomach had almost no effect upon sham drinking, i.e., the afferent impulses initiated by distention probably ascended the vagi (789); and cocainization of the gastric mucosa abolishes the inhibitory effect of distention (381, 553, 554). Towbin (789) found that while dogs normally vary water consumption by taking more or fewer drinks per day rather than by greatly changing the amount of water taken at each drink, vagotomy caused an increase in the size of the drink; thoracic sympathectomy had an effect opposite to that of vagotomy. Denervation of the stomach (vagotomy and spinal section at the level of the first or second thoracic vertebrae), according to Holmes and Gregersen (376), does not modify the drinking response to injections of hypertonic salt, nor does total sympathectomy (211).

In normal ingestion by the dog, where water reaches the stomach, intake ceases when approximately 1.2 times the deficit has been swallowed (8). If a small quantity of water is placed in the stomach of normal dogs by tube, this does not inhibit the animals from drinking at once an amount of water essentially equal to the initial deficit. Coupled with the findings of Towbin, these results suggest that the inhibitory factor of gastric distention in dogs exists, but that it operates only in extreme distention. Montgomery and Holmes (553, 554) have found, on the other hand, that the distention effect of inhibiting drinking in dogs made thirsty by hypertonic salt loads appears only after the distention has existed for some time (40 minutes); and Barker, Adolph, and Keller (74) found partial inhibition of hypertonic thirst by gastric inflation. The inhibition disappears rapidly following deflation of the stomach.

Paintal (591) has studied the rate of discharge of action currents in afferent vagal fibers presumably innervating gastric stretch receptors of the cat. In anesthetized animals there is a slowly adapting discharge following balloon distention of the stomach. The frequency of discharge is linearly related to the actual volumetric enlargement of the

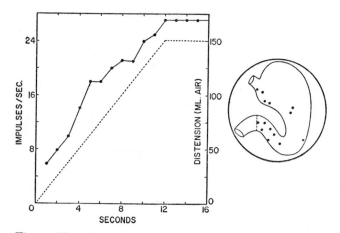

Figure 18. Frequency of action current discharge in a gastric afferent fiber with gradual distention of the stomach (anesthetized cat). The gastric balloon was distended with 150 ml. of air in twelve seconds as shown by the interrupted line. The circle inset illustrates the location of gastric stretch receptors. After Paintal (591).

stomach caused by air introduced into the balloon. The receptors could be located by digital compression of the stomach wall which caused a measured response; they are considered probably to lie in the smooth muscle rather than at the mucous or peritoneal surfaces of the stomach (Fig. 18). The effect of drugs on the response of these receptors and other vagal receptors was also studied (592).

In dogs made thirsty by intravenous hypertonic salt solutions, drinking may not occur if water is placed in the stomach 20 to 30 minutes prior to a test; if water is withdrawn from the stomach through a fistula after such an injection, drinking occurs. Unfortunately, the interpretation of studies of inhibition and satiety in hydropenia and in nonhydropenic hypersalemia suffers because these states of absolute and relative dehydration are not comparably standardized.

Species differences exist (16). While a burro (20), camel (686a), or young rabbit is similar to a dog as reflected in the observation that these animals tend to drink normally in one continuous draft to complete satiation, rats, guinea pigs, and adult rabbits (two months of age) drink slowly and interruptedly. Thus, it is found that water placed in the stomach by tube inhibits immediate drinking in proportion to the filling in the rat,[10] hamster, and guinea pig, and has little immediate effect in dog and young rabbit. It has been concluded, therefore, that rapidity of drinking and relative lack of gastric inhibition in the dog and young rabbit suggest a pharyngeal metering in these animals, while the other animals tested metered water largely in the stomach (Fig. 15).

The dog, then, is remarkable for drinking the amount of its absolute water deficit and ceasing to drink further, before any appreciable quantity of water has been absorbed (74). However, it may be a poor animal for drinking studies unless special precautions are taken to minimize psychic factors (210, 856). Conceivably satiety, as well as thirst, has a conditioned reflex component of pharyngeal, esophageal, and gastric influences which ordinarily stand in a certain temporal relation to the effects of water absorption after drinking (554).

It has been said (46) that a ruminant such as the goat offers an advantage for experiments on stimulation of the thirst or

---

[10] Water injected directly into the stomach of the rat reduces thirst promptly; water drunk normally by mouth produces an even greater reduction (550). Water drinking and the drinking of salt solutions are under the control of at least three factors: taste and other sensory mechanism of the mouth, gastric distention, and dehydration produced by the osmometric effects of hypertonic solutions on the stomach (764).

The rat ordinarily takes 15 minutes to complete 80% of its recovery from water deficit by drinking (18). It does about 80% of its drinking in the dark and devotes only about 20 minutes in every 24 hours to satisfying water needs (364, p. 125).

drinking center (p. 84). The voluminous rumen can function as a fluid reservoir which permits consumption of large volumes of water before significant inhibitory influences from the distention of the digestive tract seem to suppress thirst. Sheep with access to water every day have been noted to take 10% less water than those watered every second day. It has been supposed that they may "overdrink" when they become extremely dry (391).

Drinking may not restore entire water loss, a phenomenon which has been attributed to loss of other body materials (658). However, the view that the delay in recovery of body volume after dehydration, by drinking, relates to salt loss by sweating (689, 741) is oversimplified. The camel drinks enough water in 10 minutes for complete rehydration and sustains a precipitous drop in plasma concentration of electrolytes without ill effects (686a). Critchley (190) has stated that when dehydrated sailors have been rescued, it is a common experience for them to show polydipsia and polyuria for the ensuing two or three weeks.

Even in the dog, drinking in extreme dehydration may be quite different from drinking in moderate water deficit. A dog which had been deprived of food and water for 33 days and had lost 39% of its body weight drank back only 5.5, 5.9, and 6.7% of its initial body weight in 5, 20, and 80 minutes, respectively, when water was made available. At the end of that time, osmotic pressure of plasma and concentrations of its sodium, chloride, protein, etc., dropped about 15%, approaching normal values; the next day, concentrations had fallen another 5%, to somewhat below normal (871). Prentiss et al. (626) observed a cat to drink 7.6% of its body weight in 10 minutes and 14.3% in 4 hours after living for almost four weeks on raw salmon with no extra water (p. 328). Large drops in plasma osmotic pressure, sodium, chloride, potassium, nonprotein nitrogen, and hematocrit toward normal values were observed, of the order of 10 to 20%.

Adolph (12) states that the dog does not make up at one draft deficits exceeding 9% of the body weight. The camel maximally takes up to 33% of its dehydrated body weight (686); if a first drink is not enough to cover the loss the animal restores original body weight at the next.

An old observation of Wilks (836) associated "an inordinate stretching or distension of the stomach" with the production of intense thirst in man with diaphragmatic hernia. And Pincoffs (614) has noted patients with acute gastric dilatation who urgently want water every few minutes until the stomach has been emptied of two to three liters of retained water.

Amounts of fluid drunk do not equal the absolute capacity of the stomach (16). In rats the stomach regularly accommodates 9% of the body weight of fluid introduced by stomach tube, and the stomach regularly probably passes on about half of its water content in less than 15 minutes. The guinea pig stomach holds at least 12% of the body weight of water when filled through a tube. Even in the dog the gastric capacity is far from reached as evidenced by tests in which 8% of the body weight of water was placed in the stomach, after which the dogs immediately drank a further amount equal to 4.5% of the body weight.

Klisiecki, Rothschild, and Verney (432) have estimated that 250 cc. of water are absorbed by the small gut of a 10 Kg. dog in 36 minutes. There is evidence that water by mouth passes immediately through the pylorus. Smirk (731) estimated the absorption time of 1 liter of warm water (37° C.) as 22 to 25 minutes in man. Cold water has been said to close the sphincters of the stomach so that absorption is delayed (218).

Considering the relatively small amounts of water which may be taken under normal conditions by man, i.e., with minimal or eudipsic deficits, it seems unlikely that gastric inhibition is particularly effective in such regulation. Rather pharyngeal or other metering is suggested. Weir, Larson, and Rowntree (815) have remarked how some patients with diabetes insipidus, having been treated with pituitrin, obtained a sense of satiety and a feeling of fullness from taking small quantities of water such as half a glass; reduced from large to small water intakes, their taste for water was frequently perverted, and they referred to water as "stale" or "flat." Such a gustatory change does not occur when a man suddenly reduces the enormous water intake necessitated by his living in a hot desert environment to the intake characteristic of a temperate environment.

Taste of drinking water, however, appears to dictate how much of it will be ingested in the initial period of drinking induced by water deficit. Disgusting waters may inhibit drinking (p. 378), but hyperdipsia improves their taste (p. 406). Aside from such aberrations of thirst alluded to by E. Darwin (201), in that the desire for liquid may be diseased by indulgence in liquids grateful to the palate,[11] Adolph *et al.* (19) found that rats and rabbits ingest greater quantities of dilute salt solution than of water, the saline somehow being interpreted to require larger intakes in the interests of restoring water balance (pp. 163, 171). A similar preference may have been observed in cats (626, p. 328) but not in dogs (871). Le Magnen (471) noted that the diminution of drinking in rats in inanition was less if they were offered isotonic sodium chloride rather than water. Fig. 40 illustrates in principle how fluid requirements may vary with the concentration of the ingesta. In potassium deficiency, on the contrary, saline is taken in smaller quantities than is plain water (p. 131ff.).

It is of interest to note the demonstration (49, 892) that the tongue of frogs (*Rana temporaria* and *R. esculenta*) contains receptors which respond to distilled water or to very dilute sodium chloride, the threshold of the latter being less than 0.05%. The water response is mediated through fibers other than of pressure and touch. There are still other fibers responding to hypertonic and slightly hypotonic solutions, which may be studied by action currents in the glossopharyngeal nerve. Fresh water placed on the tongue of a pithed frog excites a massive volley of action currents. This response is abolished by Ringer's solution, isotonic saline, and some other isotonic solutions but not by isotonic sucrose. Actually, of course, frogs practically never drink water, ordinarily taking it in through their skin. Stimulation of the tongue by water is said possibly to contribute reflexly to keeping the mouth of the frog closed as well as to inhibit respiratory movement under water. No water response occurs from dorsal skin nerves.

The tongue of the cat, dog, and pig also respond to the application of distilled water to the tip of the tongue with a sudden volley of impulses for about a fifth of a second in the chorda tympani nerve. Liljestrand and Zotterman (481) posit a "water taste" in mammals which seems not to be an osmotic phenomenon but a chemoreceptor stimulation in the tongue, the stimulus being a movement of ions out of the receptor cells.

---

[11] E.g., beer," soft drinks," etc. Also called "spurious" thirst (494). The desire for flavorful beverages is not thirst but appetite based on memories of pleasant tastes and smells (467); the element of suggestion and popular fads and fancies also complicate the thirst phenomenon in man (649), not to mention the use of water as an oral lubricant.

Gastric Water Storage

Apparently men can gain practical advantage by ignoring the admonishments of satiety and drinking to nimiety with extra water, in anticipation of water restriction. Adolph *et al.* (18) believe that predrinking ("tanking up") in appropriate circumstances is not harmful and a man may convert his interior into an accessory storage tank able to carry a quart or more of additional water. Only half of any water suddenly drunk in excess of bodily needs is excreted after an hour and a half; in the desert, most of the excess can be removed by sweating within that time, so that only a small part of it is excreted in the urine instead of being used economically in sweat formation. Saline, when ingested instead of water, may be retained for a long time, even in cool climates. It has been suggested that if more than a liter is to be predrunk, a 0.5 to 0.9% sodium chloride solution be taken during 2 or 3 hours preceding the occasion on which extra water will be needed.

Water "storage" in the camel is discussed on page 359.

FREE, FACULTATIVE, AND ISORRHEIC WATER

If an organism is usefully to gain water from a solution, the volume of solution taken must supply the normal requirement of water plus any extra amount obligated in the urinary excretion of the solution's dissolved materials. Certain provisos to this generalization may suggest themselves, depending upon how we treat the question of the availability of urinary osmotic space (p. 310), but we ignore these for the present. In another way, potable solutions may be looked upon abstractly as consisting of two virtual volumetric elements: an *obligatory portion* of that highest concentration (limiting isorrheic concentration) which can just be matched by the kidney so that the organism suffers no relative retention of solute to water (857), and a *free portion* consisting of the remaining volume of pure water. Since the free water is always less than the original volume, a larger volume of solution is required than of pure water to maintain a steady state of isotonicity (except in the case of certain dilute solutions, which serve better than plain water (pp. 263, 326)). Solutions more concentrated than the limiting isorrheic concentration (p. 298, Figs. 36, 37) have a negative free water volume and are of necessity nonpotable (again, except as urinary osmotic space may be available). If f, o, and v are the free, obligatory, and total volumes, respectively, U_{LIC} is the limiting isorrheic concentration of the urine, and V is the concentration of the solution of volume v, then

$$f = v - o = v(1 - \frac{V}{U_{LIC}})$$

and

$$o = v - f = \frac{vV}{U_{LIC}}$$

In general, *free water intake* is that portion of the total of actual and potential water of an aquiferous intake (solution, food yielding preformed and/or oxidative water, etc.) which is not obligated to the renal excretion of the solutes of the intake. This definition is clearly arbitrary, reflecting the myopia of renal physiologists who do not concern themselves with larger aspects of water balance. Free water is that which is supposedly "free" to be used for other things than the obligatory urine volume (p. 15), but it does violence to the word "free" to ascribe this appellation to water obligated to sweat formation in a hot environment.

So-called free water is often calculated from maximal urinary concentrations of solutes rather than limiting isorrheic concentrations, especially since the latter are not well known. If these differ, the former yields a volume not necessarily all "free" for other purposes. In the presence of negative water loads and balances, free water may simply constitute a subminimal intake insufficient for the normal water metabolism of the organism. It may be noted that the effects of administering a volume of pure water in lieu of an equal volume of free water derived from an aquiferous potential are not identical, e.g., urinary volume and solute excretion would differ.

Where solutions contain more than one solute the problem can become complex (p. 338). Thus, increased salt excretion might condition increased urine volume, but in so doing it would provide "osmotic space" for increased nitrogen excretion. It may be seen that water obligated to salt may yet be free water for nitrogen.

By way of further definition we note that *facultative water intake* is that portion of the water intake which gives rise to and, in water balance, equals, the facultative urine volume (857, Table I, p. 15). Loosely, it is water intake in excess of needs; it is truly free water and should not be confused with the "free water clearance" of the nephrologists (741a).

Isorrheic water intake (p. 302) is that which permits the maintenance of physiologic water balances and loads, i.e., isorrhea for water. Any water intake, minimal or in excess, but consistent with the maintenance of normal concentrations of solutes in body fluids and thus with the well being of the organism is isorrheic.

SATIETY IN HYPERSALEMIC THIRST AND DRINKING

Fig. 9 is a diagram which can be employed in osmometric analysis of thirst. A similar diagram has been used by Ladell (461, 462) to interrelate water and salt balances, and cellular fluid volumes. Geometric construction on the diagram indicates the volume of water required to restore any state of hypertonicity of body fluids, dipsogenic or not, to isotonicity. Such information, however, can be directly obtained by so-called "equations of thirst" (856). These equations, derived elsewhere (857), are as follows: Q_N, the quantity of water required to bring an individual to isotonicity, is given by

$$Q_N = \frac{L}{A} - L_{H_2O}$$

where L is the load of sodium salt (more strictly, the load of osmotically effective particles); A is the normal, "isotonic" concentration of sodium in plasma, reflecting concentrations in body fluids (more strictly, effective osmolality); and L_{H_2O} is the net load of water in the body in liters at the moment preceding drinking. For example, if 2 liters of a solution containing 300 mEq. of sodium chloride per liter were in net positive load and if 150 mEq./L. were the analytical concentration of the plasma equivalent to its normal effective osmotic pressure,

$$Q_N = \frac{2(300)}{150} - 2 = 2 \text{ liters.}$$

This is not a volume that one predicts would be drunk under the given conditions, but is simply the volume which would have to be added to the body to restore its fluids to isotonicity. The locus of all Q_N values of a given magnitude is a line on the osmometric diagram called an *isodip*, or better, an *isodipsic*. It describes all of the possible combinations of salt (sodium chloride) and water loads which are theoretically consistent with "equal" thirst in the sense that equal volumes of water would be necessary to restore isotonicity. One of the possible uses of isodipsics designated in this way is in the study of volume factors in thirst and satiety (Chapter IV), since deviations in actual quantities of water drunk from quantities predicted according to isodipsic points, at widely disparate water loads, can be interpreted to reflect some measure of independent volumetric influence.

The equation of thirst which describes the quantity of water, Q_τ, required to modify a given state of hypertonicity to that prevailing at the thirst threshold, τ, is given as

$$Q_\tau = \frac{(1-\tau)(WA-L)}{A} - (W + L_{H_2O})$$

where W is the number of liters of water normally in the body before loading. Equations of the isodipsics (lines) of the Q_N and Q_τ types, as well as an extended treatment of these, have been given by Wolf (857).

The finding of Holmes and Gregersen (374) that an intravenous injection of 300 cc. of 5% sodium chloride produces severe thirst in man, and that ingestion of 400 to 600 cc. of water 20 to 30 minutes before the injection alleviates this thirst, is largely consistent with osmometric interpretation. The latter condition, in effect, is roughly equivalent to the administration of 800 cc. of 2% salt (uncorrected for urinary excretion), the cellular dehydration from which would be appreciably less than (ca. half of) that caused by 300 cc. of 5% salt. In any case, the high satiety value of water entering the system is also a factor.

We have noted elsewhere the phenomenon of voluntary absolute dehydration in man which results from his failure to drink back all of his water deficit initially. He characteristically takes 30 minutes or more to complete 80% of his recovery drinking. The thirst sensations of a man sweating rapidly during activity (p. 108) at high temperatures are inadequate to keep his water intake up to output, and he drinks only about one-half of what he loses during this period (18). Only when he has food and rest does he desire the water missing from his body. The dog, to the contrary (p. 159), keeps its water intake closely matched to output when stimulated by absolute dehydration or hydropenia. It is therefore interesting to observe that with hypersalemic thirst there can exist a condition of *voluntary relative dehydration* in both man and dog (210, 374, 376, 856).

Tables VII and VIII compare the actual water drunk (Q_A) with the Q_N values calculated to restore the body fluids of dogs and men to isotonicity. Particularly in the dog it is seen how less (half as much) water is drunk than would appear to be required. This has been reported also by Holmes and Gregersen (376) but these investigators observed one dog to drink to isotonicity and another to overdrink consistently. In man, fail-

TABLE VII

Comparison of actual quantity of water (Q_A) drunk by dogs with the quantity theoretically required (Q_N) to restore their body fluids to isotonicity. L_{Na} and L_{H_2O} are net loads of sodium and water, respectively, after intravenous administration of hypertonic sodium chloride (856).

Dog	L_{Na} (mEq.)	L_{H_2O} (L.)	Q_N (L.)	Q_A (L.)
D	202.	0.200	1.147	0.660
K	79.4	0.046	0.484	0.346
Q	93.2	0.143	0.478	0.585
O	82.0	0.027	0.520	0.150
Q	67.6	0.119	0.332	0.200
R	56.5	0.059	0.318	0.330
O	112.	0.256	0.491	0.172
K*	131.	0.454	0.419	0.000
D	308.	0.978	1.075	0.210
Q	135.	0.081	0.819	0.264
O	54.3	0.049	0.313	0.5
Average			0.598	0.342

* No drinking. Not included in averages.

ure to restore isotonicity is not so striking for ingested water but water given by vein as 5% glucose has a higher satiety value. Presumably water by vein brings into play no processes reflexly to inhibit intake as does ingested water; the former works immediately and directly to reduce the dipsogenic influence of hypertonicity and thus to bring one to or below the thirst threshold.

TABLE VIII

Actual quantity of water (Q_A), drunk ad libitum or given by vein as 5% glucose, which just caused thirst to disappear in men at the thirst threshold (Exper. No. 1 to 4) and in slightly thirstier men (Exper. No. 5 to 9). Q_N is the quantity of water theoretically required to restore their body fluids to isotonicity. L_{Na} and L_{H_2O} are net loads of sodium and water, respectively, after intravenous administration of hypertonic sodium chloride (856).

Exper. No.	Subject	L_{Na} (mEq.)	L_{H_2O} (L.)	Q_N (L.)	Q_A (L.)
		Water, ad libitum			
1	W.H.	255	0.372	1.328	0.645
2	J.W.	92	0.079	0.534	0.560
3	L.P.	132	0.096	0.784	0.560
4	W.B.	51	0.094	0.246	0.747
Average				0.723	0.628
		Glucose, by vein			
5	W.H.	120	0.058	0.742	0.065
6	W.H.	175	0.088	1.079	0.281
7	J.B.	72	0.054	0.426	0.082
8	S.D.	130	0.058	0.809	0.340
9	S.D.	150	0.108	0.892	0.338
Average				0.790	0.221

Ingested water cannot enter the system and act so quickly in this way so that its initial effect rather represents the bringing into play of other dipsoinhibitory factors such as pharyngeal metering, gastric distention, etc. In any case, men sweating profusely and working hard may drink quantities of water which dilute their body fluids below normal isotonic levels, causing at times water intoxication or heat cramps (p. 201).

Although there is a linear relation between subsequent water intake and the amount of sodium chloride injected into dogs in hypertonic solution (376), particularly when the concentration of infused solution is constant (211), and the response of an individual dog is remarkably consistent, there are still categories of drinking responses observable. Most dogs either complete their drinking promptly after the injection of salt or drink the major share of the eventual intake within 5 minutes. However, some animals consistently drink small amounts at frequent intervals for 30 to 60 minutes. Two animals were observed by Holmes and Gregersen (376) to wait 15 to 30 minutes before starting to drink. Di Salvo (210) classified the latent periods of drinking by hypersalemic dogs in three categories: *immediate* (almost always drink within a minute); *intermediate* (sometimes drink within a minute but may delay up to 10 minutes); *delayed* (rarely drink within 10 minutes). These categories appear to be characteristic of the individual although handling of the dog or removing it from and replacing it in its cage just prior to a dipsogenic injection of salt greatly increased the latent period in those dogs which were normally immediate drinkers. An intravenous injection of 2 cc. of 2% procaine preceding salt injection also increased the latent period of immediate drinkers (211). Neither vagotomy nor complete sympathectomy altered the magnitude or latency of the drinking response, nor did 10 pressor units of pitressin.

Hypodipsia: Modulations

Hypodipsia, as indicated by the area in Fig. 9 between the thirst threshold and the isotonic line, has been defined only in terms of the osmometric diagram, and not mechanistically. Tables VII and VIII show that the quantity of water actually drunk initially in hypersalemic thirst often fails to bring the organism back to isotonicity but brings it generally below the thirst threshold (with intravenous glucose the individual is brought only slightly below the threshold). Hypodipsia is then a sort of "insensible" or "twilight" thirst, and, in a sense, a voluntary relative dehydration (p. 167). It is insufficient to initiate drinking as the animal is brought toward but not to the thirst threshold from isotonicity; yet it suffices (in osmometric theory) to sustain drinking once that is initiated by such conditions as food taking, rest, etc. Hypodipsia occurs under various circumstances: in the ordinary course of dehydration; as a result of infusing subthreshold quantities of hypertonic saline (insufficient to precipitate thirst); or by failure to drink back to isotonicity from a dipsic condition. It is a transient state which readily resolves into adipsia or eudipsia depending on stimuli presented to the organism. Suggestive of hysteresis in the thirst-drinking-satiety triad of water metabolism, it may conceivably be described in terms of a highly variable threshold, i.e., not one triggered to give rise to a thirst sensation at an immutably fixed τ value, but one which reflects the modulation of multiple potentiating and inhibitory nervous factors, all interacting.

One of the most curious modulations is seen in the man on the desert—hot, dehydrated, and thirsty—who will only reluctantly drink warm or hot water from an insolated canteen (18, 168, 339, 617, 869), but will take cool or cold water with alacrity. It is convenient to state the physiologic problem as one in which the man must discharge simultaneously a positive load of heat and a negative load of water in such a way as to minimize the potential effects of unfavorable combination of these stresses. Hot water ingestion reduces mainly, or only, the latter load toward zero; cold water reduces both. In polar or other cold regions, and where the microclimate (clothing, shelter) is on the cool side, the fact that hot drinks, contrariwise, are preferable to cold may be subsumed under the same principle. Nevertheless, it is recognized that in the desert hot tea may be a welcome beverage at a time when warm water is rejected by a dehydrated person. Since the time factor precludes the possibility of exhilaration from the tea alkaloids, except possibly as a conditioned response, it may be that taste exerts an important modulating influence here (p. 235). Taste, even of water, may be affected by temperature, and in this indirect way, also, temperature may modulate thirst and drinking.

Tancredi (780) opined in 1607 that thirst is an appetite for cooling or for moisture, whichever is required. Galen stated, Tancredi tells us, that thirst is excited at one time by lack of fluid, at one time by abundance of heat. It is interesting in this regard so to interpret the excessively frequent drinking sometimes manifested by the unacclimated newcomer to the hot desert (18, 66). The frequency of thirst sensations is lessened with one's acclimatization. At first, a man is continually taking small drafts of water, but after a few days he is content to allow an hour or two between drafts, and each draft is larger. He may then allow less water deficit to accumulate, a fact suggesting that while large amounts of fluid are unwelcome to the alimentary tract, it can adjust so that large drafts become pleasurable (18).

Moreover, the intensity of thirst may be geared to the heat of the day (66, 339, 632, 675, 786, 831, p. 152), as if elevated heat loads enhanced the thirst sensation at a given level of hydropenia or cellular hypovolia; or even as a conditioned reflex. In cold climates men may not feel thirst readily (p. 234).

Another modulation illustrating multiple factor interaction is seen in the fact that when dogs made hypertonic by injections of 20% sodium chloride are offered certain other fluids than water to drink, they may elect to take considerably more. Holmes (368) showed that such dogs offered 0.9% saline took two to three times as much as they did of water; with 1.8% urea, intake was 1.3 times as much; with 5% glucose, 1.3% sodium sulfate, 0.9% magnesium chloride, 0.85% ammonium chloride, 0.9% sodium bicarbonate, and 1.15% sodium acetate intake was the same or slightly less than with tap water. The temperature of the liquid did not appreciably alter the drinking response.

It appears that fluid ingestion is not simply determined by the requirement to reestablish normal tonicity of body fluids immediately. And it is clear that problems of thirst and problems of satiety are in various degrees independent and distinct. As Starkenstein (754), Janssen (398), Wolf (851), Kanter (405, p. 205), and others have observed, the quenching of hypertonic thirst, to be lasting, involves excretion as well as intake. This "metabolic" control of thirst differs from the one reflected in the transient antidipsic effects of cocaine, opium, or other such agents. Regulation by drinking, within limits, is quicker than by excretion, but both processes are complementary; the latter is at times indispensable, as where hypersalemic thirst is so great that the taking of sufficient water to slake it is physically precluded by the limited capacity of the gut.

CHAPTER IV

THE REGULATION OF FLUID VOLUME

The regulation of the quantity of the body fluids (857), and the size of their compartments, has come to be called "volume regulation." It has the same claim to recognition (104, 630, 741b, p. 345) as a physiologic entity as does the regulation of temperature, blood pressure, plasma sodium concentration, or body weight. Unfortunately, there are few conventions for treating this subject and we presently want for a sensible understanding of volume regulation. But there is no dearth of ideas for scrutiny. The same reasons which compelled physiologists to recognize the role of the kidney in such regulation favor their considering the possible parallel role of the thirst apparatus. It is relevant, therefore, to summarize palpable information on this subject even if, in so doing, it appears necessary to depart somewhat from those lines of evidence one naturally thinks of as relating to thirst, per se.

The regulation of fluid volume is one aspect of the larger regulation of body size of which Adolph (5) has observed:

> Every kind of living organism is distinguished by its size. Size is one of the chief of its properties, and the bodies of individuals belonging to one kind are alike in bulk. Even a giant or a pigmy is not so different from the average individual as is usually the average individual of another species. Among men, for instance, all adults fit the same doorways and the same beds; Procrustes had to be excessively particular to find any cause for mutilating his victims. A hasty comparison with all men of all the inorganic objects of some one kind, such as all crystals of a single kind of

172

salt, all granite rocks, or all dolomite mountains, reveals the extent to which size characterizes men. . . . Uniform size of body and of its parts is not, however, peculiar to living things. Drops of water and grains of sand are each similar to one another in volume as well as in shape. But a living body does not keep its component materials as does the grain of sand, nor depend upon isolation for its integrity as does the drop of water.

The organism is, in fact, continually exchanging its constituents for new ones. Thus, its water is constantly being thrown away, only to be replaced by other molecules which are the same in every respect. The living body is like a river; its content is ever changing but its shape and its size remain unmodified to any large extent. A river is contained in a bed which limits it; but the mold in which the individual organism is confined is invisible, for its boundaries and its skeleton are also changing. It is independent of any particular structural constituent and maintains its individuality in a medium composed of the same substances as itself.

ON VOLUME IN BIOLOGY[1]

In one respect this subject is time-honored. Herbert Spencer and many others since his day have recognized the biological importance of the principle of similitude. Bulk increases as the cube of length; surface as the square. Hence the limitation of the size of cells, the minute canalization of the body, and the prodigious jumps of the flea, as well as the variation in metabolism with the size of the organism. Yet even this subject is by no means exhausted. For example (a fact which appears to be of some importance in describing the internal regulation of temperature) the difference in temperature between center and surface of a sphere which is producing heat uniformly throughout its whole mass, when equilibrium has been established with a surrounding liquid medium of constant temperature, is proportional to the square of the radius.

But apart from this great principle and certain superficial discussions of the nature of oedema and similar phenomena, the regulation of volume has remained without any physico-chemical analysis. Yet, from the standpoint of physical science, this is perhaps the most universal and fundamental of all organic regulations.

---

[1] This section, On Volume in Biology, omitting original reference notes, is reprinted from L. J. Henderson's statement of the problem (345).

I believe that this strange neglect may be traced to three facts. In the first place, the chemist is accustomed to vary the volume of his systems to suit his convenience. This is a justifiable practice, because, if the phases are so large that capillary phenomena may be disregarded, and so small that gravity need not be taken into account, the division of a phase into two parts does not change its energy. Thus, volume hardly enters into our calculations except as an indirect expression for that which is regarded as the true variable, *viz.*, concentration. This, however, is to disregard the real question as it presents itself in biology. Secondly, *when equilibrium has been established* in a heterogeneous system, as Willard Gibbs rigorously proved, the volume of the phases—capillary and gravitational phenomena being absent—is not relevant to the state of the system. But it may be at once observed, first, that until equilibrium has been attained the volume is of great moment, and, secondly, that equilibrium is never attained within the organism. Finally, the ordinary conception of the process of diffusion is based upon a mathematical discussion, which, though leading to a consistent description of the phenomena, is nevertheless a false representation of the actual occurrences. And nearly all physiological changes of volume depend upon diffusion.

Contrary to a general though vague belief, the regulation of volume is theoretically independent of osmotic pressure regulation. For example, if a kidney produces a liter of urine of the same freezing point as blood, it must have diminished the volume of the body and left the osmotic pressure sensibly unchanged.

For the purpose of discussion, the activity of the kidney may be reduced to the following fiction: First there must be an excretion of all the dissolved constituents of blood plasma, including water itself, in such amounts as to bring the composition of the blood in all respects to a hypothetical normal composition; secondly, a certain portion of this normal plasma, minus the colloids, must be removed in order to regulate the volume.

Statistically the volume of the urine must vary with the magnitude of the volume regulation, although, in particular cases, it need bear no relation to this quantity. Now sodium chloride is the principal constituent of blood plasma. Hence, statistically the ratio Δ:NaCl (i.e. the ratio of freezing point depression to sodium chloride concentration in urine) will be small when the volume is large, and large when the volume is small. Thus we arrive at a theoretical deduction *a priori* of Korányi's coefficient. This coefficient tells us, therefore, nothing about the mode of action of the kidney mechanism. It has no bearing on the question of the functions of glomeruli and tubules. For the ratio is seen to be, as existing evidence proves, necessarily liable to indefinite fluctuations in particular cases. There is involved merely a statistical truth, expressing the conditions under which any kidney must operate in case sodium chloride is the chief constituent of the blood.

The practical importance of this theoretical discrimination of volume regulation from the excretion of the several urinary constituents appears to be established by the fact that in pathological conditions the daily volume of urine may be constant during variations in amounts of water or salt ingested, even when such experiments lead to fluctuations in the physico-chemical properties of the urine. For this shows that the regulation of volume may be deranged more or less independently of the proper excretory functions.

If the final stage of volume regulation has been neglected, the intermediate stages have been generally misconceived. Neither the swelling of colloids nor the pressure which results from osmosis can furnish the basis for an analysis of such phenomena. In their stead we must turn to the kinetic theory and to Willard Gibbs' thermodynamics. But it should be first remarked that osmotic 'pressure' and colloidal swelling 'pressure' hardly act as important sources of mechanical tension, in the living organism. Even oedema involves very small magnitudes of such pressures. Secondly, changes in volume merely consist in the passage of material from one phase to another (except in so far as physical and chemical changes within a phase may produce very slight fluctuations in volume). Finally, apart from the operation of special secretory mechanisms which we do not understand, such processes consist in the diffusion through phases and across interfaces from points of higher to points of lower potential. In the internal phenomena no less than in the exchanges with the environment, and in the internal phenomena of a single phase no less than in the heterogeneous process, water is quite as much in question as the dissolved substances.

This fact has been generally overlooked, by the physicists even more than by the physiologists. We may consider a simple diffusion experiment in which a layer of water is placed above a layer of sugar solution. It is true that the sugar must diffuse up into the

water, but it is also true that the water must diffuse down into
the solution. Yet the phenomena of diffusion have always been
discussed with the help of the mathematical theory of heat con-
duction as exactly defined by Fourier. Thus Fick's theory of
diffusion overlooks the rôle of the solvent. This has been possible
because the process takes place *as if* the solvent were inert and the
dissolved substance possessed a higher diffusibility. But the diffusion of the solvent is probably greater than that of the solute, in
that water is, with a few exceptions, the most diffusible of substances. In their neglect of the relativity of motion, contemporary
accounts of diffusion involve an old fallacy that occurs even in the
astronomy of Ptolemy.

It may perhaps be objected that throughout the organism water
exists at a uniform potential. This, however, is both untrue and
beside the point. For, if two phases are free to exchange material,
an exchange involving all their components will take place unless,
at the outset, all their components possess the same potential in
both phases. Thus, as Höber has shown, isotonic solutions of sodium chloride and magnesium sulphate change in volume when
brought into contact. For the chloride diffuses faster than the
sulphate. Thus the sulphate solution becomes more concentrated
and, as a result, water diffuses into it from the chloride solution.
In like manner differences of pressure and of temperature influence the potential of water and of all dissolved substances.
Finally, the processes of metabolism are continually altering the
concentrations of solutions, and therefore the potential of water.

When these facts are taken into account, it becomes clear that
the chief physical factor in the internal regulation of volume is
water, through its distribution between the infinite assemblage of
phases which make up the organism. The general concepts of the
phase rule reveal the several elements of this process—except those
which depend upon so-called selective activities—but the physical
theory of diffusion, and therefore the whole kinetic description, has
been developed from a false representation of the process, which
neglects the movements of water itself. Only when this is immediately evident, as in osmotic phenomena, is it at all taken into
account. But even here the current explanations are often incomplete. And the general theory of the diffusion of water is almost
useless for the purposes of physiology. Yet there seems to be no
reason to doubt that, in the organism, this is the most important
process of diffusion.

VOLUME RECEPTORS

One of the subtle difficulties besetting physiologic analysis of volume regulation lies in the question of how the organism assesses the magnitude of its own regional and general volumes or deviations of these from "normal," since it is commonly presumed, a posteriori, that such a process is indispensable. Some assume there must be a sort of volume-detecting apparatus, organ, or organelle on the afferent side of some moderator reflex—at least in higher animals—and the term *volume receptor* (817) has frequently been employed. If this concept is interpreted in conformity with the nomenclature of sensory physiology, "volume" becomes the *adequate stimulus* of the hypothesized receptor, after the fashion in which "temperature" receptors, "pressure" receptors, "light" receptors, and "chemical" receptors are identified as to their adequate stimuli.

To decide precisely what should be called an adequate ("appropriate") stimulus—that to which each kind of receptor responds most readily—is a matter still within the purlieus of philosophy. However, some physiologists regard an adequate stimulus as one to whose form of energy the receptor is particularly sensitive; and they exemplify this by showing that warmth end-organs are more sensitive to radiant heat than nearby pain endings. Sherrington (717) stated that the main function of the receptor is to lower the threshold of excitability of the reflex arc for one kind of stimulus, and to heighten it for all others. But there is no quite satisfactory way to compare relative sensitivities to diverse types of stimulation, such as warmth versus pressure, or cold, or light, whose units of intensity are not alike.

Even the chronaxie with its units of time, common to and derivable from all strength-duration curves, is not suitable. Blair (108), who demonstrated latent addition in nerves, using the varied mechanical (pressure) stimulation of precisely timed air jets, concluded that the state of excitation produced by mechanical stimulation is the same as that by electrical. Unfortunately, in the very generality of such a proximate analysis some physiologic significance is lost, and the penultimate analysis which settles for the use of the conventional, if inexact, terminology of adequate stimuli remains attractive. Pressure and light constitute working classifications of adequate stimuli even though stimuli, secondary or derivative to these (e.g., chemical), may seem more intimate to the excitatory process when we reflect on it. Whatever shortcomings of precision reside in the various denominations of adequate stimuli, most of the specific classes are operationally useful.

Not so with "volume" receptor. It is difficult to imagine a less discriminating appellation (341) considering that numerous other adequate stimuli depend upon, are mediated through, or are concomitant with volume changes in or about receptors. Thus, pressure changes are often (835), if not necessarily, associated with volume changes; tension, likewise. Osmotic pressure changes in body fluids are conceived to act through volume changes in "osmoreceptors," for which substantial evidence exists (p. 84). But a pressure or tension receptor presumably reacts to deformation or extension and there is dubiety about its dependence on volume change. Volume appears at times properly to constitute an adequate stimulus, but for the most part its physical correlatives are so readily recognizable that the term "volume" becomes generic rather than specific.

Consider the fish in the vessels of Fig. 19. Let us regard them in toto as receptors, unstimulated so long as oxygen concentration in the water remains at or above some value. With a constant utilization of oxygen by the fish, and at a constant temperature, this oxygen concentration will presumably depend on the size of the water surface in contact with air. Nevertheless, a first experiment may show that stimulation of the fish-receptor is highly dependent on volume in systems *A* and *B*. The fish are apparently "volume" (of water) receptors, and so hypothesize. However, stimulation of the fish in *C* is found to be essentially independent of volume; and the fish is not a volume receptor. We reformulate the hypothesis: the fish are surface (water-air interface) receptors. But by varying the temperature and thus gas solubility, and metabolic rate among other things, we show subsequently that surface, per se, is not so simply related to stimulation. In this way experimental analysis tells us in turn that our fish-receptor is now not a surface receptor but an oxygen

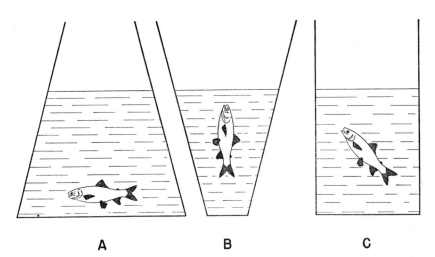

Figure 19.   Volume receptors.   A and B are two opposite types of apparently volume-dependent receptor systems.   C is a volume-independent system. See text for details.

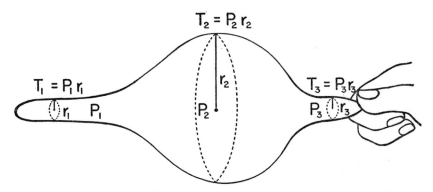

Figure 20.   Balloon demonstration and Laplace's formula.   A partially inflated "tubular" balloon has an internal pressure, P, equally transmitted to all parts of the contained air (Pascal's law; $P_1 = P_2 = P_3$); and the circumferential tension, T, in the wall of the balloon varies with the radius, r, in a given section.   After Wolf (859).

receptor; not an oxygen receptor but a metabolite receptor, etc.

Suppose a certain vital substance to be produced and utilized at a constant rate in a cell.   In a steady state, it has some mean concentration in cell fluid.   If only the volume of the cell increased, the mean concentration would fall.   Were the cell sensitive to changes in mean concentration, or were its normal behavior geared to the absolute value of the mean concentration, this would constitute a kind of volume sensitivity. In one way, such a mechanism could be envisaged to regulate the volume of the cell whose vital functions would suffer with a change of volume; in another way, changes in metabolic production or utilization rates could be envisaged to bring about volume changes.

Laplace's Formula: Heterogony

For a hollow, thin-walled (859), spherical body, there is a formula of Laplace stating $P = 2T/r$, where P is internal pressure (excess over external), T is tangential tension (hoop stress) in the wall, and r is the radius. For a cylinder,[2] $P = T/r$, the significance of which may be studied in Fig. 20.

According to Pascal's law, the pressure of gas within the balloon in that figure must everywhere be equal. The tautness of the dilated portion (under greater stretch, the rubber thinner) contrasts with the relative flaccidity of the undilated portion. This reifies the direct relation between the radius of curvature and the tension in the wall at a given internal pressure. We might suppose the pressure in a balloon less fully inflated to be lower than that in the same balloon more fully inflated; and this might be the case. However, Fig. 21 illustrates the interesting way in which pressure, tension, and radius actually behaved in one toy balloon. The tension (hoop stress) curve in the graph, which was obtained by measuring P and r and calculating Pr, is easily confirmed independently by direct determination of tension and length of a circumferential band cut from the balloon. The fact that the pressure actually *falls* as the balloon increases in size over a certain range serves to point up the care needed in assessing the supposed relation of volume changes in hollow (but not necessarily empty) viscera to pressure, tension, etc. (p. 25ff.).

There is a well known experiment, illustrated in Fig. 22, which is the "reverse" of the balloon demonstration. Two soap bubbles, shown on separate tubes, are put in communication. The surface tensions of the two soap films are essentially equal.

---

[2] The longitudinal stress in a cylinder with closed ends is only one-half of the hoop stress and so never controls rupture in an isotropic wall.

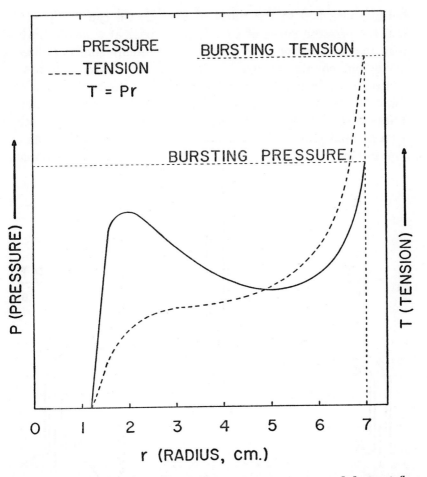

Figure 21. Inflation of a rubber balloon. Pressures measured during inflation show a complex relation to radius (and volume) and may actually fall as the volume increases over a certain range. This is a consequence of the shape of the tension-radius curve which, for a wide range of radii, deviates sharply from Hooke's law. With proper regard for units, $T = Pr$, where the radius in question is that of the largest circular crossection (see Fig. 20) and the balloon is tubular rather than spherical.

Where one bubble has a smaller radius than the other, the internal pressure in that bubble, according with Laplace's formula, is necessarily greater, and the small bubble discharges its gas into the large. If we substitute a balloon for each of the soap bubbles attached to the tubes of Fig. 22, we can easily verify that the pressure curve of Fig. 21 has a peak at a smaller radius than that of bursting. While two substantially similar balloons, partly but equally inflated, maintain their relative volumes in neutral equilibrium for a long time when connected, we can show (if the material of the balloons has the proper characteristics) that as some of the air of one is squeezed into the other by a manual pressure, a new and stable equilibrium is attained. The former loses most of its air to the latter; that is, as we make

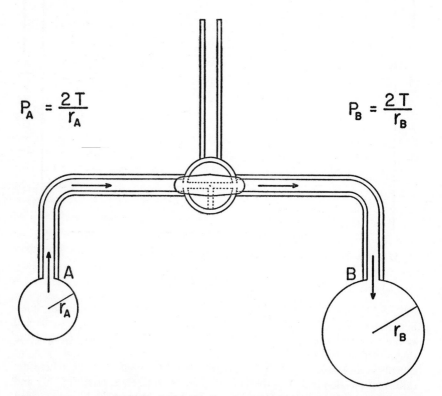

$$P_A = \frac{2T}{r_A} \qquad\qquad P_B = \frac{2T}{r_B}$$

Figure 22. Soap bubble demonstration and Laplace's formula. When two bubbles, A and B, of different radii, r_A and r_B, are connected through a 3-way stopcock as shown, gas from the smaller bubble passes to the larger until the smaller one disappears. This occurs because the tension (inner plus outer surfaces of bubbles), T, is the same in the walls of both bubbles. Since the pressure, P, is proportional to T/r, and r_A is less than r_B, P_A is greater than P_B and the gas moves from the region of high to that of low pressure.

one balloon small, and the other large, the pressure in the smaller automatically increases so that air flows with increased rapidity into the large.

If Hooke's law (i.e., $T = k(r - r_0)$), where r_0 is the radius at zero pressure and k is a constant) were obeyed in a spherical balloon or bladder, then $P = 2k(r - r_0)/r$ and, if $r \gg r_0$, P would remain practically constant at all ranges of inflation. For the case of the urinary bladder, Winton and Bayliss (845) observed that since tension would be proportional to radius, sense organs in the wall might be stimulated when the volume reached a certain value, even though the hydrostatic pressure remained unchanged. The stress on such a species of volume receptor would relate to the cube root of the bladder volume. To the extent that the bladder does not obey Hooke's law, one may modify the quantitative argument and yet preserve the central view.

It is more difficult to analyze sources of volume regulation in the "bladder" of certain unicellular organisms. Adolph (5) has presented figures denumerating the magnitude of volume regulation by the contractile vacuoles in a number of protozoa. In *Ameba proteus* the contractile vacuole averages 1% of the body volume but may be as great as 5%. The time required for the excretion of one body volume of fluid is 1.6 to 31.5 hours in this species. *Paramecium caudatum* puts out its own volume of water in 15 to 50 minutes; *Cryptochilum nigricans* in 2 minutes. It remains the case that consideration of various simple physical and geometrical factors is singularly futile in solving these problems of volume regulation. If we doubt that the "stretching" of the wall of a vacuole resembles closely that of the urinary bladder we must look elsewhere for the critical volume receptor.

This is not to say that all aspects of the matter are obscure. Fig. 23 shows a stylized cell with contractile vacuole. If the fluid in the vacuole is more nearly like that surrounding the cell than that within the cell (e. g., $C_1 = C_3$), we might assume the tensions in the vacuolar and cell walls (boundary layers) to be alike, i.e., $T_1 = T_2 = T$. Since $r_1 < r_2$, $P_1 > P_2$. The growth of the vacuole requires energy given by the product of the change in its surface area, ΔA, and the tension in its wall, a value, $(\Delta A)T$, whose lower limit is conditioned by the lower limit of T. When the vacuole touches (fuses with?) the cell surface, the tension in the common vacuolar and cell wall of radius greater than

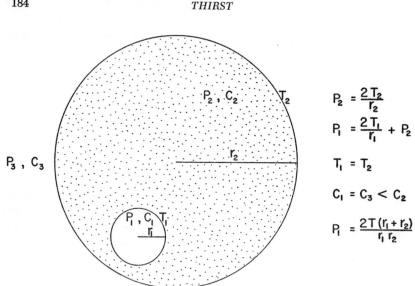

Figure 23.   Contractile vacuole dynamics.   A spherical cell of radius r_2, hydrostatic pressure P_2, osmotic concentration C_2, and wall tension T_2 contains a vacuole characterized by r_1, P_1, C_1, and T_1.   Environing fluid is P_3, C_3.
See text for discussion.

r_1 does (can?) not contain P_1. The vacuole bursts, discharging its fluid to the outside of the cell. Bursting may be delayed by manipulating the vacuole toward the interior of the cell (784). The energetics of vacuolar transport of fluid through cells has not received the attention given to "osmotic work" which, among other things, depends upon surface area (623). The reader is referred to Kitching's (425–427) articles on the physiology of the contractile vacuole in fresh water and marine Ciliates and to his theory that changes in body volume resulting from changes in ambient osmotic pressure mediate the rate of vacuolar activity (428). Prosser (630) has also reviewed this subject.

Volume reception can thus operate through, depend on, or be inextricably associated with other physical parameters. Pressure, tension, linear dimension, diffusion gradient, concentration, surface area, weight, mass, and capacity are a few examples. Volume regulation or volustasis exists as a vital phenomenon and may be as precisely regulated as other physiologic variables of its class (that precision of regulation varies is exemplified by how the coefficient of variation of body weight exceeds that of height in man); it is a highly speculative proposition, notwithstanding, that such regulation is mediated by specific receptors. Salt in our wounds may remind us of osmoreception but gives us no confidence that the pain arises in specific osmoreceptors. However, if volume receptors are will-o'-the-wisps, physiologists have had just enough success in finding other kinds of receptors to keep them looking. Even the subcommissural organ has been suspected of being the enigmatic volume receptor of the body (291a).

A potent, if not conclusive, argument against the concept of volume receptor is this: there is presently no way whatever whereby the physiologist can distinguish the regulation of volume from that of mass. In the general biologic view, mass and relative masses are the things regulated; and mass of water is presumably subject to no more precise regulation than mass of protein, mass of calcium, etc. There is no more reason to posit receptors for masses of one thing than the other. If the history of multiple factor theories in physiology tells us anything, it tells us that such primordial regulations have no unitary controls.

The excessive importance sometimes attached to the question of volume receptors is perhaps explicable in the philosophic distinction, which has been well drawn, between two types of scientific theories, viz., the physical, on the one hand, and the abstractive or mathematical, on the other. Those who are at home among the physical look for intimate mechanisms relating the processes and events of their inquiry; the others enjoy that progress which is possible even without benefit of mechanism.[3] Poincaré (619) has treated this vital point:

Suppose we have before us any machine; the initial wheel work and the final wheel work alone are visible, but the transmission, the intermediary machinery by which the movement is communicated from one to the other, is hidden in the interior and escapes our view; we do not know whether the communication is made by gearing or by belts, by connecting-rods or by other contrivances. Do we say that it is impossible for us to understand anything about this machine so long as we are not permitted to take it to pieces?

---

[3] There are those who narrowly insist on the virtue of the physical and on the futility of the abstractive (862) but this is to deny that we can learn anything about the brain through psychology or psychiatry or by observing its mediation of stimulus and response.

You know well we do not, and that the principle of the conservation of energy suffices to determine for us the most interesting point. We easily ascertain that the final wheel turns ten times less quickly than the initial wheel, since these two wheels are visible; we are able thence to conclude that a couple applied to the one will be balanced by a couple ten times greater applied to the other. For that there is no need to penetrate the mechanisms of this equilibrium and to know how the forces compensate each other in the interior of the machine; it suffices to be assured that this compensation can not fail to occur.

Where physical analysis is not yet realizable, the abstract may be useful. One example of the mathematical approach to volume regulation is seen in the heterogonic formulas, applied by Huxley (393) to constant differential growth ratios in fiddler crabs. He proposed the equation $y = bx^k$, where y is the weight of the chela, x is the total weight of the animal minus the weight of the chela (so that the part does not become, mathematically, greater than the whole), and b and k are constants. The term b merely denotes the value of y when $x = 1$, i.e., the fraction of x which y occupies when $x = 1$. The term k implies that relative change rate of x (i.e., dx/xdt) is constant with respect to relative change rate of y (i.e., dy/ydt), and the derivation of this is given by Huxley (394).

Needham (572) extended analysis of the problem of relative growth to chemical heterogony. Dry weight, y, as a function of wet weight, x, shows for mammals an average k value of 1.23; for man, $k = 1.26$. Since organisms generally dry up with age (Fig. 1), k is never less than 1 for this relation, i.e., there is no negative heterogony. The teleost in the larval stages shows $k = 1.0$. Forbes and Perley (264, p. 14) have shown by heterogonic analysis that the quantity of exchangeable sodium is directly proportional to kidney weight.

The beauty of the heterogonic[4] equation stated above lies in its analytic and descriptive power. In logarithmic form it becomes

---

[4] Needham and Lerner (573) have discussed the terminology of relative growth rates with attention to "heterogony," "allometry," and "heterauxesis" but since the scope of these relations is now broader than that encompassing merely the laws of growth, we adhere to "heterogonic" as applied by Adolph (15) to widely diverse phenomena (p. 10).

$$\log y = \log b + k \log x$$

In a plot of log y against log x, k is the slope of the commonly rectilinear curve (see Sholl (720) on the actual determination of b and k statistically). Such a heterogonic or power equation is only one of many conceivable empirical equations which can express regressions between physiologic processes. However, among organ volumes, biochemical constituents, and other physiologic variables, it is the only one that has been found to apply to a large number of relations (15, 868, Figs. 2 and 3). When $k = 1$, y is simply proportional to x. When k is greater than 1, y increases more rapidly than x and when k is less than 1, the reverse. Every positive heterogonic exponent has a corresponding negative value, numerically equal, and characteristic of the reciprocal of y because

$$\frac{1}{y} = \frac{x^{-k}}{b}$$

For example, if y is heartbeat frequency, $1/y$ is beat duration.

Thompson (784), whose discussion of Galileo's principle of similitude is also of interest for the general problem of volume regulation, has criticized Huxley's heterogony for being mathematical rather than biological. He considered the law limited in range and observed that simple interest rather than compound often holds in nature.

VOLUME REGULATION: VOLUSTASIS AND VOLUDYNAMICS

Evidence

McLean (537) first described clearly the idea that edema was a disturbance in the regulation of the volume of fluids constituting the internal environment. He traced the concept of volume regulation, inferentially, back to Claude Bernard's *milieu intérieur*. Recognizing that the advance in knowledge of local mechanism is greater than that of physiologic regulation, he introduced for consideration his view of *volume-disturbing* and *volume-restoring* forces, observing:

. . . . It is by no means certain that elucidation of the significance of the local forces involved, from the purely physico-chemical

standpoint, will lead to the solution of the problem of regulation, which is, after all, of primary importance. The method of analysis may not be capable of distinguishing cause from effect, and may even lead one astray . . . . some understanding of the regulation of volume [may] be reached, long before the intermediate steps in the process are determined.

More recently, Lowe (489–491a) and Lowe and Sayers (492) have pressed in favor of McLean's volustatic forces. Their observations of fluid balance in patients with congestive failure led them to distinguish at least two separate mechanisms controlling water loss. First a day to day, quickly acting control possibly related to ionic concentrations and osmotic pressure of body fluids; second, taking many days, a slowly acting control of total body water content. They supposed that the latter control is disturbed in these patients by an unknown agent, and may be returned to normal by bed rest alone. This control is thought to be cyclical; as a positive or negative water load is dissipated, the direction of action of the control appears to reverse, becoming effective after overshooting of the zero water load occurs; and the oscillation of water load and balance damps out gradually. The pattern is disturbed by febrile states.

These workers pointed out that mechanisms which determine normal electrolyte content in body fluids cannot be expected to control the total volume of water in the body since their receptors are sensitive to ionic concentrations or osmotic pressure, and these may be normal in gross edema. The suggestion of Borst and de Vries (120) that control is by means of a receptor sensitive to blood volume was thought of doubtful value because of the low correlation between blood volume changes and total fluid retained. The variable response to mercurial diuretics is interpreted in terms of the action of these drugs on different phases of volume-restoring or volume-disturbing forces, conceived as biochemical reactions. These processes are described in terms of complex exponential formulas using five constants. However, intake, secondary to thirst, is taken to respond separately to the osmotic pressure of body fluids. Fowler (269) has extended the observations of Lowe to rabbits.

Early experimental evidence systematically interpreted to implicate the kidney specifically as an organ of volume regulation was presented by Wolf (851), confirmed (712, 860, 861, 869), and reviewed (857, 862, 877). It was observed in dogs that the excretion of chloride, following intravenous injections of sodium chloride solutions, was not simply dependent on the load of salt but varied directly with the concentration of the infusion fluid, i.e., the rate of excretion of salt per unit load of salt increased with the infusion fluid concentration. Since osmotic concentrations are directly concerned in the relative magnitudes of cellular and extracellular fluids, the following hypothesis was proposed: although the rate of excretion of salt is otherwise proportional to load, the kidney might be obligated not only to discharge loads in proportion to their size but also to maintain the bulks of fluid compartments normal, and in normal relations to each other. The imbalance of normal ratios of bulks of cellular and extracellular fluids was called *distortion*. Urea produces no appreciable distortion in body fluid compartments generally and the basic exponential (law of decay) type of excretion of urea loads is uninfluenced by the concentration of urea in the infusion fluid.

Difficulties inherent in the Verney theory (798) of water diuresis have been used to support further a case for volume regulation. According to this theory, there exist in the central nervous system, in the bed of the internal carotid artery, osmoreceptors which are possibly tiny vesicular bodies—or even neurons— capable of swelling or shrinking with changes in the effective osmotic pressure of their ambient fluid. When water is taken in positive load, these osmoreceptors, behaving as osmometers, respond to the resulting dilution of body fluids by swelling. They may then act as stretch receptors for afferent nerves, impulses along which reflexly cause the neurohypophysis to reduce below normal its rate of secretion of antidiuretic hormone. Following a latent period during which already circulating hormone disappears from the plasma, there results a decreased reabsorption of water by the renal tubules and a consequent diuresis. As the kidney excretes this urine which is more dilute osmotically than body fluids, the osmotic pressure of the remaining body fluids rises toward normal and again stimulates (or perhaps fails to stimulate) osmoreceptors as before. Antidiuretic hormone re-appears, reducing the diuresis to normal (homaluric) flow.

This theory does not tell us why a load of normal saline is excreted, even in slight diuresis, if it causes no appreciable change in the effective osmotic pressure of body fluids; and the fact of its excretion has been the basis for considering the *volume* of saline load (or the distortion it produces) as a specific stimulus. The excretion of such saline loads has been repeatedly examined (110, 120, 752, 753, 772, 773, 857, 862, 870) and, with few exceptions, is considered not to be simply or characteristically associated with any specific nephrodynamic function such as glomerular filtration or tubular reabsorption (118, 187, 487, 753, 773, 821).

Seldin and Tarail (712) have supported one aspect of the distortion theory. Noting that hyperosmotic glucose and mannitol differed from urea in promoting natriuresis, they concluded that cellular dehydration, per se, was a regulatory factor in sodium excretion. It may be noted, however, that the effect of urea on sodium excretion has not been found to be uniform (857). And iso- and hypotonic mannitol may also augment salt excretion even more than sodium chloride solutions of comparable tonicity, suggesting specifically different actions of mannitol and sodium chloride on the renal tubules (838).

Green and Farah (303) stressed the rate, rather than the absolute degree, of cellular dehydration to be of the greater importance for sodium regulation and suggested that a major physiologic object is the maintenance of osmotic homeostasis.

These views ignore the effectiveness of the distortion associated with loads of isotonic and hypotonic solutions. Darragh *et al.* (199) have recognized that dilution of body fluids may be associated with decreased excretion of sodium, chloride, and potassium and considered the stimulus as either a decrease in effective osmotic pressure (or associated overhydration of cells), or decreased sodium concentration in extracellular fluid.

Cellular dehydration, at least of renal cells, was thought by Goodyer and Glenn (297) not to be a stimulus for natriuresis. They based their view on observations of solute excretion following injection of various hypertonic solutions into the renal artery of the dog. It need not be conceded, however, that such meta-physiologic studies (857) provide information as to the ordinary regulatory responses which affect loads of iso- and hypotonic solutions or excretory adjustments over long periods.

In extension of the cellular dehydration hypothesis of renal excretion it has been shown that antidiuretic hormone activity, ordinarily diminished in hypotonicity, may also be diminished in recumbent subjects by isotonic expansion of the extracellular space (772) or may fail to occur in hypertonicity (4, 100); that hypotonic expansion of extracellular space may lead to increased sodium excretion (101, 468, 773, 822); and that antidiuretic activity is not necessarily regulated by extracellular fluid tonicity (100, 101, 182, 469). Moreover, Ladd (454) discovered that in normal subjects hydrated 8 to 13 hours previously by oral tap water, rapid intravenous injection of "isotonic" saline produced a diuresis like that following water ingestion. Paradoxically, how-ever, this diuresis was associated with an increased osmotic pres-sure of the plasma, rather than with a decreased pressure as in water diuresis (p. 128).

Localization of Mechanism

Peters (605, 609) was one of the first to suggest that the volume of the bloodstream could affect renal excretion, although at one time he considered the idea banal (607). At another time (606), and later, he conceded that it might not be the actual volume of circulating plasma but some function usually related to it—such as renal blood flow—that apprises the kidney of the need to con-serve water.

The blood volume-renal excretion concept was elaborated by Borst (117–119). In this view, an essential factor in the genesis of edema is a regulation of urinary excretion of water and salt which effects the maintenance of cardiac output. Retention of water and salt when the amount of circulating blood is insuffi-cient to maintain normal cardiac output is not thought to be "dis-turbed" function, but rather an accommodation of function serv-ing the regulation of body volume, venous pressure, and cardiac output. Following hemorrhage (118, 404, 809), or extrarenal depletion of blood volume (182), there is found a fall in sodium and chloride excretion and an increase of potassium excretion, all thought to favor the maintenance or raising of blood volume. Rapid transfusion of blood so as to increase blood volume results in increased chloride and water excretion (286) the effect of which supposedly tends to minimize the possible increase in blood volume.

Young *et al.* (882) have observed diuresis in anesthetized dogs after intravenous infusions of dextran and of plasma but not after whole blood. A nephrodynamic account is given of the diuresis, but the adiuresis following blood is not otherwise explained than with the suggestion that expansion of blood volume alone is not a sufficient stimulus to augment urinary flow.

Welt *et. al.* (610, 817) considered that uncomplicated expansion of the plasma volume might provoke diuresis by suppressing the production of antidiuretic hormone and speculated on the possible existence of volume receptors or oncoreceptors in the vascular tree, which could affect renal excretion. Greiner and Podhradszky (312) raised the question of whether the Verney type of osmoreceptor responded to changes in colloid osmotic pressure of the plasma, but a response to such necessarily minute pressure changes seems unlikely from what is known of osmometric thresholds (798, 856, p. 75). On the other hand, Kessler and Nelson (417), by comparing the effects of injections of isoncotic albumin in 5% glucose with buffered isotonic saline, found that even considerable increase in plasma volume may not be a stimulus to renal excretion of sodium whereas relatively minimal expansion of interstitial fluid volume seemed to be a definite stimulus. And Prentice *et. al.* (625) showed that plasma volume is not controlled by the rise and fall of interstitial volume; the two can vary in opposite directions simultaneously. The latter study was of congestive failure and, although plasma volume did not rise and might fall as interstitial space expanded, it could be considered in Borst's analysis that the plasma volume might have fallen even more than it did if interstitial volume had not increased.

These views are supplemented by numerous others, and there is a considerable literature, for example, on the effect of posture on plasma volume and renal function which is treated elsewhere (739, 857). It may be noted that Brun, Knudsen, and Raaschou (137–140) have described the antidiuretic effect of the passive erect posture in man and suggested that the posterior pituitary is affected directly through nervous channels fed by pressoreceptors in appropriate blood vessels. They also saw the reduction of diuresis as a factor contributing to maintenance of circulating blood volume.

Epstein *et al.* (242, 245) studied the antidiuresis and antilyuresis or diminished solute excretion of quiet standing and found that these effects do not require a contraction of total plasma volume; they considered them possibly related to the effective distribution of the blood. Further evidence of the importance of distribution was found in a study of arteriovenous fistulas. Occlusion of an established arteriovenous fistula in man results in increased sodium excretion with no change in the values for glomerular filtration, renal blood flow, or renal venous pressure, which are usually normal in these subjects. The conclusion was drawn that renal excretion of sodium may be conditioned by the degree of filling of some portion of the arterial tree. If the legs are wrapped in elastic bandages before the orthostatic position is assumed, the reduction of salt excretion which would otherwise occur in quiet standing is inhibited. Alcohol is said to inhibit orthostatic antidiuresis and enhance orthostatic inhibition of salt excretion, from which findings it has been suggested that there are separate postural adjustments of water and salt excretion, the former under postpituitary control and the latter under control of some mechanism sensitive to the distribution of interstitial fluid (602).

Epstein (240) has related these curious phenomena to thirst, noting that when blood pressure cuffs are placed high on the thighs and inflated to 70 mm. of mercury, and when a glass of 0.14 to 0.2% sodium chloride (minimal isorrheic concentration) is ingested every 30 minutes, there sets in after half an hour a vague feeling of discomfort and restlessness. The saline begins to taste better. Release of the tourniquets is accompanied by subsidence of symptoms and some loss of the saline's palatability. Patients under somewhat similar conditions asked for water in the second half hour of congestion. With the release of the cuffs they had less interest in water.

A related phenomenon may have been observed by MacNeill and Doyle (505) in the course of an ultrafiltration of fluid from the blood of a patient being treated with a Mark XI-d dialyzer. The patient, in a good psychic state, freely able to discuss her sensations, had edema of the legs. Within a few minutes of the beginning of ultrafiltration, she stated she was very thirsty. Her legs were wrapped with elastic bandages to mobilize the edema and her thirst diminished during the remainder of the ultrafiltration which reduced her weight six pounds in 6 hours.

Harrison *et al.* (477, 487, 497) examined the effect of posture and of congestion of the head on sodium excretion in normal subjects and patients with congestive failure. Their subjects drank minimal isorrheic sodium chloride solutions continuously for several hours to attain a baseline against which the effects on excretion of sitting and recumbency could be compared. In sitting, there was a decline of salt and water excretion, which could be partially but not entirely overcome by compression of the neck by blood pressure cuff at 15 to 35 mm. of mercury. They believed this constituted evidence for a volume regulating mechanism or center in the cranial cavity. However, bandaging the legs of sitting subjects increased sodium excretion which fell after removal of the bandages. This was taken as evidence that distribution rather than total extracellular fluid volume was concerned in the regulation of salt excretion. They concluded that an intracranial mechanism is not the only nor most potent mechanism of volume regulation. The work of Netravisesh (578), Bull (142), Fishman (262), and Epstein (241) does not support the idea of a cranial volume regulator and leaves the significance of the aforementioned experiments in doubt.

Gauer *et al.* (286, 287, 288), Sieker *et al.* (726), and Drury *et al.* (214) proposed the existence of volume or stretch receptors in the cardiovascular system within the thorax (pulmonary circulation, heart chambers, great veins). Engorgement of these, as by negative pressure breathing, coincides with diuresis in man and dog, while positive pressure breathing is oliguretic and reduces kidney function. These manifestations were regarded as evidence for a sensitive mechanism linking hemostatic events with urine excretion for the control of plasma volume. Surtshin *et al.*

(777), while confirming the experimental findings, do not believe the mechanism has great importance in the regulation of body fluid volume. They considered the effect to be hormonally mediated, possibly by reflex inhibition of vasopressin secretion.

Strauss et al. (772, 773) and Smith (740) favored the view that the cephalad portion of the body is the locus of action of expanded fluid volumes, but they stressed the extracellular fluid rather than the plasma volume as primary, and emphasized the significance of the distribution factor as well as the absolute magnitude of the volume. In this concept, expansion and contraction of the extracellular space are thought to be linked to increased and decreased excretion of sodium, respectively (313). Welt and Nelson (816) suggested something of a similar, but independent, relation of extracellular volume to water excretion, while Bull (142) felt the need to postulate some receptor sensitive to changes in total body water.

Bartter et al. (77, 78) have adduced evidence suggesting that the secretion of aldosterone, with consequent effects on sodium excretion, is primarily regulated as a function of, and in response to, changes in body fluid (chiefly extracellular) volume; and that serum sodium concentration, per se, does not have any effect on the secretion of this hormone. It has been stated (313) that the influence of volume (receptors) on the kidney is exerted for water primarily through the posterior pituitary; for salt, through the adrenal cortex.

On the other hand, Kellogg and Burack (408) found in rats that increased urine flow and urinary excretion of sodium and chloride after isotonic saline administration is merely retarded in chronic adrenal insufficiency (in which water diuresis was completely suppressed). Thus, these three responses to extracellular hypervolia caused by saline loads can proceed with considerable effectiveness despite the absence of adrenal hormones.

For all the interest of the foregoing experimental observations it is well to remark that many of these are, in the life of the organism, extremely brief. Initial responses to posture changes, shifts of body fluid, infusions, etc., which are recorded over a period of a few hours can hardly be expected to reflect adaptations and compensations by the organism which might occur much later if these applied stresses were maintained (857); Fowler

(269) has also made this point. And these adaptations and compensations might not, on further analysis, be volume regulations at all. For example, cold diuresis has been interpreted (21) to be a manifestation of general fluid loss from the plasma as intense vasoconstriction tends to reduce the space within which the blood is confined. With continued exposure, urine reaches a maximal flow in the second hour and rapidly diminishes thereafter. However, intermediate air temperatures may arouse stronger diuresis than very low temperatures. Moreover, the fluid volume shift in cold diuresis is opposite to that in recumbence diuresis and it is seen how easily cause and effect may be confused. In some cases experiments purported to elucidate volume regulation are metaphysiologic (857) and it is doubtful whether the strains or responses engendered should be interpreted as if they were physiologic.

Finally, it is well to remember that disturbance of volume may be manifest in more ways than are presently imagined. The significance of the curious phenomenon discovered by McClure and Aldrich (28, 529), wherein the time required for the disappearance of intradermal blebs of normal saline is related to the state of hydration of the body, is hardly compromised by the mechanical interpretation given it by Govaerts and Bernard (301).

ISORRHEA, DISTORTION, AND KINETICS OF VOLUME REGULATION

The theory of isorrhea (857), as described briefly and employed in this book (p. 298), touches, but has not been integrated with, the theory of volume regulation. A minimal isorrheic solution of 0.1 to 0.2% sodium chloride can be administered steadily and bring on isorrhea, but solutions more dilute than this, or pure water, exert a dehydrating action on the body (852, 853) in which body fluid volume may be sacrificed with the effect of preserving salt concentration of the remaining fluid. Exceptions to this, particularly when rate or duration of administration is excessive, generally take the form of water intoxication (409, 857).

All solutions of sodium chloride between the minimal and limiting isorrheic concentrations (0.1 to 1.7%) are potentially isorrheic.

If administered steadily, not too rapidly, and over a sufficiently long period of time, output of salt and water become equal to their intakes. However, solutions such as 1% sodium chloride, which are edematigenous in man, may expand body fluid volume considerably, before isorrhea is reached. Indeed, before isorrhea is finally attained, output overshoots intake, reducing the saline load, whereupon output falls toward intake. Stewart and Rourke (768) have observed this type of volume regulation in patients receiving 6.5 liters of normal saline per day. An occult, maximal increment of 80% was added to the extracellular fluid volume by the third or fourth day with a gradual subsidence thereafter.

These adjustments vary among different species, and it is also recognized that they are upset in disease. Ladd and Raisz (455) have shown that renal excretion of salt by the dog is so efficient that intakes of sodium chloride up to 4 g./Kg./day can be maintained for considerable periods (six days) without increase in body weight or elevation of plasma sodium or chloride concentration, and with no significant salt retention. In man, however, increases of less than 0.5 g./Kg./day are attended by significant retention of salt and water. Expressed on the basis of surface area rather than weight these figures lose some of their force, but the lesser hydropigenous effect of normal saline in the dog, compared with man, is well known.

The velocity constant, γ, is a parameter used in the study of relative excretion rates. It is defined as the rate of excretion of a substance per minute per unit load. For no-threshold substances such as urea, it is also defined (851, 857) as the ratio of the clearance of a substance to its volume of distribution, i.e., $\gamma = C/b$. In man, for sodium (when sodium chloride is loaded), γ is reported of the order of 6×10^{-4} min.$^{-1}$ (854, 857). However, per unit load, salt tends to be excreted more rapidly if it is administered as a more concentrated (e.g., 3%) solution than as a less concentrated (e.g., 1%) solution.[5]

---

[5] The matter is put this way for emphasis. Actually, the excretion of salt depends more on salt load than on water load so that with moderate, similar loads of salt administered at different concentrations, very little difference of salt excretion is observed (869) and exceptions to the above statement are found (595). However, when variable loads of salt are given in fixed volumes of water, it is as if the small

After priming a dog with a load of saline it is observed that the disappearance of the loads of salt and water is essentially a first order process, i.e., γ for a given solution is essentially constant (860). This accords with the general behavior of physiologic regulations (9). In seeking to distinguish the apparent influence on urinary salt excretion of a load of salt from that of the distortion in fluid compartments produced by its effective osmotic pressure, an attempt has been made (861, 869) suitably to express the distortion factor quantitatively.

Excretion rates of sodium, chloride, and potassium for several hours following priming loads of different strengths of sodium chloride solution were examined in the dog for correlation with load and with calculated extracellular and intracellular volumes. Preliminary studies based on 144 measurements (860, 861) showed that the coefficient, r, correlating salt excretion with the cellular volume decrement, ΔV_i, was +0.657. With extracellular volume increment, ΔV_e, it was +0.772. Such figures suggest an evaluation of the hypotheses previously noted (p. 187 ff.) to explain volume regulation, *viz.*, those which assert that excretion of osmotically effective substances depends on expansion of the extracellular space (772, 773) and on shrinkage of the cellular volume (712). If anything, the correlation coefficients point to the expansion of extracellular space as the more important.

However, the correlation coefficient for excretion rate and the algebraic sum of the changes in extracellular and intracellular fluid, where *increase* in V_e is considered positive and where *decrease* in V_i is considered positive, was better still, *viz.*, + 0.803. The rationale of combining these volumes algebraically lies in taking advantage of the likelihood that excretion of osmotically effective material will tend both to shrink the expanded V_e and expand the shrunken V_i, and in weighing both of these elements in the distortion of body fluid compartments.

If the change in V_e is relatively accented by using, instead of

---

effect of pure water cancelled out, leaving only the effect of the variable salt loads. In such experiments the rate of excretion of salt per unit load of salt (γ) is clearly a function of load or, equally, of concentration of infused saline (851, 857). The output of minerals, unlike that of urea, is recognized to be regulated by factors other than plasma concentration (526, 851).

$\Delta V_e + \Delta V_i$, the value $2 \Delta V_e + \Delta V_i$, the coefficient with salt excretion becomes $+0.812$. Arbitrarily, the latter algebraic sum was called the distortion, D, and employed in further correlations. A higher linear correlation was found ($+0.874$) between salt excretion and the product of load and distortion, LD, than between salt excretion and L ($r = +0.822$) or D ($r = +0.812$) alone. In consequence it was proposed that the rate of urinary excretion of osmotically effective material is proportional to the product LD, and that load and distortion factors have the same relative importance in excretion.

Numerous refinements which cannot be considered here would be needed if such an approach to volume regulation were to become broadly useful. The foregoing discussion glosses over many technical difficulties relating to the algebraic sign of L and D, the fact that D is almost proportional to L, etc. Suffice to note that in such a scheme is sought the generality to encompass all possible combinations of positive, zero, and negative values of loads and distortions: where extracellular fluid, as with isotonic loads, is alone affected; where both phases are augmented or diminished in proportion in water loads or deficits; or, in any of the nine combinations possible to two phases (Fig. 8) which may each, independently, assume one of three states ($+, 0, -$). Such a scheme recognizes that forces act to reduce the displacement from normal of either or both phases; and it may provide a practical means of answering the question of what excretion rate of osmotically effective material may be expected with any given positive, zero, or negative load of both water and salt.

Volume regulation by the kidney is not a function of fixed magnitude relative to such regulation by other channels. Whatever may be its role for the man in a temperate climate, it must certainly be assessed differently in a hot desert. The man in the desert has a minimal urine volume and an insensible water loss several or many times as great; and his thirst becomes a dominant influence in the maintenance of body volume.

We may conceive of a load factor without a distortion factor in the case of radioactive or tracer materials. In such instances it is known that excretion rate is essentially proportional to load and, for radioactive sodium, is relatively independent of load or concentration infused.

An interesting example of the application of this type of analysis of volume regulation is found in the excretion of heavy water. Direct measurement shows this material to have a biologic half-life in man of approximately 8 to 14 days with an average of about 10 days (615, 680). However, this half-life can be accurately deduced without recourse to deuterium oxide itself, assuming it behaves like ordinary water in distribution and excretion. Being a no-threshold material excreted for the most part in simple exponential manner, it obeys the relation $\gamma = C/b$ (p. 197). The clearance of deuterium oxide may be taken as equal to that of ordinary water, ca. 1 cc./min. To allow for extrarenal excretion which behaves like urinary excretion in that deuterium oxide is removed by all routes in proportion to ordinary water (355), let us call the total heavy water clearance 2 cc./min. In a 70 Kg. man, 60% of whose weight is water, $b = 42,000$ cc. Thus $\gamma = 2/42,000 = 0.0000476$. The equation for postequilibrium, biologic decay is $L_t = L_0 e^{-\gamma t}$, where L_t and L_0 are, respectively, the loads of deuterium oxide at t minutes and at zero time after loading. At the half-life, $L_0/L_t = 2$, so that (ln 2)/0.0000476 is the half life in minutes. This amounts to 10.1 days, an acceptable estimate considering the variables involved.

In this case, the behavior of a tracer dose of heavy water exemplifies exponential decay uncomplicated by a distortion factor. If we now imagine, neglecting the toxicity factor, how the excretion of heavy water might be increased by ingesting a macroload of it sufficient to produce water diuresis, we can see how the decay will be modified by what is essentially a volume factor. That is, the rate of excretion of heavy water would not simply be proportional to its load but would also be augmented in a way which would relate to the distorted volume of the body fluids. If $D = 2\Delta V_e + \Delta V_i$, a water load would produce, it would seem, practically no distortion since, approximately, $2V_e = V_i$ and the partitioning of the load is such as to produce positive distortion in V_e and negative distortion in V_i proportional to their initial volumes. D, however, has been correlated with salt, not water excretion. Admittedly, no consistent or generally useful definition of distortion has been given.

The excretion of a microload of radioactive sodium is also presumably characterized by a velocity constant relating its clearance to some volume of distribution. The latter may vary from an extracellular volume to some large "volume" reflecting exchanges of radioactive sodium throughout the total body sodium. However, a macroload of sodium, radioactive or otherwise, has an osmotic volume of distribution which is numerically equal either to total body water or to an expanded extracellular volume, depending on whether concentration increments of sodium are measured chemically or by detecting radioactivity (530, 873).

VOLUSTASIS AND THIRST

The relation of renal function to the regulation of body volume, although acknowledged in elemental form as long ago as 1842 by Bowman (123), has only recently been seriously studied in man and higher animals. We have noted how confusion of volume— as a stimulus—with correlated or colligated parameters, and the lack of powerful methods for analyzing its relation to those emunctories and paths of intake which carry on volustasis, still plague the subject. If it has been difficult to clarify the role of the kidney in volume regulation, the situation is even less satisfactory with regard to the role of intake and thence thirst. Some of the evidence for the latter follows.

The removal of both kidneys, tolerated by the rabbit for a few days, does not result in edema (613). It has been said that edema occurs only after poisoning the animals with arsenic or phosphorus which may injure capillaries, liver, etc. That anuria is not associated with edema suggests volume regulation through intake and the thirst sensation. The anuric animal may drink only enough to maintain a constant effective osmotic pressure or sodium concentration of its body fluids; it does not increase its drinking as blood urea rises. Peters (609) held that the anuric animal had not been sufficiently considered by those who attribute edema to faulty action of the kidneys, and that the anuric patient does not develop edema if left to follow his instincts; he drinks only enough water to replace extrarenal losses.

After profuse sweating men may drink enough water to precipitate cramps and colic (561) referable to the induced cellular hypervolia along with the induced hypochloremia and hypotonicity (459) of body fluids (water intoxication). Such is evidence for the operation of a volume-restoring factor in the face of some presumptive antidipsic influence of hyposalemia. Possibly it is supplemented by the fact of the (at least often admittedly) more agreeable "taste" of dilute saline as compared with plain water, after heavy exercise, presuming the saline is somewhat more

effective in restoring fluid volume.[6]   However, men working in
humid heat and losing water and salt do not drink enough water
voluntarily to replace their loss ("voluntary dehydration," p. 151),
and thirst fails to measure need (229).   After extended water and
salt deprivation also, men (842) and animals (626, 871, p 160)
quench their thirst by ingesting an amount of water much less
than has been lost; and plasma sodium falls below normal concentration notwithstanding, presumably because of unreplaced
salt loss.   The curious dehydrating action of continuously administered water, associated with salt loss (299, 796, 852, 853),
is a related phenomenon from which it has been argued that the
need for maintenance of plasma electrolyte concentrations at normal levels takes precedence over the need to preserve body fluid
volume.

Peters (609) concluded that the metering of volume must be
a function of some particular part of the circulation or property
of the blood.   He thought that thirst in salt-depleted subjects
might be a reaction to diminished blood volume or, better, a
diminished "effective" volume.   After a large paracentesis with
reduction of abdominal pressure fluid is immediately passed into
the peritoneal cavity from the blood, causing hemoconcentration.
Patients, if not restrained, will often drink enough water then to
produce hyponatremia (p. 105).

Gregersen (308) has related postprandial thirst[7] to temporary
dehydration (reduction of the "volume" of certain body fluids)
resulting from rapid accumulation of secretions in the digestive
tract after food is taken.   Since digestive fluids are essentially,
if not exactly, isosmotic to plasma (480, 521, 719), postprandial
thirst can be regarded as a manifestation of volume rather than
of osmotic regulation.   If the offering of water to a dog is delayed
for several hours after feeding, the 24 hour intake is ordinarily
much less than when water is given ad libitum throughout the

---

[6] Salt solutions approximating human serum in composition are said to be more
palatable than equivalent sodium chloride solutions (628).   Moss (561) recommended drinking ca. 0.2% sodium chloride rather than water to prevent miner's
cramps since he considered sweat to have this salt content (p. 326).

[7] Also called "thirst of alimentation" (150, 673) and "gastric thirst" (516).

postprandial period, presumably because the secreted fluid is largely reabsorbed even if no water is taken after the meal.

The removal of isotonic fluid in hemorrhage and the thirst which sometimes attends it (p. 134) suggest their volustatic relation. Hemorrhage results not only in direct reduction of blood volume but also in interstitial volume by autoinfusion to the circulation. However, there may be concurrent reduction of cellular volume which makes it difficult to rule out this factor or an osmometric basis for thirst.

In short periods following a drop in the concentration of extracellular electrolytes, thirst may not occur although dryness of tongue and mucous membrane and loss of skin turgor signify dehydration, according to the observations of Darrow and Yannet (200). However, absence of fluid intake in dogs may be succeeded by a rise to polydipsic levels after several days (Fig. 13). Remington et al. (645) found that positive balance of water was not attained, and extracellular volume was still reduced, while cellular fluid volume was above normal. Although in the latter experiments intake of water was best correlated with shrinkage of cellular rather than extracellular volume, there are seemingly contrary reports (pp. 103ff., 132). Thus, McCance (519, 520), Holmes and Cizek (372), and Cizek et al. (172) reported in man and dog that water intake is increased in salt deficiency in which state cellular fluid may be expanded at the expense of extracellular on an osmotic basis. While Semple (713) found the rat to behave somewhat differently in that it tends, despite salt deficiency, to restore normal fluid composition at the expense of body water (while the dog merely sustains a permanent shift of fluid), these data, along with those of Brokaw (133) on potassium deficiency (p. 132), remain consistent with a diminished volume of extracellular fluid as a factor in thirst.

However, McCance (519) and Soloff and Zatuchni (749) noted that hyponatremic thirst may not be relieved by plain water. Ingestion of salt is reported to relieve this "false" thirst which may subsequently be followed by "true" thirst capable of being relieved by water. Wolf (862) has offered an interpretation of hyposalemic thirst on an osmometric basis (p. 109), but it is not established that sodium levels in plasma really measure those of effective osmotic pressure or reflect the volume of cellular fluid in such conditions (530, p. 108).

The extent to which hypotonicity is correlated with extracellular hypovolia and the significance of the one or the other, or the conjunction of these factors, for thirst remains unsettled. There is reason to believe that hyposalemia, to the contrary, and extracellular hypervolia, as in acute renal failure or cardiac edema, are also compatible with dipsic state; and that thirst may be relieved in these conditions as serum sodium rises and total body fluid diminishes (240, p. 109).

Nelson *et al.* (576, 577) have stated that hyponatremia alone may not be entirely responsible for symptoms of the low salt syndrome (700, 749, p. 105) and that reduction in "effective extracellular volume" is necessary for its pathogenesis. Hypertonic saline relieves both sodium concentration deficit and reduced extracellular volume, as well as the low salt syndrome. But isotonic saline is also effective in preventing the syndrome, including thirst, following paracentesis, suggesting the primacy of the volume factor. The progressive formation of ascites following partial constriction of the inferior vena cava (464) relates clearly to an augmentation of drinking, regardless of the effect on urine flow and a correlation with sodium retention. Observed decreases in renal function after venous congestion of the legs or phlebotomy have been regarded as homeostatic responses to a "suboptimal effectively circulating blood volume" (404).

The concept of effective volume, unfortunately, has been abused by some proponents who beg the question. If total blood or extracellular volume is not found actually to be less than normal under circumstances in which positive fluid balance prevails, the argument that fluid retention must be a response to some undefined diminution of "effective" volume is certainly inconclusive, if not circular. It does not follow that if a nonvolumetric "stimulus" to retention cannot be specified, the "stimulus" must therefore be volumetric. The fluid intake of dogs can be increased from five to eight times by thyroid feeding, yet no consistent change in plasma volume or thiocyanate space is detected (371) and there is no reason to suppose that "effective" volumes have changed in a way to provoke thirst. Again, the relative increase (to fasted weight), or constancy (to normal weight), of plasma and extracellular fluid volume in starvation may be accompanied by excessive water consumption (421).

None of the foregoing evidence and arguments settle the role of volume and the localization of volustatic mechanisms. Consider the complexity of these mechanisms as suggested in the studies of Kanter (405). He recognized two classes of dogs called *minimal internal regulators* and *maximal internal regulators.* The former, following hypertonic salt loading, drink water almost sufficing to restore their body fluids to isotonicity, and excrete large volumes of urine of low chloride concentration. The thirst apparatus in this group was thought to be particularly sensitive to cellular hypovolia. The latter group drinks less and puts out smaller volumes of more concentrated urine, regulating its body fluid tonicities largely through renal activity. Whatever may be the relation of volustatic activity to water balance, it has no fixed relation either to thirst or renal excretion. The kidneys themselves are not primary thirst receptors, since a dog with and without kidneys drinks similar amounts of water in response to identical salt loads.[8]

The integration of thirst and renal function in a striking instance of volume regulation was reported by Clarke (174). The sexual skin of the baboon (*Papio hamadryas*) achieves turgescence with little change in cellular fluid volume (if anything, it decreases) but with a large change of interstitial volume. The increase in weight of this organ derives 20% from the animal's body and 80% from exogenous fluid intake. Thirst and urinary activity are closely coordinated with the changes in water balance in that the animal exhibits thirst and relative oliguria during swelling and the reverse while reabsorption goes on. During swelling, water intake from all sources exceeds urine output by severalfold but, promptly at the beginning of shrinking, urine flow is augmented and appetite for water disappears. For 11 consecutive days one animal did not drink, and during 17 days from the start of

---

[8] Nevertheless, Linazasoro *et al.* (482) consider water intake ("thirst") in nephrectomized rats to be not up to requirements. It is stimulated to occur normally, however, in nephrectomized animals given active renal extract of the pig. These workers think it is a function of the kidney, in the presence of sufficient cellular dehydration, to liberate a "thirst hormone" (p. 92) which conditions the sensation of thirst by acting on "centres."

shrinking to the next menstruation, only 0.25 liter of liquid water was imbibed. The animal's lowest weight was 10 Kg. and the highest weight 14 Kg. The sexual skin weight varied in the menstrual cycle (ca. 36 days) from 2 to 35% of the total body weight.

Correlations of this sort between body volumes and intake-output activities are not necessarily helpful in clarifying cause and effect. We may be willing to agree that heightened fluid intake and diminished urine output bring about an increase in fluid volume of the sexual skin, but we cannot thereby rule out the possibility that the shrunken volume of the sexual skin determines that intake-output shall take the pattern it does; nor that a fully swollen sexual skin does not initiate the reverse intake-output pattern, whatever the hormonal intermediation may be.

SUMMARY

The regulation of fluid volume, like that of body size and the masses of all body constituents, is rooted in primitive physiologic processes. We know little of its mechanism, but something of its modus operandi; and we believe that it is theoretically independent of the regulation of osmotic pressure. To seek the nature of volume regulation simply in "volume" receptors and hypothetical moderator reflexes is not meaningful inasmuch as "volume," like electricity, is not an adequate stimulus. For the present, volume regulation appears to be more amenable to abstract than to physical analysis. The excretion of water and/or salts or osmotically effective material can be suggestively correlated with volumes or "effective" volumes of plasma or blood, interstitial, extracellular, and intracellular fluids, or combinations of these.

Preoccupation of investigators with the idea that stubborn problems of voludynamics can somehow neatly be resolved in terms of "diuresis" or "antidiuresis" to the neglect of over-all body losses ("ecuresis") or gains ("emuresis") of water (857), has caused confusion. Furthermore, salt figures equally or even more importantly than water in volume regulation since its quantity and concentration in body fluids largely determine not only the absolute but also the relative magnitudes of body fluid compartments (distortion).

A general theory of volume regulation should describe quantitatively not merely the processes of discharge of positive and negative loads of water and salts but also the processes whereby all possible distortion of body fluid volumes are resolved. It might subsume volume also, as has been remarked, as a factor of satiety (19) as well as of thirst. The volume of water drunk affects, among other things, gastric volume, an increase of which, even before water absorption has occurred, inhibits drinking; and this may be a factor in voluntary relative dehydration (p. 167.

The conceptual difficulty of distinguishing the effect of the mass of salt and water of a load of saline from the distortion of volume produced by the load has been examined in the light of isorrheic and osmometric analysis. Quantitative relations (correlations) have been drawn between renal excretion and volume regulation; similar ones may be forthcoming for thirst and volume regulation. While it remains easier to see how drinking or renal excretion affects the body volume than to see the reverse, the conviction that volume does influence thirst and renal excretion continues to fertilize physiologic researches.

*A quart of water per day has the high utility of saving
a person from dying in a most distressing manner.*

—WILLIAM STANLEY JEVONS

CHAPTER V

PROBLEMS OF THIRST

THE WORDS thirst and torrid are cognate; indeed, in its extreme
form, thirst is often described in terms appropriate to a conflagra-
tion. Relatively few are so unfortunate as to experience the full
agonies of thirst but many are aware of dreadful accounts of "burning" or "raging" thirst and apprehend how its "fire" is quenched
only by water. If we think mainly of the man in the desert or the
castaway at sea as those to whom befalls this fate, we recognize,
nevertheless, that the stresses and exigencies of thirst are multifarious. They present problems of the greatest complexity,
subtlety, and physiologic significance. We turn to some of these
now.

HYDROPENIA

The association of thirst with a paucity of water in the body
leads us to inquire further about hydropenia (p. 113). A vast
literature treats of the functions of water in the organism and its
singularities for metabolism, but only a meager portion of this
deals specifically with the physiology of water deprivation.

A garter snake in normal water balance is supple and quick.
Deprived of water long enough, it becomes a study in slow motion;
allowed to drink, its serpentine agility returns promptly. An earthworm suspended from a thread or hook spontaneously and repeatedly contracts, a phenomenon which has endeared this creature to anglers and fish alike. The activity changes little as by
exposure to air we deprive the worm of water up to a fifth of its

body weight but, thereafter, the amplitude of its contractions falls off in direct proportion as water loss progresses, and immobility sets in when two-fifths of the body weight has been lost (850). The worm can actually lose more than half of its body weight in this way before succumbing (9).

Deficit of body weight incurred rapidly is one measure of hydropenia in the dog, rat, and rabbit if we may judge from the fact that these species drink when in deficits up to 5% of the body weight, and not too much, to restore body weight to within 1% of its initial value. Sheep (547), hamster, guinea pig, cat, and

TABLE IX

Limiting tolerance of negative "water" loads in diverse species, as represented by fractional weight loss (weight loss/initial body weight) (9, 18, 319, 626, 686, 686a, 868, 871, 874). Many animals deprived of "drinking" water lose weight, especially if their food has a low aquiferous potential. Rapid weight loss, as of a man in a hot desert (given below) reflects, and is equivalent almost to, pure water loss. Relatively slow weight loss entails loss of water and substantial amounts of body solids, especially if food intake is (as often) cut down sharply in water deprivation, or if both food and water are withheld. Commonly, however, the larger part of weight loss, following deprivation of drinking water in hydrodipsic animals, is water loss.

Species	Fractional Weight Loss
Man	$1/5$
Rat, white mouse,* deer mouse, vole, camel, snake, turtle	$1/3$
Dog, cat, chicken, frog, cockroach	$2/5$
Pigeon, lizard, ameba	$1/2$
Earthworm	$3/5$
Slug	$3/4$

* See Fig. 24.

man, however, require food and time in recovering initial body weights (308, Figs. 15, 16), the latter taking 6 to 12 hours, or a night's sleep, and a meal or two, to recover from rather severe dehydration (18).

Table IX and Fig. 24 indicate limiting deficits of "water" and/or weight tolerated by various species, i.e., consistent with survival, but the data must be qualified insofar as rate of dehydration is an uncontrolled factor. Thus, with slow desiccation (120 hours) frogs withstand 40% weight loss; with rapid desiccation (0.7 hours), 12%. Similar differences are noted, for example, in cats dehydrated in dry air at rates corresponding to different ambient temperatures; but temperature and water may have unique, complex, and variable interrelations in different species (12). Food is commonly refused by sufficiently desiccated mammals (Table V, p. 110), leading to greater deficit of weight but relatively less deficit of water than would occur from lack of

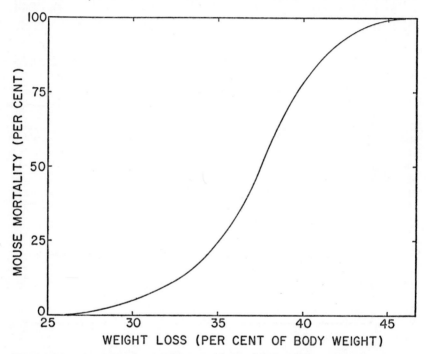

Figure 24. An ogive for intolerance of white laboratory mice to water and food deprivation. A cumulative frequency distribution; death rate as a function of weight loss at environmental temperatures of 25° to 30° C. The mean weight loss and standard deviation at death for 96 animals was 38.16 ± 3.69% of body weight. Mice died at weight deficits from 26 to 46%; half of the animals survived 37.5% weight loss. Wolf and Meroney (874).

water alone (9). This is less the case, for example, with the camel and donkey than with certain other animals, and the weight losses of these two former may be almost pure water (686).

It has been noted (p. 5) that rats deprived of water until death contain approximately the same percentage of water in their bodies as normally, since fat and other solid loss proceed extensively along with water loss; rats also keep practically the same percentage composition of their tissues in dehydration-starvation with respect to nitrogen, sodium, potassium, chloride, and phosphorus (57).

Hibernating animals go for several months without food or water, obtaining oxidative water from fat and sustaining small water losses (63); but their metabolic rates are then only 1 to 3% of that of the "resting" homeothermic state.

Fig. 25 illustrates theoretically how water loss may vary with weight loss as the fraction of water in the body varies or not with de-

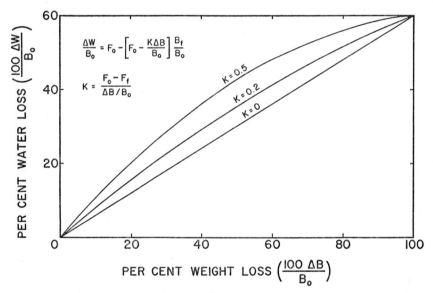

Figure 25. Relation between water loss and weight loss during deprivation of food and water, both as per cent of initial body weight (see text for use of symbols). F_0 is taken as 0.600. When $K = 0$, the fraction of water in the body at any time up to that of death from dehydration and starvation is the same as the fraction of water in the body initially so that the percentage water loss is obtained directly from the product of the weight loss and that fraction. The maximum tolerable weight loss in the dog is about 50% under these conditions, representing a water loss of 50% of the initial body water if $K = 0$; more if $K > 0$.

With rapid evaporative dehydration of an organism of the sort possible in man but not rat, loss of body solids is negligible compared with that of water. It is sometimes assumed in such cases that $\Delta W/B_0 = \Delta B/B_0$, and K would not then be a constant of dehydration.

hydration. Let F be the fraction of water in the body; B, body weight; K, a constant; Δ, signify "change of"; and 0 and f be subscripts denoting "initially" and "finally," respectively.

$$W_o = F_o B_o \tag{1}$$

$$W_f = F_f B_f \tag{2}$$

$$W_o - W_f = \Delta W = F_o B_o - F_f B \tag{3}$$

$$\Delta W/B_o = F_o - F_f B_f/B_o \tag{4}$$

From (1), $\Delta W/W_o = \Delta W/F_o B_o \tag{5}$

From (4), and if $F_f = F_o$,

$$\Delta W/B_o = F_o \Delta B/B_o \tag{6}$$

and $\Delta W/W_o = \Delta B/B_o \tag{7}$

If, arbitrarily, $F_o - F_f = K\Delta B/B_o, \tag{8}$

$$\Delta W/B_o = F_o - [F_o - K\Delta B/B_o]\, B_f/B_o \tag{9}$$

Such relations have been applied to the following case of a dog deprived of food and water and killed when moribund, after losing 42.2% of its initial body weight (871). The water content of its comminuted carcass was determined by oven drying to be 47.3%. Assuming the body had initially contained 60.0% water, it follows that the water loss in hydropenia amounted to 32.7% of the initial body weight, or 54.5% of the initial body water; and water loss would have been 77.5% of weight loss. Estimates of Elkinton and Taffel (232), based upon metabolic data rather than direct body water measurements, showed that water loss averaged 78.3% of weight loss in dogs similarly deprived of food and water. Gamble, Ross, and Tisdall (281) calculated that water loss was almost two-thirds of weight loss in simple fasting in two young girls. If the fraction of water of the body of the aforementioned dog had remained either 0.600 or 0.473 at all times in the course of hydropenia, a constancy already noted rather to be charactistic of rats and mice, then the water loss would have been 25.3% or 20.0% of the initial body weight, respectively, and in either case the water loss would have been 42.2% of the initial body water. Water loss would have been only about half of weight loss.

In cats, there is some evidence (626) that the percentual water content of the whole body is lowered on a regimen of total inanition but not when the animal is deprived of food and allowed water ad libitum. The great variability of the water content of cats and dogs precludes a definitive conclusion on how it may be modified by the regimens tested. In white rats and mice, it has been clearly shown (874) that slight but statistically significant changes occur as follows: increased body water with water ad libitum and no food; decreased body water with no water and "dry" food ad libitum; with no water and no food, rats showed a slight diminution and mice a slight increase in percentual body water. Such results concur with those reported for the white rat (689).

Tables IV and V record some of the effects of progressive hydropenia in dogs. Pernice and Scagliosi (604) autopsied the dog of Table V which died after 11 days with a loss of 24% of its body weight. They reported a general loss of flesh; pale, dry muscle; fat partly wasted (p. 118), especially in the omentum; brain, spinal cord, nerves congested; no traces of fluid in the pericardial sac; pleura apparently normal; lungs pale, anemic; kidneys of normal size, hyperemic, slightly knobby surface; etc. Histologic modifications of diverse organs of dogs dehydrated by access to food but not to water are also given by Garofeanu and Derevici (283).

Autopsy of a dog (756) which had undergone deprivation of food and water for 37 days, sustaining a weight loss of 49.7% (626, 871) revealed deep red, dry muscle which did not bleed on sectioning; deep red spleen; little or no subcutaneous, mesenteric, or perirenal fat; no free fluid in peritoneal cavity or pericardial sac; some inspissated feces; normal gross appearance of kidneys, gall bladder, and brain. Loss of skin turgor and elasticity and an increased susceptibility to exterior surface infection, and lipuria may be observed in such extremely dehydrated animals. Chemical and pathological changes in tissues, blood, and urine are mentioned by Straub (770) and by Morgulis (560); and Pribor (627) has described alterations in autonomic ganglion cells of the dehydrated cat, including decreases in chromidial substance, glycogen, alkaline phosphatase activity, and ascorbic acid.

Bodies of men dead from thirst have been said to show viscid, concentrated, coagulated blood, both in the heart and beginning of the great vessels; dryness of all structures; inflammation of the stomach and peritoneum, and the brain and its membranes; and the stomach and liver to be covered with livid and gangrenous spots (150, 216).

Elkinton and Taffel (232), Wolf and Eddy (871), and Prentiss *et al.* (626, Table IV) observed that prolonged water deprivation in the dog caused urinary sodium and chloride to diminish, or vanish, even as plasma concentrations of these ions rose. Thus, in contrast to the usual physiologic response whereby increased plasma concentrations lead to increased urinary excretion, the thresholds of retention of sodium and chloride appear to rise in water deprivation and thirst. If, according with osmometric theory, thirst is a function of increased effective osmotic pressure of body fluids, this phenomenon must be considered remarkable since the urine changes from an antidipsic to a dipsogenic influence (p. 305) by virtue of changing effectively from hypertonic to hypotonic in the course of water deprivation. It is possible to interpret this as a physiologic mechanism serving to enhance thirst, and the drive to obtain water, almost without limit. Dill (208) has interpreted the decreased salt content of sweat with acclimatization (p. 73) in this manner. The relative disappearance of sodium and chloride from the urine is possibly related to the well known fall in glomerular filtration rate which occurs in dehydration in man, dog, and other animals (739, 857).

The total water loss in their dogs was found by Elkinton and Taffel to be in excess of the original extracellular volume. Loss of water from the cells was seen to consist of three parts: osmotic; water lost with cell destruction in fasting; and water lost with potassium released in excess of nitrogen. In this latter regard, the increased potassium concentration of the serum in extreme hypertonia is especially interesting (530, 873).

Eudipsia and Hyperdipsia

Black, McCance, and Young (105) studied dehydration in man by means of balance experiments in which subjects took food but not extra water for three and four days. In this period there was no reduction in plasma volume although the men lost over 3.5 liters of body water. Apparently none of the extracellular sodium was lost and only a little of the potassium from the cells.

The amount of urea produced by the body increased. Osmotic pressure of body fluids rose along with the serum sodium, but serum potassium fell with a negative potassium balance. Characterizing experimental dehydration in eight men and two women they stated:

. . . . The experience of voluntary dehydration is inseparable from some degree of "self consciousness." Even allowing for this, the subjects exhibited a change in behavior which could be interpreted as an exaggeration of their temperamental type. Serious people became positively sombre; while others, normally cheerful, exhibited a somewhat hollow vivacity. The subjects were intellectually capable of performing estimations and calculations, but their concentration was impaired. They found that the days of dehydration were not actually uncomfortable but they seemed very long. The experimenters were never unbearably thirsty, but by the third day their mouths and throats had become dry, their voices husky, and they had begun to find it difficult to swallow. By the third or fourth day their facies had become somewhat pinched and pale and there was a suggestion of cyanosis about their lips which was rather characteristic. This general appearance of ill-being vanished within a few hours of the restoration of fluid, and the symptoms of dehydration passed off long before physiological rehydration was complete. Many of the subjects lost all their desire to drink as soon as the first pint of fluid had been taken.[1]

Sodium and chloride were found to be retained in the after-period of the experiment, even while drinking was diluting body fluids, possibly as a general reaction to dehydration. The events in moderate dehydration are contrasted with those of salt deficiency. In water deficiency, mineral excretion does not keep pace with water loss (although negative nitrogen and mineral balances may be associated with anhydremia (512)), osmotic pressure of body fluids rises, potassium leaves cells, and plasma volume does not fall. In salt deficiency, water excretion does not keep up with salt loss, osmotic pressure falls, water enters cells, extracellular and plasma volumes fall.

McCance and Young (527) have elsewhere commented:

---

[1] See "voluntary dehydration," pp. 9, 151, 224.

Man is surprisingly sensitive to a reduction in his water intake. Anyone can demonstrate this to himself and his friends by a very simple and perfectly safe experiment. All he (or she) has to do is abstain from all liquid for three or four days, and to eat only "dry" food such as biscuits, cheese, jam, sugar and chocolate. By the third day the experimenter will probably have lost from 8 to 16 pounds (about 3.5 to 7 Kg.) of weight. He will be very thirsty, but not perhaps inordinately so, and he may even maintain that he feels quite well, though he can no longer eat the dry food, and finds it a little difficult to talk for long at a time. His friends, however, will have observed a gradual change in his appearance. His cheeks will have become paler than they ought to be, and some-what sunken; his lips will look dry, and they will probably have developed a slightly bluish tint. If the subject of this experiment decides to bring it to an end, and drinks two or three cups of tea, his friends will probably notice the most dramatic change in his appearance, and within 10 minutes he will have recovered all his characteristic colouring and be looking the picture of health once more.

A degree of salt deficiency has been observed by Consolazio and Pace (177) in men on little food and limited water. Such men, taking 500 to 1500 cc. of water per day showed slightly lower plasma concentrations of sodium and chloride after four days than at the start of the experiment. This was correlated with negative balances of these ions and "salt hunger" by the end of the fast.

These subjects had no food but 30 g. of carbohydrate as "Charms" candy. There were three groups of five men each, assigned 500, 1000, and 1500 cc., respectively, for four days. The dry bulb temperature averaged 75.8° F., relative humidity 28%, and the men did laboratory work. Any volume of fresh water taken in excess of 1000 cc. per day was lost almost quantitatively in the urine. The 500 cc. ration was sufficient to clear the body of nitrogenous wastes but it did not quite prevent thirst from developing; 1000 cc. per day did. This defined a minimal and most economical optimal intake of water and is similar to the water intake of Benedict's (87) fasting subject (Table VI, p. 116).

Men found it difficult to drink as much as 1500 cc. per day under these conditions and evinced a distinct antidipsia. Almost invariably the first two days of fasting brought on moderately severe temporal and frontal headache (671) which disappeared after the second day. After the third day appetite was lost and hunger was almost absent. No significant effect on blood pressure, or body temperature was noted. Although the men retained physical fitness, there was lassitude, slight leg edema, and a reduction of visual form and color fields. Hunger cramps in one man brought about vomiting. To all groups of men, water tasted flat after two days and the flavor was unpleasant although the moistness was appreciated. The men lost between three and one-half and four kilograms during the four days(the greatest loss was in the 500 cc. group), not more than 25% of which was estimated as due to metabolism of fat and tissue; the chief loss of weight was water.

After four days the respiratory quotient of 0.757 and the low urinary excretion of nitrogen suggested that the greatest portion of the energy dissipation derived from stored body fat. No ketonuria or acetone on the breath was observed. Salt hunger was manifest in all subjects terminating the fast. Having lost an average of 3 g. of salt per day during the experiment, each consumed approximately 10 g. of salt within 2 hours after the end of the fast. In all cases serum sodium and chloride had dropped during the fast, least in the 500 cc. group (1.3 mEq./L., sodium; 2.9 mEq./L., chloride), most in the 1500 cc. group (3.6 and 5.0 mEq./L., respectively).

It has been observed of men with wasting disease that the "chronic energy deficit state" of starvation is associated with hyponatremia, hypotonia, and slight hyperkalemia. The hyponatremia is not necessarily related to sodium loss and has been ascribed to the low energy available to "pump" mechanisms as a result of which, it was supposed, sodium might leak into cells (558).

Desert Thirst: Effects of Hot Environments

From their expeditions in the deserts of the United States during World War II, and from their organized researches in laboratory "hot rooms," Adolph and his scientific parties gleaned great stores of information subsequently organized in the monograph *Physiology of Man in the Desert* (18). One of the significant con-

tributions of these studies was to place the thirst sensation in perspective. Everyone who goes to the desert becomes water conscious and has his drinking habits modified (20). But members
of these research teams, and the large number of desert troops who
served as experimental subjects for water deprivation, as during
hiking in the heat of the day, suffered many discomforts in addition to thirst. Dryness of the mouth usually was not the most
grievous complaint of a dehydrated man. Among recorded quotations of hikers we find:

> Walking was mechanical, and a matter of will power. The
> symptoms of thirst were most severe during the early phases of
> the walk . . . . At the conclusion, the thirst symptoms were mild.

Again:

> At 4:30 to 4:40 p.m., I felt first-rate, and felt I could walk for
> hours. At 4:45 my legs felt weak, my pace broke, it became diffi-
> cult to continue. At 4:50 I had but one desire—to sit down. To
> cease exercise seemed far more important than to drink.

TABLE X

Complaints or symptoms of 16 men walking in the desert without water (18).

Complaint or Symptom	Number of Times Reported	Frequency of Occurrence, Per Cent of Total Men	Number of Times, Primary Cause of Distress	Number of Times, Secondary Cause of Distress
Muscular fatigue	13	81	5	7
Thirst	11	69	3	3
Heat oppression	8	47	2	1
Intestinal ache	6	35	2	0
Nausea	4	24	3	0
Headache	4	24	1	1
Dyspnea	3	18	0	0
Dizziness	2	12	0	0
Foot ailments	2	12	0	0

Table X gives the relative frequency of complaints in one group
of men studied. Only one man in five found thirst his most serious
symptom. In contrast, excessive muscular fatigue was reported by
12 men, and five of them ascribed their inability to walk farther
to physical exhaustion. In general, men cannot continue to walk

in the desert heat unless they replace their water losses with certain minimum frequencies. Dehydration augments the signs of physical fatigue until merely standing erect is an intolerable strain. Men dehydrated to this extent retain their mental faculties; they are not crazed with thirst (18):

The order of appearance of the signs and symptoms . . . . is particularly characteristic. Thirst is noticeable very early, but does not increase much in intensity as the water deficit continues to increase. Vague discomfort, not experienced by controls who drank water, gradually becomes defined in the flushing of the skin, heat oppression, weariness, sleepiness, impatience, anorexia, and dizziness. At about the time that the walking pace can no longer be maintained, dyspnea, tingling, and cyanosis, as well as a suggestion of tetany, appear. Still later, a man cannot stand alone, either because of impaired coordination or fainting.

What the signs are when the water deficit is greater than 10 per cent of the body weight we know only from the reports of men who were lost in the desert for some days. King obtained his information from a troop of cavalry, and McGee drew upon the reports of several desert travelers for his pointed discussion [see Chapters VII, VIII] . . . . There may be extreme restlessness, accompanied by delirium and hysteria. The tongue swells,[2] swallowing becomes impossible, and the mouth loses all sensation. The skin shrivels and shrinks against the bones, the eyes become sunken, vision is dim, and partial deafness is the rule. Micturition is painful,[3] and is probably followed by anuria. The skin turns numb and bloody cracks appear. Apparently, this is the irreversible stage, from which there is no recovery. It is not certain whether the lethal point is nearer a 15 per cent or a 25 per cent deficit; much depends on air temperature, exposure, and speed of dehydration. With the onset of inability to swallow at about 12

---

[2] Chalfant (165) tells of a man on the desert who, "believing that he was likely to perish, cut his palate with a knife so that the dripping blood would keep his tongue from swelling." And Snow (745) quotes Captain Riley of the ill-fated brig *Commerce*: "I broke my bottle and spilled the little water it contained, and my tongue, cleaving to the roof of my mouth was as useless as a dry stick until I was able to loosen it by a few drops of my . . . urine." See page 402.

[3] Skattebol (727) describes this process among castaways. ". . . . it was an extremely painful process, causing some men to cry aloud. The product was small and rusty-looking, and the period of waiting for urination, the letting go, sometimes took as long as ten minutes."

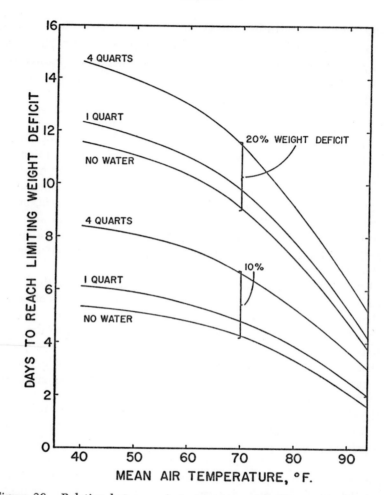

Figure 26.   Relation between air temperature and time required to reach limiting weight deficits on various initial water supplies.   Calculated from data for Fig. 27.   Weight deficit of 20% corresponds approximately to most men's limit of endurance without work; 10% corresponds to the limit of ability to work.   Evidence exists (228, 523) that actual survival rates may be higher than suggested by information based upon laboratory and field experiments.   After Adolph *et al.* (18).

per cent water deficit, the individual can no longer recover without assistance.   A man dehydrated to this point must be given water intravenously, intraperitoneally, by stomach tube, or through the rectum.

Most of the above signs cannot be measured quantitatively at present. In the field, where precision instruments are hard to use, people rely on qualitative observations. This fact, however, is an advantage, since anyone may promptly deduce from comparable observations the probable water deficit in a given individual. The stages of dehydration recognized by McGee may also be designated approximately in our series of signs. It is accurate enough to suppose that each of McGee's stages—clamorous, cotton-mouth, swollen-tongue, shriveled-tongue, blood-sweat—corresponds to ranges of deficits covering about 5 per cent of the body weight [see (865)]. In our experience, the cotton-mouth stage usually ends in exhaustion.

In the desert the average man tolerates water deficits up to 3 or 4% of body weight with moderate impairment of efficiency; at

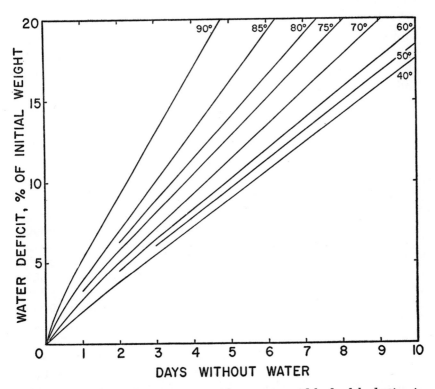

Figure 27. Relation between time without water and body dehydration in men at various temperatures. See Fig. 26. After Adolph *et al.* (18).

5 to 8% he is fatigued, spiritless, prone to complain about his situation, and predisposed to physical collapse; at more than 10% dehydration cooperation from men cannot be expected and gross deterioration, physical and mental, sets in (18, 458, 620). Accurate observations on man do not extend to deficits greater than 11%. It has been estimated above that the limiting deficit compatible with survival in acute (rapid) dehydration is about 20% (15 to 25%) (18, 801, Figs. 26, 27, Table IX, p. 395), but tolerance to dehydration as a function of the rate of losing water has not fully been assessed (p. 209). Rate of dehydration may influence the thirst threshold in man, but not in the dog (658).

The cause of death in desiccation has been attributed by Kerpel-Fronius and Leovey (416) to cell injury resulting from increased osmotic pressure of tissue fluids; Babcock (63) thought that death was uremic and, in one sense (Table IV), but not in another (p. 275), it so appears. Generally, little attention has been given this subject and little evaluation has been made of secondary effects of dehydration, as on the reduction of the circulation and the elevation of the body temperature (18, p. 81), for the morbidity and mortality.

Water from Desert Plants

MacDougal (502) has written:

The Indian and the desert traveler often seek relief in the juices of plants when water fails. The fruits of some of the prickly-pears are slightly juicy, the stems of the same plant or the great trunks of the sahuaro contain much sap, but for the most part it is bitter, and while it would save life, in extremity, yet it is very unpleasant to use. The barrel-cactus, or bisnaga (*Echinocactus*), however, contains within its great spiny cylinders a fair substitute for good water. To get at this easily one must be armed with a stout knife or an ax with which to decapitate the plant, which is done by cutting away a section from the top. Lacking a suitable tool the thirsty traveler may burn the spines from the outside of the bisnaga by applying a lighted match and then crush the top with a heavy stone. This or other means is taken to remove a section 6 to 8 inches in thickness and expose the older parenchyma around the small central woody cylinder. Next a green stake is obtained from some shrub or tree that is free from bitter substances, and with this or with the ax the white tissue of the interior is pounded to a pulp and a cavity that would hold two gallons is formed. Squeezing the pulp between the hands into this cavity will give from 3 to 6 pints of a drinkable liquid that is far from unpleasant and is generally a few degrees cooler than the air . . . . Scouting Indians have long used the bisnaga, and a drink may be obtained in this manner by a skilled operator in 5 to 10 minutes. Some travelers are inclined to look with much disfavor on the liquid obtained in this manner, but it has been used without discomfort by members of expeditions from the Desert Laboratory . . . .

The sap of the sahuaro (*Cereus giganteus*) and of other cacti contains bitter substances that make it impossible to be used to allay thirst by man, although it may be given to burros. A supply is usually obtained by felling the heavy trunk and elevating the ends a few inches above the ground, while the middle is allowed to sag lower over a bucket or vessel that has been suitably placed in a hole in the ground below. A cut is made above the bucket to allow the liquid to exude, while the process is hastened somewhat by building a fire under the ends.

A supply of the pulp of the barrel cactus has been carried by some (382a, 620), wisely, since this particular plant is not always readily located. Chunks carried for several days may still contain moisture. Rubbing the body with chewed pieces reportedly helped keep one man cool (620).

Ways of obtaining water from cacti, from the surface roots of some desert plants such as the "water trees" of arid Australia, from sap, and otherwise are detailed elsewhere (571a).

An experiment illustrating the dissociation of hydropenia and thirst is cited by Adolph *et al.* (18). Fourteen men were weighed soon after breakfast whereupon they played ball or sat in the sun until each showed a body weight deficit of more than 2%. They were then allowed to drink enough water to bring their weight deficits to exactly 2%. During the first few hours the men drank all that was given them and complained vociferously of thirst, but after 4 to 5 hours, they were no longer thirsty at a 2% deficit. After 7 hours the men drank ad libitum for 30 minutes at the end of which period the average weight deficit was 2.5%. Thus, while the men were at first hyperdipsic on a 2% deficit, their thirst gradually disappeared until after 7 hours a deficit of 2.5% was not dipsogenic.

One of the key factors in this apparent accommodation is possibly the steady salt loss which occurred with time and which was unreplaced. As has been noted earlier (p. 73), the higher concentration of salt in the sweat of unacclimated men may actually be consistent with the development of considerable absolute, but negligible relative, dehydration, with collapse occurring in the absence even of eudipsia. This is an aspect of voluntary dehydration (p. 151).

Bean (80) has described the reactions of men in a hot room undergoing acclimatization. A man's first morning's work found him about a liter behind his zero water balance level, when water

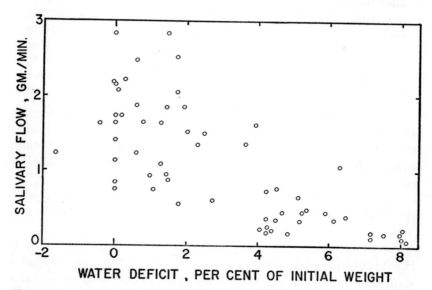

Figure 28. Salivary flows at diverse water deficits in man. After Adolph *et al.* (18).

was given as desired. In five days this deficit was only about half a liter and, if one enforced restriction to the amount of fluid taken voluntarily the first day, there was a tremendous complaint. The pattern of thirst had shifted.

The best performance of fully acclimatized young men doing intermittent hard work in heat is achieved by replacing hour by hour the water lost in sweat (80, 617). Any amount of water less than this leads in a matter of hours to serious inefficiency and eventually to exhaustion. Replacement of salt hour by hour under such circumstances has no demonstrable advantage but without salt, water ad libitum will not be great enough to compensate sweat loss.

Salivary flow diminishes with water deficit (Fig. 28) almost linearly until at 8% deficit it has almost ceased. At this stage the breath may become fetid (150, 825, 889), the tongue saburral (632, p. 410), and the individual can no longer spit even though he may be chewing. This constitutes a method of estimating a dangerous degree of water deficit (18). Ladell (461), however, found little change in salivary activity until a subject in a hot and humid environment had been without water for 24 hours and had a deficit of 2 liters of water. He posited the existence of a store of about 2 liters of "free circulating water" which may have to be used up before bodily functions are appreciably impaired.

In water deficit (33, 150) and in starvation (87) visual acuity and other senses (785), and the faculties of perception and understanding (769) may actually be sharpened (p. 296); but amblyopia or meropia, total blindness, and some loss of hearing have also been observed in severe deprivation (112, 249, 422, 567, pp. 377, 387). Adolph et al. (18) listed various measurements which, in experimental tests, showed no significant correlation with water deficit, including acuity of bright vision, area of color fields, rate of dark adaptation, and auditory acuity. There may be dysuria with a small volume of rusty colored urine passed but once a day (18, 150, 727), and bradycardia (339, p. 144). (See Richet's (648) note on death by thirst in prisoners headed for Germany locked in trains.)

Lachrymation can still occur even in severe hyperdipsia, although not in terminal water deficit (339, 567, 769). Gibson (290, p. 250) recounted how, nearing land after 26 days in a lifeboat in the Indian Ocean, the parched survivors were in tears. Whittaker (831), of the Rickenbacker party (Chapter X), stated that when their rafts in the Pacific were overlooked by a passing plane, they didn't weep only because there was not enough moisture available in their bodies for tears. But this may have been rhetorical. However, McGee (pp. 401, 405) recorded of the "blood-sweat" phase of dehydration that:

> . . . . tears fall until they are gone, when the eyelids stiffen and the eyeballs set themselves in a winkless stare . . . .
> [later] . . . . the eyeballs are suffused and fissured well up to the cornea and weep tears of blood . . . .

Under the stress of desert heat, but with free access to water and salt, the body maintains with considerable tenacity its normal percentual salt content (18, 95) in the plasma. The urine may become chloride-free (20, 406) and the rate of its formation may decline to 10 cc./hr. in man; ordinarily the lowest daily output is of the order of 400 to 500 cc. (20). However, the obligatory volume is known to fall (458), even in a temperate climate, as low as 300 cc. on a carbohydrate diet when water intake is less than enough to prevent water deficit. Winkler *et al.* (234, 842) stated that dehydrated men on a carbohydrate diet may actually have daily urine volumes of less than 100 cc./day.

So long as we employ the conventional but arbitrary assumption that an animal is in water balance (zero balance) after a meal, it appears that hydropenia is the ordinary state except for this point (9, 18, 658); and the water balance is continually changing in relation to body weight. Nevertheless, aside from this effect of an otherwise convenient reference, there is evidence that man (in the desert) and dog, for example, do not ordinarily drink more water than they need. Thus, constancy of urine composition and specific gravity may be taken to oppose the view that much water is taken in excess. Of man in the desert, Adolph *et al.* (18) state:

> The concept that man ordinarily drinks more water than he needs may arise both from wishful thinking and from inexperience. Those interested in saving water hoped to achieve economy by depriving men of the supposed excess. But whenever man keeps himself in a state of overhydration (e.g., by copious beer drinking), his kidneys constantly spill over the excess water in the form of a very dilute urine. This is true even in the desert. Overhydration thus is detectable in large daily urine volumes (diuresis) and low urinary specific gravities . . . . average urinary output of man in the desert is less than in a temperate climate, and the average

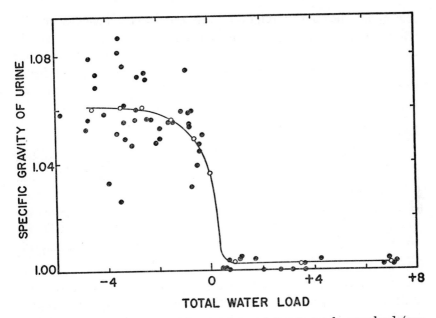

Figure 29. Specific gravity of dog urine in relation to total water load (per cent of body weight). Constant diet. Each black dot represents a separate day; in negative loads, three individuals deprived of water; in positive loads, two other individuals given water repeatedly by stomach. Each white dot represents a mean specific gravity for a 1% interval of load. After Adolph (9).

specific gravity of the urine is somewhat greater. Even some of the highest fluid intakes measured were not excessive in the sense that any more than the necessary quantity was drunk.[4]

---

[4] This, of course, is the key to the question of handling limited water rations when the effective ambient temperature exceeds the mean skin-lung temperature in such a way that heat can be lost from the body only by evaporation (p. 267) of water: ". . . . drink as often as you like. In fact you had better drink more and oftener than you think your thirst requires . . . ." (620).

An older, supplanted view, once held by the armed forces, is exemplified by the following Field Manual statement (804): *"Restricted water consumption must become a habit.* Training must condition troops to live on a limited water ration and must develop such self-discipline in the use of water as will assure the maintenance of combat efficiency on the limited water supply available. Rapid drinking during the day must be avoided as nearly all the water thus consumed is quickly thrown off in excessive perspiration and thus wasted. The first cravings for water are lessened by moistening the mouth and throat. Small sips from the canteen will accomplish this."

Fig. 29 shows the relation between urinary specific gravity and water load. A single measurement of specific gravity may do more to identify the existence of a water increment than any other measurement (9). Curiously, in positive water loads, samples of urine vary around one concentration and in negative loads around another, with a steep transition in between.

Dying of Thirst

If thirst is not of necessity the worst feature of severe hydropenia, it may indeed occupy this role. The horrors of unmitigated thirst are amply attested in literature, scientific and other (Part II). "For the first few days the tortures of thirst are so poignant that you are on the brink of losing your senses," recorded Hedin (339) of his experience in the Taklamakan desert. An experienced desert dweller, Chase (168), wrote:

> How long could I go without water, if by any chance I were left without it? In that fierce heat, and struggling with that terrible country, a few minutes was as long as one could go without drinking. In a flash I saw what would be my condition *in a single hour* —torture: two hours—delirium: after that raving madness, till agony passed into insensibility, and that into death.
>
> Let not the reader think that I am overdrawing here. Those who travel the desert in the middle of summer, and *on foot (which makes all the difference)*, know well enough that to be two or three hours without water brings a man within the grasp of death. In that terrific temperature one's bodily moisture must be constantly renewed, for moisture is as vital as air. One feels as if one were in the focus of a burning-glass. The throat parches and seems to be closing. The eye-balls burn as though facing a scorching fire. The tongue and lips grow thick, crack, and blacken.

One day's deprivation of water on the desert is known to have disturbed men's mental balance such that these sufferers from thirst have forded streams waist deep to wander out on the dry plain beyond to death (502).

Nevertheless, as might be expected, distress does not persist to the end. Gautier (289), speaking of the Sahara, observed that the reality of suffering is not so terrible as could be imagined; and, in the agony of thirst, consciousness appears to be lost, perhaps for a considerable period, before death. The ghastly accounts of McGee (535, Chapter VIII) and others also suggest this kind of termination. Larrey (465), Surgeon-in-Chief of Napoleon's Army of the East in Egypt and Syria, gave the following account of the 1798 expedition:

> Without food or water, the army corps entered the dry deserts bordering Libya, and arrived only with the greatest difficulty on the fourth day of the march at the first place within Egypt which offered supplies (Damanhour). Never has an army undergone such great vicissitudes or such painful privations. Struck by the burning rays of the sun, marching always afoot on still more burning sand, crossing huge, terrifyingly dry plains where only a few puddles of almost solid mud were found, the most vigorous soldiers, consumed by thirst and overwhelmed by heat, succumbed under the weight of their arms.
>
> Some watery plains (effect of a mirage) seemed to offer an end to our troubles; but it was only to plunge us into deeper gloom, resulting in the dejection and prostration of our forces, which was borne by many of our brave men to the last degree. Called too late for some of them, my help was useless, and they died as if snuffed out. This death seemed to me sweet and peaceful; as one of them told me in his last living moment, he experienced an inexpressable comfort. However, I revived a considerable number of them with a little fresh water fortified with a few drops of alcohol which I always carried with me in a small leather bottle. I also used advantageously some Hoffmann's anodyne mixed with sugar.

A remarkable record, cited by Bardier (71) and others (154, 250) is that of Antonio Viterbi, a Judge Advocate under the first Republic. Compromised in an affair of "Vendetta" during the Restoration, he became a political prisoner, sentenced to death on December 16 [sic], 1821, by the court of Bastia. The following (including inconsistencies) is translated from Bardier:

> He wanted to avoid the shame of the scaffold by letting himself die of hunger, and he executed his project with a remarkable will power. He took notes upon himself from which we will extract the passages of interest to us.
>
> "*November 27, 1821*—I fell asleep around one o'clock and my

sleep lasted until half past three. At half past four I fell asleep again for more than an hour. On awakening, I found myself strong and without the least feeling of discomfort, except that my mouth was slightly bitter. This is the end of the second day I have been able to go without eating: I feel no discomfort and experience no need."

(There is a blank here: the copy does not speak at all of the four days between November 27 and December 2, the day when Viterbi interrupted his first fast which had lasted 6 days. The second fast started December 3, lasted until the death of Viterbi on December 20.)

"*December 2.* Today, at three o'clock, I ate with appetite and spent a very quiet night.

"*3. Monday.* No food of any kind; I do not suffer from this privation (second fast).

"*4. Tuesday.* Same abstinence; the day and night passed in a way that would have given courage to anyone not in my situation.

"*5. Wednesday.* The preceding night, I did not sleep at all, although I did not feel any physical restlessness; my mind alone was extremely disturbed. In the morning it became calmer, and this calm continues. It is now two o'clock in the afternoon and for the last three days, my pulse has not shown any febrile movement; it is slightly more rapid and its palpitations are stronger and louder. *I feel no discomfort whatsoever. The stomach and intestines are in perfect rest.* My mind is clear, my imagination active and ardent; my vision is extremely clear; *absolutely no desire to drink or eat;* it is positive that I feel no longing for one or the other.

"In an hour, it will be three days since I began abstaining from all food. My mouth is without bitterness, my hearing sharp; I have a feeling of strength all over. Around half past four, I closed my eyes for a few moments, but a general trembling soon woke me. Around half past five, I began to feel vague pains in the left part of my chest. After eight o'clock, I slept peacefully for an hour; when I woke, my pulse was perfectly calm. From about half past nine till eleven o'clock, sweet and deep sleep, *very noticeable* weakness in the pulse, but regular and deep; no other alteration.

"At midnight, absolute tranquility in all the animal economy, particularly in the pulse. At one o'clock, *very dry throat, excessive thirst.* At eight o'clock, same sensation, plus a very slight pain in the heart.

"The pulse on the left side gives oscillations different from that of the right side, which indicates the disorder produced by absence of food.

"6. *Thursday. The doctor advised me to eat, assuring me that the abstinence, in which I persist, would prolong my life for fifteen days. I decided to fill my stomach, in the hope that an excess would produce the desired effect.* It produced exactly the opposite, and the diarrhea stopped; in a word, I was completely miserable. No fever, and yet *for four full days, I have not drunk nor eaten.*

"*I endure a thirst, a devouring hunger,* with an unchanging courage and an inexorable constancy." (Here details on the pulse.)

"At nine o'clock, prostration of strength; pulse fairly regular, mouth and throat dried; sleep for about half an hour.

"7. *Friday.* (Quiet night from six o'clock on). On awakening some dizziness, *a burning thirst* . . . . At nine o'clock, thirst diminishes . . . . at two o'clock, *ardent thirst* . . . . at six o'clock, mouth bitter . . . ."

8. *Saturday.* During the whole day, he suffers exclusively from thirst.

9. *Sunday.* He has a few dizzy spells, pulse is weak, thirst is always vivid. "At three in the afternoon, a half hour of good sleep after which the pulse is intermittent; dizziness, *continuous and ardent thirst.* Then the head is quiet, *the stomach and intestines without any agitation;* regular pulsations. . . .

"At eight o'clock, the pulse is strong and regular, the head clear, *the stomach and entrails in good condition;* vision is clear, hearing good, *a terrible thirst; the body is full of vigor.*

"10. *Monday.* During the day of the tenth, same pain caused by thirst.

"I continue to take tobacco with pleasure; *I feel no desire to eat* . . . . At ten o'clock, *continuous and always more burning thirst.*

"A strong desire to eat seized me many times during the afternoon, aside from that, I felt *no trouble or pain* in any part of the body."

11. *Tuesday.* He is still preoccupied by thirst.

"At six o'clock, my intellectual faculties have now all the customary energy; *thirst is burning, tolerable; hunger has completely ceased.* My strength is failing noticeably . . . . The stomach, intestine cause no pain. At ten o'clock, weak and regular pulse; *horrible thirst, no desire to eat.*

"*12. Wednesday.* Same condition. *No desire to eat, but thirst is more ardent.*

"*13. Thursday.* Thirst is perhaps a little more tolerable; same indifference to food."

18. December. He finally remains always tormented by thirst from 12th to the 18th, when he writes:

"At eleven o'clock, I arrive at the end of my existence with the serenity of the just. *Hunger does not torment me any more; thirst has entirely ceased; the stomach and intestines are quiet,* head without cloudiness, vision clear. In a word, a universal calm reigns, not only in my heart and in my conscience, but also in all my organism.

"The little time I have left passes sweetly like the water of a

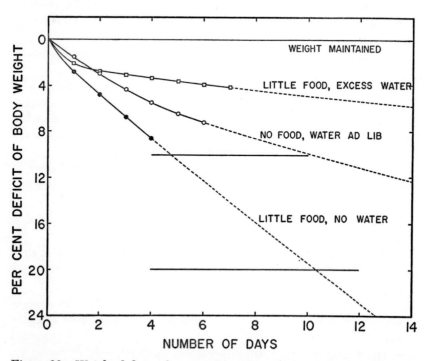

Figure 30. Weight deficits of men on life rafts. Broken lines are extrapolations. Temperature 80°–88° F. Deficit of 20% corresponds approximately to most men's limit of endurance without work; 10% corresponds to the limit of ability to work. After Adolph *et al.* (18).

small brook through a beautiful and delightful meadow.[5]   The light is failing for lack of oil."

Viterbi lived two more days and died on December 20.

So Antonio Viterbi died after seventeen days of fast during which he abstained from all beverage.   This observation seems very instructive; for it shows that if, after a certain time, hunger may be tolerable, it is not the same for thirst.

A diary was also recorded by Falls (249).   This 22 year old U. S. sailor died of thirst and starvation 11 days after his light plane crashed in the Mexican desert of Baja California, and after he had been driven to drink sea water from the Gulf of California.   His last expressed wish was for water or ice cream (p. 400).

Adolph *et al.* (18) have suggested on theoretic and experimental grounds that 12 days is about the limit of man's endurance without water (Figs. 26, 27, 30).   According to the researches of McCance *et al.* (523) the longest voyage of castaways at sea without a supply of fresh water lasted 15 days, although no statement was made as to whether rain fell.   Evidence exists that survival rates may be higher than suggested by information based upon laboratory trials (228, 523).

Thirst of High Altitude and Polar Regions

In some ways hydropenic thirst is no less a problem at high altitudes or in the far north or south than on the desert.   Of mountain climbing in rarefied air, Hyde (395) stated:

> . . . . the heart thumps irregularly, the pulse goes up to 100, your knees knock together, and your poor legs seem unwilling to carry you.   Your throat is parched, you feel suffocated, your chest seems to be loaded down with a great weight, and such a feeling of utter exhaustion!

At high altitude water is scarce despite the richness of ice and snow (807).   The only source of water may be melted snow, and fuel (gasoline) is required to melt it.   Some mountain climbers,

---

[5] This reference to water, however poetic, may have physiologic significance.   See McGee's account, p. 400, dealing with water in its inexpressibly captivating aspects.

and others, state that eating snow makes one thirsty. This allegation needs qualification. There is, of course, no substance to the Hippocratic idea (164) that:

> Water from snow and ice is always harmful because, once it has been frozen, it never regains its previous quality. The light, sweet and sparkling part of it is separated and vanishes leaving only the muddiest and heaviest part.

A comfortable man in normal water balance who proceeds to eat snow may recognize some of the curious "tickling" (162, p. 54) or burning sensation (perhaps caused by some cutting or abrasive action of the ice crystals) otherwise associated with eating salty food and, possibly, with "thirst," but he is not made strikingly thirsty (869). Actually, snow can be used directly to quench thirst (802), particularly if "wet." If its temperature is extremely low, it may be warmed in the hands or by breathing on it, as otherwise it may freeze or crack the lips. Byrd (148), alone in the Antarctic in a weakened condition, felt he could "suck snow to quench thirst" but he also remarked, "I licked the snow until my tongue burned."

The dehydrated, thirsty man is subject not only to such oral stimulation but also is exasperatingly aware that large volumes of "dry" snow provide small volumes of water (ca. 17:1 for uncompacted snow) which will not, for the effort involved in ingestion, produce any palliation comparable with that to be expected from taking water; also, at low temperatures the absolute humidity is so low that respiratory water loss is greatly enhanced, providing in this regard a greater dipsogenic influence than otherwise. The significance of the failure of snow eating to provide the usual conditioned stimulus which ordinary drinking offers to satiety should not be discounted.

It is sometimes remarked that melted snow is tasteless and gustatorily uninteresting, and that this accounts for failure to take sufficient fluid voluntarily. Also likely a reason is the oligodipsia noted below, not to mention the inhibiting effects of the hostile environment on the potency of the thirst reflex.

To man, a disadvantage of eating snow may be the lowering of body temperature caused thereby. However, Davis (202) has observed the Emperor penguin (*Aptendoytes forsteri*) eat snow in the Antarctic. And pine siskins in the Far North have also been observed to eat snow, as have starlings, evening grosbeaks, and white-breasted and red-breasted nuthatches; starlings and cedar waxwings are reported to catch snowflakes on the wing as if they were insects (29, 504). Some animals in less rigorous climates, e.g., sheep (391), eat snow in winter in lieu of water, if necessary. It is not harmful for cats and dogs to eat snow. In the Far North dogs eat snow as they would food. In areas where water and snow are simultaneously available, dogs often prefer snow to water (830).

It has been stated that thirst cannot be satisfied by sucking ice in the cold (295); the relief it provides in patients has been attributed to the cooling of the inspired air (780).

Breathing deeply and hyperventilating the dry air at high altitudes causes climbers to double or triple their intake of fluid to offset dehydration, and the need for liquids grows more pressing with height. Nevertheless, the general dysgeusia which prevails may lead to the use of powdered fruit juice to make water more palatable. The report of the British Medical Research Council on the Everest expedition (540) states:

> Above 18,000 feet, the production of cooked meals and adequate quantities of fluid becomes increasingly difficult.[6] The diet seems unpalatable and monotonous, appetite is depressed by altitude, and food intake is consequently much reduced. Many climbers develop peculiar food preferences and crave foods usually not available, such as salmon, sardines or tinned fruit. Large quantities of sugar are taken, mainly in beverages which even then seem to taste less sweet than at sea level. The average intake of sugar on Cho Oyu in 1952 was as great as 12 oz. per man per day.
>
> Owing to the dryness of the air and the increased rate of respiration at high altitudes, loss of water from the lungs is greatly increased. There is much indirect evidence in accounts of previous expeditions to suggest that climbers have suffered from dehydration. Besides the difficulty of satisfying fluid requirements because of inefficient cookers and shortage of fuel, the sensation of thirst, like the appetite for food, may be impaired at high altitude so that

---

[6] All water above 18,000 feet had to be obtained by melting snow. Cooking could be done over wood fires up to 18,000 feet; above, paraffin stoves had to be used. The process is a long one, partly because the heat generated by the average cooker is reduced and much of it is wasted.

men are apt to overlook the importance of fluid intake. It had been shown on Cho Oyu that five to seven pints of liquid per man per day were in fact necessary.

As at high altitude, thirst may be expected where the low temperatures of the polar regions freeze all available potable fluid (190) unless a source of heat can be employed to counter this. Thus, men are advised to carry a canteen under their outer clothes.

Scott (709), writing of the antarctic voyage of the *Discovery*, remarked that the first task of the day was to obtain ice from a "quarry" for daily water consumption. The harder and bluer the ice, the better it is adapted for melting and the less fuel is required to melt it. Had they been obliged to use snow, their task would have been much heavier since the properties of snow (volume, low thermal conductivity, low density) make it long, costly, and difficult to melt.

One can get good drinking water from old sea ice, icebergs and, of course, glaciers. Young sea ice is salty although less so than the water from which it is formed; it consists of pure ice containing small cavities filled with brine. It has angular corners, a milky appearance, tough texture, and is difficult to splinter. After a year it loses its salt and becomes "fresh." Old sea ice ("paleocrystic") can be distinguished by its smooth corners, rounded by the rains and thaws of one or more summers (758), bluish color, glassy or glare surface, and ease of splintering when pecked at with a knife.[7]

---

[7] Stefansson (757) wrote of the Arctic: ". . . . When sea ice forms it is salty, although perhaps not quite so salty as the water from which it is made, and probably during the winter it loses a certain amount of its salt, although even in April or May ice formed the previous October is still too salty for ordinary cooking uses. But in June and July when rains begin and snow melts and little rivulets trickle here and there over the ice, forming in the latter part of summer a network of lakes connected by channels of sluggishly flowing water, the saltiness disappears, or at least that degree of it which is perceptible to the palate, and the following year this ice is the potential source of the purest possible cooking or drinking water. The ponds on top of the ice are also fresh. During the melting of summer the pressure-ridges and the projecting snags of broken ice change in outline. When the ice has been freshly broken it may well be compared with the masses of rock in a granite quarry just after the blast, or if it is thinner, with the broken-bottle glass on top of an English stone wall. But during the summer all the sharp outlines are softened on the pressure-ridges, so that at the end of the first summer they are no more jagged than a typical mountain range, and at the end of two or three years they resemble the rolling hills of a western prairie. The old ice is easily recognizable at a distance by its outline and on closer approach by the fact that the hummocks are frequently glare. That can never be the case with salty ice, which is sticky and therefore always has snow adhering to it."

In summer, drinking water can be obtained from pools in the old sea ice, particularly away from the edge of the floe where salt water spray may have blown in (538, 570). Fresh water on floes is largely derived from the melting of fresh snow. Nevertheless the aging of sea ice itself is a factor in making it potable since the trapped brine moves slowly down with resultant freshening of the top layers. Thus, as the crystals of pure ice grow together, the dissolved salts are given off to the unfrozen sea water below.[8] Moreover, salt-water ice thaws more readily than pure ice and the salt is leached out and excluded in successive meltings and refreezings.

When sea water is frozen in the laboratory, salts concentrate at the bottom of the container. If a lump of such ice is allowed to melt and the fluid separated into fractions, the concentration of solutes in these fluids may range from over twice that of the original sea water in the first fractions to less than one-tenth (869). The last 30% of the original volume of sea water from the melting ice is potable when the brine is drained from the ice (575, p. 244).

That drinkable water could be obtained from frozen sea water was known in Aristotle's day (543).

MARIPOSIA[9] OR SEA WATER DRINKING

Composition of Sea Water

The composition of sea water, particularly at the ocean surface, is important to dipsologists. Because of its chemical complexity, the "total solid" of sea water is difficult if not impossible to determine by direct analysis, and reproducible results are not obtained by evaporative methods (75, 778). Oceanographers more commonly deal with *salinity*, defined as the total amount of solid material in grams contained in one kilogram of sea water when all the carbonate has been converted to oxide, the bromine and iodine replaced by chlorine, and all organic matter completely oxidized. The salinity is of slightly smaller numerical value than

---

[8] Ice containing entrapped salt can eliminate this salt under the influence of a temperature gradient through the ice. The salt diffuses as a brine through the ice toward the warmest part of the ice cake, a process independent of gravity. However, diffusion will not occur where the ice is below the eutectic temperature of $-6°$ F. (829).

[9] I shall use the term mariposia ($=$ thalassoposia) to designate sea water drinking either as the dipsologic phenomenon peculiar to the castaway at sea or desert shore, as in experimental tests with natural or artificial sea water, or, generally, as it may characterize behavior in animals.

the total quantity of dissolved solids but is obtained by a technique yielding more reproducible results.

In another way, the salinity of sea water is the weight in grams in vacuo when the solids have been dried to constant weight at 480° C., the quantity of chloride and bromide lost being allowed for by adding a weight of chlorine equivalent to the loss of the two halides during the drying. Thus the salinity equals the weight of the total salt per kilogram of water, less most of the weight of the bicarbonate and carbonate ions and less the difference between the bromine and its equivalent of chlorine (336).

Salinity, S, expressed in parts per thousand ($^0/_{00}$), is related to total salt, Σ, whose units are similarly expressed, by the ratio $\Sigma/S = 1.00456$. Regardless of the absolute concentration of sea water, the relative proportions of the different major constituents are virtually constant except at low salinities where minor deviations may occur. Determination of salinity is a relatively difficult procedure but, because of the constant composition of dissolved solids, the chemical analysis of any element present in relatively large quantity can be used as a measure of other elements and salinity.

Chloride ions constitute by weight about 55% of dissolved solids and are measured easily by titration with silver nitrate. Originally defined, the *chlorinity* was the total amount of chlorine, bromine, and iodine in grams contained in one kilogram of sea water, assuming that bromine and the iodine had been replaced by chlorine. A more strict definition making chlorinity independent of future changes in atomic weights is given by Sverdrup, Johnson, and Fleming (778). It is well to remember that salinity is not the same as total salt content, and chlorinity is not the same as chloride content.

An empirical relation has been established between salinity and chlorinity, *viz.*:

$$S = 0.030 + 1.805 \ Cl$$

where Cl is the chlorinity ($^0/_{00}$). *Chlorosity* is the property of sea water corresponding to the chlorinity expressed as grams per 20°-liter; it is the product of the chlorinity and the density of a sea water sample at 20° C. Thus, for a chlorinity of 19.000 $^o/_{oo}$, the density being 1.024, the chlorosity is 19.46 g./L. Other important chemical and physicochemical relations follow (499, 778):

$$\Sigma = 0.073 + 1.8110 \ Cl$$

Where Z is the total salt per kilogram of solvent water,

$$Z = \frac{1000 \ \Sigma}{1000 - \Sigma} = \frac{73 + 1811 \ Cl}{999.927 - 1.8110 \ Cl}$$

Where τ is the freezing point in degrees C.,

$$\tau = -0.05241 \ Z$$

The osmotic pressure in atmospheres at 0° C., π_0, is

$$\pi_0 = -12.08 \ \tau,$$

and at any temperature, t,

$$\pi_t = \frac{\pi_0(273 + t)}{273}$$

At 25° C. the osmotic pressure of average sea water is about 25 atmospheres with an osmolality of approximately 1.0. Barnes (75) has tabulated osmotic pressures of sea water at 25° for chlorinities from 10 to 22 $^o/_{oo}$.

TABLE XI

Major constituents in sea water of chlorinity 19.000$^o/_{oo}$, salinity 34.325$^o/_{oo}$, total salt 34.482$^o/_{oo}$, and specific gravity, at 20 °C., 1.02427. Same data as in Table XII. After (499).

Positive Ions	g./Kg. of Sea Water	mEq./Kg. of Sea Water	mEq./L. of Sea Water (20°C.)	Negative Ions	g./Kg. of Sea Water	mEq./Kg. of Sea Water	mEq./L. of Sea Water (20°C.)
Na	10.559	459.134	470.277	Cl	18.980	535.303	548.295
Mg	1.272	104.605	107.144	SO$_4$	2.649	55.146	56.484
Ca	0.398	19.857	20.339	HCO$_3$	0.139	2.285	2.340
K	0.380	9.712	9.948	Br	0.064	0.806	0.826
Sr	0.013	0.303	0.310	F	0.001	0.071	0.073
Sum	12.622	593.611	608.018	Sum	21.833	593.611	608.018

TABLE XII

Formula for "Artificial Sea Water" based on same data as Table XI.* After (499). The osmolality of this fluid is ca. 1.006. It has the same freezing point ($-1.87\,°C.$) as a 3.16% sodium chloride solution; its milliosmosity is 541 mM sodium chloride. So-called plant nutrients and heavy metals are lacking.

Salt	Grams	mEq./Kg. of solution	g./L. of solution (20°C.)	mEq./L. of solution (20°C.)
NaCl	23.477	401.632	24.047	411.380
MgCl₂	4.981†	104.605	5.102‡	107.144
Na₂SO₄	3.917	55.146	4.012	56.484
CaCl₂	1.102	19.857	1.129	20.339
KCl	0.664	8.906	0.680	9.122
NaHCO₃	0.192	2.285	0.197	2.340
KBr	0.096	0.806	0.098	0.826
H₃BO₃	0.026	¶	0.027	¶
SrCl₂	0.024	0.303	0.025	0.310
NaF	0.003	0.071	0.003	0.073
Sum	34.482	593.611	35.320	608.018
H₂O to	1000.000			

* It is exceedingly difficult to prepare solutions exactly duplicating the properties of sea water because of the likelihood of introducing contaminants, even in reagent grade chemicals, that far exceed the ordinary concentration of these elements in sea water, and especially because of the difficulty in dispensing salts containing water of crystallization. Thus, the three decimal places of the recipe represent an exercise in "chemical mathematics." Slight disagreements in the last decimal places between figures in this table and Table XI and those of Lyman and Fleming (499) and Sverdrup, Johnson, and Fleming (778) are in consequence of using atomic weights of 1942 instead of 1939. The latter authors may be consulted for details of preparation and other recipes for artificial sea water.

For the preparation of several liters of this recipe at one time the following volumetric method may be preferred. Use 11.060 grams of $MgCl_2 \cdot 6H_2O$ and 1.040 times the quantity of the compounds listed above (omitting $MgCl_2$). Add these quantities (or any multiple thereof) to 1000 ml. (or the corresponding multiple thereof) of distilled water at $20\,°C$. Adding the calcium and magnesium chloride after the other salts have been dissolved in nearly, or in all of, the required quantity of water minimizes the formation of precipitates; or, if such form, they tend to dissolve completely after several hours.

† One may use approximately 10.635 grams of $MgCl_2 \cdot 6H_2O$ instead; or, a stock, concentrated solution of known strength may be added in the required volume. Anhydrous magnesium chloride may be prepared by decomposition of magnesium ammonium chloride or by dehydrating the hexahydrate in an atmosphere of hydrogen chloride (498).

‡ One may use approximately 10.893 grams of $MgCl_2 \cdot 6H_2O$ instead.

¶ Boric acid undissociated.

Where the increment of sea water density above 1, multiplied by 1000, is called σ_0,

$$\sigma_0 = -0.069 + 1.4708 \; Cl - 0.001570 \; Cl^2 + 0.0000398 \; Cl^3$$

at atmospheric pressure and 0° C. At the surface, at 0° C. and Cl = 19.0 °/$_{00}$, sea water has a specific gravity of 1.02758; at Cl = 19.4 °/$_{00}$, specific gravity is 1.02816 (see Table XI).

The pH of the sea is 7.5 to 8.4, the higher values generally being found near the surface.

The major constituents of sea water are given in Tables XI and XII, the latter serving as a recipe for an artificial sea water where the minor constituents are unnecessary (e.g., nitrogen, phosphorus, and silicon needed by marine plants, and heavy metals). For a review of the analysis of sea water see Barnes (76).

Making Sea Water Potable

Although there are those who imagine that ordinary sea water in its natural state is "potable" (see Glossary), scientific consensus and general experience has it that pure sea water is harmful if ingested in quantity to the exclusion of fresh water (pp. 274, 292). Numerous methods of making sea water fit to drink have been devised.

An obvious step toward potifying sea water would be to precipitate the salts in some chemical reaction. It would not do to add silver nitrate to sea water to precipitate the chloride (664) since the effect is simply that of substituting the nitrate ion for the chloride (332). Osmotically, the sea water would remain essentially unchanged. A similar difficulty inhered in the use of the "De-salinating" (Goetz) kit the function of which was to remove about 70% of the chloride and 10% of the sulfate as silver and barium precipitates, with substitution of the citrate ion (396a).

Spealman (750) suggested a two-step process, first using silver oxide (Ag_2O) to precipitate silver chloride according to the reaction:

$$2Na^+ + 2Cl^- + Ag_2O + H_2O = 2Na^+ + 2OH^- + 2AgCl.$$

Calcium and magnesium ions are partly or wholly precipitated as

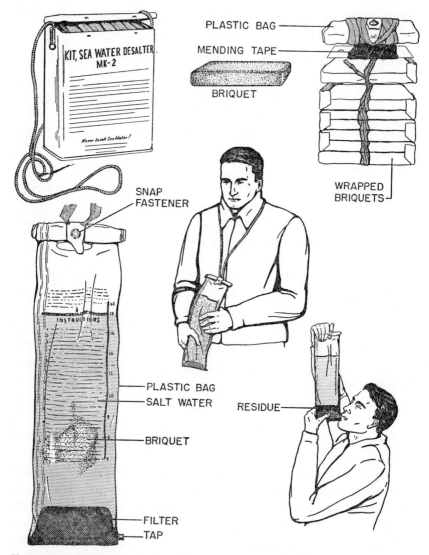

Figure 31. Sea water desalter kit, arrangement of packaged contents, and an unwrapped briquet are shown in upper portion. A briquet is composed of silver zeolite (silver aluminum silicate), barium hydroxide, a small amount of activated carbon for taste and odor removal, a lubricant used as a mold release, and a swelling polymer to facilitate its disruption in water. One briquet is added to approximately one pint of sea water in a plastic bag where it disintegrates. The bag is folded closed and snap-fastened. Gentle kneading and agitation of the bag for 45 to 60 minutes results in the removal

hydroxides in this first reaction. In a second reaction, after AgCl is filtered off, uric acid precipitates sodium urate:

$$Na^+ + OH^- + \text{uric acid} = Na\text{-urate} + H_2O$$

A potable fluid is now filtered off. It contains about 0.6% of dissolved materials (urates and sulfate). The Spealman process has the disadvantage of being a two step process and of requiring a longer time and greater manipulation than is thought desirable for life raft conditions.

Hurran (390) found a silver zeolite which, shaken with 3% sodium chloride and filtered, gave pure water.

Consolazio, Pace, and Ivy (177a, 178) have reviewed various methods of making water potable, including the use of stills and permutit, and have discussed the development and use of silver zeolite in desalting kits of the U. S. Navy (571). Zeolites are highly porous chain-like double silicate structures to which sodium and calcium ions are readily accessible by means of fine pores. Ions small enough to diffuse through these pores may then exchange reversibly with the base of the crystal (450). By compressing silver zeolite (AgZ), or high capacity resins, into compact briquets and by incorporating some barium hydroxide, reactions such as the following obtain with the salts of sea water:

$$AgZ + Na^+ + Cl^- = NaZ + AgCl$$
$$Ba(OH)_2 + Mg^{++} + SO_4^{--} = Mg(OH)_2 + BaSO_4$$

All the products on the right hand side of these equations are insoluble precipitates. Fig. 31 illustrates the principle and operation of such desalting kits, as do photographs of Consolazio et al. (178) and Allen (31).

---

of about 90% of the dissolved solids: sodium and potassium replace silver becoming insoluble zeolites; chloride precipitates as silver chloride; sulfate as barium sulfate; and magnesium as magnesium hydroxide. Clear, potable water may then be sucked from the tap, the muddy residue being held back by the filter. The bag is rinsed out with sea water before re-use. Where space is at a premium, as in collapsible rubber life boats, storage of desalter kits is preferable to storage of water. A package of seven briquets converts about six times its volume of sea water.

In addition to chemical precipitation and ion exchange, other methods by which sea water can be made potable are known. Parker (596) has discussed distillation (31), absorption of water vapor as by silica gel with subsequent removal of water by heating, freezing (ice separates until the remaining liquid is saturated with salts), use of hydrates from which water of crystallization may be recovered, and electroosmosis. See also similar, and some older, methods noted by Howe (382b).

Nelson and Thompson (575) reported a laboratory study of removal of sea salt by freezing processes. Ice formed at —5° to —35° C. contains 20 to 25% of the salts originally in the sea water. Salts concentrate in the brine at the bottom of the container when sea water is frozen in the laboratory. The last 30% of the original volume of sea water from the melting ice is potable when the brine is drained from the ice; the yield may be increased to 50% by reprocessing the brackish water from the melting ice. If an ice "cube" made from sea water in a refrigerator is allowed to melt, several fractions of the melt being separated, it will be found that the salts effectively leach out of the ice, the first portions being more concentrated than the original sea water, the last portions being almost pure water (869).

Ellis (237) has treated of the methods and possibilities of extracting fresh water from the ocean on a large scale. The least amount of work which can produce 1000 gallons of fresh water under idealized conditions is 2.6 kilowatt-hours (extracting this volume from 1,000,000 gallons of sea water at 60° F.). Thus one watt could produce 1.46 liters of fresh water per hour. If greater extractions of pure water volume are made from a given volume of sea water, the energy requirements rise. It is of some interest to note that, taking the osmotic "work" of human kidneys at an estimated 0.70 Calories per day, this energy expenditure for the production of urine is 2160 foot pounds per day, a rate of $1/_{30}$ of a watt; the total metabolism of the kidney dissipates power of the order of 3 watts. Fenn (254) has estimated the energy of oxygen utilization of a man at rest as 107 watts.

One of the remarkable developments in the realm of desalting sea water is the discovery of cellophane membrane which, when sufficiently compressed (e.g., 600–700 lbs./sq. in.), are almost perfectly semipermeable (399, 641) and can be used as filters to separate the salts from the water of sea water. With sea water on one side under such hydrostatic pressure, which exceeds the osmotic pressure of that liquid (ca. 370 lbs./sq. in.), there is a flow across the membrane of fluid whose salt concentration may be less than 1% of that of the original sea water. The applications of such membranes are potentially numerous and may include the creation of sea water presses for lifeboats. The advantages and disadvantages of these membranes are discussed by Breton (126a).

Thirst at Sea

From the scarcity of cold water survival stories, it is evident that a man doesn't last long after shipwreck in northern or southern latitudes (331). Critchley (190), in his small medical monograph on *Shipwreck-Survivors,* ranks cold above thirst as the most distressing and dangerous hardship in this situation; and McCance *et al.* (523) concur in stating that, once in a lifeboat, cold is the greatest hazard. Frequently, however, men adrift contend with an inadequate stock of drinking water for prolonged periods. It is difficult to determine the longest time that has been endured by castaways without water, but Critchley's estimate was 11 days, and that of McCance *et al.* 15 days (p. 233). Actually, a man may have access to some, but insufficient, water and may suffer more and longer than one with no water at all.

Time of survival is critically dependent upon air temperature and insolation, other things being equal. But rates of dehydration may be vastly different on the sea and in the desert. If 10 days or so of complete water deprivation at sea are required to reduce the weight by 20% (Fig. 30), a lethal limit (p. 222), enough other substances are lost so that water loss, per se, is less than 20%. The relative importance of body water and solids for survival is not precisely known (18).

The enormous, though not astonishing, number of extant accounts of shipwreck and of castaways at sea is greatly reduced when considered for their dipsologic significance.[10] Among these latter, some are of interest as background and will be set out briefly (see also Chapters X, XI).

The *Pandora.* Hamilton (327), Surgeon of the Royal Navy, described the distress experienced by the shipwrecked crew of the

---

[10] Accounts of starvation among castaways and others are given by Keys *et al.* (421), including that of the survivors of the *Medusa* (p. 246) and seaman Izzi (p. 250), and by Duncan (217).

frigate *Pandora* in 1792.   Under command of Captain Edwards, with 160 men, this vessel set out to bring to punishment the mutineers of the late ship *Bounty,* and to survey the Straits of Endeavor (Southern Arm of Torres Strait) to facilitate a passage to Botany Bay.   Some of the mutineers were taken in Tahiti. Afterwards the *Pandora* struck a reef and sank.

One hundred and two survivors in four open boats began an enforced voyage of 1,100 miles in the Indian Ocean (Arafura Sea) to the island of Timor.   Thirst and famine accompanied them.   Those who drank urine died in the sequel of the voyage. The effect of thirst on one man was so strong that he became delirious, and continued so for some months after.[11]   The men found respite on an island of which Hamilton wrote:

> After having gorged our parched bodies with water, till we were perfectly water-logged, we began to feel the cravings of hunger; a new sensation of misery we had hitherto been strangers to, from the excess of thirst predominating.

The *Medusa*.   Famous in the literature of dipsology is the shipwreck of the French frigate *La Méduse* (68, 484).   The narration of this tragedy by Savigny and Corréard (675), as it relates to thirst, has been summarized by Meigs (541):[12]

> An expedition, consisting of four vessels, sailed from the Isle d'Aix, on the west coast of France, on the 16th of June, 1816, for the French possessions at Senegal, on the west coast of Africa, which had just been restored to France by England, through the treaties of 1814–15.   The only vessel of the fleet concerning us, the frigate Medusa, carried about 240 souls.   The ship ran on a dangerous reef, not very far from her destination, the port of St. Louis, on the

---

[11] Persistent mental effects of severe dehydration are also mentioned in the account of McGee (p. 406ff.).

[12] There are a number of discrepancies, insignificant for our purposes, between Meigs' account and that of Savigny and Corréard who were actually aboard the raft mentioned.   Thus, according to the latter, the *Medusa* sailed on the 17th of June and carried 397 people; there were six boats; the flour was thrown into the sea before the raft left the *Medusa* in order to accommodate more passengers; the woman and her husband are not mentioned; on the fourth day nearly 300 flying fish were caught and eaten raw, dried, and cooked; flesh from dead bodies was eaten similarly (a fire was built on the raft for cooking); there is no mention of M. Griffin as drinking sea water, although Griffin du Bellay was among the survivors.   Other accounts of this episode also differ in details.

2d of July. They tried to heave the vessel off the reef, but failed, and on the 5th of July it was resolved to abandon her. The chief officers, and some of the crew, took to the boats, four in number, while from 147 to 150 persons, officers, soldiers, and crew, were placed on a large raft which had been constructed, the intention being that the boats should tow the raft to the shore. In the hurry of the embarkation, six casks of wine, and only two of water were placed on this raft. The only provisions they had were twenty-five pounds of biscuit, and some barrels of flour. The boats towed the raft for a short distance, and then, under the influence of selfish terror, and want of proper discipline, abandoned the raft, and made the best of their way to the shore, where they all arrived in safety.

The raft floated helplessly on the sea for thirteen days. On the second night the soldiers broached one of the wine-casks, and, becoming wild with wine and delirium, attacked the officers, who were collected together in the middle of the raft. A furious hand-to-hand combat took place, and many were killed or thrown into the sea. In the height of this strange delirium the soldiers threw the two casks of water, some of the wine, and the barrels of flour, into the sea. They cast overboard the only woman on the raft, with her husband; the two were rescued, only to undergo the same fate afterwards. On the morning of the third day, only 60 of the 150 persons, remained; of the wine, but two casks had been preserved; on this day they began to devour the dead bodies left upon the raft. As the sun rose on the morning of the fourth day, it shewed the survivors ten or twelve of their companions extended lifeless upon the wreck; their bodies were cast into the sea, except one which was retained to feed those who, as the narrator says, 'the day before had clasped his trembling hands, vowing him eternal friendship.' The fifth day arrived; only thirty persons remained—of this number but fifteen seemed likely to survive some days; the others were covered with wounds, and had almost entirely lost their reason. The fifteen who retained some strength, held council together, and resolved that, to save their own lives, the others must be thrown into the sea; they were aiding to consume the only drink they had, the small amount of wine remaining,—so they were cast into the sea. Amongst those sacrificed, was the one woman on the raft, who had twice already been rescued from the water, when cast overboard by the mad and infuriated soldiers.

It was about this time that the narrator of the story gives some account of the character of the sufferings they endured: 'A raging thirst, which was redoubled in the daytime, by the beams of a burning sun,[13] consumed us; it was such, that we eagerly moistened our parched lips with urine, which was cooled in little tin-cups— we put the cup in a place where there was a little water, that it might cool the sooner; it often happened that these cups were stolen from those who had prepared them—the cup was returned to him to whom it belonged, but not till the liquid it contained was drank.' M. Savigny, a young Swiss surgeon, and one of the narrators, observed that the 'urine of some of us was more agreeable than that of others. There was a passenger who could never prevail on himself to swallow it; in reality, it had not a disagreeable taste; but in some of us it became thick and extraordinarily acrid; it produced an effect truly worthy of remark: namely, that it was scarcely swallowed when it excited an inclination to urine anew.[14] We also tried to quench our thirst by drinking sea-water—M. Griffin used it continually; he drank ten or twelve glasses in succession. But all these means failed, or diminished our thirst only to render it more severe a moment afterwards.' They put sea-water into their hats and washed their faces with it at frequent intervals; they moistened their hair with it, and plunged their hands into it; they reserved their small portions of wine in their tin-cups, and sucked it through a quill. This mode of taking it was very beneficial, and quenched the thirst more than when it was all taken off at once. 'Three days passed in inexpressible anguish; we despised life to such a degree, that many of us did not fear to bathe in sight of the sharks, many of which swam about the raft; others placed themselves naked in the front of the machine which was still submerged; these means diminished, a little, our burning thirst.'

On the morning of the thirteenth day, a ship appeared—one which had been sent out from St. Louis, to search for them. They were saved. 'Let the reader imagine,' says the narrator, 'fifteen unfortunate men, almost naked; their bodies and faces disfigured by the scorching beams of the sun; ten of the fifteen were hardly able to move; our limbs were excoriated, our sufferings were deeply imprinted on our features, our eyes were hollow, and almost wild,

---

[13] The connection between the intensity of thirst and the height of the sun or the heat of the day is repeatedly mentioned by sufferers and is described in some detail by Pujo (Chapter IX). See page 152 also. Tiira (786), who concurred in distinguishing the intensity of thirst between day and night, nevertheless stated that the cool of afternoon did not relieve his raging thirst.

[14] See pp. 15, 456.

and our long beards rendered our appearance still more frightful; we were but the shadows of ourselves.'

Thus, of the 147 or 150 persons on the raft, only fifteen were saved, and of this small number, five died after reaching St. Louis. Those who still exist, it is said, were covered with scars, and the cruel suffering which they endured had greatly impaired their constitutions.

The *Dumaru*. Men surviving the wreck of the *Dumaru* (783) in 1918, off Guam, drifted 1,300 miles in 24 days to the island of Samar. Their water stores ran out and there was scarcely any for the last nine days. When they reached the stage where the tongue was dry and the lips cracked and the mouth was irritated from repeated rinsings with salt water to cool the mouth and throat, unrest grew. On the thirteenth day, under the provocation of the hot sun, some of the men began to drink sea water, a process which, once started, seemed impossible to stop. When one man's throat became so dry that his endless profanity ceased to come forth, he would gulp down salt water until he could again start talking.[15] The men were described as maddened by hunger and thirst and driven to cannibalism (p. 337).

The *Trevessa*. Foster (267), captain of the shipwrecked *Trevessa*, logged a 1,700 mile voyage in open boats in the Indian Ocean in 1923. From previous experience with shipwreck, Foster thought that thirst could be "kept down" by drawing sea water into the nostrils and blowing it out again, and also by keeping the face and head wet (p. 152) but not taking sea water into the mouth. The men sucked small lumps of coal and buttons, thinking the latter helped to keep the mouth clean. Nevertheless all had a horrible taste in the mouth, and the mouth and tongue were thickly coated with white slime. They desired water not merely to revive themselves but also to clean their mouths of the slime; and there never seemed to be enough for this purpose. When salivary flow ceased, the men could chew biscuits and blow them out of their mouths, dry as dust (337). To catch rain, the hair was pulled down over the face and the water allowed to run through it, down a tin chute held under the chin, into an empty biscuit tin.

---

[15] Tiira (786) also lost his voice in this way but found it hard to swallow water when he was parched (see pp. 377, 387, 411ff.).

The *Rooseboom*, Etc. At midnight, March 1, 1942, the Dutch steamer *Rooseboom*, halfway between Padang in Sumatra and Ceylon, was torpedoed. A single lifeboat from this vessel, built for 28 but choked at the start with 80 castaways, men and women, traveled 1,000 miles in 26 days in the Indian Ocean. Gibson (290), one of four survivors, has described uriposia, hemoposia, and anthropophagy[16] attending what must rank along with that of the *Medusa* (p. 246) as one of the most frightful episodes of water deprivation known to man.

He observed that the drinking of urine, once started, became imitative. At first taste he found urine nauseating. Mixed with salt water, it seemed to improve; but later it tasted like gasoline, became intolerable, and was abandoned. Others also have terminated uriposia through disgust (506).

Other accounts of thirsty castaways include that of Trumbull (791) which tells of three fliers who covered 1,000 miles on a raft in 34 days, eating raw fish (including, reluctantly, shark) and birds; Tiira (786), adrift in the Indian Ocean and Straits of Malacca near the equator; and the article of Harby (331). The latter noted the claim of Lt. (jg) George H. Smith (733a), 20 days adrift, that greasing his mouth and throat with bird fat (31) enabled him to drink a pint of sea water daily for five days. However, when Smith began to drink sea water he was not badly dehydrated and rain came in time to relieve his condition. Harby also cited the cases of seaman Izzi (421, 567, 569) who survived chiefly starvation for 83 days on a life raft, his weight having dropped from 145 to 80 pounds, and of Poon Lim, Chinese steward of the torpedoed *Benlomond*, who was 133 days afloat and who has been called the world's champion survivor. Jones (402) noted the drinking of sea water by a castaway. It was said to help for a moment but not to satisfy thirst; no ill effects appeared to follow from such drinking except excessive purgation.

---

[16] See Critchley (190) for other references to the drinking of fresh blood, whether from seabirds or other animals, from dead men, or from the living; he also notes the licking of perspiration and the swallowing of fluid within giant blisters raised by the tropical sun. Whittaker (831) tells of the discussion of the Rickenbacker party as to the possibility of butchering themselves (i.e., cutting off the ball of the little finger, a piece of toe, etc.) to provide bait for catching fish.

It is difficult to obtain reliable information as to the water and salt intakes of individuals alleged to drink sea water along with rain water, fish juice, etc. Moreover, it is not difficult to misinterpret certain reports such as the following (881):

An interesting case of prolonged starvation was recently reported in the *Naval Military Surgeon* by Capt. P. Yeressko Jr. of the Naval Medical Corps of the Black Sea. Captain Yeressko left the Crimea in July 1942, when the Nazi troops invaded the peninsula, in a small boat with three comrades; they had only one small flask of fresh water and three cans of preserved fish for food. The crew rowed in turn during the first three days, but rowing soon became impossible. They decided to lie quietly without moving or speaking. The feeling of hunger was very strong for the first week, but later it diminished; nevertheless, the thoughts of the crew were continually about eating. By the end of the third day all fresh water was gone. Captain Yeressko proposed that they drink sea water, to which all four men gradually became accustomed. By chance it was noticed that tablets for chlorinating water gave it a somewhat better taste. Later the four men became so accustomed to sea water that on the fifth day all could drink about a quart and a half daily. However, when it was possible the crew enthusiastically drank rain water.

During the first fifteen days there was a keen feeling of starvation, backache, ache in the muscles of feet, fatigue, shortening of work capacity, reduction of weight, decrease of the pulse rate (about 56 per minute), decreased sweating, and dryness of the skin. These symptoms became more intense after the fifteenth day, and nervous and psychic symptoms such as hallucinations and loss of consciousness were added. The first member of the crew died on the nineteenth day, the second on the twenty-fourth day and the third on the thirtieth day of starvation. Captain Yeressko was rescued unconscious by a passing ship on the thirty-sixth day of starvation. He lost 22 Kg. during those five weeks. On the seventh day after rescue, when eating meat for the first time instead of the usual tea, gastric distress with diarrhea developed and was controlled only after treatment with hydrochloric acid and pepsin.

Although more than two years have passed, Captain Yeressko notes that fresh water and ordinary food still taste undersalted.

Unless it is recalled that the Black Sea contains only 1.8% salt and the Sea of Azov considerably less (Table XIII), this case may be mistakenly used to argue the merits of drinking "sea water." It is interesting to add that even volunteers who had been drinking sea water-fresh water mixtures for a few days in experimental studies (671) thought the taste of fresh water taken thereafter to be rather "flat."

TABLE XIII

Approximate surface salinity of various bodies of water (g./Kg. of sea water, $^0/_{00}$).

Aral Sea	10.2
Atlantic Ocean (near equator)*	35.7
Azov, Sea of (northern to southern parts)	1 to 16
Baltic Sea	7
Black Sea (generally)	18
Black Sea (near Danube mouth)	10 to 16
Caspian Sea	12 to 13
Dead Sea	280
Finland and Bothnia, Gulfs of	1 to 3
Indian Ocean (near equator)	35.1
Marmara, Sea of (central part)	21 to 22
Mediterranean Sea (eastern basin)	39.0 to 39.5
Mediterranean Sea (western basin)	37 to 38
Mediterranean Sea (near Gibraltar)	36
Pacific Ocean (near equator)	34.9
Persian Gulf	35 to 40
Red Sea	37 to 41
Suez, Gulf of	41

* For 60 to 120 miles off the mouth of the Amazon River the sea surface salinity maybe only 10 to 14$^0/_{00}$, but it rises rapidly beyond these distances and is "normal" at 200 miles (month of March).

The report of Haynes (338) on the sinking of the USS *Indianapolis* and the full story of Rickenbacker (655) are recounted in Part II. For additional material in this vein the reader is referred to Duncan (217), Farrell (251), Hunter (389), Wall (802), Hawkins (337), Skattebol (727), and Madden (506).

Diadermic Drinking

It is known that water can diffuse from the body through the skin as an insensible perspiration or transepidermal water loss (665), showing a certain permeability of the integument. Less clear is the factual basis of the old thesis, which recurs repeatedly in the literature of thirst, that water may be supplied to the body through the skin (176). Callenfels (150) stated that thirst is relieved by placing aqueous fluid on the skin, or by baths. He told of sailors castaway on the Pacific, who, wetting their garments with sea water, obtained some relief of their extreme thirst. Tiedemann (785) also mentioned baths as relieving thirst, but he did not specifically recommend sea water in this connection; he recognized sea water to be harmful, causing nausea, vomiting, diarrhea, and more thirst if drunk. Hallay (321), by "reasoning" alone, concluded:

> . . . . fresh water can be drunk through the dehydrated skin . . . . a survivor . . . . may be able to quench the thirst by immersing the body in sea water, which would result in absorption of the water without immediate incorporation of the sodium chloride . . . .

Critchley (190), however, presents a more sober view. Of imbibition of water by the skin he says the most superficial layers may take up water and become sodden—the process being maximal in 1 to 1.5 hours. It is greater in tepid or warm water than in cold, and less in sea water than in fresh water. But there is no evidence that the deeper layers of the skin take up water or that any appreciable quantity can pass into the blood vessels (6). A review of the question of percutaneous absorption of water is given by Rothman (665).

Nevertheless, in McGee's account (p. 387) is found the statement regarding a case of severe hydropenia—the "shriveled tongue phase"—that water was slushed over the victim's body and rubbed into his limbs and extremities. The skin first shed, then absorbed it "greedily as a dry sponge—or more exactly, as this season's rawhide. . . ." And Pujo's narrative (p. 415) is likewise relevant. These writings, of course, do not indicate that water is actually taken up systemically.

Whitehouse, Hancock, and Haldane (828) showed that the human subject in a bath of water evidences only slight absorption ("osmotic") of fluid through the skin. There is practically none from a bath of isotonic sodium chloride; and in 11.5 to 20% sodium chloride baths, water passes outward through the skin (ca. 30 g./hr.). The well known swollen and furrowed appearance of the skin on the fingers and toes was noticed in ordinary water and isotonic salt solution but not in 10% (586), 11.5%, and

20% saline. These studies have been criticized (151) but the results not refuted.

Pinson (615), in a review of water exchanges and barriers as studied by the use of hydrogen isotopes, reported that transfer of water vapor (traced by tritium) across the skin occurs from a saturated atmosphere at a rate approximating that at which water normally passes out through insensible perspiration. There is no difference in the rate of absorption if the skin is immersed in water. This suggests that even in the face of the osmotic gradient between tissue fluid on the one side and water on the other, no bulk filtration of water occurs (p. 18), at least in euhydration.

The separation of fresh from salt water by the skin is, physically as well as physiologically, a highly improbable process, involving as it must, the expenditure of "osmotic (concentration) work" (p. 244) by a membrane not noted for this characteristic. For practical purposes the integument of the dog appears to be impermeable both to water and sodium chloride as suggested by the following experiment. Skin from the thigh of a dog was removed in the form of a tube. Sealed at the ends by clamps and filled with nearly saturated sodium chloride solution, the skin sac was placed in tap or distilled water for two days. At no time during this period did an appreciable change in weight of the sac occur nor did salt appear in significant amounts in the ambient fluid (869).

Buettner (141a) has found that water may be gained by the skin of human hands or arms from solutions osmotically less concentrated than 5.5% sodium chloride; stronger solutions extract water from the skin. Since it would thus appear that water could be abstracted from sea water, he suggested that this process might be useful to shipwrecked individuals. But it is not clear how a steady state of water absorption through the skin could be sustained against the osmotic gradient from sea water outside the skin to body fluids inside the skin even if, as is noted, there may be a layer of high osmotic pressure below the skin surface.

As Portier (622) observed, the skin of marine mammals must be essentially impermeable in order to sustain the large differences in osmotic pressure which exist between their body fluids and sea water; at least the insignificant variations in weight undergone by these animals as a result of being transferred from fresh to salt water, or the reverse, is strongly suggestive on this point. Moreover, the skin lies over a thick layer of poorly vascularized blubber (256).

Sea Water Enemas

Even less tenable than diadermic drinking, on physiologic grounds, is the belief that the mammalian intestinal mucosa is able to extract fresh water from sea water. To be sure, the intestinal wall is permeable to water, and fresh water enemas can relieve thirst (494). But these facts make it even less likely that, when the intestinal wall separates body fluids from sea water, there can be effected a passage of water against an osmotic gradient.[17] Assuming the intestinal wall could to a degree selectively absorb water from strong saline, we should still have no evidence that any human membrane, including renal, can transport water against an osmotic gradient of salts equal to that between sea ("open ocean") water and body fluids, viz., a gradient of 700 mOs./Kg.

The history of the sea water enema may be said to have begun with the following letter by Mr. Morley Roberts (657) to the *British Medical Journal* in 1918:

In 1910 the idea occurred to me that death at sea from thirst when there was no fresh water could at any rate be postponed, and possibly altogether avoided, by rectal injections of pure seawater. I founded the view on the fact that when sea-water is actually drunk it sets up reverse peristalsis, locks up the pylorus in a tonic spasm such as occurs in acute abdominal cases, and hence is not absorbed; while hypotonic and isotonic injections, though unpleasant to drink and likely to cause vomiting, serve every purpose in subduing thirst. Thirst is in practice thus avoided when malignant disease or obstruction of the oesophagus prevents deglutition. I considered that the salines not needed by the blood plasm would be excreted by the kidneys, and that the heavy work thrown on them for short periods would be unlikely to damage them. I communicated these opinions to many medical men, and even to one medical paper—not the *British Medical*

---

[17] What may be the case of the intestinal mucosa of birds that drink sea water (p. 363ff.) remains to be seen.

Journal—in 1911, but was unable to get them published without some proof. One well-known physiologist who thought them rather interesting suggested I should try the experiment on myself. This I did not do for reasons with which I need not trouble you. I am, however, now in a position to quote evidence that my theoretical views were sound, and Mr. R. Graham, for whose bona fides many well-known men will vouch, has kindly permitted me to adduce it. The following are the facts:

While returning to England from the United States in 1916 he undertook a fast, and while fasting injected daily two gallons of pure sea-water. During the first five days he did not take anything whatever to drink, although on the fourth and fifth day he washed his mouth out with ordinary water. He did not feel in the least thirsty till the sixth day, when he took half a tumbler of water. Such thirst as he experienced was, however, very slight. On the seventh day he drank one and a half glasses of water, although he felt he could have gone without had he chosen to do so. During this period his pulse was normal, his general condition good, his strength well maintained, and though the injections resulted in the usual evacuation, there was no tendency to diarrhoea or any other disturbance. On the eighth day he resumed his normal life. I think there can be no doubt that these facts are highly important. Even this last year, owing to the U boat campaign, English seamen have died of thirst. With a Higginson syringe as part of a boat's normal equipment, I submit that such disasters could be avoided or, at the very least, postponed, thus affording castaways a better chance of being picked up.

The same mail which delivered Roberts' letter to the editors also brought one from Wherry (824) suggesting:

. . . . the injection of sea water into the lower bowel, if slowly done, would give some relief and prolong life in such cases. We use saline injections in our hospital wards with great advantage and the apparatus needed is of a simple kind:—a glass syringe or a rubber tube to be used as a siphon; the nozzle and bowl of a tobacco pipe in emergency might answer. As I cannot gather from any navigator that the plan has ever been tried, I make the suggestion as above for the slow injection of sea-water as an enema for absorption.

Interest in Roberts' suggestion grew slowly and continued for

years (223, 225, 664, 711, 805), resurging at the beginning of
World War II when the problem of castaways again came to the
fore. Pittard (616), basing his opinion on the text of Warbasse
and Smyth (805), and on an inconclusive experiment upon himself, gave credence to the allegations of Roberts respecting Mr.
Graham's "demonstration." It is of some interest to restate the
imaginative precepts of Warbasse and Smyth:

> In the absence of a fountain syringe, apparatus may be extem-
> porized. A bottle with its bottom removed, to act as a funnel; a
> piece of rubber, wooden or metallic tubing; a tobacco pipe; or a
> piece of rubber cloth or tarpaulin, rolled into a tube about a piece
> of spirally wound wire, may be used for insertion into the rectum
> for the purpose of introducing the sea water. A funnel may be
> extemporized from any of the above mentioned materials. For
> lubricating purposes, grease, oil, soap, saliva or other glairy or
> viscid fluid may be used.
> When no material for constructing a tube is at hand the individ-
> ual may be placed in the exaggerated knee-chest position with the
> anus in the superior position; the anus may be opened by means of
> three or four lead pencils, pegs, or rolls of cloth of a similar size,
> inserted about 5 or 6 cm. (2 or $2^1/_2$ inches), and salt water poured
> through the interstices. If no such apparatus is available two
> fingers may be inserted into the rectum, slightly separated, and the
> water poured between. If no receptacle is to be had the water
> may be dipped up in the hand.
> An ingenious person who is alone should be able to carry out one
> of these technics upon himself. Where several persons are to-
> gether, at least one should master the technic. The operation
> should be carried out with great patience and gentleness. The
> best possible cleanliness should be observed. Extemporized ap-
> paratus should be smooth and not permitted to cause abrasions.
> If the skin and mucous membrane are not wounded it is possible
> to teach the anal sphincter to relax under slight outward pressure.
> The amount of sea water introduced should if possible be a meas-
> ured quantity, so that the operation may be carried out regularly
> and with scientific accuracy, according to the above principles of
> proctoclysis. No person should go to sea without this knowledge.

Subsequently, attempts to assess these claims were made. Foy,
Altmann, and Kondi (270), noting that by 1942 there had been

little actual evidence for or against the therapeutic value of sea water enemas, studied six volunteers. Deprived of water for 80 hours, three received enemas and three were controls. It was proposed to use sea water containing 2.8% chloride as sodium chloride in volumes of 1,500 cc. per day, divided in five to six doses; but it was found impossible for this quantity to be retained. The maximum retention in 24 hours was 1,300 cc. and two of the three sea water subjects returned 150 to 200 cc. more from the rectum than they received. Thereafter, four doses of 200 cc. were given per day but these could be retained only with the greatest effort. Roberts' commended use of two gallons daily, they remarked, "seems to us absolutely fantastic."

In any case, no clinical difference between the two groups of subjects was found. All had decreasing pulse rates and a tendency to lowered blood pressure. None had "thirst-fever." Thirst and objective signs of dehydration (dry mouth, sunken eyes, unelastic skin) were the same in both groups. Sea water (salt) was believed to have been absorbed as shown by higher plasma and urinary chloride concentrations in the experimental group. Chloride excretion was also greater in that group as was the urine flow (2,000 cc./day compared with 1,400 cc./day in controls); and the sea water group lost an average of 10 pounds per person compared with 6 pounds in controls. It was concluded that enemas of sea water were of little or no value in maintaining water balance (265).

Adolph, Wolf, and Kelly (24), cited by Pearson (603), came to similar conclusions from studies on themselves and two dogs. Sea water was not observed to become more concentrated in chloride while in the rectum; usually it became more dilute, but this does not necessarily reflect differential absorption of solutes to water.[18] One test showed marked absorption of chloride and urinary excretion of it in a dog. They considered the procedure

---

[18] It may reflect admixture of sea water with essentially isotonic fluid in feces. Bradish *et al.* (124) instilled sea water both rectally and into one distal, completely divided portion of a colostomy, in the latter case with no water loss or fecal contamination. Such enemas became more dilute in chloride with time indicating the colon does not concentrate sea water. No subjects showed diminution of thirst, but seemed to get progressively worse (headache, weakness, fogging of mental processes). Cramps prevented retention of 600 cc. of fluid in the rectum.

to be of no benefit, or deleterious, to the individual, even though he be dehydrated. Actually, most individuals are unable to hold appreciable quantities of sea water in the rectum or colon long enough to absorb much, and the procedure recommended by Pittard was said to rest without foundation.

Allison and Critchley (33) injected sea water rectally in two patients with diabetes insipidus. The procedure gave no relief of thirst and produced great discomfort.

One further report (227) cited an experiment on a young man without food or water. On the third day of his total fast, while hungry and thirsty, he was given a slow proctoclysis of artificial sea water. Cramps set in by 30 minutes and there was expulsion of some of the fluid before all could be administered. The procedure was continued later, thirst became worse, and analysis of expelled material showed it more dilute than the administered fluid.

An editorial (226) reviewing this question stated, "Graham must have had an exceptional mucosa." The British Medical Research Council Committee on the Care of Shipwrecked Personnel concluded the sea water enema was harmful (538).

Sea Water Drinking: Testimony, Tests, and Opinions

Good (296) presented a clinical evaluation of five survivors who had been 15 days adrift on a raft. He obtained testimony that drinking sea water in "great quantities" was followed by irrationality. One man who drank copiously of sea water two days before rescue drank an abundance of fresh water after rescue such that on the second day following, both feet became edematous. After the edema cleared up in the next three days there still persisted some polydipsia. No one who had abstained from drinking sea water developed edema. When dehydrated sailors have been rescued, it is a common experience for them to show polydipsia and polyuria for the ensuing two or three weeks (190).

Mitscherlich and Mielke (551) took note of Nazi experiments in sea water drinking. Several witnesses at the Nuremberg trials gave accounts of investigations which were conducted at Dachau in the summer of 1944 under the direction of Beiglböck:

Individually the patients [gypsies] suffered from gnawing hunger and dreadful thirst, which was only made worse by drinking salt water. This thirst was so intense that some patients did not shrink from drinking the dirty water used in mopping the floors . . . . from the first day to the last, the participants were issued salt water four to five times daily to the total quantity of a pint. The forty-four persons were subdivided into five or six groups. Two groups received pure sea water, two others pure sea water with an added salt preparation, the remaining group received distilled water without addition. From the outset daily blood specimens were drawn from the participants. In individual patients weakness and especially thirst took such extreme forms that only after a few days they could no longer leave their beds. In one case I remember that the patient broke out into paroxysms of screaming.

Futcher, Consolazio, and Pace (273) reported the effects of taking sea water in three men:

Subject 1—On the first day this man drank a liter of sea water (1 to 2 g. of citric acid added per liter to make it more palatable) in 8 hours; this resulted in sensations of marked peristaltic activity. He awoke very thirsty on the second day. In the course of half an hour he drank 300 cc. of sea water and almost immediately passed a watery stool. Despite this he drank another 500 cc. of sea water in the next hour, with resultant nausea, and the passage of another liquid stool, accompanied by intestinal griping . . . . At the end of 3 hours of the second day he had drunk a liter of sea water. During the afternoon his bowels moved twice more with tenesmus, and he experienced a gradually increasing occipital and orbital headache. Thirst was severe in the evening, as was hunger. Sleep was very broken. During days 1 and 2 he had ingested 100 g. of peanut butter, 21 g. of "Charms" (candy) and 280 g. of matzos (salt free crackers). On the third day, the headache persisted, and the subject was irritable. Attempts to drink more sea water resulted in vomiting. During the day he felt moderately weak, and noted moderate thirst and hunger, but made no further attempt to eat or drink. Thirst was severe during the night of this third day. The subject experienced no untoward experiences during the breaking of the fast on the fourth day. (Total sea water drunk, 2,000 cc.)

Subject 2—This man chose to drink sea water only when thirsty. During the first day he drank 620 cc. of sea water; throughout the day he had a frequent desire to pass a (liquid) stool. The morning of the second day, after drinking 150 cc. of sea water, he passed involuntarily a small amount of liquid stool. During this second day he ingested 210 cc. of sea water, having experienced slight thirst and dryness of the mouth in the evening, with broken sleep. On the third day he drank only 60 cc. of sea water; he passed a formed stool in the evening. He experienced no marked thirst at any time; during the third day there was moderate fatigue incurred by the ordinary laboratory duties. Intake of food during the three days was 93 g. of "Charms," 42 g. of plum pudding, and 26 g. of peanut butter; there was little appetite. He experienced less lassitude than during a previously reported experiment when he forced himself to drink a liter or more of 3.5% solution of sodium citrate daily. At the end of the third day of the present experiment he felt that he could continue on his regime (which was essentially one of water deprivation plus small amounts of sea water) for several more days. (Total sea water drunk, 890 cc.)

Subject 3—On the first day this subject drank 400 cc. of sea water (citrate added as above) in divided amounts. He experienced no thirst. Early in the second day, before ingesting any food, he drank 200 cc. of sea water and immediately passed a stool, the last part being watery. During the whole day he was thirsty, although a total of 800 cc. of sea water was consumed. There were persistent intestinal rumblings and calls to stool, which were allowed to go unanswered. Facial pallor was noticeable. On the third day thirst was marked, but was unrelieved by drinking sea water; during this day 1,200 cc. of sea water was drunk. The subject did not feel fatigued as on the second day, however. A call to stool was frequent though unanswered. Sleep was disturbed during the night of the third day. During the experiment he consumed 33 g. of "Charms," 112 g. of matzos, 49 g. of peanut butter, and 80 g. of plum pudding; as thirst and dryness of the mouth increased, only Charms and plum pudding could be swallowed with any ease. At the close of the experiment the subject believed he could persist on the regimen for another two or three days, but did not feel sure he could prevent diarrhea. (Total sea water drunk, 2,400 cc.)

Sundry Views: Rationing Water. Scientific consensus holds pure sea water to be a nonpotable liquid, a cogent view which has been most detailed and best epitomized by McCance and his associates (347, 348, 352, 523, 526, 527). Thus, if "open ocean" water is osmotically equivalent to 3.2% sodium chloride (Table XII) and if the salt concentration of human urine cannot exceed the equivalent of 2% sodium chloride (Table XX), then a man drinking 100 cc. of sea water would have to eliminate 160 cc. of urine in order to remove all of the ingested salt by the renal emunctory. He would thereby suffer a net loss of 60 cc. of water. Ignoring minor defects in these premises (p. 301), we infer that if the man did not lose all of the ingested salt he might (1) sustain a salt excess which would steadily augment for the worse with continued sea water drinking and (2) suffer a higher than normal concentration of salt in his body fluids which, as is known, tends to provoke thirst (16a, 526, 867).

An almost opposite view, discussed later, holding that physiologic advantage may be derived from drinking sea water has been represented by Bombard (112, 113), Aury (60, 60b), and Longuet (488a), and may be inferred from Willis (839). While the polarity of these views is by no means absolute, an important middle ground which has not been adequately investigated would recommend that sea water be admixed with fresh water for the purpose of extending the total ration, as for example, Heyerdahl (357) has suggested. The use of fish juice (113, 387, 531) is, in some ways, a special case of admixture (p. 331).

Biske (103) inquired if it would not be advantageous to determine to what extent fresh water might be admixed with sea water before becoming undrinkable. Since isotonic salt is approximately 1%, and "open ocean" contains total salts to about 3.5%, he supposed it might be 2 or 3 parts of fresh to 1 part of sea water which would serve to eke out supplies of fresh water. Moreover, he supposed that slightly salted water might be a better drink than fresh, where perspiration is heavy.

Ratios of 6:1 to 4:1, and 1:1, of fresh to sea water have been suggested (167, 230, 483, 832). Pond (620) stated that a man can drink brackish water, that is "water with half as much salt as sea water—and get a net gain of moisture for the body." This contention is based on the fact that maximal urinary salt concentration may exceed half the salt concentration of sea water; it makes no allowance for insensible water loss. It was intended to suggest that brackish water (p. 326), possibly up to half strength sea water, should not necessarily be discarded in emergencies (p. 272ff.); there are records of sea castaways who threw away their fresh water supplies because sea water had splashed into them (620a). The ratio of 240 cc. of sea water to 400 cc. of fresh water per day diminishes or prevents nitrogen retention (456).

It is interesting to recall Heyerdahl's account[19] (358) of the *Kon-Tiki* in this regard:

> When tormented by thirst in a hot climate, one generally assumes that the body needs water, and this may often lead to immoderate inroads on the water ration without any benefit whatever. On really hot days in the tropics you can pour tepid water down your throat till you taste it at the back of your mouth, and you are just as thirsty.[20] It is not liquid the body needs then, but, curiously enough, salt. The special rations we had on board included salt tablets to be taken regularly on particularly hot days, because perspiration drains the body of salt. We experienced days like this when the wind had died away and the sun blazed down on the raft without mercy. Our water ration could be ladled into us till it squelched in our stomachs, but our throats malignantly demanded much more. On such days we added from 20 to 40 per cent of bitter, salt sea water to our fresh-water ration and found, to our surprise, that this brackish water quenched our thirst.[21] We had the taste of sea water in our mouths for a long time afterward but never felt unwell, and moreover we had our water ration considerably increased.
>
> One morning, as we sat at breakfast, an unexpected sea splashed into our gruel and taught us quite gratuitously that the taste of oats removed the greater part of the sickening taste of sea water!

On the other hand, on Shackleton's last expedition to the Antarctic, he and his men became dependent upon water which had turned brackish in its breaker from the entrance of some sea water. He wrote (714):

---

[19] From *Kon-Tiki: Across the Pacific by Raft.* Copyright 1950 by Thor Heyerdahl.

[20] See Note 34, Chapter II.

[21] Albrecht (27) observed that rats brought nearly to the point of water intoxication manifested no specific urge to drink sea water, though presumably it would have been to an animal's advantage to increase its salt intake.

Thirst took possession of us. I dared not permit the allowance of water to be increased since an unfavorable wind might drive us away from the island and lengthen our voyage by many weeks. Lack of water is always the most severe privation that men can be condemned to endure, and we found, as during our earlier voyage, that the salt water in our clothing and the salt spray that lashed our faces made our thirst grow quickly to a burning pain. I had to be very firm in refusing to allow any one to anticipate the morrow's allowance, which I was sometimes begged to do. We did the necessary work dully and hoped for the land . . . . Our mouths were dry and our tongues were swollen . . . . but any thought of our peril from the waves was buried beneath the consciousness of our raging thirst.

When Macdonald (501) wrote a letter to the *British Medical Journal* stating that Bombard's advice to drink sea water (p. 269) was not backed by any acceptable evidence that our present concepts of renal function are inaccurate, and that Bombard's own evidence was unsatisfactory and contradictory, he pointed out that such heterodox opinions had caused alarm among those who had responsibilities in advising on survival policy. McIlrath (536) replied by letter, citing evidence from *Kon-Tiki* and observing that one should not ignore the need for salt replacement which might well be met by a certain amount of salt water.

Chapman (167), basing his remarks on two investigations cited in brief, recommended for temperate climates a mixture of sea to fresh water of 1:5.7 to save some fresh water. Without reviewing his experiments, we may observe that they reflect a type of reasoning frequently applied to this problem. He imagined that since the kidneys put out 450 cc./day of 2% salt, then no matter the dehydration, any volume of sea water (3.5%)[22] less than 257 cc./day should be adequately handled with respect to salt $(450 \times 2 = 257 \times 3.5)$. And he objected to a letter of Hervey (347), in reply to McIlrath (536), which categorically rejected the idea that any real benefit should be ascribed to the use of sea water.

The idea of replacing salt is not relevant to castaways, Hervey

---

[22] Sea water containing approximately 3.5% total salt is osmotically the equivalent of only 3.2% sodium chloride (Table XII).

said, because they would seldom (unlike on *Kon-Tiki*) have adequate water supplies.[23] Elkinton and Winkler (234) have stated also that persons can drink little if any pure sea water without becoming further dehydrated, although indefinitely large amounts can be taken if sufficient diluted with fresh water. Again, replying to Chapman, Hervey (348) considered that individual's experiments inconclusive, but agreed with him that nothing is to be gained by "spinning out" a small fresh water ration unduly; and he reiterated the view that even limited amounts of sea water are harmful.

Whillans and Smith (825) experimented with human subjects taking 10 ounces of sea water and 16 ounces of fresh water per day and compared them with controls taking 16 ounces of fresh water alone. Both groups had food rations. It was reported that subjects felt the extra supplementary sea water to result in less loss of stamina and to facilitate chewing and swallowing of rations. Also, their subjects supposed that if they were in a dinghy at sea, and had only a small supply of fresh water, they would drink sea water along with fresh. No significant differences in blood sodium and chloride were shown between the two groups. Saliva had become almost solid in consistency toward the end of the six day test and had a distinctly foul taste and odor. After the tests, subjects showed rapid recovery. Slight epigastric discomfort, consisting mainly of a feeling of distention and occasionally of burning, was noted during the first day after the experiment (thought due to mechanical dilatation of stomach by unaccustomed volume of food and fluid).

Ladell (458, 460) has also presented a case for drinking sea water, qualified in that his recommendations were made with object to maintain survivors in the highest possible physical condition for 7 to 10 days, and not to prolong over-all survival time (p. 288ff). Ladell does not wish to overemphasize the possibility of benefit from drinking sea water in small quantities and agrees

---

[23] The desalting kits used by the U. S. Armed Forces (Fig. 31, p. 242ff.), and on some private yachts, are intentionally designed to leave the purified sea water with approximately one-tenth of the original salt content since experiments showed a more favorable water balance to result from ingestion of such fluid than of distilled water (178). Also, there is a favorable reduction in the amount of chemical needed to desalt the sea water, when this salt residue is allowed.

that although no immedate deleterious effects may follow from drinking small, strictly limited quantities of sea water, it is highly dangerous to exceed these limits. The theory behind this recommendation is that sea water intake may have the effect of sustaining blood volume at the expense of cellular fluid for an initial period, cellular dehydration appearing not to cause much physical disability until it becomes gross (488a, p. 292). (However, serious hyperdipsia may accompany cellular dehydration.) Ladell stated (460):

> The real touchstone of sincerity in this matter is for the worker himself to say what he would do if he found himself adrift with the Board of Trade water ration of 112 oz. (240 ml./day for 14 days). If my chances of being picked up at all depended on my keeping fit and alert for the first week I would certainly drink some sea-water, but not more than 250 ml./day. If my chances of rescue depended on my remaining alive for the maximum length of time I would avoid sea-water. I would refrain from drinking anything at all for the first 24 hours, or until my urine had become concentrated and my excretory rate was down to 0.5 ml./min., as any water taken before this point is reached is lost in a diuresis. If allowed, I would drink most of my allotted water in the first 10 days. I would refuse protein or salty foods such as pemmican. My own ideal shipwreck ration would be 75% carbohydrate and 25% fat, the latter for palatability and interest, important even on a 500-calorie daily diet. As air temperatures at sea level are the same as the water temperature, which rarely exceeds 29° C. even in the Indian Ocean, provided there was some shelter from the sun (most important in a lifeboat), and I was not rowing, I would be unlikely to sweat no matter where I was. But if I did sweat, I would, paradoxically it must seem to Dr. McIlrath . . . . immediately stop taking sea-water. Sweat is only about one-third as concentrated as body water; hence when body water is lost as sweat two-thirds of the salt that was dissolved in it remains in the body, further increasing the concentration. Losing a litre of sweat is roughly the equivalent of taking 5 or 6 g. of salt, which would indeed hasten the onset of lethal intracellular dehydration.

Ladell (458) had previously found that the water ration of 8 ounces per day referred to above led, experimentally, to rapid deterioration[24] (p. 288ff.). In actual practice there have been cases where survivors succumbed to water lack while on this ration, lifeboats being found with people dying of thirst while there was still water in the breakers; in other cases, self-denial of water had been carried to the point where death could have occurred with water on hand (483).

Ladell has suggested the following plan for rationing water at sea: Day 1, no water;[25] days 2 to 6, 18 ounces (512 cc.) per day; thereafter, the remaining 22 ounces (625 cc.) to be given in token quantities only, e.g., 2 ounces per day to maintain morale. On the token intake only, deterioration was not so rapid as expected, suggesting that there might be some acclimatization or habituation to water lack in slow dehydration (p. 209), while in rapid dehydration, there is not time for this and weight loss is sometimes greater than expected.[26]

Obviously, at high effective temperatures where no protection from the sun is afforded, this time scale cannot be considered valid (539). Water loss augments steeply with increase in air temperature and insolation (Fig. 39) and certain physical relations govern this loss in a fixed manner. For example, when ambient temperature is greater than the mean skin-lung temperature (p. 227), the only way in which metabolic heat can be dissipated from the body is by the evaporation of water which requires about 0.58 Calories per gram of water vaporized (386). In order

---

[24] According to U. S. Coast Guard regulations, lifeboats fitted on vessels in ocean and coastwise service are required to be equipped with three quarts (U. S.) of water, and two pounds of food, per person. These provisions are required to be packaged in hermetically sealed cans approved by the Coast Guard. British regulations call for similar water stores (538); Hunter (387) states that 500 cc./day is allocated per person in naval survival practice.

[25] Shipwrecked personnel have been thought almost invariably not to desire to eat or drink for the first 24 hours (733a, p. 429); in any case the establishment of bradyuria (p. 15) appears to be desirable so that water will not be wasted in diuresis or as a facultative urine volume.

[26] It is interesting, and possibly germane, to note Kenney's (411) observation that water may be saved by subjects exercising in humid heat if small volumes are taken at frequent intervals rather than larger volumes less frequently. Thus, there may be a most economical method of rationing a given water supply (462), but this has only been ascertained where water debts were small, the period of observation of subjects was only 90 minutes, and the water supply was one liter. It remains to be tested for other circumstances.

to prevent body temperature from rising it is necessary, therefore, that approximately 1,730 cc. of water be evaporated for each 1,000 Calories gained either by insolation, metabolism, or otherwise. There is no way to reduce this water loss without impairment of body efficiency (18). This irreducible physicochemical fact precludes any possibility of "training" or acclimatization with a view to getting along with less water for indefinitely protracted periods. At high temperature, water loss is mandatory. Hence the value of cooling by wetting the clothes with water, keeping in shade if possible, and avoiding unnecessary exertion (571). Unfortunately, after the first day or two, salt water may sting and irritate the body surface (831) particularly if one is sunburned.

In one way, and it may so seem from a "physiologic" point of view, the quantity of water taken per day is the essence of a water ration (p. 227). Yet, when supplies of water are quite short, it has often been felt that the manner in which they are consumed is important (p. 248). Skattebol (727) stated:

> We found that the best way to get the most out of three ounces of water was to take a tiny sip at a time, keeping each sip in the mouth for half a minute or so before allowing it to trickle down the throat. Objectively it would seem that three ounces were three ounces, and that it made no difference how fast these were sent into the system. But actually the pain of thirst is concentrated in the mouth and throat, and it is better to give it direct relief in this way than indirect relief by swallowing the water quickly.

Volhardt and Schütte (801) felt that mariposia might be unobjectionable under certain conditions, if pure water is obtainable to control threatening symptoms; and that the danger and horror of such experiments are greatly exaggerated. They studied several groups of people on a dry diet to which was added 500 cc. of sea water daily for approximately five days. On the first day sea water was repelling. Thirst began that day (evening). On the second day thirst was greater, the mouth was dry, there was a diminished antipathy to sea water, and bradycardia developed, reaching 46 beats/min. On the third day not much change was observed and the desire to drink could easily be suppressed. There was a strong urge to rinse the mouth. Sea water drinking was now a pleasure. Appetite slackened, bradycardia continued.

On the fourth day the mouth was so dry that food could not be taken without sea water. Subjects were apathetic. The fifth day saw paresthesias, twitching of calf muscles. On the sixth day the dry mouth burned and there was loss of appetite. In one of the older subjects, albuminuria (0.5%) was manifest on the third day. Urinary chloride, expressed as sodium chloride, was said to be 2.3 to 2.6%; the 24 hour specific gravity, 1.033 to 1.038. Daily weight loss of 600 to 1000 grams was essentially a water loss. Plasma chloride rose an average of 4%.

Bombard's Voyage: Aury's Experiments. A most active proponent of the idea that sea water not only can but should be used by castaways has been Bombard (112, 113), a French physician who set out to determine what procedures would help to insure survival when one is adrift. Bombard conceived that he could drink one and one-half pints of sea water per day since this contained the "permissible daily intake of salt," a belief with no foundation whatever in physiology, disregarding as it does consideration of the relative quantities of salt and water in sea water. He argued further that sea water should be drunk early by the castaway, if fish have not been caught to supply juice, to prevent dehydration.

The relief of absolute dehydration, regardless of the state of relative dehydration, may indeed have some importance for survival as Ladell has suggested (p. 266) and as Barker and Adolph (73, p. 290) have shown in rats. It is not unlikely that, within limits, the keeping up of the extracellular and blood volumes has an effect on sustaining physical strength, if not on over-all survival time.

In any case, armed with his conviction that the sea provides sufficient food and drink to enable the battle for survival to be fought with perfect confidence (p. 332ff.), and to test his theory, Bombard and a companion set forth in the Mediterranean in a dinghy appropriately name *l'Hérétique*. From Monte Carlo on May 25, 1952 in an 18 day journey to Minorca they drank sea water (10 days) and fish juice (four days) squeezed from the flesh of sea perch in a fruit press. They also ate sea perch during these four days and made good use of the pint or so of fresh water which condensed on the bottom of the boat at night. Bombard did not find thirst a problem and stated it was a bearable one for his companion until he drank a few mouthfuls of sea water; the day following his thirst had gone. They did not vomit and had no diarrhea but rather constipation. Bombard had not a single bowel movement for 11 days. Whatever might be the diarrheic effect of sea water taken on land,[27] at sea, he alleged, it was not laxative (see also Willis' statement, p. 273).

The raft was then shipped to Tangier from whence Bombard took it over alone, making Casablanca and then the Canary Islands. On October 19, he left Las Palmas alone in *l'Hérétique* and drifted across the Atlantic to Barbados. This voyage took 65 days during which time he subsisted on fish, fish juice, rain water, and some sea water. Unfortunately, it is impossible to tell from his accounts just how much of the various fluids were taken; indeed, on the 52nd day the S. S. *Arakaka* took him aboard whereupon he had a meal. However, he stated that for three weeks at sea he took no fresh water but only fish juice, which quenched his thirst. He ate about 100 g. per day of plankton[28] to supply vitamin C (p. 334) and regularity of bowel movement. His attacks of diarrhea on the Atlantic were said to be independent of sea water drinking.

During the Atlantic voyage he lost 55 pounds in weight and suffered various "minor ills" (p. 333). He became anemic, his erythrocyte count dropping from five million at the start to two and one-half million on arrival. His blood pressure seemed to vary with his spirits, being maximum with hope and minimum with despair and exhaustion. He was wracked by diarrhea for 14 days from November 26th, with sizable hemorrhages. His skin became dehydrated and a rash covered his whole body. He lost his toenails and developed serious defects of vision and loss of muscular tone; and he was hungry. "But I got there." .... "I had conquered the menace of thirst at sea." (112).

---

[27] Sea water has been drunk since olden times, indeed, by the ancient Romans (295a), for therapeutic ends, chiefly as a purgative. It is still used today, notably in certain German resorts on the North and Baltic Seas.

[28] Heyerdahl (357, 358) ate plankton which tasted like shrimp paste if made up chiefly of copepods, or like caviar or oysters if composed largely of eggs. Four of the six men of the raft, *Kon-Tiki*, liked it; the others didn't like sea food.

Aury (60, 60a) has reported results of studies in which men, experimentally "adrift" on rafts off the St. Raphael Naval Air Base and off Dakar drank sea water in regulated doses, 50 cc. portions taken 10 times per day, one portion every hour and a half. Sea water was reportedly easy to drink in this way, with or without emergency rations of food. In one experiment of three days duration, three men found no nausea, diarrhea, or thirst.

In all, 12 volunteers made two, three, and four day studies of this sort with similar results. On the basis of these essentially uncontrolled studies, Aury conceived that the "prejudice" about the harmfulness of sea water used temporarily (up to five days) must disappear; and that it might be useful to instruct on the benefits to which men could attain by a reasonable consumption of sea water in case of necessity. He felt that the notion that ingestion of sea water necessarily entails digestive troubles was not valid.

No comparison was made between the effects of taking such small quantities of sea water[29] and of taking no water, or with taking similar quantities of fresh water. Although it was admitted there may be a point beyond which sea water drinking could be dangerous, these far reaching and serious conclusions about the value of such ingestion are hardly proved experimentally, particularly the notion that more sea water might be permissible in a hot than in a temperate climate (460, Fig. 42, p. 324). It should be noted that these experiments were conducted at relatively low ambient temperatures: 7.2° C. at night to 16° during the day in one experiment (although the thermal insulation of the tented raft made for higher temperatures); 15.2° to 24.6° in another. Chapman (166) has also observed that at air temperatures of 12° to 13° C., thirst was not a constant factor in men on limited water (average 300 cc./day) and food intake until the sixth day of deprivation. And Llano (483) states that in the cold, men went 12 to 80 hours without thirst.

---

[29] Gibson (290), survivor of a 26 day lifeboat voyage (p. 250) in the Indian Ocean observed that those who drank sea water in tiny quantities seemed to suffer no ill effects, but the effect of drinking large quantities was coma from which one never emerged except crazed or suicidal.

Aury's uncontrolled experiments were repeated under laboratory conditions by Longuet (488a) who accords generally with the former's conclusions (60b). Longuet states that one ought to drink sea water from the first day (of shipwreck) even if he has a fresh water supply. If he has not drunk at all for three or four days, then it is thought dangerous for him to drink sea water.

Willis' Voyage. William Willis (839, 840), seaman, undertook a remarkable 115 day, 6,700 mile voyage on a raft, the *Seven Little Sisters,* as an adventure of the spirit. His only companions were a cat and a parrot. Sixty-one years old, "in the full strength of body and mind, I wanted to put myself to the great test, the test to which each man must put himself sometime. I would test myself in endless labor and sleeplessness, on primitive, scanty food, in exposure to the elements that I loved, in the terrors of loneliness and, like a soldier in battle, living under continual threat of death. And this thought also inspired me: I would perhaps contribute some knowledge about survival at sea."

Willis sailed his raft from Callao, Peru to Pago Pago, Samoa June 23 to October 15, 1954. On August 6, 45 days out, he discovered the greater part of his water supply to have been lost through the corroded seams of the water cans. He then had 36 quarts of fresh water left; at two and a half of his cups per quart, 90 cups. This was far less than the cup a day he had counted on for the duration of an initially estimated 200 day voyage.

He considered that he might squeeze a little water out of the flesh of the smaller fish he caught, but only a little; and knew that if he cut a hole in the sides of the big ones—50 pounds or more— "fresh" water from their flesh would slowly fill it. That might help some; but there were days when he did not get a bite.

However, he recalled that many old sailors took sea water as a laxative, and recollected that the capacity to drink sea water seemed to vary with men. From experience he knew he could drink some without ill effects and, believing he did not have enough fresh water to keep himself going, he felt he had to try drinking sea water. In view of certain errors in the newspaper accounts (839) of his mariposic habits, the following composite of information is presented, based upon his book (840) and personal communications (841):

From August 6th to September 8th, when I was north of the Marquesas and had my first rain I drank from two to two and a half cups of salt water a day. During this time I drank about 30 cups of fresh water. On September 8th I collected seven gallons of rain water. I gathered up my cans and eagerly drank my fill. Together with the 60 left I had now about 130 cups of drinking water. From this time to the end of the voyage I drank approximately about one and one half cup of fresh water a day and about one to two cups of salt water.

I never drank less than two full cups a day and suffered not the slightest ill effects. I drank it only when really thirsty and just enough to quench my thirst. Fresh water I used sparingly—for coffee or flour paste, and now and then I took a sip . . . . Sea water did not cause undue thirst in me. I do not recall a single case of diarrhea during my voyage—I cannot even complain of looseness of stool.

The above figures are approximately correct. Throughout the voyage I was under great physical and mental strain, perhaps without realizing it fully, and my mind, also due to my primitive diet, was hardly in a condition to make tests. My faculty of mental concentration had quite a bit deteriorated. There were no doubt some days during my acute water shortage when I drank less than two cups a day but there were also days when I drank in excess of three cups. Perhaps I would have taken closer note of the amount of salt water consumed if I had considered it important. As I brought out in my book I have always been able to drink salt water and so could approach my dilemma without attaching any momentous importance to it. I took it in my stride after the first shock had worn off. This attitude eliminated entirely the sense of fear and of doing myself any bodily harm . . . . I wish to point out again that I practically use no salt. In earlier years and later on ships, while living in hot climates and doing extremely heavy labor and sweating enormously, I never used salt pellets in my drinking water.

Willis' food stores consisted chiefly of roasted and ground *cañihua* flour, a cereal growing in the Andes above the 12,000 foot level; similarly roasted and ground barley flour (*máchica*); and unrefined sugar (*chancaca* or *raspadura*). He also ate fresh fish before and after August 6th.

Critchley's Summary. In Critchley's monograph (190) on *Shipwreck-Survivors* we find the following:

. . . . Belief as to its [sea water's] toxicity is wide-spread and much of the clinical evidence is strongly corroborative. Experience shows that for a dehydrated person to drink sea-water, cut off from liberal supplies of fresh water which might serve as a diluent, is to risk delirium and death, perhaps within a few hours. This observation is not contradicted by the fact that men may on occasions drink sea-water without harm resulting; indeed, many who have been swimming in the water before reaching their lifeboat or raft, have in all probability swallowed many mouthfuls of sea-water. Of my series of 279 survivors nineteen have admitted that they deliberately drank sea-water (usually small amounts) while adrift, while another seven have gargled or rinsed their mouths with it. In spite of this, sea-water poisoning must be accounted, after cold, the commonest cause of death in shipwrecked sailors. One ascribes the death to sea-water ingestion rather than to simple lack of water, because it is probable that there comes a breaking point in a dehydrated person's resistance, when more or less consciously he succumbs to the temptation of drinking the fluid which is all around him.[30] This giving way of inhibition varies in time, occurring very early in Lascar seamen and late in the men of stouter morale, more especially if they are in a position of authority within the lifeboat. The drinking of sea-water is very difficult to control, as it is usually carried out furtively, after nightfall or during the process of bathing the head and face. Sometimes, a rag will be steeped in sea-water and then sucked.

The train of clinical events—when sea-water is taken by a very dehydrated subject—is immediate slaking, followed quite soon by an exacerbation of the thirst which will require still more copious draughts. The victim then becomes silent and apathetic ". . . with a peculiar fixed and glassy expression in the eyes." The condition of the lips, mouth and tongue worsens and a peculiarly offensive odour has been described in the breath. Within an hour or two delirium sets in, quiet at first, but later violent and unrestrained; consciousness is gradually lost; the colour of the face changes and froth appears at the corners of the lips. Death may

---

[30] Gibson (290, p. 250), one of a group of castaways, observed that some wildly imagined sea water was fresh and drank. Almost everyone experimented with drinking it.

take place quietly—and if at night-time—unnoticed; more often it is a noisy termination, and not infrequently the victim goes over the side in his delirium and is lost. Vomiting does not typically occur, neither does purgation, though it was mentioned as a complication by Peirce (1752) and in one of the survivors of the *Anglo-Saxon,* 1940.

Such a description is, of course, a composite one based upon the accounts afforded by a large number of laymen. One knows of no medical officer who has had the opportunity of observing the terminal phases. Two American Red Cross nurses, however, among this series, adrift for nineteen days in a small lifeboat, witnessed the behaviour of a lad of 17 who began to drink sea-water on about the third day. This he continued to do, on and off, surreptitiously. He became dazed and "peculiar" and afterwards delirious, dying on the fifteenth day after being comatose for seventy-two hours. There was incontinence but no suppression of urine. Both of the nurses were impressed by his strange bloated appearance, and the bright cherry-red colour of his lips. The tongue was heavily coated and the skin was clammy and cold. He held his jaws tightly clenched and would not accept or swallow the nourishment they tried to give him. They are satisfied that the mood of exitus did not resemble a uraemia, a condition with which they were familiar.

In some of the older accounts of shipwreck, we read of sea-water being mixed with other fluids to form a less toxic beverage. Thus, equal parts of brandy, salt-water and vinegar were tried by survivors from the S. S. *Tweed* (1846). The crew of the *Fattysalam* (1761) drank a mixture of three-parts of pig's blood with one of sea-water . . . .

McCance *et al.* (523, p. 325), in a valuable statistical analysis of the hazards to men in ships lost at sea in 1940–44, have reasonably demonstrated that the indiscriminate drinking of sea water is accompanied by a sizable rise in the death rate. Their report is based on interviews with, and abstracts of the depositions of, men who survived the loss of their ships. It includes investigations of the death rate of sea water drinkers compared with that of "controls" as a function of length of voyage, temperature of the sea, and amounts of fresh water issued per head per day. As they observe, actual proof that drinking sea water will hasten a man's end is clearly impossible to obtain in an experimental setting, but the information of their inquiry provides new evidence on this point.

PHYSIOLOGIC ANALYSIS OF MARIPOSIA: FOOD RATIONS

Diuresis normally following ingestion of water relates to the fact that a positive load of water is created along with a diminished tonicity of body fluids. Under these conditions, antidiuretic hormone disappears from the system with resulting water diuresis. Water diuresis usually does not follow drinking when the intake is insufficient to pay off an existing water debt. However, when sea water or saline is drunk, urine flow often increases in volume, presumably as a "saline diuresis."

Ladell (456, 458, 460) found an increase in urine flow when human subjects, totally or partially deprived of fresh water, drank up to 400 cc. of sea water daily. However, he showed that the body gained water in the transaction because the extra water lost in urine was less than the extra water taken as sea water. He also observed in these circumstances that nitrogen retention was diminished or prevented, possibly with some benefit to the man on a raft. Men drinking sea water, as compared with those taking no such supplement to a dry diet, had somewhat higher plasma chloride, and sodium (273), concentrations but outwardly showed no significant difference, both groups of men being on their feet at the end of 10 days when they had weight losses of 10 and 11% respectively. Ladell has emphasized the possibility that the drinking of sea water, while perhaps not to be recommended for any favorable influence on the time of survival (p. 266), may serve to keep one fit and alert for an initial period of perhaps a week. Presumably, this follows from the fact that the ingestion of sea water with its attendant hypertonicity and cellular dehydration serves to maintain extracellular and plasma volumes higher than they would be under conditions of enforced dehydration.

Gamble's (276, 277) discussion of the water requirements of castaways has also brought out the fact that, at least initially, sea water drinking does not cause a net withdrawal of fluid from the body (ecuresis) but rather a positive balance (emuresis); the increase in urine flow brought about by sea water ingestion does not offset the quantity taken in. Thus in a thirsting period a subject's urine flow averaged 501 cc./day. After drinking 500 cc. of sea water, the urine volume was 860 and not 1001 cc./day as would be the case were no water gained by the body.

In accord with certain animal experiments, Gamble assumes that a loss of 38 to 40% of body water marks the survival limit for dehydration by thirsting. For a 70 Kg. man this could be about 19 liters and, at the rate of a daily loss of 1300 cc., survival expectancy would be 14 days. This depends on the old assumption that a man contains 70% water rather than 60%. Actually, it is not known what the limit of absolute dehydration is. Rubner (672) gave it as 20 to 22% of the body water (p. 209). Adolph *et al.* (18) estimated the limit for man in the hot desert at a loss of water approximately one-fifth of the body weight (Table IX, p. 219) or one-third of the body water. But it may well be more when conditions of dehydration are slower, and less if sea water is drunk. We have noted earlier that Viterbi survived 17 days without water (p. 229ff.).

Gamble (277) reported that subjects taking sea water could drink no more than 500 to 600 cc./day without gastrointestinal disturbance. If the maximal concentration of urine were 1.4 osmolal under conditions of drinking sea water, the quantity of urine required to remove the solutes from a liter of sea water of osmolality 1.0 might appear to be approximately 0.71 liter, leaving 0.29 liter of urinary water "free." However, about half of the osmolality of the urine would be represented by urea and non-saline material with little effective osmotic pressure. In terms only of salt content, urine might be 0.6 osmolal (Table XX); and the fallacy of this argument in its simple form is clear (p. 307ff.). Gamble recognized this fact, pointing out also that ingestion of sea water sets up a process of alteration of the composition of intracellular fluid and of reduction of its volume relative to the volume of extracellular fluid. He wrote:

. . . . Whether or not this process, which will proceed gradually, is of such physiological disadvantage as to offset a small but valuable overall water gain from sea water we are quite unable to say.

Judging the evidence conservatively the verdict of legend against the ingestion of sea water by castaways would seem to be sustained.

Gamble also presented a most important evaluation of the use of limited quantities of glucose. When glucose is taken the losses of solutes normally incidental to the state of fasting are reduced by about one-half with corresponding reduction of obligatory urine volume. The absence of the abnormal solutes which derive from the ketosis of fasting produces some further reduction of the renal water requirement but does not alter expendable body water as determined by the extent of loss of normal solutes.

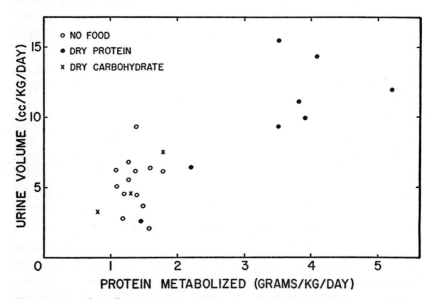

Figure 32. The effect on urine volume (water loss) of protein metabolism in dogs. See Fig. 33. After Danowski *et al.* (196).

It was shown that with 100 g. of glucose the reduction of the water (intake) requirement is 83 cc. or that one can substitute approximately 100 g. of glucose for 100 g. of water at almost no cost to the water exchange. Since 100 g. of glucose completely prevents ketosis, this substitution cannot be carried further. But there is a large saving of body fluids which reflects conservation ("sparing") of protein and reduction of catabolism almost by half (352, Fig. 43), with resulting extension of survival beyond the expectancy for fasting.[31] Indeed, with a carbohydrate ration, men deprived of water may early restrict below 100 cc. of urine per day (842).

There is also an important contribution to morale. The cheerfulness and sense of physical effectiveness of subjects given glucose

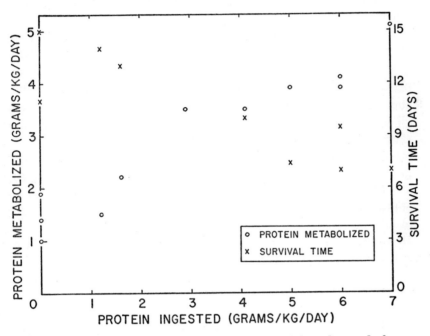

Figure 33. Protein metabolism and survival times of dogs deprived of water as a function of protein ingestion. Protein fed in excess of 1.5 g./Kg./day stimulates protein metabolism, accelerates urinary water loss (see Fig. 32), and shortens the period of survival. Ingestion of smaller amounts of protein fails to increase protein metabolism. After Danowski *et al.* (196).

---

[31] In starvation three grams of "preformed" water (87, 579) may be released from the destruction of each gram of tissue protein (19 grams with the liberation of each gram of nitrogen); one-tenth of a gram of water for every gram of body fat. If oxidation of each gram of protein is equivalent to the addition of 0.653 cc. of 52.5% urea solution (p. 117) then, in starvation, each gram of body protein utilized might yield 3.65 cc. of 9.4% urea solution. This exceeds the maximal urinary urea concentration in man. Moreover, water released when protein is destroyed is not "free" (p. 163) but contains electrolytes, and is a solution almost isosmotic with extracellular fluid. No account is here taken of the urinary water obligated by the ash of the protein, e.g., sulfate, phosphate (6).

contrasts with the unhappy lassitude of fasting; glucose prevents the "sour stomach" which may develop after the first day of fasting. Dry protein when eaten spares body protein but accelerates dehydration (Figs. 32, 33, p. 328). Gamble discussed also the finding that the loss of extracellular fluid incidental to fasting can be completely prevented by giving sodium chloride along with glucose.

Butler (147) recommended the use of a candy type ration, resembling butterscotch, containing only carbohydrate (80% glucose) and 15 to 20% fat (p. 266). Less nauseating, it is superior to carbohydrate alone (although it may not keep so well), and has a higher caloric and aqueous yield per gram ingested than glucose. Higher fat intakes may also lead to protein sparing (702).[32]

Life boats of commercial vessels are often considered to have "ample" storage space so that canned water rather than desalting kits (Fig 31, p. 243) may be stocked. It is possible that even this space could be put to better use by substituting glucose solution (867), or sucrose, for plain water. The specific volumes of these sugars are such that for a given weight dissolved in water, less than two-thirds their weight of water is displaced. Upon oxidation in the body a quantity of water almost equal to that displaced is formed so that little is sacrificed from the aquiferous store of fluid. Yet the nutritive and spiritual value of the sugar may be transcendent.

Glucose displaces 0.648 cc. of water per gram and yields 0.600 cc.

---

[32] On a weight basis (p. 353), fat provides more oxidative water than carbohydrate. Accordingly, it was once considered that laying down body fat was a way of storing body water (p. 359ff.) and, in practice, if the limited carbohydrate reserves are exhausted before severe water deficiency develops, the presence of large stores of a nonnitrogenous water forming metabolite may contribute to survival (462). Mellanby (542) pointed out, however, that since water loss is proportional to oxygen uptake, an animal living on fat may be worse off than one living on carbohydrate, so far as protection against desiccation is concerned. For each 1000 Calories derived from fat, approximately 120 grams of water form; for carbohydrate, 130 grams of water form. Thus, on an activity basis, less water is produced by fat utilization. And the effect of the urinary excretion of fat metabolites on the water balance is far from clear. Kaunitz, *et al.* (407a) have shown that of rats kept on diets calorically sufficient only to maintain body weight, and with water ad libitum, those on a high fat (or on a high protein) diet required only three quarters as many calories as those on a high carbohydrate diet; and the water intake was lowest on the high fat diet.

of oxidative water; sucrose displaces 0.630 cc. of water per gram and yields 0.579 cc. of oxidative water. Table XIV suggests how little water need be sacrificed per Calorie of sugar added to the ration. It may be noted that, for equal percentage concentrations, sucrose provides about 5.6% more Calories than glucose, per unit volume of solution.

For equal percentage concentrations, also, sucrose solutions have about half as much osmotic pressure as glucose. This may be a factor

TABLE XIV

Aqueous and caloric yields of 1 liter of variously concentrated sugar solutions, based upon the following constants for glucose and sucrose, respectively: specific gravity, 1.544, 1.588; water of oxidation, 0.600, 0.579 g. water/g. sugar; heat value, 3.75, 3.96 Cal./g. sugar.

% Sugar (g./100 cc. solution)	Preformed Water (L.)	Water of Oxidation (L.)	Total Water Yield (L.)	Total Calories
		Glucose		
0.00	1.000	0.000	1.000	0.0
5.00	0.968	0.030	0.998	187.5
10.00	0.935	0.060	0.995	375.0
20.00	0.870	0.120	0.990	750.0
30.00	0.806	0.180	0.986	1125.0
40.00	0.741	0.240	0.981	1500.0
50.00	0.676	0.300	0.976	1875.0
		Sucrose		
0.00	1.000	0.000	1.000	0.0
5.00	0.969	0.029	0.998	198.0
10.00	0.937	0.058	0.995	396.0
20.00	0.874	0.116	0.990	792.0
30.00	0.811	0.174	0.985	1188.0
40.00	0.748	0.232	0.980	1584.0
50.00	0.685	0.290	0.975	1980.0

in oral stimulation, along with taste, stickiness, etc., affecting the desirability or palatability of sugar solutions. Other carbohydrates, or even certain soft drinks might have advantages over plain water (867).

Burggraf (143a) has raised the question of the desirability of incorporating substantial quantities of glucose in desalting briquets (p. 242).

An evaluation of sea water drinking, important for its incisive conclusion, is that of Hervey and McCance (352), summarized as follows:

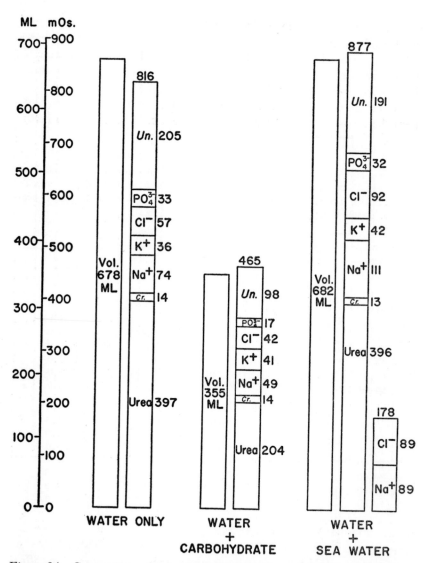

Figure 34. Composition of urine in man under three experimental regimens. The left hand columns represent the 24 hour urine volumes for the third day (see text for details). Right hand columns show amounts of urinary constituents in milliosmols. Figures at heads of columns are total solutes, calculated from freezing point depression. Figures for undetermined constituents (*Un.*) were obtained by difference. *Cr* is creatinine. Figures are means for six subjects. The small column at extreme right indicates the daily intake of ions on the ration containing sea water, regarding this as equivalent to 3.45% sodium chloride. After Hervey and McCance (352).

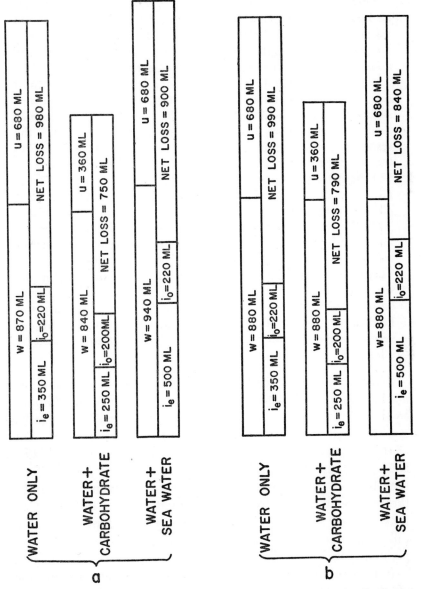

Figure 35. Mean water balances found on three rations for the third day. Same subjects as Fig. 34. (a) measured water balances. (b) water balances after substitution of average value for extrarenal losses, to eliminate change differences in extrarenal water loss. w, extrarenal water loss; u, urine volume; i_e, drink; i_o, oxidative water. After Hervey and McCance (352).

Three rations, 350 ml. distilled water, 250 ml. distilled water plus 96.5 g. carbohydrate, and 350 ml. distilled water plus 150 ml. sea water, were given daily for 3-day periods to six subjects receiving no other food or drink. The experiment was fully 'crossed-over' and was carried out in a constant environment.

On the carbohydrate ration the water balance over the third day of exposure was about 200 ml. better than on the ration consisting of water only, and the rise in the total osmotic pressure of the body was smaller. The improvement in water balance was the result of a reduction in urine volume, which was in turn due to the effects of carbohydrate upon metabolism. These effects were (1) the sparing of body protein, (2) the prevention of ketosis and (3) a reduction of the basal metabolic rate. It is suggested that all three may have been brought about by a common mechanism.

On the sea-water ration the water balance for the third day was improved by 80 to 150 ml., but the rise in the osmotic pressure of the body was greater than when distilled water alone was given. These effects were due to the retention of most of the water of the sea water, together with the salt which it contained. It is suggested that the effects of sea water drinking on body tonicity and fluid distribution are deleterious, and that the gain of water observed on the third day would eventually have been replaced by a loss.

Some of the analytical results of these investigators are summarized in Figs. 34 and 35 and Tables XV and XVI. Although by the third day their subjects were pale, tired-looking and lethargic, they had lost only 4.4 to 5.4% of their body weights. None of them agreed with the subjects of Whillans and Smith (825, p. 265) that they would add sea water to their water rations if ever they became castaways. However, there is obviously a limit to the confidence which investigators ought to place in the declarations of their subjects. During the study of Rubini *et al.* (671), following, one subject taking quite pure artificial sea water complained of its "fishy" taste.

In the preliminary phase of an attempt to analyze the question of whether a person possessing limited supplies of fresh water can usefully augment his water ration by admixing it with sea water, Rubini, Wolf, and Meroney (671) carried out experiments somewhat similar to those of Hervey and McCance, above. Follow-

TABLE XV

Packed cell volumes and serum chemistry. Means of observations on six subjects, immediately before and at the end of 72 hr. periods on each ration, and mean changes (except where marked *, when results were available from five subjects only). Standard errors of the mean in parentheses. The values of t and P immediately below each figure for mean change indicate whether this differed significantly from zero, i.e., whether a significant change took place over the 72 hr. period. Values of t and P in separate lines indicate the significance of the differences between the mean changes on water only and on each of the other two rations (352).

	Packed Cell Volumes (%)	Serum Proteins (g./100 ml.)	Serum Urea (mg./100 ml.)	Serum Sodium (mg./100 ml.)	Serum Potassium (mg./100 ml.)	Serum Chloride (mg./100 ml.)
Water only						
Initial	47 ($\pm$1.5)	6.78 ($\pm$0.11)	33.1 ($\pm$2.0)	332 ($\pm$5)	15.8 ($\pm$0.6)	354 ($\pm$4)
Final	52 ($\pm$1.5)	7.24 ($\pm$0.16)	43.6 ($\pm$3.4)	336 ($\pm$6)	16.6 ($\pm$1.0)	345 ($\pm$3)
Change	+5 ($\pm$1)	+0.46 ($\pm$0.10)	+10.5 ($\pm$2.5)	+4 ($\pm$3)	+0.8 ($\pm$1.4)	-9 ($\pm$4)
	$t = 5.28$	$t = 4.42$	$t = 4.23$	$t = 1.45$	$t = 0.59$	$t = 2.63$
	$P < 0.01$	$P < 0.01$	$P < 0.01$	$P = 0.2$ to 0.3	$P = 0.5$ to 0.6	$P = 0.02$ to 0.05
Water + Carbohydrate						
Initial	45.5 ($\pm$1)	6.52 ($\pm$0.12)	33.6 ($\pm$2.5)	334 ($\pm$2)	16.5 ($\pm$0.7)	357 ($\pm$3)
Final	51.5 ($\pm$0.5)	7.27 ($\pm$0.15)	35.2 ($\pm$2.0)	338 ($\pm$4)	17.2 ($\pm$1.3)	350 ($\pm$2)
Change	+6 ($\pm$1)	+0.75 ($\pm$0.13)	+1.6 ($\pm$1.0)	+4 ($\pm$3)	+0.7 ($\pm$1.3)	-7 ($\pm$4)
	$t = 7.05$	$t = 6.00$	$t = 1.69$	$t = 1.27$	$t = 0.55$	$t = 1.79$
	$P < 0.01$	$P < 0.01$	$P = 0.1$ to 0.2	$P = 0.2$ to 0.3	$P = 0.6$ to 0.7	$P = 0.1$ to 0.2
t Water/carbohydrate	0.87	1.81	3.34	0	0.05	0.32
	$P = 0.4$ to 0.5	$P = 0.1$	$P < 0.01$	$P > 0.9$	$P > 0.9$	$P = 0.7$ to 0.8
Water + Sea water						
Initial	47.5 ($\pm$0.5)	6.81* ($\pm$0.23)	32.0 ($\pm$3.1)	336 ($\pm$6)	16.8* ($\pm$0.7)	352 ($\pm$3)
Final	49.5 ($\pm$1)	7.27* ($\pm$0.25)	41.2 ($\pm$2.8)	336 ($\pm$7)	20.3* ($\pm$1.3)	349 ($\pm$2)
Change	+2 ($\pm$1.5)	+0.46* ($\pm$0.16)	+9.2 ($\pm$1.3)	0 ($\pm$2)	+3.5* ($\pm$1.2)	-3 ($\pm$2)
	$t = 1.54$	$t = 2.86$	$t = 7.02$	$t = 0$	$t = 3.01$	$t = 2.10$
	$P = 0.1$ to 0.2	$P = 0.02$ to 0.05	$P < 0.01$	$P > 0.9$	$P = 0.02$ to 0.05	$P = 0.05$ to 0.1
t Water/sea water	1.91	0	0.46	1.22	1.47	1.54
	$P = 0.05$ to 0.1	$P > 0.9$	$P = 0.6$ to 0.7	$P = 0.2$ to 0.3	$P = 0.1$ to 0.2	$P = 0.1$ to 0.2

ing a control period, men were deprived of food for three days and either deprived of water also, or allowed amounts of distilled and/or artificial sea water (Table XII) as indicated in Table XVII. Essentially all of the data of these experiments is contained in Tables XVII, XVIII, and XIX.

Serum concentration increments of sodium, chloride, total solids, and osmotic pressure tended to rise in experimental periods, roughly in proportion to the quantity of sea water supplement taken at any level of fresh water intake. By calculation from ionic and estimated water balances in their experiments, Hervey and McCance inferred that an increase of osmotic pressure in body fluids occurred when 150 cc. of sea water and 350 cc. of distilled water were taken daily over comparable periods of time. This rise was greater than when 350 cc. of distilled water alone was given. However, the latter workers did not report the osmotic pressure of serum directly. They actually found no change in the concentration of serum sodium and a small drop in that of chloride (Table XV).

So far as the data of Rubini *et al.* go, it would appear that the addition of sea water in relatively large quantities is deleterious by virtue of its tendency to promote hypersalemia, and in this they concur with Hervey and McCance. Whether this effect would continue at the lower sea water percentages (less than 30%) had such experiments been prolonged is not certain. Hervey and McCance assumed that augmentation of osmotic pressure would continue without limit, presumably until a fatal termination. Unfortunately, the effect of relatively small loads of sea water compared to that of no sea water at given levels of fresh water intake cannot be evaluated from any data on hand. This appears to be a crucial point to be decided in future tests particularly since capacities of the adaptive responses of the renal concentrating processes (243, 244) are still not well known (p. 340).

Winkler *et al.* (842) studied men in slightly more extended water deprivation. No clear advantage of hypotonic saline (0.6% sodium chloride, diluted sea water) over fresh water could be demonstrated in the amelioration of dehydration. They considered intake of diluted sea water as psychologically undesirable

TABLE XVI

Weight losses and urine volumes. The values of *t* and *P* below each column relating to the carbohydrate and sea water rations indicate the significance of the difference between the mean of that column and the corresponding mean on the ration of water alone (352).

Subject	Initial Weight (Kg.)	Water Only			Water + Carbohydrate			Water + Sea Water		
		Loss over Whole 72 hr. (Kg.)	Loss during 3rd 24 hr. (Kg.)	Urine during 3rd 24 hr. (ml.)	Loss over Whole 72 hr. (Kg.)	Loss during 3rd 24 hr. (Kg.)	Urine during 3rd 24 hr. (ml.)	Loss over Whole 72 hr. (Kg.)	Loss during 3rd 24 hr. (Kg.)	Urine during 3rd 24 hr. (ml.)
B.	82.73	5.28	1.13	445	3.75	1.09	395	4.33	1.95	675
G.	68.63	4.23	1.53	927	3.89	0.96	342	3.83	1.25	877
H.	72.00	4.85	1.56	685	4.08	0.72	386	3.90	1.00	684
L.	65.77	3.68	1.23	801	3.48	1.00	322	3.39	0.91	545
M.	69.47	4.22	1.28	742	4.27	0.88	387	3.88	1.16	840
T.	60.78	3.52	0.79	465	2.88	0.85	300	2.83	0.76	470
Mean	69.90	4.30	1.25	678	3.72	0.92	355	3.69	1.17	682
Standard error of the mean		($\pm$0.28)	($\pm$0.12)	($\pm$77)	($\pm$0.20)	($\pm$0.05)	($\pm$16)	($\pm$0.21)	($\pm$0.17)	($\pm$65)
t					1.67	2.66	4.07	1.74	0.39	0.04
P					0.1 to 0.2	0.02 to 0.05	<0.01	0.1 to 0.2	0.7 to 0.8	>0.9

on the ground that it might lead, among real castaways, to the drinking of more concentrated solutions as the fresh water supply dwindled. Certainly, dehydration is known to make it difficult to limit the intake of sea water (273, 783, p. 274). Neverthless, the psychologic argument that, under stress, the temptation to add more than allowable quantities (assuming such were demonstrated) of sea water would be insurmountable does not cut to the heart of the question. The argument itself is debatable (867), not the least reason being that suitable discipline to control water rationing not uncommonly prevails (p. 267).

Elkinton and Danowski (230) have uncritically stated that the castaway can supplement his water supply by diluting sea water, volume for volume, with whatever meager amounts of fresh water that he may have, since, as they glean from older literature, the kidney can handle the extra salt in the less concentrated solution; but McCance and Morrison (522) have given reasons to deprecate this advice. This question is analyzed further on page 307ff.

Numerous concrete suggestions as to quantities of water and rations best suited to shipwreck survivors or others with limited supplies, have been made (539, 550a). These matters cannot be reviewed here at length; indeed, no fixed rules apply in all situations. Futcher, Consolazio, and Pace (274) studied men on pneumatic life rafts in the Gulf of Mexico in July, in weather such as to cause the daily requirement of water to approach the maximum on any ocean. Curiously, the average daily evaporative loss was calculated to be 730 ml., an unusually low figure. They estimated that as long as exertion is minimal, seasickness is not excessive, clothing is kept moist with sea water, a light breeze blows, and there is some protection from the sun, a supply of 500 to 1,000 cc. of water a day will prevent the occurrence of dehydration in semifasting (p. 116) survivors on lifeboats and rafts in the tropics. McCance (539) considers 18 ounces (ca. 500 cc.) of water per man per day to be an absolute minimum for temperate zones but inadequate for tropical conditions.

Glaser and Hervey (294) suggested that a total of 2.5 liters of water and 500 grams of sugar should enable men to remain reasonably fit for five days on a tented float in tropical waters, also provided they wet their clothes to cool themselves, minimizing perspiration losses. They recommended, as did Ladell (460) and others, refraining from drink

TABLE XVII

Effects of sea water on the metabolism of men without food or sufficient water. See text and Tables XVIII and XIX. *C*, control period; 1, 2, and 3, experimental days; *R*, 2 hour rehydration period. The figures under "Fluid Intake" for the *R* period are fresh (tap) water intakes at 10, 60, and 120 minutes (cumulative), respectively (671).

Subject	Age	Initial Body Wt. (Kg.)	Wt. Loss (%)	Distilled Water (L./day)	Sea Water (L./day)	Conc. (% Sea H₂O)	Period	Na (mEq./L.)	K (mEq./L.)	Cl (mEq./L.)	Osmotic Pressure (mOs./L.)	Total Solids (g./100 g. serum)	Hematocrit
G	21	65.35	0.00	...	0	0	C	140.7	4.42	105.8	281.8	9.02	45.2
			1.99	0	0	...	1	146.7	4.62	105.9	287.9	9.53	45.7
			3.67	0	0	...	2	148.9	4.62	108.0	293.5	9.80	46.4
			5.35	0	0	0	3	149.4	4.35	108.4	293.9	10.14	46.3
				0.880, 1.125, 1.150			R	143.1	4.54	105.7	283.4	9.09	45.8
D	21	80.40	0.00		0	0	C	139.7	5.23	102.0	274.0	9.09	52.3
			1.49	0	0.500	100	1	150.8	4.61	108.9	290.9	8.36	52.0
			2.99	0	0.500	100	2	151.1	4.33	111.6	291.5	8.85	52.0
			4.85	0	0.500	100	3	153.6	4.28	114.8	300.6	8.81	53.3
				0.740, 1.235, 1.660			R	143.5	3.72	109.7	283.5	9.18	47.0
	21	73.65	0.00	0.250	0	0	C	144.1	3.99	108.3	282.0	8.11	47.0
			1.70	0.250	0.050	17	1	144.7	4.15	106.4	285.1	8.50	49.0
			3.53	0.250	0.050	17	2	144.2	4.28	108.1	288.7	8.59	50.7
			4.89	0.250	0.050	17	3	144.0	4.09	108.2	293.0	8.93	50.6
				0.450, 0.600, 0.850			R	146.2	4.18	106.1	283.3	8.77	50.3
M	24	80.25	0.00	0.250	0	0	C	143.0	4.09	104.0	281.8	8.77	44.5
			1.37	0.250	0.125	33	1	142.4	4.21	106.9	288.8	9.12	44.2
			2.98	0.250	0.125	33	2	145.2	4.26	105.8	286.8	9.34	44.5
			4.29	0.250	0.125	33	3	146.1	4.32	105.2	286.8	9.30	45.0
				0.100, 0.200, 0.200			R	145.0	4.28	103.8	296.1	9.14	45.1
P	20	66.46	0.00		0	0	C	149.9	4.83	104.3	296.7	9.43	51.6
			2.12	0.500	0	0	1	145.5	4.96	103.4	294.1	9.63	51.2
			3.02	0.500	0	0	2	149.5	4.90	101.6	291.6	9.73	51.4
			3.93	0.500	0	0	3	148.2	5.18	102.9	291.0	9.69	50.9
				0.440, 0.490, 0.540			R	145.4	4.35	107.7	282.3	8.67	49.0
H	22	51.20	0.00		0	0	C	142.8	4.23	108.8	289.6	8.79	48.5
			1.17	0.500	0.100	17	1	145.6	3.90	107.8	287.6	9.22	50.0
			2.34	0.500	0.100	17	2	146.2	3.87	102.7	292.2	9.26	51.7
			3.32	0.500	0.100	17	3	145.8	3.71	108.6	284.4	8.83	49.5
				0.375, 0.825, 0.980			R	143.9	4.32	107.7	283.3	8.26	52.7
S	21	69.40	0.00		0	0	C	141.9	4.20	109.3	287.0	9.00	56.5
			2.02	0.500	0.250	33	1	144.1	4.68	110.2	291.5	8.97	56.5
			3.24	0.500	0.250	33	2	144.1	4.45	104.5	300.2	9.34	54.0
			4.32	0.500	0.250	33	3	147.7	3.95	106.0	282.3	8.95	51.0
				0.500, 1.500, 1.650			R	140.9	5.02	113.7	290.0	8.22	49.0
	20	72.85	0.00	0.500	0	0	C	148.6	4.01	113.7	296.1	8.20	49.0
			0.96	0.500	0.500	50	1	149.7	3.79	113.7	293.0	8.85	52.0
			1.92	0.500	0.500	50	2	147.8	4.02	113.8	294.3	9.18	52.0
			3.05	0.500	0.500	50	3	150.3	4.05	...	293.0	...	49.5
				0.500, 0.690, 0.780			R	142.4	...	...	285.5	...	...

in the first 24 hours so as not to lose facultative urine volume in water diuresis (p. 267).[33] Actually, in conditions of extreme heat or insolation, this advice could be dangerous since severe dehydration could result in less than that time (808). However, once the urine flow has become minimal (obligatory volume) it may be better to drink water moderately quickly than to save it too long, since the latter course brings on inefficiency more quickly without delaying death.

Hervey and McCance (353) have given the composition of three levels of emergency rations, expressed per man per day, for provisioning expeditions in the field: the first should prevent deterioration in a healthy man at rest; the second, or compromise, should maintain a man in a reasonable state of efficiency for three weeks or even longer; and the third, is a minimum ration on which a man would lose between 1 and 2% of his body weight a day, but on which he ought to remain fairly well for one week and survive for two or more.

For those short of water, jelly candy is a better carbohydrate store than hard candy which tends to produce mouth sores (93, 671). Chocolate bars have been considered thirst provoking (p. 65) and otherwise unacceptable (93). McCance *et al.* (523) have reported of shipwreck survivors that when water supplies were short, fruit and sweets were the only foods that could be eaten with enjoyment.

Adolph (10) showed that rats survived slightly longer, while losing the same amount of body water, when allowed to drink sea water than when denied all water. The maximum urinary chloride concentration in the albino rat is greater than in man, dog, or some marine mammals, and exceeds that concentration in sea water (Tables XI, XX, p. 358). Half strength sea water or its equivalent of sodium chloride allowed indefinite maintenance of body weight in rats, with augmented turnovers of water and salt.

Barker and Adolph (73) confirmed the finding that these animals survive longer (optimally) when given sea water ad libitum than when given no water or when sea water was forced. The voluntary intake of sea water was one-third the voluntary intake of tap water, but this could be doubled if the rats were required to take sea water while acquiring food. Curiously, rats

---

[33] It has been said that if protein, carbohydrate, or fat is taken with water, certain amounts of the fluid are retained and stored with the food until it is oxidized. Water taken before food is promptly excreted; taken with or soon after food (or salt) it may be retained (6). Taking protein may (or may not) be contraindicated on other grounds (p. 330).

TABLE XVIII

Effects of sea water on the metabolism of men without food or sufficient water. See text and Tables XVII and XIX. C, control period; 1, 2, and 3, experimental days; R, 2 hour rehydration period (671).

Subject	Period	Volume (L./day)	Specific gravity ($D^{20}_{15°}$)	Total solids (g./100 g. urine)	Urine Na (mEq./L.)	K (mEq./L.)	Cl (mEq./L.)	Osmotic pressure (mOs./L.)	Accumulated Sensible H_2O Load (fluid intake—urine output) (L./day)
G	C	2.352	1.0131	3.18	84.7	41.5	88.7	514.3	0
	1	0.516	1.0213	5.90	96.0	62.3	102.8	843.7	−0.516
	2	0.305	1.0294	8.02	75.6	76.6	88.2	1113.0	−0.821
	3	0.378	1.0313	7.90	76.9	116.4	66.3	1187.1	−1.199
	R	0.057*	1.0278	6.85	58.5	77.6	...	1084.2	...
D	C	1.190	1.0239	5.60	158.3	65.8	156.3	929.3	...
	1	0.849	1.0248	5.58	187.2	85.0	225.8	981.0	−0.349
	2	0.848	1.0271	5.67	239.1	90.9	290.8	1054.6	−0.697
	3	0.833	1.0274	5.80	289.3	88.9	275.0	1100.2	−1.030
	R	0.045*	1.0302	7.34	235.9	92.9	...	1260.7	...
J	C	3.552	1.0088	1.81	85.9	19.4	75.1	310.4	...
	1	0.612	1.0140	3.40	134.9	52.2	185.6	626.8	−0.312
	2	0.625	1.0269	6.77	118.2	71.0	163.5	1037.5	−0.637
	3	...	1.0287	...	84.2	105.7	133.4	1243.8	...
	R	0.049*	...	...	56.1	101.9	74.7	1196.7	...
M	C	1.344	1.0212	4.94	227.7	39.4	184.9	861.2	...
	1	0.563	1.0204	5.04	172.7	68.5	226.9	934.1	−0.188
	2	0.579	1.0272	6.63	189.2	75.1	201.5	1093.3	−0.292
	3	0.487	1.0279	6.82	171.5	80.2	171.4	1140.0	−0.404
	R	0.030*	1.0269	6.95	144.3	122.7	176.2	1180.0	...
P	C	2.296	1.0101	2.74	104.2	36.0	97.8	481.9	...
	1	1.296	1.0084	1.98	59.7	21.8	52.8	316.6	−0.796
	2	0.402	1.0241	6.34	103.9	55.7	110.8	961.2	−0.698
	3	0.343	1.0270	7.59	50.6	83.0	54.9	1106.3	−0.541
	R	0.050*	1.0276	6.70	31.5	66.5	16.8	1043.7	...
H	C	1.360	1.0178	4.14	134.5	65.3	127.3	694.3	...
	1	0.610	1.0209	4.68	155.2	85.4	146.4	835.9	−0.010
	2	0.658	1.0177	4.51	156.8	78.4	183.0	800.9	−0.068
	3	0.583	1.0218	5.04	194.4	75.6	240.8	899.1	−0.051
	R	0.050*	1.0242	6.14	210.0	45.0	218.1	1045.5	...
S	C	1.967	1.0163	7.19	111.5	42.8	105.1	590.4	...
	1	0.965	1.0210	8.42	145.7	62.5	143.5	795.9	−0.215
	2	0.468	1.0292	10.84	146.4	76.7	144.7	1109.7	0.067
	3	0.436	1.0331	11.85	128.1	88.0	130.9	1200.0	0.381
	R	0.175*	...	...	12.5	22.6	...	...	...
B	C	1.390	1.0176	4.11	113.9	50.0	116.6	708.3	...
	1	0.826	1.0260	5.71	180.7	79.6	209.8	1008.5	0.174
	2	0.888	1.0254	5.46	246.5	57.6	277.0	1026.9	0.286
	3	0.918	1.0236	5.21	286.3	45.6	299.8	1005.5	0.368
	R	0.048*	1.0247	5.29	291.9	43.6	...	1051.3	...

* 2, not 24, hour sample.

deprived of food drank three times as much fresh water in the second half of their survival period as in the first half, resembling in this regard the state of increased water consumption in extremes of human inanition (421, p. 116); it was considered doubtful whether such excessive water consumption is necessary for the animals' continued life. Dehydration without salt intake never gave such high urinary chloride concentrations as with salt, when values up to 760 mM./L. were obtained.

THE TOXICITY OF SEA WATER AND HYPERTONIC SALINE

Elkinton and Winkler (234), reviewed "clinical" observations of castaways who drank sea water, emphasizing that the reported irrationality, delirium, and attempts to jump overboard all point to disturbances of the central nervous system. This suggestion is supported by experiments on dogs given hypertonic saline in which tremors, hyperactive reflexes, motor incoordination and finally irregular and failing respiration set in. On the other hand, dogs with access to sea water as their only ingesta may drink sparingly and die only weeks later in the tranquil manner characteristic of dogs with no food or water (871).

Under some conditions, cells appear to function until they have lost 40 to 50% of their water (234), although a loss in excess of 25% has been estimated to carry a high mortality (530, 869).

In experimenting with dogs, Elkinton and Winkler chose to test them with 5% sodium chloride rather than 3.5%, which might appear better to simulate sea water, since dogs are able to produce a urine 1.5 times as concentrated as man (Table XX). While this may not provide a valid basis for extrapolating to human regulation[34] it yielded evidence that under such condi-

---

[34] In this experimental category may be placed the 5/6 nephrectomy by McCance and Morrison (522), performed to make the concentrating power of the rat kidney resemble that of man (Table XX). Different pulmocutaneous water lossses of rat and man per unit of body weight suggest that it does not do merely to equate their renal emunctories concentrationwise to provide different species with comparable water and electrolyte metabolisms. Among the subtle difficulties to this end we may observe that it may not leave the w/Z ratio (p. 313ff.) unchanged when one increases urinary flow and decreases urinary concentration by nephrectomy. Increase of urine flow results not merely from nephrectomy, per se (which could simply be offset by a corresponding increase of water intake, i_e), but is increased also by increase of salt intake, Q, which varies with both the concentration, I, and the volume of saline ingesta.

TABLE XIX

Effects of sea water on the metabolism of men without food or sufficient water. See text and Tables XVII and XVIII. C, control period; 1, 2, and 3, experimental days (671).

Subject	Period	Accumulated Sensible Ion Loads (intake − output)			Saliva				Thirst	Other Predominant Symptoms and Signs without Regard to Onset or Duration
		Na (mEq.)	K (mEq.)	Cl (mEq.)	Vol. (cc./min.)	Na (mEq./L.)	K (mEq./L.)	Osmotic Pressure (mOs./L.)		
G	C	0	0	0	1.00	20.6	23.6	124.0	0	Hunger, abdominal cramps, headache, weakness, euphoria, insomnia, dry mouth, palpitations
	1	− 49.5	− 32.1	− 53.0	0.45	13.0	22.0	86.2	+	
	2	− 72.6	− 55.5	− 79.9	0.15	16.3	21.6	96.2	++	
	3	−101.7	− 99.5	−105.0	0.10	10.7	23.0	82.7	+++	
D	C	0	0	0	1.49	20.9	17.4	79.9	0	Nausea, headache, euphoria, insomnia, diarrhea, dry mouth
	1	76.1	− 67.2	82.3	0.71	26.9	22.9	121.9	+	
	2	108.3	−139.3	109.7	0.08	36.4	33.6	175.8	++	
	3	102.3	−208.4	154.6	>0	...	...	...	+++	
J	C	0	0	...	1.27	27.0	22.8	106.5	0	Hunger, weakness, euphoria
	1	− 59.1	− 31.4	− 86.2	0.86	14.5	22.7	86.3	0	
	2	−109.5	− 75.3	−161.0	0.49	11.5	22.4	80.3	0	
	3	...	...	...	0.33	8.5	23.6	66.3	+	
M	C	0	0	...	1.51	12.1	18.1	75.7	0	Hunger, lethargy
	1	− 38.4	− 37.4	− 59.2	0.69	7.3	13.2	49.1	0	
	2	− 89.1	− 79.7	−107.4	0.55	13.3	19.5	87.0	0	
	3	−113.8	−117.5	−122.4	0.45	9.1	13.9	56.0	0	
P	C	0	0	0	0.86	16.4	23.9	111.3	0	Hunger, headache, lethargy
	1	− 77.4	− 28.3	− 68.4	0.43	8.7	22.5	65.2	0	
	2	−119.2	− 50.7	−112.9	0.65	5.8	21.6	79.0	0	
	3	−136.6	− 79.2	−131.7	0.40	5.5	22.0	188.0	+	
H	C	0	0	0	1.51	20.1	20.0	106.4	0	Hunger, abdominal cramps, headache, lethargy, euphoria, insomnia, palpitations
	1	− 47.7	− 51.1	− 34.5	1.06	33.7	17.7	114.3	0	
	2	−103.9	−101.7	−100.1	0.70	25.1	20.0	126.8	+	
	3	−170.2	−144.8	−185.7	0.70	24.8	20.0	164.7	+	
S	C	0	0	0	0.96	29.9	18.6	92.9	0	Hunger, headache
	1	− 23.0	− 57.8	− 1.4	0.90	28.5	18.8	88.2	0	
	2	− 26.1	− 91.2	− 68.0	1.14	30.0	18.4	95.8	+	
	3	− 87.9	−127.1	−148.0	0.80	30.5	19.6	104.2	0	
B	C	0	0	0	1.53	12.7	18.3	76.8	0	Hunger, abdominal cramps, headache, dry mouth
	1	86.0	− 60.7	100.1	1.02	14.9	18.6	86.0	0	
	2	102.3	−106.8	129.1	0.88	19.3	20.4	119.9	0	
	3	74.7	−143.1	128.1	...	...	...	...	...	

tions extracellular fluid volume was maintained while intracellular fluid bore the brunt of a fluid loss which increased steadily to the end. The circulation continued to function well (27). There was no collapse of plasma volume, renal function remained good, the pulse was vigorous, and the electrocardiogram was normal.

The toxicity of sea water in mammals has been studied by Albrecht (27) using rats, guinea pigs, mice, dogs, and seals. In addition to testing artificial sea water (336, 499, Table XII) and natural sea water from Woods Hole and the Gulf of Maine, she also studied solutions of magnesium chloride, sodium chloride, sucrose, and urea. The lethal dose of sea water or of equiosmotic sodium chloride solution for 50% of rats, mice, and guinea pigs when given a single intraperitoneal injection was 16% of the body weight. After such a dose no rat drank enough fresh water to save itself. The LD 50 of molar sucrose solutions for these species under the same conditions is less than half of equiosmolal salt solutions. For rats the LD 50 of sea water by stomach tube, given in divided doses at half-hour intervals, is essentially the same as by intraperitoneal injection, although more gradual administration increases the total LD 50.

Dogs and seals retain more sea water by stomach if it is given in repeated small doses (0.33% of body weight) than if it is given in a single large dose (3.3%). This is probably true in man also (pp. 271, 277). Vomiting of sea water is due to gastric irritation, not merely to distention by fluid.

The total dose of intravenous sea water required to kill seals varies with the infusion rate, but is of the order of 4 to 9% of body weight. Death occurs very quietly, as from deep anesthesia. The heart slows gradually but continues beating for some minutes after breathing stops, suggestive of magnesium intoxication with parenteral solutions (635, 636). Seals are no more resistant to the effects of sea water than are other mammals. Although they are not known to drink it directly, they unavoidably swallow a little sea water when feeding (p. 345). Men, dogs, and seals will vomit if they take enough into their stomachs; not so the rat which never vomits.

Dogs given 5% of the body weight of sea water at one time commonly vomited (27); vomiting could be delayed by giving the same amount of fluid in 1% doses at half-hour intervals. Diarrhea was not a prominent feature in dogs after oral sea water. With these nonfatal doses, plasma chloride did not rise more than 50% and at the end of such experiments dogs showed intense thirst and drank large drafts of fresh water. During the following 24 hours it was not unusual for them to drink three times their control water intakes. Appetites for food were unaffected by sea water.

In rats, convulsions usually followed intraperitoneal injections of hypertonic salt or sucrose solutions, but rarely followed oral salt solutions. The convulsions consisted of an explosive hyper-irritability, the rat running about wildly if not closely confined. Rats that survived those intraperitoneal injections which were lethal for at least 50% of the animals seemed often to be the ones that excreted the most urine within the first 2 hours after injection.

The cause of death following large loads of sea water is not always clear (p. 275). The nervous system seems primarily to be affected, possibly initially stimulated, but ultimately depressed. When 15% of the body weight of sea water and food is forced in rats, death may succeed gastrointestinal difficulties, large amounts of undigested food being found in the stomach (73). Increased osmotic pressure which possibly injures cells has been given as a cause of death in exsiccation and uremia (416), but urea in hyperosmotic solution, which presumably does not produce much cellular dehydration is also toxic and convulsive in rats (27). There is evidence the cells can sometimes function until they have lost 40 to 50% of their water (843). Histologically, death from hypertonic sodium bromide is associated with more dehydration of brain cells than is death from water privation in rats (284).

Whereas Barker and Adolph (73) found plasma chloride in rats made moribund by administration of sea water to be about 170 mEq./L. as compared with a normal of 103, Albrecht (27) found values of 175 to 200 and even 244 mEq./L., terminally. In unanesthetized dogs killed by intravenous administration of 5% sodium chloride, Winkler *et al.* (843) observed values of plasma chloride as high as 193 mEq./L.; of plasma sodium, as high as 213. Values almost as high were determined in anesthetized dogs. Death results from respiratory failure (234); the cardiovascular system and electrocardiogram are little affected. No critical lethal concentrations of sodium or chloride are apparent (843).   Plasma potassium rises in dogs with ligated ureters, or nephrectomized (530, 873), under such treatment.   Where urine may form freely, such dogs elaborate urinary chloride up to 600 mEq./L., but the concentration ratio does not much exceed that found commonly.   In anesthetized cats and dogs, an osmosity (p. 342) of plasma, following salt injections, of 220 mM./L. (ca. 410 milliosmolal) is compatible with life (530).

In dogs and rats, moribund from deprivation of food and water, terminal concentrations have been measured: sodium, 178 and 169 mEq./L.; chloride, 140 and 135 mEq./L.; and milliosmosity, 259 and 181 mM./L., respectively (871, 874).

It is curious, but repeatedly reported, that visual acuity of men fasting (87) and thirsting (33) is for a time improved (p. 225).   The visual acuity of Levanzin, Benedict's famous faster, increased rapidly in starvation, doubling within two weeks.   However, visual fields (form and color) have been reduced in dehydration (177).   Epstein (240) has noted reports of several dehydrated subjects, who were given concentrated mannitol infusions, to the effect that the light in the room looked more yellow.   After a couple of hours of this, an intense headache appeared, which was worse on standing and completely relieved by lying down, possibly because of lowered cerebrospinal fluid pressure.

Diarrhea

It is said that rats, dogs, seals, and men get diarrhea from ingested sea water if there is no previous severe water deficit (27), but Rickenbacker noted purgation (p. 455) after drinking salty water when he was presumably dehydrated.   Two seamen, survivors of the sloop *Betsy* shipwrecked in 1756, and undoubtedly dehydrated, drank sea water notwithstanding remonstrances.   It purged them so excessively, according to Captain Aubin, that they fell into a kind of delirium and were of no more service (217).   Jones (402) also noted sea water catharsis (p. 250).

On the other hand, Bombard (112) and Willis (841) deny any diarrheic influence of sea water ingestion on the basis of their personal experience at sea in rafts (pp. 270, 273).   Critchley (190, p. 275) and Aury (60, 60a, p. 271) also stated that purgation is not typical of sea water drinking; and Llano (483a), in a two day test patterned (50 cc. at approximately 2 hour intervals) after Aury's, observed no diarrhea or even loose stool after 850 cc.

of sea water, 400 cc. on the first day (spent on a raft in Mona Passage) and 450 cc. on the second day.

Diarrhea from drinking sea water in limited quantities is hardly different from that following equiosmotic sodium chloride[35] (ca. 3%) and little special emphasis need be placed on the content of magnesium and sulfate in the former (869, p. 325ff.).

However, if an ingested kilogram of sea water contains 55 milliequivalents of magnesium sulfate and 50 milliequivalents of magnesium chloride (Table XI), and none of these salts are absorbed from the gut, then approximately one-third of a kilogram of ingested fluid will remain unabsorbed in the gut at isosmotic equilibrium across the blood-gut boundary. This would be fluid "permanently" marked for diarrhea as distinguished from the water which might temporarily be drawn into the gut by the presence of hypertonic ingesta. The latter, along with the other two-thirds of a kilogram of ingesta, should in time be absorbed unless absorption is aborted in a general saline diarrhea.

The absorbed fraction (two-thirds) of the ingested sea water would load the system with nine-tenths as many osmols as was contained in the original kilogram, but the virtual osmotic concentration of the absorbed fluid would be 35% greater than the original sea water. The osmotic stress (i.e., cellular hypovolia), thus, can be shown to be greater than if no fluid had remained unabsorbed in the gut (assuming in the osmometric calculation (p. 75) that renal and extrarenal excretion of osmotic material is zero).

The actual diarrheic influence of sea water has not been definitively quantified under any, not to say varying, conditions (p. 325). Experimentally it has been shown (178) that sea water, from which all of the magnesium but none of the sulfate is removed may not be so cathartic; all of the sulfate from such an ingested fluid has been found to be completely absorbed from the intestinal tract and excreted in the urine. Magnesium ion, itself, is believed actually to be absorbed slowly.

In the author's laboratory (875) medium sized cats have been

---

[35] Indeed, even fresh water will sometimes cause diarrhea if drunk too fast when one is dehydrated (272a, p. 412).

sustained for weeks on partially dried fish (p. 330) and sea water ad libitum (taking 50 to 100 cc./day and more), maintaining body weight and normal osmotic pressure of body fluids, keeping urine volume in excess of fluid drunk, and showing no signs of diarrhea. Diarrhea has been more likely to occur in a situation where an animal had been led into a hyperdipsic state by deprivation of fluid but not of partially dried fish and then offered sea water ad libitum. It might then drink excessively and get diarrhea (p. 328).

SEA WATER DRINKING: APPLICATIONS OF ISORRHEIC THEORY

The theory of the isorrheic state has been treated in detail elsewhere[36] (857) and will be reviewed here only as necessary. If the components of a solution infused into an animal at a constant rate appeared in the urine in the same relative concentrations of solute and solvent, it could be expected that in time (neglecting extrarenal losses) a load of solution would build up to the point at which output would equal input, that is, the isorrheic state (isorrhea) would be attained. Any solution of sodium chloride containing between 15 and 290 mEq./L. (0.1 to 1.7% sodium chloride) is potentially capable of reaching equality of intake and output for water and salt if administered long enough. These limits of concentration are called the minimal isorrheic concentration (MIC) and the limiting isorrheic concentration (LIC), respectively (Figs. 36, 37). Solutions concentrated below and above these limits cannot reach isorrhea for both solute (sodium and chloride) and solvent of the administered solution, although chloride appears to have a higher LIC than sodium.

Thus, LIC solutions of sodium chloride of approximately 1.7% represent a physiologic limit. No stronger solution can be administered without the body suffering a retention of salt relative to water. If a solution less than 1.7% but greater than 0.85% (= 145 mEq./L.) is taken, e.g., 1.4% (= 240 mEq./L.), the

---

[36] Smith's (739) summary and analysis of isorrhea are mistaken. Apparently, in converting to mEq./L. from the original units of chloride concentration which were reported as mg. of sodium chloride per cc. (851, 853), the given chloride concentrations were erroneously taken to be mg. of chloride per cc.

urine concentration will be greater than 1.4 and less than 1.7% (Fig. 36). The effect of excreting a solution (urine) more concentrated than that administered is to remove relatively more salt than water and to reduce the concentration of any retained fluid toward the normal plasma concentration of sodium or chloride. Uncorrected for extrarenal water and salt loss, if the administered solution is 1.7%, the urine is 1.7% and, although the urinary func-

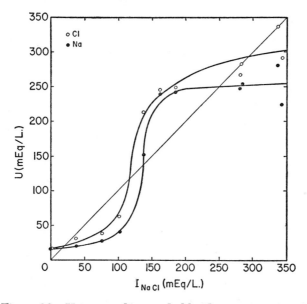

Figure 36. Urinary sodium and chloride concentrations in man (U) at the third hour of infusion of sodium chloride of concentration I_{NaCl}. Rate of intravenous administration of fluid, 7 cc./min. Critical isorrheic concentrations are those at which the sigmoid curves cross the diagonal isopleth. After Wolf (857).

tion is not acting to reduce the concentration of retained fluid, the physiologic situation concentrationwise is at least not worsening thereby. However, if a solution of 1.8% is administered, the urine concentration might in theory rise to 1.75% but could no longer match the intake, and the physiologic situation would deteriorate steadily. In this way it is seen how the maximum urinary concentration (MUC) of salt, generally just over 2% in

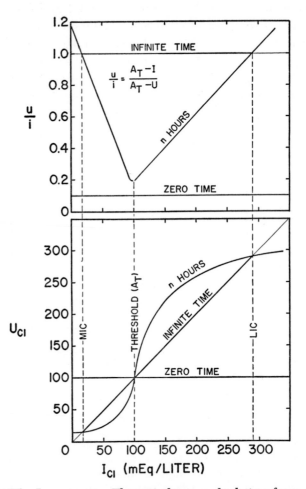

Figure 37. *Lower curve:* Theoretical temporal relations for man between urinary chloride concentration, U_{Cl}, in mEq./L. and infusion concentration of sodium chloride, I_{Cl}. At zero time after beginning infusion, U_{Cl} is arbitrarily taken as 100 mEq./L., and remains the same regardless of I_{Cl}. Several (n) hours after beginning steady infusion the sigmoid curve can be obtained, intersecting the line passing through the origin which is the locus of all points at which $U_{Cl} = I_{Cl}$. The points of intersection are the critical isorrheic concentrations indicated by labeled, vertical, interrupted lines. At "infinite" time, for any value of I_{Cl} between the *MIC* and the *LIC*, $U_{Cl} = I_{Cl}$.

man and 2.5% in dog (Table XX), is not wholly germane to a discussion of the problem of taking sea water.[37]

In general, maximum urinary concentrations appear to exist only under conditions which cannot be maintained without deterioration of the organism. A man with such loads of salt and water as to show a maximum urinary concentration of salt is in a state, perhaps not difficult initially, which by its nature promotes an increasing retention of salt relative to water and requires, for example, an intake of water which would reduce this urinary concentration to some lower value. Although maximum urinary concentrations certainly occur in what are not abnormal or unphysiologic situations, these are commonly transient, and are usually followed by intakes which neutralize the systemic conditions responsible for them. In terms of a LIC of 1.7% salt, the intake of sea water is seen to be even more hazardous than in terms of the MUC of 2% in man. Unfortunately, the way in which the LIC of salt may vary, as with a diminished urea output in starvation, is not known. Conceivably the LIC approaches the

---

[37] If one expresses urinary sodium ("salt") as if it were all sodium chloride one might also express sea water salts as if they were in effect (osmotically) sodium chloride. A sea water containing 3.45% salts, with an osmotic pressure equivalent to about 1.01 Os./Kg., has the same freezing point as a sodium chloride solution of 541 mM./L., or 3.16% (Tables XI, XII).

Upper curve: Theoretical temporal relations for man between ratio of rate of urinary flow to rate of intake of infusion fluid (u/i) and infusion concentrations (I_{Cl}). At zero time (u/i) has some value arbitrarily taken as 0.1. After several (n) hours the V-shaped curve is seen to intersect the horizontal at $u/i = 1$ at the MIC and the LIC, indicated by labeled, vertical, interrupted lines. At "infinite" time, for any value of I_{Cl}, between the MIC and the LIC, $u/i = 1$.

The n hour and infinite time curves in upper and lower graphs are related by the steady state equation indicated on the upper graph, that is, for every value of U_{Cl} and I_{Cl} in the lower curves, and with A_T taken as 100 mEq/L., the corresponding value of u/i is plotted in the upper graph. The interrupted lowest portion of the upper n hour curve indicates the insolubility of the equation $u/i = (100-100)/(100-100)$ in that region. These curves are uncorrected for insensible loss of water. After Wolf (857).

MUC under certain conditions, and we need not stress such differences between LIC and MUC as appear in laboratory studies.

In terms of isorrheic theory, water regularly ingested by animals
under "normal" conditions, along with the salts of the diet, may be
considered in the abstract as a component of a steadily administered salt solution whose composition lies between the MIC and
the LIC. However, all such solutions are, in steady state, isorrheic. And water intake thus useful to the organism, even in
excess of need, is called *isorrheic water*. Isorrheic water is not
synonymous with "free water," values of which are sometimes im-
properly calculated from "maximal" osmotic pressures of the
urine with no regard for water balance (p. 164).

Gorham *et al.* (299) and Wolf (857) have applied the concept of the
MIC to the determination of the relative importance of salt and water
in the genesis of cardiac edema. They consider the daily total net salt
intake as if it were dissolved in the daily total net water intake. The
concentration of such a virtual, abstract solution, whether above or below the MIC, is considered specifically to determine the pattern of renal
excretion of body fluid.

Analysis of Water and Solute Metabolism, and Thirst, by Means of Algebraic Inequalities

A powerful tool which can be used to investigate interrelations
of water and electrolytes, for our purposes as they relate to thirst,
exists in the extension of isorrheic (equality) theory to cases of
inequality. The elements of this method have been presented in
several places (852, 853, 857, 863, 864) and will be reviewed here
briefly.[38]

Using osmometric theory as a reference, we assume that thirst
is precipitated when the effective osmotic pressure of body fluids
rises to a point called a thirst threshold (p. 75), and worsens
as this point is exceeded. Let us examine first a simplified dipso-

---

[38] The reader is reminded that an algebraic inequality is an expression resembling
an equation except that in place of the sign, $=$, it employs the sign, $>$ ("greater
than"), or $<$ ("less than"), and occasionally $\gg$ ("much greater than"), $\not>$ ("not
greater than"), etc. Inequalities are subject to similar rules of transposition, cross-
multiplication, division, etc. except that, unlike the case with equations, inequalities
cannot have both sides multiplied by -1 without changing the sense of the inequality. Thus $5 = 5$ and $-5 = -5$; but $5 > 4$ while $-5 < -4$.

genic situation in which a man with no initial excess or deficit of water or salt simply rests at room temperature, losing his usual pulmocutaneous water and his usual obligatory urine volume. Loss of osmotically effective material ("salt") in the urine only is represented by the product uU_{eop} where u is rate of urine flow (cc./min.) and U_{eop} is urinary concentration in terms of effective osmotic pressure (eop), i.e., osmolality or other equivalent units. Rate of water loss is represented by $u + w$, where w is the rate of extrarenal water loss (cc./min.), chiefly pulmocutaneous. These expressions describe mathematically the salt removed from the body and the water removed from the body.

Imagine the salt removed to be dissolved in the water removed so that, in effect, a solution is removed whose virtual concentration is $uU_{eop}/(u + w)$. If this solution is less concentrated than body fluids of concentration A_{eop}, its removal tends to leave the remaining body fluids more concentrated osmotically. To posit a condition of salt and water loss which, in theory, proves dipsogenic,[39] let

$$\frac{uU_{eop}}{u + w} < A_{eop}$$

and solve this inequality for

$$\frac{w}{u} > \frac{U_{eop}}{A_{eop}} - 1$$

From the latter inequality we might infer a curious rule, *viz.*, in hydrodipsic mammals (those which normally drink free water) undergoing ordinary dehydration, and which have a concentration ratio for effective osmotic pressure greater than 2, the rate of extrarenal water loss exceeds the rate of urine flow. If the concentration ratio were 2,

$$\frac{w}{u} > 2 - 1 = 1$$

or, $$w > u$$

[39] Thirst and osmometric analysis are conveniences of the argument. What is important in this inequality analysis is the determination of conditions which favor the rise of *eop* without limit. In this sense the analysis concerns survival primarily; thirst secondarily.

Under the conditions of dehydration in man, described above, w might be of the order of 0.7 cc./min., and u might be 0.5 cc./min., which would satisfy the inequality. Where w is extrarenal loss in a hot environment, w/u is capable of attaining in man (18) a ratio in excess of 30. In the frog which produces a hypotonic urine such that $U_{eop}/A_{eop} < 1$, $U_{eop}/A_{eop} - 1$ is negative, reflecting the fact that the frog, which practically never drinks, *gains* rather than loses net water through its skin. In diabetes insipidus, with negative values of $U_{eop}/A_{eop} - 1$, however small w/u may be because of the polyuria, the latter term is always positive. Thus it is always greater than $U_{eop}/A_{eop} - 1$, and the dipsogenic nature of this disease is formalized.

This analysis illustrates the antagonism between the dipsogenic effect of the extrarenal water loss which always tends to concentrate body fluids osmotically, and the antidipsic effect of the removal from the body of a hypertonic urine. The dipsogenic (potogenic) element in most mammals is usually the stronger so that, at intervals, they drink.

The formation of saliva, always hypotonic (65, 362) is in a sense dipsogenic but actually, because of its return to the system, has no net osmotic effect. The facultative urine flow in water diuresis is also dipsogenic, i.e., ingestion of a positive water load changes the urine from antidipsic to dipsogenic.

A more detailed and general analysis (863) by means of inequalities will now be treated.

Consider again the man with no initial excess or deficit of water or *eop*. He proceeds to lose extrarenal and urinary water, and *eop*; he gains metabolic (oxidative), preformed, and exogenous (e.g., drinking) water, and exogenous (e.g., dietary) *eop*. The net *eop* lost from the body per minute is $uU_{eop} + E_{eop} - Q_{eop}$, where E_{eop} is rate of extrarenal loss of *eop*, and Q_{eop} is rate of intake of *eop*. The net rate at which water is lost from the body is $u + w - i$, where i is rate of intake in cc./min. Where m, p, and e, refer, respectively, to metabolic, preformed, and exogenous water, $i = i_m + i_p + i_e$. All (net) water removed from the body in a unit time is regarded as if it were a physical unit of volume. If the *eop* removed could be dissolved in this virtual volume of water removed then, in effect, the resulting solution of concentration $(uU_{eop} + E_{eop} - Q_{eop})/(u + w - i)$ would be removed from the body. By the rules of partition,[40] only if the concentration of this removed *eop* solution is less than that of the parent body fluid can this body fluid develop an elevation of *eop* consistent with the onset of thirst. Thus, if thirst is to set in,

$$\frac{uU_{eop} + E_{eop} - Q_{eop}}{u + w - i} < A_{eop} \qquad (1)$$

from which it follows that

$$\frac{w}{u} > \frac{U_{eop}}{A_{eop}} - 1 + \frac{E_{eop} - Q_{eop}}{uA_{eop}} + \frac{i}{u} \qquad (2)$$

Example I. For a man, we might find the following values of the variables: $U_{eop}/A_{eop} = 1.3$; $E_{eop} = 0$; $Q_{eop} = 0$; $i = i_m = 0.2$ cc./min. (no preformed or drinking water taken); $u = 0.5$ cc./min.; and $w = 0.6$ cc./min. Substituting in (2),

$$\frac{0.6}{0.5} > 1.3 - 1 + \frac{0.2}{0.5}$$

or,
$$1.2 > 0.7$$

This inequality reflects the fact that the dipsogenic influence of the extrarenal water loss is greater than the antidipsic influence of the hypertonic urine.[41] If w were unknown, we could solve for

$$w > \frac{uU_{eop}}{A_{eop}} - u + \frac{E_{eop} - Q_{eop}}{A_{eop}} + i \qquad (3)$$

---

[40] Rules of partition (857): From a parent solution of concentration P, remove some solute and some water to form a daughter solution of concentration D. If $D = P$, the residual parent solution is of concentration $R = P = D$. If $D > P$, $R < P$; if $D < P$, $R > P$.

[41] The assumption that $U_{eop}/A_{eop} > 1$, in the absence of food and water intake, is only valid (and then not necessarily) in the first few days at most. It is known for dogs (232, 871), cats (626), and men (671) that urinary sodium and chloride concentrations under such conditions fall with time (Tables IV, XVII, XVIII) so that U_{eop}/A_{eop} is probably less than 1 (although urinary potassium rises). Thus the urine shifts from an antidipsic to a dipsogenic influence, in theory, and the inequality tends to become even greater.

This yields a minimal value for w of 0.35 cc./min. under the given conditions and constitutes a unique method for obtaining such an estimate of extrarenal water loss. U_{eop}/A_{eop} determines the antidipsic or dipsogenic influence of urinary flow by being, respectively, greater or less than 1; the clearance of effective osmotic pressure, uU_{eop}/A_{eop}, explicit in the latter inequality, determines these influences by being greater or less than u.

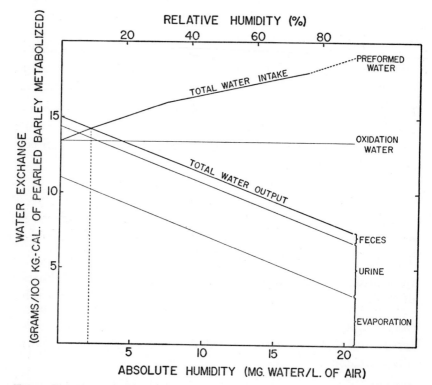

Figure 38. Water balance of kangaroo rat at various atmospheric humidities at 25° C. The calculations are made for the metabolism of 25 grams of dry pearled barley (100 Calories metabolic value). *Ordinate:* water intake for metabolism of barley and the simultaneous water output. *Abscissae:* atmospheric humidity. Water derived from oxidation of the 25 grams of barley is 13.4 grams, always constant and independent of atmospheric humidity. But the free water absorbed in the grain increases with humidity. In the graph the absorbed water is superimposed on the oxidative water, giving the top curve of total water intake as a function of humidity. After Schmidt-Nielsen and Schmidt-Nielsen (684, 689).

In some animals, practical considerations may preclude determination of w other than by inequality (3); and a minimal value may suffice for some purposes. In theory, it is possible, by actually increasing total water intake, i, until (3) becomes an equation (i.e., thirst is indefinitely postponed), to estimate the actual value of w mathematically.

Example II. Data for the point of water balance in kangaroo rats (681, 684, 689, Fig. 38) are given as follows: $w = 10.3$;[42] $i_m = 13.4$; and $u = 3.5$. These values are relative, expressed as g./100 Calories of pearled barley metabolized. Omit factors for fecal, preformed, and drinking water, and take $E_{eop} = Q_{eop} = 0$ to parallel Example I. Choose $U_{eop}/A_{eop} = 2$, although even a value as low as 1 would not change the inference. Substituting in (2).

$$\frac{10.3}{3.5} \ngtr 2 - 1 + \frac{13.4}{3.5}$$

or,
$$2.9 \ngtr 4.8$$

The fact that inequality (2) is *not* satisfied suggests that there is no tendency to concentrate *eop* and that the kangaroo rat is not hydrodipsic, i.e., has no necessary tendency to drink under these conditions. Such is the case in these animals.

Sea Water-Fresh Water Admixtures

About the view that the castaway at sea with a limited fresh water supply can beneficially add some sea water to his store, Hervey and McCance (352, pp. 261ff., 284) simply and categorically concluded:

. . . . it is urged that belief in the desirability of castaways drinking sea water, even in small amounts added to fresh-water rations, be finally abandoned.

This proposal has been affirmed by McCance and Morrison (522), McCance, Ungley, Crosfill, and Widdowson (523), and Margaria (510a).

---

[42] Excluding fecal water. Note that w consists of subfactors such as fecal, pulmonary, sensible, and insensible water, etc.

As Hervey (348) has explained the matter, sea water is strongly hypertonic to human body fluids and the first effect of absorption of any quantity of it, large or small, must be to increase for the worse the salt concentration of the body. This cannot seriously be challenged. However, Hervey went on to remark:

> Diluting sea-water with fresh-water rations makes no difference to the result: men who do this will become more dehydrated than if they drank the same ration of fresh water alone.

At present there is no conclusive evidence for or against this latter view (228) although it should be said that some reports appear to contravene it (177, 178, 840, pp. 265, 272ff.). It cannot easily be said to be self-evident, however, because there are mixtures of sea and fresh water which are hypotonic and do not, by virtue of their simple addition to the body, increase the tonicity (relative dehydration) of body fluids; nor is it obvious that a larger volume of sea-fresh water admixture must cause a greater absolute dehydration than the smaller volume of fresh water alone.

Ladell (456, 460) supposed that the total osmotic space available in the urine might, in diuresis resulting from drinking a quantity of sea water, accommodate both the obligatory urea and metabolite excretion of a semistarving individual, and also the salt of the sea water. This idea is subtle and powerful, and it is proposed shortly to examine some of its implications. Its extension to larger questions of drinking in animals can only be broached (p. 327ff.).

McCance and Morrison (522) have attempted in the following way to clarify objections to the castaway's use of sea water in any amount as an additive to fresh water rations. They picture the ingestion of diluted sea water as a two stage operation: (1) ingestion of the limited ration of fresh water which is insufficient to relieve dehydration, has no effect on urinary osmolality, and merely dilutes body fluids to a small extent; (2) ingestion of sea water. Since pure sea water promotes an admittedly undesirable hypersalemia, these authors ask of stage (2), ". . . . what good can it do?"[43]

This analysis presumes in effect that the dehydrated castaway's body is a static system, a receptacle containing slightly hypertonic fluid, into which fresh water and strongly hypertonic sea water are poured. Obviously the final tonicity of the total body fluid will be higher (and less desirable to the castaway) if sea water is added than if it is not added. This conclusion, however trivial, may, of course, be correct in actuality. But the as yet undetermined quantitative differences between this static picture and the actual behavior of the body are what logically sustain the argument about admixing.

Not only may urinary salt be removed from the body at different rates depending on volumes and salt concentrations of ingested fluids (Tables XVII–XIX) but the urine volume may vary also as part of a dynamic system. It should be agreed that in marked dehydration the effects of small amounts of fresh water which do not affect the urinary output cannot be favorably modified by adding sea water, as McCance and Morrison hold. But where the fresh water ration is relatively plentiful and dehydration has not become substantial, the addition of sea water may have appreciably different effects.[44]

It is well to note that in starvation, both water deficit (with oliguresis) and water excess (with diuresis) are attended by low urinary salt concentration; the production of urine is thus a dipso-

---

[43] McCance and Young (526), in affirming that sea water drinking is deleterious in dehydrated man, extended this concept to uriposia. ". . . . a dehydrated man can do himself no good by drinking his own urine. By so doing he is merely asking his kidneys to repeat work which they have already done, and cannot be expected to do better." However, it is not to be overlooked that small amounts of urine or sea water used for moistening or as a gargle, or even blood, have been used gratefully by sufferers (pp. 219, 248, 378, 392, 404).

It is of interest that water stored in the bladder of frogs and toads need not be irrevocably lost. Hypotonic urine can largely be reclaimed, presumably usefully, by these animals when subjected to dehydration (677).

[44] Bombard's idea (p. 269) that sea water should be drunk before dehydration sets in was intended to be applied even where no fresh water or fish juice was yet available. This may appear to relate more to Ladell's physical fitness concept (p. 265) than the one here considered; however, see page 321ff.

genic process (p. 304) in both instances. However, in the ab-
absence of dehydration and with the administration of even hypotonic salt solution, the urinary salt concentration may be high
(especially as extrarenal water loss is high) and the production
of urine may be an antidipsic process.

   Urinary Osmotic Space. Were salt the only solute of the urine
it would not be surprising if the urinary volume varied from zero
to certain considerable quantities essentially in proportion to the
salt excretion, although at extremely high excretion rates a linear
relationship would not be expected (739, 857). At low to moderate rates of salt excretion (and intake), urinary salt concentrations could be expected to be at the limiting isorrheic concentration (ca. 1.7% sodium chloride or somewhat higher (p. 298ff.))
where small degrees of absolute and relative dehydration coexist.
It is only for this hypothetic case of pure saluria in the dehydrated
individual, actually, that arguments against the use of sea water,
alone or in admixture, are incontrovertible. With the proviso
(for the moment) that all salt leaves in the urine, any given
increment of sea water(osmotically equivalent to 3.2% sodium
chloride) to the body must obligate a still larger increment of
urinary volume if salt balance is preserved, making for a negative
water balance (p. 262). If enough salt were eliminated extrarenally, as in sweat, to keep the urinary volume increment equal
to the sea water increment, water balance would still be negative
by virtue of the concomitant extrarenal water loss. It is not possible, therefore, under these conditions to preserve simultaneously
zero salt and water balances.

   In point of fact, of course, salt is not the only solute of the
urine. A large fraction consists of urea and other materials which,
although they may exert no effective osmotic pressure in the body
fluids at large, obligate a urinary volume to some extent independently of salt. This exposes the inadequacy of the simple argument,
based on salt intake being equal to urinary salt output, to bring
out the real problem. Where s and S are volume and salt concentration of a saline intake, respectively, and u and U are the
same for urine, the statment $sS = uU$ suggests properly that if
$S > U, u > s$. But it also implies that as s approaches zero while
$S > U$, that u should approach zero (since U will not). This is

not the case because a value of $u > 0$ is obligated by excretory products other than salt.

Suppose the ordinary, metabolic excretion of all solutes with no *eop*, designated as "urea+" for simplicity, to be 480 mOs./24 hours. If the limiting isorrheic concentration of these as a whole were taken at 1,200 mOs./L. (ca. 7.2% "urea+"), then 480/1,200 or 0.40 L./24 hours would be the virtual, salt free, obligatory urine volume. This minimum volume of urine would be produced even if salt excretion were zero. It is this salt free volume which potentially constitutes the available osmotic space of Ladell (456, 460) into which some extra salt can escape and still keep beneath its own urinary concentration ceiling. Hervey's (348) interpretation of Ladell's osmotic space, as that urinary volume of submaximal salt concentration to which salt could be added, raising the concentration to maximum without an increase in volume, is somewhat misleading and was clarified by Ladell (460).

Although the concept of osmotic space took root from studies of Gamble *et al.* (279, 280), its formulation by Ladell, and its reformulation as given here and elsewhere (875), is quite independent of the idea of "economy of water in renal function referable to urea" (p. 74). We proceed to detail a theory of osmotic space as follows.

Consider a daily intake of 480 mOs. of salt (*eop*) which when excreted only by the kidney brings the total urinary solute (*eop* + "urea+") to 960 mOs./24 hours. For a limiting osmolality of the urine still at 1,200 mOs./L., and salt balance, 960/1,200 or 0.80 L./24 hours of urine must necessarily form. But the 480 mOs. of salt dissolved now in 0.80 L. yields an *eop* concentration of 600 mOs./L. This latter approximates to a limiting isorrheic concentration for *eop* (Table XX), i.e., of all salts which might exert *eop*, but largely for "sodium chloride." Thus the virtual volume of urine obligated by "urea+" provides water available for the solution of salt, and the virtual volume of urine obligated by salt reciprocates in providing water available for the solution of "urea+."

It may now be seen that if the above intake of 480 mOs. of salt were provided by 0.48 L. of sea water of concentration 1,000 mOs/L. (assumed here to be entirely *eop*), that volume of sea water would actually obligate only 0.40 L. of extra urine, i.e., a relative gain of water to the body of 0.08 L. would be obtained unlike the case if no fluid were drunk. In another way, sea water intake would exceed its self-obligated water output; and this excess of water would be "free" (p. 163) since all of the salt of the intake fluid would have been removed.

Nothing is more clear than that experimental facts of urinary excretion requisite to analysis of the type we undertake, as these might apply to castaways in starvation or semistarvation, are quite meager or do not exist. If "urea+" excretion falls in starvation (Table VI. But this may not occur during mariposia, according to Aury (60); indeed, urea excretion may increase.), then the osmotically available space for salt falls with it. But this is largely offset by the fact that the urinary volume falls also, saving water directly.

However thin the argument in support of the potential systemic benefit of mariposia, there is much less to be said for uriposia (p. 309). It is not merely that the osmotic pressure of the urine of a dehydrating man ordinarily exceeds that of sea water. It is rather because there is no osmotic space in the urine, forming in dehydration, for the solutes in ingested urine which are already at their limiting concentrations. Thus, any volume of ingested urine obligates no less than an equal volume of newly formed urine. Urine may be less salty (and possibly less dipsogenic on that score) than sea water but is otherwise of a lesser aquiferous potential, and is possibly also more toxic. Conceivably the urine of certain diabetic or nephritic individuals might be less dangerous if drunk by normal persons. The use of urine to moisten the throat is still another matter (p. 219).

The Admixture Problem. The complexity of the admixture problem is pointed up by observing that when a given volume of sea water is added to fresh drinking water, several variables in the salt-water metabolism are simultaneously and differentially changed: the volume of intake fluid is increased; its concentration is increased; the intake of *eop* is augmented; and the urine volume is increased (60, 526, 671, 825). The combined effect of all of these, which by no means comprise all of the pertinent variables, on body fluid composition and thirst is not to be inferred easily.

Thus, if we know that half-strength sea water can prevent relative dehydration in the fasting dog (871) and perhaps in man, to judge from Willis' account (p. 272), can we tell whether an intake of fresh water alone, half as great as of this half-strength sea water is equally beneficial?

Inequality (3) on page 305 may be modified as follows, taking its right hand side equal to Z:

$$w > \frac{uU_{eop}}{A_{eop}} - u + \frac{E_{eop} - Q_{eop}}{A_{eop}} + i_e + 0.3 = Z$$

All symbols are as before, but volumes per unit time will now be referred to in L./24 hours. Here i_e represents the total volume of fluid (of any concentration) drunk per 24 hours, 0.3 is an assumed daily average formation of oxidative water, Q is the total daily intake of *eop* or salt contained only in i_e and defined by $i_e I_{eop}$. I_{eop} is the osmotic concentration of fluid i_e in osmols per Kg. (or, more loosely, per L. of water).

We now discuss the case of a man without food at various mean environmental temperatures, making no allowances for preformed water of tissue breakdown, enteral water or salt losses, changes in nitrogen excretion, etc. Fig. 39 shows a curve of extrarenal (pulmocutaneous) water loss, w, as a function of temperature, adapted from Adolph *et al.* (18). Since Z is the ordinate, every point of the water loss-temperature curve is a Z value and the w curve is also the locus of all points $w = Z$.

The purpose of the following theoretic analysis is to illustrate broadly yet quantitatively the effect of the capacity of the kidney to eliminate *eop* (chiefly salt, e.g., chloride and its electroequivalent cations) at either low or high values. Depending on the relative loads (availability) of salt and water, the urine will either be salt poor or salt rich. If salt supplied by sea water can be removed in a salt rich urine, under conditions to be described, without resulting in a retention of salt relative to water in the body fluids at large, then the ingestion of sea water by virtue of its salt content need not be proscribed; and the ingestion of the water contained therein, per se, can act to promote a state of absolute and relative euhydration.

The interaction of the variables in Z is involved. In the absence of sufficient experimental data, the following assumptions are made:[45]

(1) w can be found from the curve $w = Z$ in Fig. 39, at any mean temperature.

(2) $E_{eop} = 40(w - 0.7)1.86 = 74.4w - 52.1$, where w is pulmo-cutaneous water loss at a given temperature, derived from the curve $w = Z$; 0.7 is minimal, nonsweat, insensible water loss (no salt therein) in L./24 hrs.; 40 is average salt content in sweat in mEq./L.; and 1.86 confers upon E the units of mOs./24 hrs.[46]

(3) $Q_{eop} = i_e I_{eop}$

(4) There is water balance, $w + u = i_e + 0.3$. This restriction was not applied by Ladell.

(5) There is salt balance, $u U_{eop} + E_{eop} = i_e I_{eop}$. U_{eop} varies from 0 to 600 mOs./L. and its values satisfy also assumption (6).

(6) "Urea+" excretion is 480 mOs/24 hrs. and

$$u = \frac{480 + i_e I_{eop} - E_{eop}}{1200},$$

where 1,200 mOs./L. is the limiting isorrheic, osmotic concentration of the urine and u has a minimal value of 0.40 L./24 hrs. Higher values of u are determined by the solution of this equation so long as those values of u satisfy the condition

$$\frac{i_e I_{eop} - E_{eop}}{u} < 600 \, \text{mOs./L.}$$

When the left hand side of this inequality is ≥ 600, we derive, instead,

$$u = \frac{i_e I_{eop} - E_{eop}}{600},$$

from assumption (5). That is, as soon as the LIC of *eop* is reached,

---

[45] Admittedly the parametric values chosen for calculations are not firmly based in experimental fact at this time. Nevertheless they permit us to block out tentative conclusions not readily derived by other means.

[46] Obviously the calculation of E_{eop} is subject to various qualifying conditions. The eccrine chloride concentration increases with the duration of sweating (329) although it is reduced with acclimatization (25, 26, 208, 209, 663a) possibly (663), though not necessarily (18), because of chloride deficiency. Sweat rate may be lower in men drinking saline if they are active in a hot humid environment (461), and also during water restriction (782). Loss of magnesium salts in or through the gut are unaccounted (p. 297, 325).

further *eop* excretion augments urinary volume in accord with that concentration restriction; urea excretion no longer determines *u*.

(7) A_{eop} is a constant for purposes of this analysis, i.e., 300 mOs./L. (The "normal" value in man is somewhat lower (Table XVII).) Since Z is given by the expression on page 313, from assumptions (2) and (3),

$$Z = \frac{i_e I_{eop}}{A_{eop}} - \frac{E_{eop}}{A_{eop}} - u + \frac{E_{eop}}{A_{eop}} - \frac{i_e I_{eop}}{A_{eop}} + i_e + 0.3$$

so that

$$Z = i_e + 0.3 - u$$

It is interesting to note that I_{eop} and *w* enter simply to determine *u* through assumptions (2), (5), and (6), and Z follows directly therefrom.

By choosing values of i_e and I_{eop} as desired, the values of Z as a function of temperature and the curves of Fig. 39 are derived. Where the curve of Z at given i_e and I_{eop} values crosses the $w = Z$ curve, the conditions defined thereby are those of zero water balance, zero salt balance, and maintenance of a constant A_{eop} value. Where the Z curve falls in the region below the $w = Z$ curve so that $w > Z$, the conditions defined are those of zero salt balance, negative water balance, and the tendency to elevate A_{eop}. The latter presumably predisposes to intensification of thirst and a steadily deteriorating condition (p. 303). Where the Z curve lies above the $w = Z$ curve, i.e., $w < Z$, the conditions defined predispose to zero water balance, negative salt balance, and the tendency to diminish A_{eop}. But the availability of salt, however, is not a problem here, and water diuresis would permit water balance at widely varying fluid intakes. If so corrected, certain Z curves would coincide with the $w = Z$ curve up to the same point (temperature) of intersection as indicated by the assumptions actually employed e.g., presently shown in Fig. 39.

We notice in Fig. 39 that the curve $i_e = 0$ lies everywhere below the $w = Z$ curve, indicating that lack of water must inevitably lead to deterioration. Precious mathematical lucubration is assuredly not necessary to elicit this fact, but it serves, by pro-

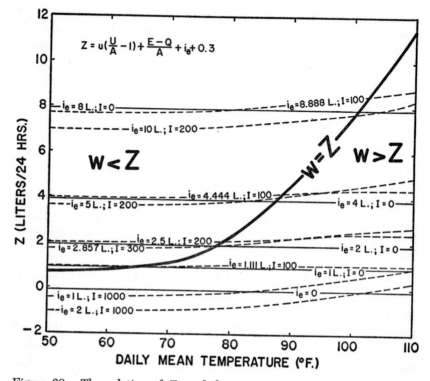

Figure 39. The relation of Z to daily mean air temperature. Values of evaporative water loss, *w*, for men at rest in shade, are plotted as a function of mean air temperature (heavy line, $w = Z$). This curve divides the diagram into two areas, an upper one in which $w < Z$ and a lower one in which $w > Z$. With 24 hour intakes of drink, i_e, of salt concentration *I* mOs./L., with extrarenal salt losses (sweat), *E*, and with salt intakes, *Q*, values of Z can be determined from the equation in the upper left of the graph for various temperatures. All concentrations and rates of salt exchange refer to effective osmotic pressures. Where curves of Z (lighter lines, solid or interrupted) intersect the heavy line, $Z = w$. Z curves in the area $w > Z$ designate conditions of salt and water balance which predispose to relative dehydration, presumably to thirst, and to a steadily deteriorating condition. Where Z curves intersect $w = Z$, the highest temperature theoretically consistent with zero water and salt balances is indicated. Solid Z curves represent fresh water (or none); interrupted curves represent salt solutions. See text for details.

viding other less obvious conclusions, to point up the power of inequality analysis. For the chosen parameters, when $i_e = 2$ L.

of fresh water per 24 hours ($I = 0$), the Z curve intersects the $w = Z$ curve at about 77° mean F. (reflecting a higher maximum temperature). Without considering this point of intersection to have absolute significance, we discover by this method how a certain intake may prevent hydropenic deterioration up to a particular mean temperature, but not beyond. We see how $i_e = 4$ L. of fresh water intersects the $w = Z$ curve at about 87° F.; 8 L. carries us still higher.[47] Taking sea water milliosmolality as 1000, it is seen how i_e values of 1 and 2 L. of this fluid per 24 hours yield Z curves lying below $w = Z$. It is instructive to observe that the curves for which $I = 1000$ cross the curve $i_e = 0$.

If we now consider a volume of fresh water of 2 L. to which we add 0.5 L. of sea water, so that $i_e = 2.5$ and $I = 200$, we find that the intersection of this Z curve with the curve $w = Z$ is at a higher temperature (78.5° F.) than that of the curve for 2 L. of fresh water alone, suggesting a beneficial effect of the admixing in sustaining normal water and salt balances at the higher temperature. On the other hand, the addition of 0.857 L. of sea water to 2 L. of fresh water gives us a Z curve for $i_e = 2.857$ and $I = 300$, which intersects $w = Z$ at the same temperature as the curve for 2 L. of fresh water alone, suggesting less benefit than provided by the more dilute admixture. Compare also sea water:

---

[47] The upper range of temperatures considered in our analysis is in considerable measure hypothetical although mean temperatures of 110° F. or higher in hot rooms have provided information on extrarenal water losses for such unnatural conditions. Actually, air temperatures of the open ocean do not differ much from surface temperatures of the water which rarely exceed 86° except, for example, in parts of the Indian Ocean (90°) or of large bodies of water like the Gulf of Mexico (91°). While direct radiation from the sun augments water loss, total evaporative weight losses during a 24 hour period are only about a third greater for unshaded men than for those in good shade. However, provision of adequate shade is said to be able to lengthen survival time by as much as 40%, not including the secondary effects which flow from this in increasing the chance that rain will be caught and further prolong life (18).

The use of atropine to reduce water loss by limiting sweating has not been evaluated in connection with the problems of the castaway although it is said to be dangerous in the desert (18). Cullumbine and Miles (193) found that 2 mg. of atropine sulfate administered intramuscularly to men in warm environments augmented their general distress by increasing restlessness and irritability, and by promoting dryness of mouth and circulatory embarrassment (increased pulse rate, general vasodilatation). Even when body temperature was not increased, the feeling of heat might be intense.

fresh water admixtures of 1:9 (curves $i_e = 1$ versus $i_e = 1.111$, $i_e = 4$ versus $i_e = 4.444$, and $i_e = 8$ versus $i_e = 8.888$) and 1:4 (curves $i_e = 4$ versus $i_e = 5$ and $i_e = 8$ versus $i_e = 10$).

Pursuing the analysis further, let us examine Figs. 40, 41, and 42. Based upon the same information as Fig. 39, these depict the threshold condition of $w = Z$. In this case, since $Z =$

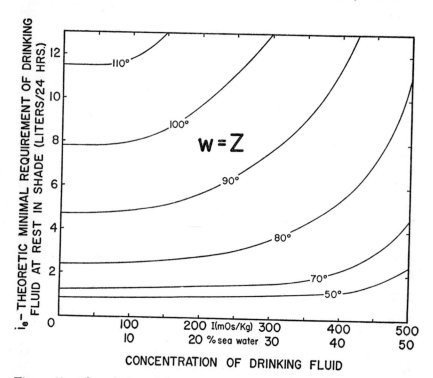

Figure 40. The relation of theoretic minimal drinking fluid requirements to the concentration of drinking fluid mixtures of fresh and sea water at various mean air temperatures (°F.). See text for details.

$i_e + 0.3 - u$, we have $i_e = w + u - 0.3$. In order to obtain the relations of Fig. 40, u is determined as before (assumption (6)), and thence i_e for the ordinate. By simply choosing various and appropriate values of $i_e I_{eop}$, we determine $i_e I_{eop}/i_e = I_{eop}$, which provides the abscissal values corresponding to i_e. Figs. 41 and 42 are now readily derived from the volume-concentration formula for admixtures, $sS = i_e I = (f + s)I$, where S is the osmotic concentration of sea water (taken as 1,000 mOs./L.), and f and s are, respectively, the volumes of fresh and sea water mixed, in L./24 hrs.

Fig. 42 illustrates strikingly the theoretic advantages and disadvantages of admixtures. Given the assumptions, it follows that, with variable temperature, there is a variable fresh water requirement for maintaining water and salt balances and con-

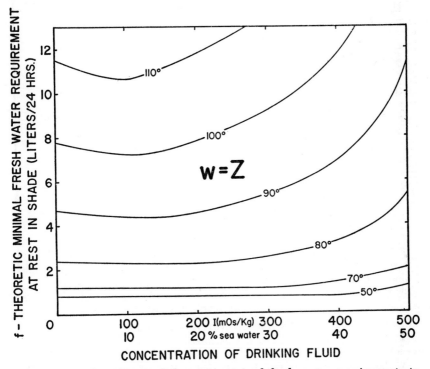

Figure 41. The relation of theoretic minimal fresh water requirements to the concentration of drinking fluid mixtures of fresh and sea water at various mean air temperatures (°F.). See text for details.

stancy of salt concentrations in body fluids. This requirement passes through a minimum as the quantity of sea water admixed is increased from zero, although the quantity of sea water required to minimize the fresh water requirement is not numerically equal to the quantity of fresh water saved per 24 hours. However, the maximal quantity of fresh water saved at a given temperature is

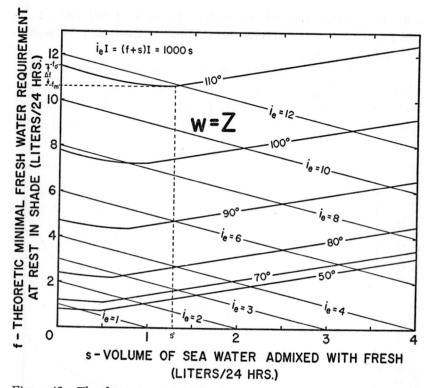

Figure 42.   The theoretic minimal fresh water requirement as a function of the volume of sea water admixed with fresh water.   The family of parallel i_e lines are equipotes.   Each equipote is the locus of all points representing a fixed total volume (in liters per 24 hours) of fresh and sea water, i.e., $i_e = f + s$.   The maximal volume of fresh water theoretically saved per 24 hours, Δf, is measured by the difference between f_o when $s = 0$ and the minimal fresh water requirement, f_m, at the optimal sea water volume, s', in a curve for a given temperature.

An important consideration here is that if the values on the ordinate be called water deficit/24 hours, instead of f, and the values of the abscissa be simply sea water intake/24 hours, the same family of curves provides minimal negative water loads and corresponding optimal sea water volumes where no fresh water is taken.   Thus, in theory, 0.48 L. of sea water taken at 50° F., in the absence of fresh water, would yield the smallest possible water deficit (slightly smaller than if no fluid at all were taken) and a zero salt balance.

Formulas for calculating Δf, s', and other details are given in the text.

greater as the quantity of fresh water alone ($s = 0$) required at that temperature is greater; it is actually proportional to extrarenal salt loss as shown following.

In salt balance,

$$sS_{eop} = uU_{eop} + E_{eop}.$$

According to the basic premise in the foregoing analysis, the optimal volume of sea water, s', consistent with the maximal volume of fresh water saved in an admixture, depends upon filling with *eop* a urinary osmotic space of 0.8 L. from 0 to 600 mOs./L., or in the amount of 480 mOs. Therefore, if $s = s'$ and $S = 1{,}000$ mOs./L. then

$$s' = \frac{480 + E_{eop}}{1000}$$

Now let f_o be the theoretic minimal fresh water requirement for water balance at a given temperature when $s = 0$; let f_m be the theoretic minimal fresh water requirement for water balance, at the same temperature, in admixture with s'; let Δf be that maximal quantity of fresh water theoretically saved by admixture with s'; and let u' be the volume of urine formed when any volume, $i_e = s'$, of pure sea water is taken alone.

When fluid intake is fresh water only, $i_e = f_o$. In water balance

$$i_e = f_o = w + u - 0.3$$

When fluid intake consists of f_m and s', then, in water balance,

$$i_e = f_m + s' = w + u' - 0.3$$

Thus, $$\Delta f = f_o - f_m = u - u' + s'$$

Since $u' = 0.8$ and $u = 0.4$ L./24 hrs.,

$$\Delta f = s' - 0.4 = \frac{E_{eop}}{1000} + 0.08$$

This relation holds in Fig. 42.

Thus, the saving in fresh water is proportional to the extrarenal salt loss which increases as a function of temperature. The minimal value of Δf is 0.08 L./24 hrs. Since the lowest possible value of s' is 0.48 L./24 hrs. (when $E_{eop} = 0$), it follows that even with the smallest intake of fresh water which, alone, would be consistent with water balance, it should be possible theoretically to reduce this by 0.08 L. by admixing 0.48 L. of sea water.

A curious point is this: if osmotic space is available for salt in the urine, a certain quantity of salt, taken as a corresponding volume of pure sea water, might just fill the osmotic space and augment urine volume in addition, but not by an amount exceeding the volume of sea water drunk. Thus zero salt balance would be obtained and the negative water balance resulting from drinking sea water only would be the same as (i.e., no greater than) if no fluid were taken.

Equal negative water balances are defined for these states as

$$i_e + 0.3 - (w + u') = 0.3 - (w + u)$$

or, $$i_e + 0.3 - (w + u') = 0.3 - (w + 0.4)$$

When sea water alone is drunk so that $i_e = s''$,

$$s'' = u' - 0.4$$

Salt balance is defined by

$$u' = \frac{1000s'' - E_{eop}}{600}$$

so that

$$s'' = 0.6 + \frac{E_{eop}}{400}$$

If the degree of dehydration involved did not interfere with the urinary concentrating power for salt, it would appear that, at low temperatures where $E_{eop} = 0$, up to 0.6 L. of sea water could be taken per 24 hours with no worse effects than if no water were taken (the water deficit in both instances would be 0.8 L./24 hrs.). At 100° F., where $E_{eop} = 521$ mOs., 1.9 L. of sea water could be taken in 24 hours, causing, in theory, exactly the same negative water balance, *viz.*, 7.8 L./24 hrs., as would obtain were no fluid taken. If, however, a developing negative water balance (and/or even adrenocortical stress) precipitated the "dehydration reaction" (105, Table IV) in which the kidney fails to concentrate urinary salt in spite of elevated concentrations of salt in the plasma, then serious consequences could be expected following mariposia.

On the other hand, some of Aury's and Longuet's results (p. 271ff) may be explicable on the basis of this theory since it follows therefrom that quantities smaller than 0.6 L. of sea water per day could provide a more favorable water balance than no fluid at all. The subjects of the aforementioned workers took 0.5 L. of sea water per day and Aury considered the water balances similar to those which one observes in men under the same conditions but completely deprived of water.[48]

We have described the theoretic advantages of drinking an admixture of sea and fresh water over drinking fresh water alone. To complete the picture we may formally cite the theoretic advantages of drinking an admixture over drinking sea water alone. These are: 1) the negative water balance is less; 2) the dehydration reaction (restriction of salt from the urine, elevation of threshold of retention of salt) may be minimized; and 3) the disgusting, nauseating, emetic, and dipsogenic properties are less. In general, increasing the ratio of fresh to sea water is to be desired but, as we have seen above, there may indeed be a limit (p. 263).

The putative undesirable sequelae of mariposia, *viz.*, nausea, vomiting, and purgation—not to mention the hyperdipsia and other effects to be expected if this mathematical analysis is invalid—have been denied by a sufficient number of individuals (p. 296) and have been lacking in a sufficient number of animal experiments to favor still further examination of this matter.

It is of special interest to note that if the ordinate of Fig. 42 simply be called water deficit per 24 hours, instead of f, the same family of curves (omitting equipotes) for different temperatures, as drawn, holds for the new relation. Thus, the minima now represent the smallest possible negative water loads, and indicate correspondingly the optimal sea water intakes, s'. The formula for calculating s', given above, yields directly the theoretic quantities of sea water which, taken in the absence of fresh water, would be consistent with salt balance and the least possible hydropenia.

That some volume of pure sea water taken can be beneficial in tending to prolong survival time at any temperature, if the

---

[48] The practical advantage of having something to drink, rather than nothing, to moisten a parched throat ought never be overlooked (p. 219).

Three survivors of the British yacht, *Taifun,* adrift on a raft in the Mediterranean for six days were reported (646) to have tried Bombard's "method," taking three tablespoonsful of sea water every two hours from 6 o'clock in the morning until 8 at night, for six days (= ca. 360 cc./day). "It is due to this that we are now all right —," related Bergez, the engineer. Hervey (351) retorted, ". . . . they were lucky to survive in spite of it," for the reasons also given elsewhere (p. 307ff.).

negative water balance is less than when no fluid is drunk, pre-
supposes zero salt balance among other things. It may appear
dubious from the experiments of Hervey and McCance (352, p.
284) and Rubini, Wolf, and Meroney (671, p. 286, Tables XVII–
XIX), and, indeed, of Ladell himself (460) that zero salt balance
is possible generally, but the question has still not been disposed
of satisfactorily.

Examination of the equipotes of Fig. 42 clearly suggests how,
as air temperature increases, the relative volume of fresh water
to sea water must increase in order just to maintain $w = Z$,
a point already suggested by Ladell (460). The apparent con-
tradiction to this theory (228, 523) in the records (which suggest
that mortality of sea water drinkers was less rather than greater
at higher temperatures) cannot be evaluated since nothing is
indicated about the quantities of sea water drunk in these cases.

It cannot be overemphasized that the foregoing calculations
and diagrams are intended in no wise to define what will actually
be obtained in practice; they fail, perhaps seriously, in neglecting
the matter of alterations in nitrogen excretion with starvation or
semistarvation (302a, pp. 118, 329ff.) and with temperature, and
in neglecting the real hazards and complications of seasickness.
Rather, they are used to suggest that, in theory which remains to
be tested, certain optimal sea water-fresh water admixtures might
be able usefully to extend fresh water supplies. This possibility
has hitherto not been derived formally.

It can be inferred from this analysis that potential savings in
fresh water during water balance, if such there be, increase as
a function of the absolute amount of fresh water required and
available. Therefore, where these supplies are small, and if a
theoretically optimum mixture is one containing relatively little
sea water, we recognize that the gain to be anticipated by admixing practically vanishes (867). Herein lies the force of the argument of McCance and Morrison (522, p. 308). In another way,
a man with only 10 cc. of fresh water cannot hope to measure
his systemic benefit from the addition of 1 cc. of sea water. But
the real question is: can a man with 10 liters of fresh water, who
adds a liter of sea water, hope for an extra day of survival?

It has been properly remarked (31) that in emergencies a man will drink some sea water accidentally, and a certain amount of dried salt may also be taken in (571) nullifying the meager benefit that might be gained by mariposia. But there is no quantitative assessment of this matter.

Ladell (460) does not recommend rinsing the mouth out with sea water as each rinse means that at least 10 cc. of water is left in the mouth, and with frequent rinses, it is supposed, the upper safe limit of intake would soon be reached.

The statistical demonstration of McCance, Ungley, Crosfill, and Widdowson (523, p. 275) of the hazard in drinking sea water must be considered in the light of the fact that the quantities of sea water drunk by their survivors were generally not known. The man who, crazed or otherwise, consumes large quantities of sea water relative to fresh, and who becomes a mortality unit, is not necessarily in the same category as the man who drinks sparingly or takes small quantities relative to those of fresh water. McCance and his associates showed that, in their series, men did not start to drink sea water until they had been adrift three days, a procedure which, by the theory outlined above, would not maximize the value of a given fresh water supply but serve contrariwise. And it must be noted that this was the contention of Bombard (112, 113) and Longuet (488a, p. 272).

The foregoing analysis clearly points up the dangers of indiscriminate use of sea water, more explicitly, indeed, than heretofore. It exposes the nature of a few of the "metaphysiologic" problems (857) which yet remain to be resolved experimentally if physiologists are to be able to assert confidently whether admixing can be a judicious procedure even for a statistically small group of casualties; and it may be of some heuristic value for the design of crucial experiments.

The question is occasionally raised as to whether certain components of sea water finding their way into the gut are removed from the osmotic stage by virtue of precipitation as insoluble salts, e.g., calcium sulfate, or other insoluble calcium or magnesium salts. Elkinton and Winkler (234) and others state that magnesium and sulfate are excreted as isotonic (with body fluids) solutions, and the long and proud history of Epsom salts as a purgative is well known. The magnesium salts (chloride and sulfate) of sea water exert on the average approximately the same osmotic pressure per mol of magnesium salt as sodium chloride; if the former remain in solution, one-third of the volume of ingested sea water should be destined for fecal elimination (p. 297). No account of this has been made in the foregoing calculations. The osmotic effect of sea water is predominantly measured (to the extent of ca. 85%) by its content of chloride (Tables XI, XII), all salts of which are soluble.

SALINE DRINKING WATERS

Water less salty than the oceans but with more than 0.1% of dissolved salts is called *brackish;* drinking water, according to the U. S. Public Health Service standards, should have no more than 0.1% and preferably less than 0.05% of dissolved salts (399).

Saline drinking waters are used in many parts of the world by man and animals (p. 358). Shotton (721) states that water of 0.3% sodium chloride can be drunk regularly by men in a desert climate; 0.4%, unaccompanied by important quantities of other salts is acceptable; 0.5% is endurable for short periods. Man is rather less tolerant than his herds.

It has also been held (502) that saline or alkaline water containing up to one-quarter per cent of salts may be used by men in the desert for many days without discomfort, but if the proportion goes to one-third per cent, only hardened travelers may use it; at one-half per cent, water is inimical to health and comfort.

The therapeutic value of saline drinks in industrial fatigue is well attested. Moss (561) proposed the use of 0.2% sodium chloride for miners and stokers, based on the assumption that sweat in hot environments contained approximately that much salt. Oswald (588) recommended a mixture of 0.21% sodium chloride and 0.14% potassium chloride to prevent cramps and promote well being in stokers and foundrymen. The military has used 0.1% sodium chloride in hot climates.

The taste threshold of sea water (artificial, Table XII) is obtained with mixtures approximating 1% sea water containing 0.035% sea salts (869). This order of magnitude is similar to that for the taste threshold of sodium chloride in man and rat (p. 122).

Burns (145) found the 'Ababda tribespeople of the eastern desert of Egypt to drink water containing salts, expressed as sodium chloride, in concentrations of 0.2 to 0.855%. These values are based on the conductivity of the contained electrolytes relative to the conductivity of sodium chloride in a standard solution. The most concentrated drinking water tested actually contained 123 mEq. of chloride/L., 56 mEq. of sodium/L., and 224 mOs./L.

Burns found human urine as concentrated as 1,470 mOs./L. Along with the value 1,484 mOs./L., reported by Frank *et al.* (271) in a hydropenic patient, this is among the highest urinary osmotic pressures on record for man (Table XX).

Injurious effects of continued drinking of water containing various salts, simulating natural saline waters used by people and livestock, have been studied (32, 344). Heller (342) tested rats and found 1.5 to 1.7% to be the maximum amount of soluble salts (sodium and potassium chloride, etc.) that could be used with safety. The bad effects were thought more to be "osmotic" than due to any specific ion. Antagonistic effects of ions are lacking or secondary. Chloride salts are less injurious than sulfates; alkalies more deleterious than neutral salts. When various strength sodium chloride solutions were employed as the sole source of drink, no rats were alive after 10 days if they received 2.5% or higher. At lower levels of concentration, the amount of water consumed became greater with increasing salt concentration until the rats refused to drink at all. Finally, they were compelled (by "thirst") to drink a large quantity at one time, causing death shortly. Waters containing 1.5% salt were often fatal to young rats. Growth stopped. They became emaciated and had rough coats, ophthalmia, diarrhea, and inflamed intestines. If they survived, some could resume growth and rear young on this intake. Increased mineral content of drinking water, which does not seriously injure animals, augments urinary and fecal output of salt, the latter possibly because of catharsis of osmotically active salts (343).

FISH AS A SOURCE OF WATER

We proceed to examine another matter, still in some ferment, namely, the use of fish as a source of "free" or "isorrheic" water (p. 163).

If a cat were castaway at sea but provided with fish, there is little question, at least in theory, but what it could survive for an indefinite period with no access to fresh water. Cats possess remarkable ability to concentrate their urine (626, 670, 867, Table XX). The conservation of water by the renal emunctory enables them to utilize the preformed and oxidative water of food such as fish or meat to compensate for all paths of water loss. Prentiss, Wolf, and Eddy (626) kept cats on salmon or on beef with no extra water for several months and showed that they suffered no serious or progressive hydropenia. However, in some cases they developed powerful appetites for sea water, possibly for the salts therein. One cat drank an average of 143 cc. of sea water per day for a week; another drank half strength sea water up to 2.5 L./day, which was accompanied by severe sustained diarrhea (875). This accords with our knowledge that salt solutions are sometimes interpreted by animals as requiring larger intakes than water (pp. 162, 171).

Willis (840, p. 272) actually had a cat with him under conditions resembling those of a castaway and it would appear that theory in this case is practicable.

Quashnock (633) and Danowski *et al.* (196) found that the dog could be maintained in a vigorous state for at least four weeks on raw haddock. This was explained by the dog's ability strongly to concentrate nitrogen, with conservation of some of the water of the fish (842). Dry protein, administered to dehydrating dogs in amounts greater than necessary for nitrogen equilibrium (i.e., 1.5 g./Kg./day), increased urine volume and thereby dehydration, and decreased survival time (Figs. 32, 33).

Straub (770) stated that it is a known fact that dogs fed fresh meat in sufficient quantities generally have no need for additional water uptake, although partially air-dried meat effects a dehydration of these animals. And McCance and Young (527) alleged that the dog in a temperate climate, if deprived of food and water can, unlike a man, live quite comfortably on the water in its tissues which are broken down, and on its own water of metabolism. Caldwell (149) noted evidence that cats could live for long periods on a diet of flesh and blood such as might be obtained from a recently killed animal; and Colin (176) cited a cat that ate boiled meat without drink for 19 months.

A man, castaway at sea and eating fish, is no match metabolically for a cat or a dog. His urinary concentrating power is half that of these animals, the larger part of the deficiency lying in a lesser ability to concentrate nitrogen. All of the water of ingested fish (muscle) is used to excrete its protein metabolites and salts (p. 117ff.) and is not used to minimize dehydration or

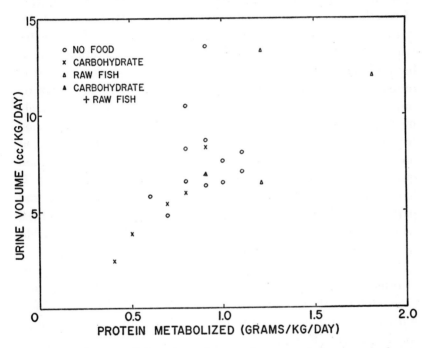

Figure 43. Average daily urine volume and average daily amount of protein metabolized as measured by nitrogen excretion in man. Subjects receiving sugar tended to conserve body protein and so to have low urine volumes. After Winkler *et al.* (842).

reverse the water balance (230, 234, 633, 842, Fig. 43). Nothing in experimental evidence contradicts the view that ingestion of whole fish or fish muscle is an unsafe practice for a man without fresh water or early prospects of obtaining considerable quantities; and it has been stated (831) that thirst is intensified by eating fish. Further, it would appear even more reasonable that dried fish should not be eaten unless water is abundantly available

(571). However, it may be important to inquire whether under certain conditions a man does better to utilize the flesh of fish rather than his own flesh (474a, 867). In semistarvation, where some raw fish is eaten, the excretion of urinary nitrogen may be no greater than in complete starvation, i.e., some body protein is spared (633).

So much for present physiologic understanding. The question of whether fish could profitably be eaten by man along with ingestion of sea water or some admixture of sea and fresh water (pp. 270, 271, 333) deserves more careful consideration than it has received. In the author's laboratory recent experiments (875) on cats indicate that these animals: (1) survive indefinitely on raw salmon, and no extra water (626); (2) become progressively more hydropenic on raw salmom which has been partially dried by removing water amounting to one-fifth of the wet weight, and no extra water; (3) become progressively hydropenic when offered no food but artificial sea water ad libitum (which is hardly drunk); but (4) may survive indefinitely when offered partially dried salmon of (2) and artificial sea water ad libitum, which is drunk in considerable quantities (p. 298). Somewhat similar results have also been found in white rats (875, p. 358).

An experimental and theoretic analysis of this matter in terms of osmotic space (p. 310) for a given extrarenal water loss, and calculated metabolic water yields of foods (p. 352ff.) is called for, but we defer this interesting subject and its implications for man for the present (875).

Fish Juice

Partly as a result of the present physiologic proscription against eating fish when one is short of water, but also for more positive reasons, much attention has been directed to the use of the juice of fish in the hope that this might constitute a potable fluid. This endeavor has been fortified by hearsay evidence that native fishermen in tropic seas, and others, have supplemented their water rations by sucking or squeezing the juice out of raw fish flesh (388, 840); and Bombard's contentions (pp. 269, 332), of course, have stimulated some recent work.

Assuming that certain strengths of saline—equivalent to an ideal, nitrogen free fish juice—are potable, and that one can simulate such solutions by suitable admixing of sea and fresh water, it does not follow on that account that it would serve the castaway equally well to mix sea water with a restricted fresh water supply as to drink fish juice. When one makes such a mixture he is adding only sea water to his total water ration; when one obtains fish juice from a catch, he is in effect adding both sea and fresh water to his total ration since fish juice, at least as regards salt, may be considered abstractly as a mixture of two volumes of fluid, one osmotically equivalent to sea water and another of pure water. These alternatives create vastly different physiologic situations.

It has sometimes been recommended that, in view of the difficulty of wringing the juice out of a fish,[49] the fluid be chewed out (531). Chewing fish may temporarily quench thirst (358) but has not been advised because it results in a simultaneous swallowing of protein also (272a, 570); indeed, with the salivation induced thereby and entering the pulp, no net yield of fluid is obtained by chewing or sucking (388).

So-called "lymph," obtained by mechanical expression from the flesh or other tissues of fish, is not true lymph (350). Thick, turbid, and often pink, it may contain plasma, cell fluid, red cells, and tissue debris, and its concentrations of electrolytes are quite unlike those of extracellular fluid. It has an oily, slightly sweet taste and a slight fishy odor unless ammoniacal compounds are present in relatively large amounts. Crude extracts of fatty fish e.g., of mackerel muscle, have the consistency of whipped cream and contain perhaps 80 g. of fat/Kg.

The viscid, collagen-containing, more or less limpid liquid left after press juice is cleared of fat and insoluble material by centrifugation or decantation is known as *stickwater* (188). This quickly decomposing liquor is given off as waste in the wet process of reducing fish to meal. It is often salvaged for its vitamins, proteins, and amino acids and condensed to be added to cattle and poultry feed.

---

[49] The "fish juice fable" (733a). It is almost impossible to wring by hand any appreciable moisture from fish.

Fish eyes contain a high percentage of water and their use has been suggested along with advice to suck spinal fluid from the backbones of birds and fish (571a); the value of the latter is dubious.

Hunter and Hughes (388) have reviewed the literature of, and at length studied, methods of production, yield, and analysis of lymph from several species of marine fish. They also designed a practical fish press yielding fluid of the order of 200 cc./Kg. of fish muscle. Accepting 400 cc./Kg. as a theoretical maximum quantity of fluid expressible, they discovered that lesser yields of fluid varied with the square root of the pressure applied.

Analysis of press juice from various species showed it to contain 5 to 20 g. of nitrogen/Kg., 19 to 100 g. of protein/Kg. From six cod the following average values were found for electrolytes (mEq./L.) in press juice: sodium, 41; potassium, 103; calcium, 3.9; magnesium, 15; chloride, 37; phosphate (as phosphorus), 49; sulfate (as sulfur), 90; bicarbonate, 2. Butler (147) obtained from sea bass only 50 cc. of fluid per kilogram of fish, largely intracellular, containing in each liter 20 g. of nitrogen (suggesting a protein content of 125 g.), 30 g. of phosphorus, and 42 mEq. of chloride.

The yield from incised fish, hanging and allowed to drip, is much less (388). When 10 or more cuts, one inch apart and one and one-half inches deep were made down the length of the fish, no more than 9 cc./Kg./24 hrs. were obtained unless the coelomic cavity was opened. In this case, no more than 18 cc./Kg. were obtained, in 6 hours for mackerel, and in 24 hours for cod. Lymph from fish incised and hung contained 15 g. of protein/Kg.

The solute concentrations of fish juice scarcely reflect the quasi-extracellular concentrations one might expect to find in true lymph. For example, as Grafflin (302) observed, the plasma of marine teleosts contains approximately 150 to 170 mEq. of chloride/L. (p. 366). The low sodium and chloride and high potassium and nitrogen (half of the nitrogen is nonprotein in nature (387)) concentrations of pressed fish juice reflect a general breakdown of cellular barriers with admixing of extracellular and cellular fluids.

Whatever reservations must remain about Bombard's theses (p. 269) and however illogical, perverse, and at variance with present physiologic evidence several of his concepts appear to be, some of his reports, facts, and suggestions are useful and interesting (113). With ingestion of sea water and fish juice of the order of 900 g./day, he found urine volume to be between 500 and 900 cc./day. The liquid which oozes from V-shaped, deep incisions in the flank of big fish (previously wiped to get rid of mucus and make it more palatable), or which fills up holes cut in the sides (839, 840), is not so rich in protein (ca. 1%) and in nitrogen (0.2%) as juice obtained from a screw type meat press. The former fluid contains fewer cells and less tissue debris than press juice. Bombard's press yielded 300 g. of liquid per Kg. of flesh; production could be improved by 70 g. by including the viscera in the pressing. By squeezing flesh in a rag (twisting, torsion) the fluid yield from flesh was said to be 200 to 250 g./Kg. Fluid yield is much better with big fish than with small. Bombard discarded fish smaller than 300 g. (Hunter and Hughes (388) remark on high press yields being misleading if fish muscle itself was extracted and included with the yield of fluid.)

An eight day experiment (113) of eating fish flesh and drinking fish juice resulted in diarrhea, gingival hemorrhages, and lesions of the mucosa. In another experiment of 10 days duration, relative constancy of blood protein was taken as evidence of constancy of blood water and the satisfactory nature of the intake. Nothing was said of analyses of the body fluids for salt or osmotic pressure, or about thirst, but the flavor of the fish was pronounced excellent. The fluid drunk per day was 0 to 500 cc. of sea water and 750 to 1800 g. of pressed liquid.

With 3 Kg. of fish daily, yielding 750 to 900 g. of liquid, and supplemented by sea water, we have a ration we may hope to obtain, Bombard stated. Accordingly, in distributing survivors of shipwreck, few people should be placed in many lifeboats rather than many in few because the number of pounds of fish caught is not proportional to the number of fishing lines (over about six) but suffers diminished increments per line in a given boat. His aim was to instil hope in individuals who are possibly lost through despair and the feeling of being abandoned (840). He would have his instructions placed on the sides of lifeboats against the time when food and water is short because the castaway should know what awaits him. The problem of survival is negligible, he thinks, if morale is high. Of his Atlantic voyage, he remarked the symptoms (p. 270) of rapid loss of taste sense, anosmia, which improved eight days after the end of the voyage; auditory hallucinations; and the need for more sleep (sleep as experienced did not bring true rest, and waking was difficult).

He also recommended use of a net with relatively large holes to catch zooplankton and eliminate phytoplankton which latter were said to be salty, difficult to assimilate, and laxative or even toxic.[50] However, the fluids of zooplankton, also, are osmotically similar to sea water (630); and his concern that these be eaten to provide vitamin C may (or may not) be misplaced. Aury (60) supposes that ascorbic acid consumption is important for its favorable influence on the resistance to cold and fatigue through effect on the production of corticoid hormones and action on the pituitary-adrenal cortex.

While no one can now say what the requirements for ascorbic acid or other vitamins would be on a diet of raw fish of various species, it is generally conceded that acute starvation has never been associated with the development of any signs suggestive of a vitamin deficiency (421). The loss of water-soluble vitamins in sweat is not a significant factor in depleting body stores of these (548). Even under severe conditions, their loss in sweat is much smaller than loss in urine (674). Moreover, although it tells us little about starvation, in man on a vitamin C-free diet, more than four months may elapse before symptoms of scurvy develop (186). Lindemann (482a), however, believed himself to suffer the initial oozing of blood from his gums as a result of avitaminosis on the 23rd day of his voyage alone across the Atlantic. He carried considerable quantities of food (evaporated milk, beer, peas, garlic, and a few oranges) and also caught and ate raw fish.

The most satisfactory laboratory evaluation thus far of the putative benefit of fish to the castaway at sea is that of Hunter (387). With the development of a suitable press for obtaining fish lymph, and with a background of information on the composition of this fluid (388), Hunter studied fasting men in two groups. In three day trials, one group had a basic water ration of 250 cc./day; the other had, in addition to this basic ration, 1 liter of fish juice from cod fillets daily.

Subjects with the supplemental ration of juice had smaller losses of body weight, nitrogen, and electrolytes, and smaller water deficits than the others. Subjectively, those on fish juice

---

[50] A discussion of the toxic plankton is given by Clarke and Bishop (173). Although only one species, the planktonic (neritic) flagellate, *Gonyaulax catenella*, is known to produce a poison fatal to man, it may be assumed that there are others more or less harmful. The dinoflagellate, *Gymnodium* sp. ("Red tide"), causes extensive fish mortality. More probably dangerous even than the suspected but questionably harmful chitinous exoskeletons of the crustacea and the sharp siliceous valves of diatoms are the stinging forms in the plankton, such as certain jellyfish, and tentacles of the Portuguese man-of-war (*Physalia*) which may be picked up by plankton nets.

felt better than those on water alone, which was attributed in part to the lower water deficit as well as to the comfortable feeling of something in the stomach after drinking the juice (after controlling their "natural repugnance" to the juice, all subjects agreed it was a refreshing drink).

It is not enough as a criterion of relative benefit, of course, simply for the water balance to be less negative or more positive (350, 352) with the fish juice ration than without it. The higher water balance should, one would suppose, also be accompanied by a state in which elevations of both total and effective osmotic pressure of the plasma are less on the fish juice and water ration than on the water ration alone. These conditions also appear to have been satisfied in Hunter's experiments, although what combination of these would be optimal is not known.

Unfortunately, a fatty pelagic (surface swimming) fish such as the mackerel tends to yield fatty juice (p. 331; see Table XXI for fat content of several species of fish). Such juice has a higher solute content in the water phase than the juice from the less fatty demersal (deep swimming) fish such as the cod. Moreover, fatty juice is repellant and difficult to ingest, and more readily produces gastrointestinal symptoms (epigastric distress, intestinal irritability) along with steatorrhea (387). Possibly also, increased urine volume results from the incomplete metabolism of the fat. Hervey (349, 350) estimated theoretically that such low water-high solute juices may increase water deficits in dehydrated starving men and not reduce them as does cod juice; and even the latter provides relatively little free water. For these reasons, therefore, and to the extent that catchable pelagic fish happen to be fatty, the practical value of these juices as a water supply remains problematic. Experimentally, cod juice may be beneficial as a water ration, but this type of fish is quite unlikely to be caught by the castaway.

The statement of Hunter (387) that fish juice from any source (exclusive of elasmobranchs, the juice of which contains too much urea, and may be thoroughly disgusting) will supplement water rations beneficially if adequate carbohydrate is available for energy requirements remains academic for the impoverished castaway.

As Hervey (350) summarized it, of the two groups of fish, the
pelagic and the demersal forms, only the former are of direct
interest to castaways:

> . . . . It has from time to time been reported that surface fish
> are abundant, and that they will congregate round and follow rafts,
> but this can only apply to the warmer regions of the sea. In our
> own latitudes [England] the only surface fish (e.g. mackerel) are
> small, confined to coastal waters, and seasonal in occurrence. On
> the other hand deep-swimming fish, such as cod, haddock, etc.,
> are numerous in places all over the world . . . .
> There is still room for experimental work, but on the information
> available now it seems unlikely that fluid obtained from fish can
> make a useful contribution to the castaway's water supplies.[51]
> Fish which castaways could catch are limited to tropical or near-
> tropical waters. A heavy press is needed to obtain any fluid, and
> the provision of one in the equipment of a rubber raft has obvious
> drawbacks. The composition of the fluid at its best is not very
> favourable for men short of water, and at its worst it might be
> deleterious. Finally, the rations, means for collecting rain, and
> sun stills should provide the castaway in a Naval raft with a rea-
> sonable supply of water, and it seems most unlikely that replacing
> any of the present rations or equipment by a fish press would on
> balance be a good exchange.

Under certain circumstances it might be possible to employ an
"osmotic press" to obtain the juices of fish. By soaking pieces of the
flesh in relatively small quantities of sea water for several hours, the
osmotic pressure and electrolyte concentrations of the ambient fluid
are reduced considerably below that of pure sea water, toward that of
fish juice, the more as the ratio of flesh to sea water is increased (869).
And the protein content of the ambient fluid should be relatively low,
particularly if the flesh is fresh. The high effective osmotic pressure
of sea water causes fluid to leave the tissues of the fish so that equilibrium is approached with a corresponding dilution of the sea water.
Actually it makes no difference whether cells of the fish behave as
perfect osmometers or not (530, 873) since substantially the same
ultimate reduction of total salt concentrations in the ambient fluid will
occur in either case.

---

[51] The castaway on the open sea, that is. The castaway or inhabitant of an island
short of water may be in another ecologic category respecting the types of catchable
fish.

Something of this dilution effect, and perhaps some additional effect of chemical or physical reaction of sea salts with tissue substance, may have been discovered by survivors of the *Dumaru* (p. 249). Driven to cannibalism in their extremity, they placed flesh of the chief engineer in a biscuit can, covered it with sea water, and boiled it to a broth; the stock was likened to tough veal. And it was alleged:

> The salt in the sea water in which the flesh was boiled was absorbed by the flesh, leaving the broth free from salt and not unpleasant to taste.

Permissible Protein Concentrations in Potable Fish Juice: Theory

To estimate the maximum permissible concentration of protein in fish juice which might be used in lieu of fresh water to sustain life in man is an interesting question. It is doubtful that a precise answer can be obtained on purely theoretic grounds in view of the uncertain magnitudes of several variables involved: e.g., the extent to which ingested fish protein actually substitutes for endogenous protein in metabolism; the actual volume of urinary water obligated in the excretion of organic and inorganic metabolites under particular conditions; the fat, electrolyte, and nonprotein nitrogen composition of the juice; and the degree to which one may actually depart from zero water and salt balances for given survival times.

Acknowledging that further empirical solutions to problems in this category are needed (p. 327ff.), we nevertheless obtain crude estimates along the following lines, using symbols largely as before in the treatment of sea water-fresh water admixtures.

In water balance, on a 24 hour basis,

$$w = i_e + 0.3 - u \qquad (1)$$

where i_e is the liters of fish juice drunk. In salt balance,

$$u = \frac{i_e I_{eop} - E_{eop}}{U_{eop}} \qquad (2)$$

As before (p. 314), $E_{eop} = 74.4w - 52.1$, $U_{eop} = 600$ mOs./L. Take I_{eop}, reflecting only the salt content of fish juice, as 300 mOs./L.,[52] and solve the above for

$$w = \frac{300 i_e + 127.9}{525.6}$$

If i_e is chosen to be 1.000 L., we calculate $w = 0.814$ L., $E_{eop} = 8.5$ mOs., and $u = 0.486$ L., satisfying all conditions of concentrations and fluid balance.

Now, $$i_e I_{op} = u U_{op} + E_{op} \tag{3}$$

where E_{op} is taken equal to E_{eop} for simplicity, U_{op} is the total osmotic ceiling, or *LIC*, taken to be 1,200 mOs./L., and I_{op} is the sum of I_{eop} and the potential osmotic pressure of the dissolved protein, i.e., the osmotic pressure of a solution which would obtain if that protein were replaced by the metabolic urea to which it will give rise. Since each gram of protein provides 0.336 g. of urea (pp. 117, 354), the potential osmotic pressure of a solution of protein of concentration I_{pr} (g./L.) is $336 I_{pr}/60.06 = 5.59 I_{pr}$. Thus $I_{op} = 300 + 5.59 I_{pr}$, and

$$i_e(300 + 5.59 I_{pr}) = u(1200) + 74.4w - 52.1$$

We may substitute the value of $u = 0.486$ L., obtained above, in this last equation to obtain $I_{pr} = 52$ g./L. for $i_e = 1.000$ and $w = 0.814$ L. Or, we may combine with $u = i_e + 0.3 - 0.814$ and express I_{pr} as a per cent.
Thus,

$$I_{pr}(\%) = 16.1 - \frac{10.9}{i_e} \tag{4}$$

For the conditions in which $w = 0.814$ L., $U_{op} \ngtr 1200$ mOs./L., $U_{eop} \ngtr 600$ mOs./L., and zero water balance, we can, from such equations, obtain the relationship between I_{pr} and i_e. The level $i_e = 1.000$ L., yielding a maximum permissible concentration of

[52] In some marine teleosts the osmosity of serum electrolytes exceeds that of mammals (p 366) and the osmotic pressure of the blood may exceed 400 mOs./L. It is difficult to assess the significance of this for our problem, along with the facts that sodium concentration may be low and potassium high in pressed fish juice (p. 332). The act of pressing, which may cause some undesirable elevation of protein and potassium concentration in fish juice, may also lead, compensatorily, to some diminution of sodium concentration and of effective osmotic pressure of the juice to values below those for extracellular fluid.

5.2% at $w = 0.814$ L. is roughly applicable to Hunter's study of cod fish juice, noted above. His juice contained ca. 3.3% protein.

Similarly, for a condition of water balance in which $i_e = 2.000$ L., $w = 1.385$ and we have

$$I_{pr}(\%) = 16.1 - \frac{23.0}{i_e} \tag{5}$$

Equations (4) and (5) are two of a family of curves for different w values which can be drawn, if desired.

The theoretic maximum of 16.1% protein, at the highest possible levels of intake of fish juice, exists because at this concentration, the potential osmotic concentration of protein is 900 mOs./L.; at large i_e values, U_{eop} approaches 300 mOs./L. and the condition $(U_{op})_{LIC} = 1200$ mOs./L. is approached. Lower values of i_e and I_{pr} than follow from the above equations where one of these variables is set, are not consistent with our arbitrary condition of zero water balance, and are therefore not further considered. The lowest value of I_{pr} consistent through the equations with a given i_e (and w) value reflects the quantity of urea required to raise the osmotic pressure of the urine from 600 to 1,200 mOs./L. with no change in its volume.

As noted previously, maintenance of water balance may be a wholly unrealistic criterion for judging the thirst quenching and other palliative possibilities of fish juice. Also, to the extent that metabolic end products of exogenous (fish) protein and fat take the place of those of endogenous (human flesh) protein, one might be no worse off for ingesting fish juice containing some protein than if none were contained therein. Indeed, a salubrious effect is more likely and is evidenced in Hunter's work (387) noted above. If human muscle is essentially a solution containing 28 g. of protein per 100 g. of water, none of its tissue water is "free" except negatively (pp. 118, 163). At a level of $i_e = 1$ L./day and an endogenous nitrogen excretion equivalent to 10 g. of protein, it is perhaps immaterial for the urine volume whether I_{pr} is 0 or 1%. However, at low caloric intakes (below 500 Cal./day) increased nitrogen intakes may promote increased urinary excretion of nitrogen (387, 701).

The foregoing calculations are indubitably speculative. To note a few of the unsatisfactory aspects we mention: that half of the nitrogen of fish juice (three-quarters with elasmobranch juice) may be nonprotein in nature (387, 388); that urinary nitrogen (presumably protein catabolism) increases with increased water ingestion (383) and in dehydration (105, 302a) but yet urea may be used for protein synthesis in protein deficiency (833); the possible existence of adaptive renal responses to protein and urea administration which lead urinary water to be conserved more efficiently (244); neglect of the urinary water obligated with respect to the sulfate and phosphate derived from protein metabolism (642); the effects of possible azotemia in spite of nitrogen balance; and the neglect of the influx of preformed water and tissue solutes into the metabolic pool in partial starvation (p. 118).

Nevertheless, such matters as the putative value of hemoposia, and specifically the advice that drinking the blood of birds and fish is useful to the castaway at sea (571a, 733a), and many kindred problems may be reassessed along these lines, not to mention the larger questions of zoologic thirst and drinking to which we now turn.

ZOOLOGIC THIRST, DRINKING, AND WATER BALANCE

Although it is futile to discuss thirst in animals insofar as sensation may be at issue, there are other relevant considerations of drinking phenomena, or the absence thereof. Accordingly, we shall touch upon some of these, chiefly as they may illuminate certain dipsologic questions. Krogh (445) and Adolph (9) have also extensively studied such matters; Colin (176) has described drinking in animals of various classes; the Schmidt-Nielsens (689) have reviewed the water metabolism of desert mammals; and Smith (741) has brightly summarized the story of animals that live without water.

Urinary Osmotic Pressure: Osmosity, Etc.

In problems of water balance of the type here to be considered it is often necessary to refer to the osmotic pressure of the urine as determined from freezing points. It may be the case that in most mammals urea is sufficiently impermeable to the renal tubule to exert an effective osmotic pressure resembling that of some salts, but urea in the body fluids at large, with some exceptions, seems to exert little effective osmotic pressure since it penetrates most cell membranes rather freely. Thus, when it is said that human urine is perhaps 1.4 osmolal (rarely, Table XX) and sea water is 1.0 osmolal, one must not be misled to imagine from these total osmotic pressures that free or isorrheic water (pp. 163, 302) is thereby made available to the organism. When we treat the daily metabolic urea production as if it were an exogenous intake dissolved in, say 0.5 or 1.0 L. of ingested sea water, the noxious properties of sea water appear in better perspective, even in terms of total osmotic pressure, since the osmotic pressure of such urea-sea water mixture exceeds that of urine. The analysis in terms of effective osmotic pressure has been given on page 277.

If one regards the renal clearance of osmotic pressure as the product of the concentration ratio of osmotic pressure and the minute rate of urine flow, then an "economy of water" (132, 890) is defined by such a clearance minus the urine flow. This definition of water economy has meaning for the regulation of the total osmotic pressure of the body fluids, but it is relatively meaningless for the regulation of their effective osmotic pressure and, to a large extent, for thirst. Inequality analysis, discussed in the previous section, has been based upon considerations of effective osmotic pressure, and it is possible to rewrite such inequalities in terms of the clearance of effective osmotic pressure.

The clearance of osmotic pressure is the so-called "osmolar" clearance (741a, 820, 890). The term osmolar is used widely in physiologic reports. Whatever its connotation, it is, strictly, meaningless and inherently contradictory, suggesting somehow that osmotic pressure is a primary function of molarity. Where one wishes to convey the intent presently sanctioned by "osmolar," "osmolal" should be used instead (857). "Osmolar" should certainly not be used as if it were a synonym of the adjective "osmotic." The commonly used cryoscopic constant for water, viz., 1.86° C., is a molal depression constant of freezing point, so that the commonly used ratio of the freezing point of a solution to 1.86 is an osmolality rather than an osmolarity.

The osmolality of a given solution is numerically equal to the molality of an ideal solution of a nonelectrolyte having the same osmotic pressure, freezing point, etc. As approximated by the ratio $\Delta/1.86$, where Δ is the freezing point depression (°C.), it is useful to physiologists chiefly for comparing osmotic pressures. Its drawbacks are twofold: its exact value can only be obtained, if at all, by correcting for activities at different concentrations; and its units, osmols/Kg. (or, less exactly, L.) of water (solvent), do not readily interconvert with ordinary molar or normal analytical concentrations, particularly because of the variability among the specific or molar volumes of different solutes.

In many instances, and for practical purposes, these drawbacks are minimized and the usefulness for comparisons retained by using as a referent the molarity of sodium chloride solutions; the advantage derived lies in that this measure of osmotic pressure is not less and is sometimes more useful to the physiologist (530).

In some ways "osmolarity" would seem an ideal term to characterize this measure except for its having been preempted (279, 280) in another context from which it could not now easily be disentangled. Moreover, that term erroneously suggests a relation to osmolality which parallels that between molarity and molality (123a, 771a).

It is considered advisable to employ such a term as *osmosity*, this being, for a given solution, numerically equal to the molarity (or, loosely, to the millimolarity) of a sodium chloride solution having the same osmotic pressure (freezing point). Thus, the milliosmosity (or, loosely, the osmosity) of plasma might be 161 mM. of sodium chloride per liter; its milliosmolality would be 300 mOs./Kg. of water.

To exemplify an advantage of the suggested nomenclature, consider a highly concentrated solution, perhaps urine, whose unknown osmosity is to be determined. It is diluted in the usual way by making a chosen volume of it up to a measured, larger volume of final solution (this is a practical consideration since the freezing point is more satisfactorily determined on the more dilute solution). Now the dilution factor times the osmosity as determined of the final solution yields the osmosity of the original unknown solution, except for such changes in activity of the unknown with dilution as differ from changes in activity of sodium chloride for the same dilution, i.e., except for a second order difference. In parallel, if a concentrated solution of sodium chloride of the same osmosity as the original unknown had been diluted by the same factor, and this factor applied to the measured osmosity of the diluted salt solution, the result necessarily is precisely the osmosity (molarity) of the original concentrated salt solution.

From the freezing point depression, osmosity is approximated by $\Delta/3.46$; from osmolality, osmosity is approximated by osmolality/1.86. Osmosity is determined exactly by the newer osmometers if their instrumental readings are calibrated against sodium chloride solutions of known molarity.

The term "isosmosity" has, unfortunately, been used synonymously with "isosmoticity" (698).

Table XX provides a comparison between total and effective osmotic pressures of urine in various species. Although it is not known precisely how to estimate effective osmotic pressure (530, 873), this has been approximated from chloride concentrations sufficiently to permit discussion of the significance of urinary excretion, as for the problem of mariposia.

It may be well, however, to call attention to some other of the inadequacies of Table XX:

It was assumed for simplicity in calculating U/A not only that total and effective osmotic pressure of plasma were the same ($A_{op} = A_{eop}$), but that they were equivalent to $\Delta = 0.6°$ C. Neither is true for all cases in the table. Ordinarily in man, $\Delta = 0.54°$; in dog, $\Delta = 0.57°$ C. The body fluid of the seal has a slightly elevated and variable osmotic pressure (622); and the highest U_{Cl} reported for the dog (234) was obtained only with substantial elevation of plasma chloride.

Urinary chloride concentrations do not measure sodium chloride concentrations; neither is strictly a measure of *eop*.

The conditions under which the various maximum urinary concentrations (MUC) in this table were obtained are not comparable; e.g., states of hydration and salt load were not the same. The MUC of chloride and (probably) the limiting isorrheic concentration (LIC), are functions of nitrogen excretion. At extremely high, metaphysiologic (857) salt loads, the MUC of chloride is depressed (osmotic diuresis). In another way, the word "maximum" has at least two meanings: (a) the highest value which happened to have been found in adventitious, unsystematic, or limited investigations; (b) the highest value found under some stress, usually unstandardized, such as moderate water privation. In theory, it is the more physiologic *LIC* rather than the more metaphysiologic *MUC* which is germane to certain specific questions, as of mariposia. But the *MUC* supplies a useful approximation and is generally the only value available.

Excretion of water and salt in the sweat and by the gut affects the functional value of the *LIC* probably more than the *MUC*. As sweat loss increases, the effect on the regulation of salt concentration of the body fluids is as if the *LIC* (tolerable intake concentration) were indeed lower; or, a higher *LIC* (urinary concentration) than exists in fact would be necessary in order that a given intake of water and salt be matched by the corresponding urinary outputs.

Marine Mammals

It has long been of interest to physiologists to learn how marine mammals such as seals and whales obtain enough water to carry out their metabolic processes. The problem is complex and has not completely been settled.

Portier (622) measured the osmotic pressure (freezing point depression) of the blood of the whale (*Balaenoptera*) and the seal (*Phoca*) and found it higher than that of terrestrial animals of the same class (255).[53] He recognized that sea water which was incorporated with the invertebrate food of these animals or, in effect, ingested, tended to elevate the osmotic pressure of their body fluids. A freezing point depression as high as 4.5° C. was discovered in one *Phoca* (Table XX) but such high osmotic pressure was uncommon and Portier felt unable satisfactorily to explain the curious difficulty which appeared to face these animals in their osmotic regulation.

The body fluids of most marine invertebrates are isosmotic with sea water. Some crustaceans and a few annelids show deviation from this rule. Some animals such as the snail (*Aplysia*) and the starfish

---

[53] Whales and dolphins belong to the Cetacea, an order in the class of mammals; seals and walruses belong to the Carnivora, another order of mammals sometimes divided into the aquatic suborder Pinnipedia and the terrestrial Fissipedia (dogs, cats, etc.). The osmotic pressure of the blood of birds is higher than that of mammals (215).

(*Asterias*) swell in a dilute medium, then shrink with loss of salts. They regulate volume with a sacrifice of concentration. As Prosser (630) states, the regulation of volume and concentration may, therefore, be separate functions. The polychaete worm (*Nereis pelagica*) and the mussel (*Mytilus*), among other creatures, remain swollen in dilute media, having no volume or osmotic constancy. Some animals remain slightly different osmotically. The brine shrimp (*Artemia salina*), widely distributed the world over, is found in the Great Salt Lake of Utah in a medium of 22% salt (elsewhere it may live in lakes of even higher concentration). It is reported that in a lake of 8.4% salt, the blood concentration of this animal was equivalent to a 1.3% sodium chloride solution; in 17.4% salt solution as a medium, the blood was equivalent to a 2.4% sodium chloride solution.

Seals have been observed to drink fresh water (396), but ordinarily they do not do this; nor do they appear to drink sea water. Smith (739) states that Eskimos are aware that seals do not drink water. Conceiving the animals always to be thirsty, a hunter who has killed a seal pours water into its mouth so that the spirit of the dead one will tell other seals who will then come to be killed.

It is usually agreed that seals, which are able to swallow fish out of water, do not drink any considerable quantity of sea water even when playing with and taking fish submerged (125, 255, 256, 359, 396, 737); in the latter case it has been said that the esophagus wipes the fish virtually dry as it goes down (741).

Actually the inference, from the apparent dryness of the stomach contents of whales, and from chloride, magnesium, or sulfate analyses of urine and feces or residual salts washed out of the rectum of seals (255, 737, 739), that these animals are not mariposic might well be strengthened. It is hardly compelling in its present form. The generalization therefrom, widely accepted, that all marine mammals refrain from ingesting sea water, remains largely based on conjecture and on a far from complete physiologic theory of salt and water metabolism in terrestrial forms. Even the finding that the feces of the cetaceous dolphin are isotonic with the blood after ingestion of hypertonic saline (256), however this may suggest that intestinal absorption of salt is much the same as in other mammals, hardly proves that cetaceans do not drink sea water. Tracer techniques (566), among others, might well be employed to resolve some of the questions about drinking in aquatic mammals.

Osmotic space analysis suggests that there is no physiologic reason why seals and whales ought not to drink some sea water; indeed, it is difficult to believe and to determine that they really do not. Even goats and cattle are known to drink from the ocean (p. 358). That the cat is able to use sea water successfully in conjunction with diets of fish too poor in water to sustain it (p. 330) may be highly significant. It may be that marine mammals do drink sea water in small but variable amounts depending, among other things, upon the items in their diet and upon how the composition of the diet varies with the season. In some quarters it is taken for granted that sea water is ingested. Kellogg (407b) has remarked:

> . . . . It is not known by what means Recent whales are able to avoid assimilating excessive quantities of salts from their food or from the sea water that they swallow.

Urinary excretion of water and solutes in the harbor seal (*Phoca vitulina*) is correlated directly with food intake (125, 359, 737). So also is the glomerular filtration rate. Thus, seal kidneys increase activity when food (fish) has supplied water to spare for renal excretion. When body water is limited, as between meals, the rate of absolute dehydration is therefore reduced along with the urine flow. The urine of the seal may contain salt equivalent almost to 3% sodium chloride when hypertonic saline is given (Table XX); and the *MUC* of urea is 6.75% (737). This suggests that, with little or no intake of sea water, the urine is sufficiently antidipsic to square with the piscatory habit of these animals. Nevertheless, the case of the seagoing seal and other oceanic mammals has not been closed.

Irving, Fisher, and McIntosh (396) presented calculations, which have been widely quoted, used, and modified, to suggest that preformed and oxidative water made available from food (herring) would be adequate for the excretory processes of the "typical" mammalian (carnivorous) kidney of the harbor seal. We shall show that calculations of this sort do not yet satisfac-

TABLE XX

Maximum urinary concentrations. Δ_{op} is the actual freezing point depression, corresponding to the total osmotic pressure, op, the latter being represented by the milliosmolality of the urine, U_{op}. Δ_{eop} is the portion of the actual freezing point depression corresponding to the crudely estimated effective osmotic pressure, eop. The eop is derived from experimental records of urinary chloride concentration, U_{Cl}, with the assumption that the total salt of the urine is sodium chloride, U_{NaCl}, and that this alone exerts effective osmotic pressure. The concentration ratios, U_{op}/A_{op} and U_{eop}/A_{eop}, for total and effective osmotic pressures, respectively, were taken arbitrarily as $\Delta_{op}/0.6$ and $\Delta_{eop}/0.6$, where $0.6°C$. was the value chosen for freezing point depression of all plasmas. (See page 343 for various inadequacies of this table.) From data in (73, 88, 125, 145, 213, 234, 256, 271, 276, 445, 475, 590, 622, 626, 686, 689, 692, 693, 737, 739, 857, 875).

Animal	Δ_{op} (°C.)	U_{op} (mOs./L.)	Δ_{eop} (°C.)	U_{eop} (mOs./L.)	U_{Cl} (mEq./L.)	U_{NaCl} (%)	U_{op}/A_{op}	U_{eop}/A_{eop}
Kangaroo rat	10.9*	5870*	3.14*	1690*	908	5.31	17.30	5.23
Cat	4.00–6.05	2150–3250	1.66–1.95	890–1050	479–565	2.80–3.30	6.67–10.1	2.77–3.25
Camel (dromedary)	4.65–5.90	2500–3170	...	...	...	...	7.75–9.83	...
Setonyx brachyurus†	4.07	2190	2.68	1440	773	4.52	6.78	4.47
White rat	4.79	2580	1.73–2.63	930–1410	500–760	2.92–4.44	7.98	2.88–4.38
Harbor seal	3.99–4.50	2150–2420	1.66–1.73	895–930	481–500	2.81–2.92	6.65–7.50	2.77–2.88
Pollack, Humpback, Rorqual whale	1.83–2.49	984–1340	1.80–2.84	967–1525	520–820	3.04–4.79	3.05–4.15	3.00–4.73
Dog	3.49–4.32	1880–2320	1.38–2.27	744–1220	400–657	2.34–3.84	5.81–7.20	2.30–3.78
Rabbit	3.56	1910	...	...	...	...	5.93	...
Porpoise	3.41	1833	1.97	1060	570	3.33	5.68	3.28
Man	2.23–2.75	1200–1480	1.14–1.42	614–764	330–411	1.93–2.40	3.72–4.58	1.90–2.37
Goat	...	...	1.11	595	320	1.87	...	1.85
Chicken	1.00	538	...	...	...	...	1.67	...

* Total electrolytes measured conductometrically have been reported at 1500 mEq./L., corresponding to the *conductivity* of 8.77% NaCl; actual chloride concentration, despite high conductivities, may be quite low. Maximal value of urea is given as 3840 mM./L. or 23.1% (685). In the gerbil (*Gerbillus gerbillus*) total electrolytes are reported conductometrically at 1600 mEq./L. as NaCl (9.4%), and urea at 3410 mM./L. or 20.5% (144).

The osmotic pressure for the kangaroo rat, which has been crudely estimated by summing the presumed osmotic contribution of the urea and of the electrolytes, measured conductometrically, assuming usual osmotic coefficients, is subject to numerous, but partly compensating, errors. Thus, pertinent osmotic coefficients at high concentrations and in complex mixtures are unknown; conductivities of electrolyte mixtures such as the viscous, semi-solid urine of these animals may not provide a suitable basis for calculating the osmotic pressure of electrolytes; at these high concentrations molarity, as determined analytically, differs appreciably from molality. Smith (739) estimates $\Delta = 10.4°C$., acknowledging that the osmotic pressure equivalent even of this is probably high for so concentrated a solution. The osmotic pressure given in this table may be too high for urea and electrolyte, although the effect of other nonelectrolytes is not considered.

† Australian marsupial, cat-sized macropod.

torily resolve the problem. Of course, the capacity of kidneys varies greatly concentrationwise, even among mammals (Table XX). As indicated (p. 327ff.), the dog and cat, but not man, can be maintained on raw fish, with no other supply of water, for a time sufficient to point up the carnivore's greater ability to concentrate metabolic nitrogen. And the kangaroo rat (*Dipodomys*) can, if necessary tolerate mariposia (p. 358).

The situation of the Mystacoceti or whalebone whales which collect plankton and small fish for food may appear more difficult than that of the Odontoceti or toothed whales which feed largely on vertebrates, but both must still be re-examined to the extent that previous physiologic analysis was inadequate (867). Krogh (445) attempted to show that an invertebrate diet could be handled without extraordinary mammalian renal apparatus, basing this view on a slight modification of the calculations of Irving *et al.* (396) but, for reasons given below, these considerations also remain inconclusive. Fetcher (255) has speculated that the invertebrate feeders have a special mechanism for the reduction of urinary salt concentration, perhaps buccal glands acting to eliminate some hypertonic, antidipsic secretion. Whales, unlike seals, have no salivary glands although the cetaceous dolphin does, and the saliva is possibly hypertonic (p. 52). Fetcher and Fetcher (256) later considered the possibility that sea water could be "filtered" in the buccal region and taken into the blood stream relatively salt free. They took issue with Krogh's view that enough water can be obtained by cetaceans simply from a diet of marine invertebrates.

Clarke and Bishop (173) have suggested that plankton in mass, with some of the sea water squeezed out, might provide enough oxidative and preformed water to cover the excretion of its metabolic end products and contained salt even in man. Their calculation is loosely based only on the total, and does not note the effective, osmotic pressure ceiling of the urine; and it employs the relatively high (rare) value of $U_{op} = 1.4$ osmolal. Salt content of squeezed plankton was estimated at 70% of that of an equal volume of sea water, which represents its fluid as over 80% as salty as sea water if one corrects for some 86% water in a wet pressed mass of plankton. Judging by metabolic calculations for, say, raw clams (Table XXI), it would appear dubious that plankton should constitute a completely sufficient aquiferous potential for man, although it well might for the whale.

In the calculations of Irving *et al.*, it is assumed that seals live in an environment of sufficiently low temperature that no water need be expended by evaporation for their body temperature regulation. Seals under their observation were fed only fresh herring, presumably the raw Atlantic variety. The composition of this fish was taken from an older table of nutritional values (715): 11.2% protein, 3.9% fat, and no carbohydrate; the fresh fish was assumed to contain 80% water. For the combination of fat and protein metabolized, the quantity of oxygen required to yield 1,000 Calories was calculated as 236 liters. With the assumption that oxygen to the extent of 6% of the respiratory volume is removed during resting respiration, it follows that for each 1,000 Calories, the expired air is 236/0.06 = 3,933 liters. This volume, if raised in water content from that of saturated air at 15° C. to saturated air at 35° C. would require approximately 100 grams of water. They estimated that the feces removed approximately 200 grams of water for 1,000 dietary Calories, but made no correction for the salt lost in this water since the chloride content appeared negligible.

One weakness of this analysis lies in its being based on a composition of food which should not be considered typical of the food seals eat. Table XXI shows the composition of raw Atlantic herring, as given by newer nutritional tables (810), to be such that the case made out by Irving *et al.* is lost. A seal might, in theory, obtain all of its water from raw Pacific herring, cod, flounder, haddock, and clams, but not from Atlantic herring, bluefish, halibut, Atlantic mackerel, or Pacific salmon. Moreover, some seals eat various molluscs and crustacea and, as with the case of the Mystacoceti, this may impose a metabolic stress still greater than where fish alone may be taken.

Seemingly more difficult is the position of creatures like the leopard seal or sea leopard of the Antarctic (*Hydrurga leptonyx*) which preys on warmblooded animals such as other seals and sea birds, and the killer whale (*Grampus*) which eats its own kind among other homoiotherms. For if we assume such a diet to be similar in composition to

TABLE XXI

Theoretic effects of ingestion of various foods, with no extra water, on urinary concentrations. Applicable to the seal, primarily, and other mammals supposed to lose no cutaneous water. No correction for the relatively lesser pulmonary water loss in the whale (page 352). The urinary osmotic pressure equivalent (U_{op}) and the urinary effective osmotic pressure equivalent (U_{eop}) may be compared with maximum urinary concentrations for various mammals. For food, alone, to be able to supply sufficient water for all metabolic requirements of water balance, the tabulated U_{eop} and U_{op} values must both be less than their respective maxima in Table XX. See page 352ff. for calculations.

Food (100 g., edible portion)	Cal./ 100 g.	G./ 1000 Cal.	Per Cent				Grams			Water Intake (g.)						Urea from Protein (g.)	Total Salt (g.) **
			Water	Protein	Fat	Carbohydrate	Protein	Fat	Carbohydrate	Pre-formed	Oxidative Water						
											From Protein	From Fat	From Carbohydrate	Total			
Fresh herring*	...	1250	80	11.2	3.9	0	139	...	0	1000	71	50	0	1121	50	12.5
Fresh herring†	80	1250	80	11.2	3.9	0	140	48.0	0	1000	55.4	52.2	0	1107.6	49.4	12.5
Raw Atlantic herring	191	524	67.2	18.3	12.5	0	95.9	65.5	0	352.1	38.0	70.2	0	460.3	32.2	5.2
Raw Pacific herring	94	1063.8	79.6	16.6	2.6	0	176.6	27.7	0	846.8	69.9	29.7	0	946.4	59.3	10.6
Raw clams, long and round	81	1234.6	80.3	12.8	1.4	3.4	158.0	17.3	42.0	991.4	62.6	18.5	23.4	1095.9	53.1	24.7
Raw bluefish	124	806.5	74.6	20.5	4.0	0	165.3	32.3	0	601.6	65.5	34.6	0	701.7	55.5	8.1
Raw cod	74	1351.4	82.6	16.5	0.4	0	223.0	5.4	0	1116.3	88.3	5.8	0	1210.4	74.9	13.5
Raw flounder	68	1470.6	82.7	14.9	0.5	0	219.1	7.4	0	1216.2	86.8	7.9	0	1310.9	73.6	14.7
Raw haddock	79	1265.8	80.7	18.2	0.1	0	230.4	1.3	0	1021.5	91.2	1.4	0	1114.1	77.4	12.7
Raw halibut	126	793.7	75.4	18.6	5.2	0	147.6	41.3	0	598.4	58.4	44.2	0	701.0	49.6	7.9
Raw Atlantic mackerel	188	531.9	68.1	18.7	12	0	99.5	63.8	0	362.2	39.4	68.3	0	469.9	33.4	5.3
Raw Pacific salmon	223	448.4	63.4	17.4	16.5	0	78.0	74.0	0	284.3	30.9	79.3	0	394.5	26.2	4.5
Raw beef sirloin	254	393.7	62.0	17.3	20	0	68.1	78.7	0	244.1	27.0	84.3	0	355.4	22.9	3.94
Raw lamb, rib chop	356	280.8	51.9	14.9	32.4	0	41.8	91.0	0	145.7	16.6	97.5	0	259.8	14.0	2.81
Raw chicken, roaster	200	500.0	66.0	20.2	12.6	0	101.0	63.0	0	330.0	40.0	67.5	0	437.5	33.9	5.00
Raw hamburger	321	311.5	55.0	16	28	0	49.8	87.2	0	171.3	19.7	93.4	0	284.4	16.7	3.12
Cooked hamburger	364	274.7	47.0	22.0	30	0	60.4	82.4	0	129.1	23.9	88.3	0	241.3	20.3	2.75
Milk, can, evaporated	138	724.6	73.7	7.0	7.9	9.9	50.7	57.2	71.7	534.0	20.1	61.3	39.9	655.3	17.0	10.9
Milk, whole	68	1470.6	87.0	3.5	3.9	4.9	51.5	57.4	72.1	1279.4	20.4	61.5	40.1	1401.4	17.3	10.3

TABLE XXI (continued)

Food (100 g., edible portion)	Oxygen (L.) For Protein	For Fat	For Carbohydrate	P.-l. monary Water Loss (g.)	Urinary Water (g.) ‡	¶	Salt in Urine (%) ‡	¶	Urea in Urine (%) ‡	¶	U_{eop} (mOs./L.) ‡	¶	(U_{op})urea (mOs./L.) ‡	¶	(U_{op}) (mOs./L.) ‡	¶
Fresh herring*	236	93.9	0	106	...	800.0	...	1.56	...	6.3	...	496.4	...	1049.0	...	1545.4
Fresh herring†	133.3	126.1	0	100.3	907.3	807.3	1.27	1.30	5.44	6.12	404.1	413.7	905.8	1019.0	1309.9	1432.7
Raw Atlantic herring	91.3	53.3	0	95.9	264.4	164.4	1.59	1.95	12.2	19.6	506.0	620.5	2031.3	3263.4	2537.3	3883.9
Raw Pacific herring	168.1	96.2	0	97.7	748.7	648.7	1.28	1.33	7.92	9.14	407.3	423.2	1318.1	1521.8	1726.0	1945.0
Raw clams, long and round	150.4	33.3	34.2	96.2	899.7	799.7	2.63	2.84	5.90	6.64	836.9	903.7	982.4	1105.6	1819.3	2009.3
Raw bluefish	157.4	62.2	0	96.9	504.8	404.8	1.41	1.51	11.0	13.7	448.7	480.5	1831.5	2281.1	2280.2	2761.6
Raw cod	212.3	10.4	0	98.3	1012.1	912.1	1.24	1.26	7.40	8.21	394.6	401.0	1232.1	1367.0	1626.7	1768.0
Raw flounder	208.6	14.2	0	98.3	1112.6	1012.6	1.23	1.25	6.62	7.27	391.4	397.4	1102.2	1210.5	1493.6	1607.9
Raw haddock	219.3	2.5	0	97.9	916.2	816.2	1.28	1.31	8.45	9.48	407.3	416.9	1406.9	1578.4	1814.2	1995.3
Raw halibut	140.5	79.5	0	97.1	503.9	403.9	1.37	1.46	9.84	12.3	436.0	464.6	1638.4	2048.0	2074.4	2512.6
Raw Atlantic mackerel	94.7	122.8	0	96.0	273.9	173.9	1.57	1.90	12.2	19.2	499.6	604.6	2031.3	3196.8	2530.9	3801.4
Raw Pacific salmon	74.3	142.4	0	95.6	198.9	98.9	1.76	2.53	13.2	26.5	560.1	805.1	2197.8	4412.3	2757.9	5217.4
Raw beef sirloin	64.8	151.5	0	95.4	160.0	60.0	1.84	3.23	14.3	38.2	585.5	1027.9	2381.0	6360.3	2966.5	7388.2
Raw lamb, rib chop	39.8	175.2	0	94.8	65.0	−35.0	2.78	...	21.5	...	884.7	...	3579.8	...	4464.5	...
Raw chicken, roaster	96.2	121.3	0	95.9	241.6	141.6	1.66	2.12	14.0	23.9	528.2	674.6	2331.0	3979.4	2859.2	4654.0
Raw hamburger	47.4	167.9	0	94.9	89.5	−10.5	2.37	...	18.7	...	754.2	...	3113.6	...	3867.8	...
Cooked hamburger	57.5	158.6	0	95.3	46.0	−54.0	3.80	...	44.1	...	1209.2	...	7342.7	...	8551.9	...
Milk, can, evaporated	48.3	110.1	58.4	95.6	459.7	359.7	2.15	2.47	3.70	4.73	684.2	786.0	616.1	787.5	1300.3	1573.5
Milk, whole	49.0	110.5	58.7	96.2	1205.2	1105.2	0.77	0.75	1.44	1.57	245.0	238.7	239.8	261.4	484.8	500.1

* As given by Irving et al. (396).

† Recalculated from Irving et al., using constants given in text.

‡ Urinary water = Total water intake − (lung loss + fecal loss); fecal loss = 100 g. water, 1 g. salt.

¶ Urinary water = Total water intake − (lung loss + fecal loss); fecal loss = 200 g. water, 2 g. salt.

** Fish and meat assumed to contain 1% salt; clams, 2%; milk, same as ash content.

beef, lamb, chicken, or hamburger (Table XXI), we must judge the "typical" carnivorous or cetacean kidney (Table XX) to be quite unable to regulate the water economy of these animals under the conditions assumed by Irving *et al.* or Krogh. Birds of prey, however, are favored in handling their diet by their ability to excrete uric acid (p. 364).

Lactation is another stressful situation (626). Krogh viewed the fact that the milk of whales is only 50 to 70% water as a manifestation of an austere water economy. Present calculations do not encompass this factor.

The conclusions of Krogh applied to whales feeding on invertebrates suffer almost in the same way as those of Irving *et al.*, depending as they do upon the same calorific and compositional values used by the latter. Krogh refined the argument in adducing that because of the increased pressure in the lungs of the whale in diving, less water need be lost by evaporation (in the face of greater than 6% oxygen extraction), and he took a somewhat smaller quantity of water loss in feces, coupling it with salt loss in fecal fluid.[54]

The method of calculation used for Table XXI follows:

A unit of 1,000 Calories of food is taken as a base. From the values of Cal./100 g. of "edible portion" of food[55] (only ones available) given

---

[54] In cats, Prentiss *et al.* (626) found much smaller losses of fecal water, between 4 and 12 grams of water per 1,000 Calories which, if applicable to marine mammals even roughly, would improve the theoretic picture.

[55] Irving *et al.* used Sherman's (715) figures for "as purchased" composition rather than those for "edible portion" (although it is not clear where they obtained 80% as the water content of fresh herring). Strictly, it makes no difference which of these two groups of figures is used in the calculations for Table XXI since the same result obtains either way. The "as purchased" composition does not, as may be supposed, reflect the composition of the whole food, i.e., "as purchased" values for herring are not those which would be found by analysis of an entire fish such as might be swallowed by a seal. "As purchased" values are found by multiplying "edible portion" values by $(1 - R)$ where R is the fraction of "refuse" of the food. That which is refuse, however, is determined with respect to human consumption and consists of inedible portions or portions usually discarded. The composition of refuse does not enter into the conversion from "edible portion" to "as purchased" value. From the standpoint of metabolic calculations, the latter values are derived rather than primary; in a sense they are artificial or unrealistic and not especially adapted to our purposes. Actually, of course, nutritional tables may be quite misleading as an indication of the protein, fat, and water taken by a seal which has ingested a whole fish.

by nutrition tables (810), we determine the grams of food, G, needed to supply 1,000 Calories.

Preformed water of food (g.) $= G \times (\% \text{ water of food})/100 = i_p$

Protein of food (g.) $= G \times (\% \text{ protein of food})/100 = G_{pr}$

Fat of food (g.) $= G \times (\% \text{ fat of food})/100 = G_f$

Carbohydrate of food (g.) $= G \times (\% \text{ carbohydrate of food})/100 = G_c$

Oxidative water[56] of protein (g.) $= 0.396 G_{pr} = (i_m)_{pr}$

Oxidative water of fat (g.) $= 1.071 G_f = (i_m)_f$

Oxidative water of carbohydrate (g.) $= 0.556 G_c = (i_m)_c$

Total water intake (g.) $= i_p + (i_m)_{pr} + (i_m)_f + (i_m)_c = i$

Fecal water loss (g.) $= 100 \text{ or } 200 \text{ g.} = r$

Water loss from lungs is based on physiologic fuel values (716) and calorific values of oxygen of

Protein: 4.27 Cal./g.; 4.485 Cal./L. of oxygen

Fat: 9.02 Cal./g.; 4.686 Cal./L. of oxygen

Carbohydrate: 4.11 Cal./g.; 5.047 Cal./L. of oxygen

(For calculations on milk, the physiologic fuel values used were: Protein, 4.27; Fat, 8.79; and Carbohydrate, 3.87 Cal./g.)

From the above figures,

Protein requires $4.27/4.485 = 0.952$ L. of oxygen/g. $= O_{pr}$

Fat requires $9.02/4.686 = 1.925$ L. of oxygen/g. $= O_f$

Carbohydrate requires $4.11/5.047 = 0.814$ L. of oxygen/g. $= O_c$

Oxygen utilized/1,000 Cal. $= G_{pr}O_{pr} + G_f O_f + G_c O_c = V_{O_2}$ liters

Total air ventilated/1,000 Cal. at 6% oxygen extraction $= V_{O_2}/0.06$ liters

---

[56] Metabolic water is commonly (and is here) identified (689) as water of oxidation (i.e., of hydrogen) although Babcock (63) originally conceived it to derive from several sources of which oxidation was the chief. Changes in molecular structure of nutrients or tissue substances (e. g., transformation of dextrose or invert sugar into cellulose or starch), formation of muscle fiber and other complex proteins from amino acids, and anaerobic breakdown of food and tissue material to molecular structures of lower order in many organisms were among these.

Complete oxidation of food (carbohydrates, fat, protein, chiefly) yields a quantity of water equal to nine times the weight of hydrogen in the original substance. Thus 100 parts of starch containing 6.17% hydrogen gives 55.5 parts of water; 100 parts of anhydrous dextrose containing 6.66% hydrogen gives 60 parts of water. Most of the fats yield more than their weight of water, while proteins when completely oxidized give 60 to 65% water. When protein breakdown results in urea excretion the metabolic water, according to Babcock is about 42% of the weight of the protein (cf. above); when uric acid is excreted, it is 53%.

Grams of water raising total air ventilation/1,000 Cal. from saturation at 15° to saturation at 35° C. $= 0.02648 \, (V_{O_2}/0.06) = w =$ pulmonary water loss

At zero water balance, urinary water (g./1,000 Cal.) $= i - (w + r) = u$

Urea from protein[57] (g.) $= 0.336G_{pr} = G_{urea}$

Concentration of urea in urine (%) $= 100G_{urea}/u = U_{urea}$

Salt intake (g.) $= 0.01G$

Salt loss in feces (g.) $= 0.01r$

Concentration of salt in urine (%) $= (G - r)/u = U_{salt}$

Osmotic concentration of urinary salt solution $= U_{salt} \, (1.86/0.005845) = U_{eop}$ (mOs./L.), of sodium chloride

Osmotic concentration of urinary urea solution $= U_{urea}/0.006006 = (U_{op})_{urea}$ (mOs./L.)

Total osmotic concentration of urine $= U_{eop} + (U_{op})_{urea} = U_{op}$ (mOs./L.)

The trouble with calculations of this type (579) is their critical uncertainty in various areas: one may not be using actual compositions of foods *consumed,* as these are usually not given in ordinary nutrition tables;[58] water and salt losses by various emunctories in the animals under particular observational or experimental conditions have not thoroughly been ascertained; and finally, there is a substantial uncertainty about the physiologic fuel values of foods (742) in mammals other than man. It may be incorrect to assume, for example, that the coefficient of digestibility is the same in man as in some of these other animals; and such coefficients may be smaller on diets consisting of relatively uniform species of protein than on varied diets (716). If the seal were to utilize an appreciably smaller fraction of the protein

---

[57] A unit weight of different proteins may yield different quantities of urea. The ratio 0.36 g. urea/g. protein was assumed by Irving *et al.* It corresponds to a nitrogen content of 16.8% of the protein (if the coefficient of digestibility were 1). Few figures are available for nitrogen content of whole fish proteins. Cod, herring, and halibut muscle, respectively, are given as 13.6, 14.0, and 16.5%; menhaden meal, 11.6%; and scallop, 17.1% (109).

The factor, 0.336, used here is the product of 0.343 (representing g. urea/g. protein (p. 117), where the protein is taken to contain 16.0% nitrogen) and the coefficient of digestibility of fish and meat (in man) taken as 0.98 (716).

[58] However, see monumental volume of Vinogradov (799). The composition of fish (and no doubt other foods) is extremely variable with season (328), etc. No table, therefore, is generally reliable.

of its food than does a man, discarding protein in feces and utilizing the preformed water of the food, the aspect of the problem would change completely (867).[59]   Fig. 44 illustrates the sharp improvement in the renal position of an animal as the per cent protein in its diet falls, a situation, in effect, somewhat as if the coefficient of digestibility were lowered.

On the other hand, if the urinary osmotic space could be shown to permit physiologic ingestion of some sea water (pp. 330, 346) the water economy of marine mammals, again, would generally appear more understandable.   In short, numerous questions remain undecided.

Desert Mammals, Et Alii

Inequality analysis accords with the observation that the kangaroo rat is a hydro-adipsic mammal (p. 307).   But this is an animal of a group which ordinarily does not expend water on heat regulation; it, like other rodents, avoids high environmental temperature, staying in underground burrows during the heat of the day. A large animal such as the antelope known as the addax (*Addax nasomaculatus*) which scarcely, if ever, drinks (130) presumably must use water to keep its body temperature from rising unduly in its hot desert environment of North Africa and the Sudan; the same may be said of the Mongolian wild ass (*Equus hemionus*) of the central Gobi which is found in abundance in parts of the desert where there is no water whatsoever (50).   And King (p. 380) has remarked the superiority of the mule over the horse in this ability to withstand drought.   In their penetrating analysis of the water metabolism of desert mammals, Schmidt-Nielsen and Schmidt-Nielsen (689) divide their subjects into two groups on this basis.

(1) Those which do not use water for heat regulation, includ-

---

[59] In man it has been shown that if 1,000 cc. of water is ingested with meals the protein constituents of the food are more completely utilized; there is a decrease in excretion of all forms of fecal nitrogen, including bacterial (513).   Such an addition of water, however, decreases also the fecal excretion both of dry matter and of moisture (514).   Water deprivation is known to diminish fecal excretion of water (p. 358) but its effects, or those attending the problem of obtaining free water from food, on fecal nitrogen excretion remain to be studied.   The total fecal nitrogen in cats taking fish or beef is negligible, even in hydropenia (626).

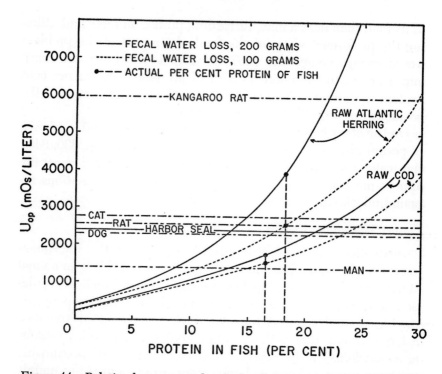

Figure 44. Relation between total, calculated osmotic pressure of the urine of the seal and the per cent protein contained in fish diets, based upon raw Atlantic herring (18.3% protein, 12.5% fat and 0% carbohydrate) and raw cod (16.5% protein, 0.4% fat and 0% carbohydrate). The vertical lines representing the actual protein composition of these fish touch the curves (black circles) at values of total urinary osmotic pressure calculated as described in the text. The remainder of each curve is "derived," i.e., keeping constant the per cent fat of the fish as given by nutrition tables (810) Table XXI, the per cent protein is varied from 0 to 30% and the per cent water is changed correspondingly. U_{op} was calculated for fish of such theoretic composition. Fecal water losses were considered at two levels, 100 and 200 grams per 1000 calories. The latter fecal water loss is that assumed by Irving *et al.* (396).

The solid horizontal line indicates the approximate maximal urinary osmotic pressure of the harbor seal (Table XX). From the location of the black circles it appears, in theory, that this animal could live exclusively on cod, but not on herring, if no other water were available. If the coefficient of digestibility of fish protein were lower than the values implicit in the calculations (= average values for man), the effect would be substantially as if the percent protein in the ingested fish were lower than in actuality. Thus, at 10% protein, "derived" herring could be utilized by the seal with no extra

ing pack rats and ground squirrels which live on juicy plants with high water content, and kangaroo rats (*Dipodomys*) and pocket mice (*Perognathus*) which live on seeds and other dry plant substances[60] generally (66) and drink no water. Desert rodents have evaporative water losses only one-half to two-thirds that of laboratory rodents of similar size; but the house mouse, canyon mouse, and hamster also have low evaporative losses (683). The evaporation of the white laboratory mouse is, curiously, higher than that of the wild mouse. The former die within a week of water deprivation (99, 689, Fig. 24) but the latter, according to legend (150), and several other rodents, scarcely ever drink (63). The rabbit rarely drinks unless it is forced to take food drier than is usual (673).

(2) Animals needing water extensively for heat regulation, including man, dog (panting), donkey, and horse. Many carnivorous animals (150) (including insect eaters) such as desert kit foxes, the grasshopper mouse (*Onychomys*), possibly some dogs and cats (149, 196, 626, 770) and, of course, the seal, can obtain sufficient water from their food, if that water is not required for heat regulation (689). Prairie dogs, goats, and sheep in pasture can go for long periods without access to drinking water (63, 502, 689). Range livestock (sheep), however, may require considerable water on winter ranges (391); or they may require none (470). Camels do not need drinking water for four months or longer when grazing in the winter (620); in hot summer weather they have gone as long as 17 days without water (686).

The kangaroo rat (*Dipodomys merriami*) is able to utilize sea water for drinking, if made to drink by being placed on a high protein (40%) soy bean diet which obligates unusually large

---

[60] The coefficient of digestibility of plant proteins, at least in man, is often lower than that of animal proteins. This may contribute to a more satisfactory water balance than has been assumed (p. 354).

---

water. U_{op} values calculated for low protein diets reflect no allowance for endogenous protein metabolism.

The interrupted horizontal lines approximate maximal urinary osmotic pressures for some other animals (Table XX), facilitating rough comparisons. However, actual curves for these animals would be somewhat displaced in their entirety if calculations of U_{op} had been based, for example, on the relevant fecal and pulmocutaneous water losses per 1000 Calories (p. 352ff.).

amounts of water as urine (682).[61]   The Australian marsupial, *Setonyx brachyurus,* another remarkable concentrator of urinary electrolytes (Table XX), is able to drink 2.5 sodium chloride and maintain water balance, when on a "dry" diet, but when offered 3% salt, its intake of fluid falls (88).

The white rat (Table XX) is somewhat less able to handle strong salt solutions when on a dry diet but can drink and utilize effectively (maintain weight) half strength sea water (10) (sea water of chloride concentration 512 rather than 548 mEq./L. (Table XI)). The fasting dog utilizes half strength sea water well (871). The camel is known to drink brackish water (339) and wild goats (729) and cattle are known to walk into the sea to drink (840), although whether the latter is primarily for the purpose of getting water or salt is not clear.

Schmidt-Nielsen *et al* (684a, 686, 686a, 690) carried out studies of the camel in the Sahara desert which at last show physiologically that this animal can actually tolerate prolonged water deprivation better than some other large mammals. It is able to do so because its expenditure of water is low and it can tolerate a high degree of bodily dehydration. Its low total water losses reflect low urine output, low water content of feces,[62] and low evaporative water loss; it never pants or breathes with mouth open in the hottest Saharan weather. The camel can sustain a loss of water of

---

[61] This is less remarkable if we realize that cats, also, are able to utilize sea water if made to drink appreciable quantities by being placed on a "high protein" diet (p. 330). This mariposic ability does not simply depend on the capacity to form a urine more concentrated in salt than sea water. Indeed, such capacity is neither necessary (as in cats) nor sufficient to invest an animal with this faculty. Were urine volume small enough in relation to extrarenal water loss, the excretory potential (concentrating power) for salt would be of no avail (10, 875). Actually, the urinary concentration of salts in the cat can at times approximate and even exceed the concentration of salts in sea water (Tables XI, XX) but, without food, the cat cannot and does not so profitably drink sea water.

White rats also show somewhat similar effects of taking sea water (875); even with dried whole milk as the sole caloric intake, survival time is greater if sea water is taken ad libitum than if no fluid is taken (73, p 290).

[62] Lower in periods of water deprivation than in periods of euhydration. The distribution of water among different emunctories may be a function of the type of ration. Holsteins on timothy hay have been observed to lose more water in the feces than by evaporation; on linseed oil meal and bran, and on maize meal, several times as much was lost by evaporation as in feces (470).

30% of its body weight even in desert heat while other mammals dehydrated in a hot environment die from explosive heat rise at lesser degrees of desiccation (12). It is reported that the plasma volume of the camel is not appreciably reduced during dehydration while the interstitial fluid volume suffers relatively large water loss. The dehydrated camel drinks to complete rehydration in 10 minutes, ordinarily. A drop in plasma concentration follows, minimum values being reached 48 hours after drinking (p. 160). Electrolytes are conserved after rehydration and urine flow falls rather than rises.

Plasma volume is maintained in moderately dehydrated men (105). It is difficult to interpret the significance of plasma protein and total solids (refractometric) measurements in the plasma of men, dogs, and rats deprived at length of food and water (18). In the dog with a low protein intake, but with free access to water, protein concentration and the volume of plasma fall (812). Deprived of both food and water, rats and dogs show relative constancy of plasma protein concentration (57, 626, 871, 874); when food is allowed but water withdrawn, rats may show a rise in plasma protein and total solids (57, 874). Cows kept for two days on hay (relatively water-poor) but deprived of water show hemoconcentration and a rise in serum protein level (813). But the dehydrated (and rehydrated) donkey shows no change in protein concentration (208, 689). Men who lose weight by rapid sweating show a loss in plasma volume and a corresponding increase in its total solids; plasma loses a greater proportion of its water than the body as a whole (18).

The old conception that the camel "stores" water in some exceptional manner is without foundation. There is no evidence that this animals drinks more than necessary to bring the water content of its body to normal after water deprivation. Fluid found in the rumen (stomach) and digestive tract of desert camels (*Camelus dromedarius*) was not greater than normally found in other ruminants such as cows (687).

In the Sahara desert, native herdsmen start training camels when they are calves to take water at intervals of about four days. Then, when full grown, they can go six, eight, or 10 days without a drink (620).

Storage of fat in the hump and elsewhere is another matter.

Upon oxidation, fat yields more than it own weight of water (p. 353) and at the end of a trip much fat may have disappeared (63). In experiments, however, it has been found that camels use water faster than it is formed by oxidation (686).

Another important reaction of the camel (and certain passerine birds, p. 362) is manifest in the way its body temperature fluctuates with the heat of the day. The diurnal variations in rectal temperature may exceed 6° C., being a minimum of 34.2° in the morning with an afternoon maximum of 40.7°. On a hot day, body temperature steadily increases to a maximum whereupon further increase is prevented by sweating. Two advantages are indicated: heat stored in the body during the period of increasing body temperature does not use water for its dissipation and, once maximum body temperature is attained, the temperature gradient from the hot environment to the body is less steep than if the body temperature had remained lower. The amount of water required to maintain body temperature is now less than would have been required had the body temperature been kept low. This reaction is typical for a camel in water shortage; with free access to water, diurnal temperature variations are only about 2° C.

The terminus of camels by dehydration is described by Hedin (339).

In the kangaroo rat (*Dipodomys merriami*) the rectal temperature increases and stays above ambient temperature as the latter increases. When body temperature approaches the lethal limit of about 41° to 42° C., an emergency mechanism for heat regulation is activated, namely, a copious salivation which wets the fur under the lower jaw and throat thoroughly. Similar salivation reactions have been observed in other small mammals which do not sweat (mouse, rat, guinea pig, and opossum), in the cat which does not sweat appreciably but coats accessible parts of the body with saliva, and to some degree in the rabbit, although the latter does not spread the saliva over the fur (360, 689). Rodents, in response to high ambient temperatures, do not pant like man or dog, and their evaporative water losses do not increase greatly (12); even the dog has been described as reluctant to pant when dehydrated (306).

The pig also, like the rabbit, largely wastes its profuse flow of saliva (662), up to 500 cc. per day, although a principal avenue of heat loss in hot atmospheres is from the moist mouth and snout. The moist muzzle of cattle, sheep, goats, pigs, dogs, and cats is due to the presence of modified sweat glands (803).

Kuno (451) writes as follows:

> Evaporation from the mucous membrane of the mouth and the tongue can successfully control body temperature when these organs are large in proportion to the size of the body, as is the case in the dog. In animals with a small mouth, the skin must be entrusted with the responsibility of controlling the body temperature by evaporation. As a matter of fact, the sweat glands are developed in such animals, namely the horse, sheep, goat, monkey etc., man being also included.
>
> There are, however, many species of mammals with a small mouth, which have no sweat glands, and which do not pant. In some such animals, saliva is used as substitute for sweat. On hot summer days the body of a mouse is entirely wet. Salivation is copious and the frontal surface of the chest and the abdomen of the animal are first made wet. The animal then busily rubs saliva all over the body with its legs . . . .
>
> The elephant is an animal with an enormously large body and a small mouth and it seems to show neither panting nor strong salivation. By histological examinations, no sweat glands could be detected in its skin. I have long been puzzled to know how this animal gets rid of the effect of heat. At last I have had an opportunity of observing several elephants on warm summer days and found that they frequently suck water into the trunk and at once spray it over the head, the back and the sides. If there is no water to secure, they introduce the trunk into the mouth, use saliva in the same way.

Birds

It is well known, and had been said by Aristotle, that birds of prey (in contrast to the granivores) practically never drink (176, 445, 780).[63] Callenfels (150) noted parrots and quail as scarcely

---

[63] Mr. Malcolm Davis (202), Assistant Headkeeper of the National Zoological Park of Washington, D. C., informs me that, among falconiform birds, he has never observed drinking in the bald eagle (*Haliaeetus leucocephalus*), the red-tailed hawk (*Buteo jamaicensis*) nor in other species of *Buteo*.

ever requiring water, and Babcock (63) cited the case of a hen that lived for six weeks with no food or water. Poultry were the only creatures of the ill-fated Hedin caravan (339) which kept up their spirits, sauntering about in the blazing sun of the Takla-makan desert while man, camel, and dog were dying (Table IX). The hens feasted on the carcass of a dead sheep. Yeates *et al.* (880), however, observed that fowls can safely withstand a dry bulb temperature of 105° F. for only a few hours and, as the temperature mounts, tolerance time falls off rapidly. Birds cannot use accelerated respiration effectively for cooling, and have no sweat glands. The "private atmosphere" of the feathers retards heat exchange but the stance of holding the wings out increases the effective radiating surface and exposes less densely feathered parts. Fowls definitely take advantage to dip the head into water for cooling; it may be more important that they wet their heads than that they drink.

Dawson (203) has studied the temperature regulation and water requirements of the brown and Abert towhees (*Pipilo fuscus senicula* and *P. aberti dumeticolus*). The former is a resident of the relatively cool coastal slope of southern California; the latter of the hot Colorado Desert. Neither dissipates through evaporation more than half of the heat it produces at high air temperatures although slight physiologic advantages of the Abert over the brown towhee are noted. Although birds pant, this appears to produce too much heat at high air temperatures to be an efficient process for heat dissipation. Their capacity for evaporative cooling is thus insufficient to prevent body temperature from rising at high air temperatures, and the survival of these passerine birds during very hot weather depends primarily on their ability to tolerate elevated body temperatures and on behavioral patterns which tend to minimize heat stress. They may become inactive, seek shade, and may bathe in water in the middle of the day. Both species were found to tolerate elevations of body temperature of over 3° C.; the mean lethal temperature for both is 46.9° C. In a way, these birds react as does the camel (p. 360) but their small size and heat capacity suggest necessarily different physiologic adaptive details. Numerous desert birds seem to be almost independent of a supply of drinking water, e.g., thrushes and desert larks and the ostrich (741),

A puzzling problem awaiting clarification concerns the sea birds which have been said to be adapted to drink sea water and are known to drink it, although not usually in large quantities (445). Lockley (485) has observed Manx shearwaters (*Puffinus puffinus puffinus*) on first taking to the sea as fledglings. Their "first action is to drink, then to wash, then suddenly they discover they can dive." Fisher and Lockley (261) write:

> In order to carry on a sailing life upon the ocean it is obviously necessary for a sea-bird to be adapted to operate for a considerable time from base, even though, in ordinary rough weather, it may be able to sail very swiftly and make perhaps twenty or thirty miles an hour. Some sea-birds, and particularly the tube-nosed, in their early years before they make their first journeys to breeding cliffs, spend certainly two and up to seven years at sea without visiting land at all, possibly even without a sight of it. They are therefore adapted to drinking salt water and many have been recorded as doing so (shearwaters, petrels, auks and gulls).

Krogh (445) cites Lockley for statements particularly on the shearwater (*Puffinus*), the storm petrel (*Hydrobates*), the puffin (*Fratercula*), and the razorbill (*Alca*) which habitually drink small amounts of sea water. The albatross (*Diomedea*) and the booby bird (booby gannet, *Sula*) have also been observed to take sea water. Nevertheless Smith (741) remarks:

> It is sometimes asserted that marine birds drink sea water in captivity—because they have been observed to give the appearance of doing so; but it seems more likely that they are merely gargling it for fun, or perhaps using it to reduce the body temperature by taking it into and expelling it from the mouth.

As Smith further indicates, the maximal osmotic concentration of the urine in the chicken is only about 60% above the osmotic concentration of the blood so that unless unanticipated concentrating power is present in marine birds, we must look entirely to their renal excretion of uric acid to explain their ability to live

away from land.[64]   Not only does uric acid remove from the body
in each molecule twice as much nitrogen as does urea (it also has
the least hydrogen of any nitrogenous excretory product), for
which product it substitutes, but it thereby reduces osmotically the
obligatory urine volume (63).   Moreover, uric acid is relatively
insoluble in water, and forms a supersaturated solution which
yields a precipitate of fine crystals.   Being out of solution, these
exert no osmotic pressure.   Unfortunately, uric acid excretion reduces not only the obligatory urine volume but also, necessarily,
the osmotic space available for salt (pp. 310, 330).   The explanation of mariposia in sea birds thus becomes more difficult purely
on a renal basis and, indeed, is quite unresolved.

Sea birds feeding on marine fish would seem to be independent
of drinking at all inasmuch as the water content of fresh fish is
much higher than necessary for the renal excretion of the salts of
this food.   It has been supposed that ingestion of sea water
would impair an otherwise favorable water and salt balance
(688), unless, of course, such ingestion is actually a means of
providing salt rather than water (p. 358).   We cannot draw an
equilibration diagram (Fig. 4) for the water balance of a marine
bird, and it has not been shown how its metabolic and preformed
water may cover extrarenal losses.   These latter may relatively
exceed those of the seal (p. 352ff.) because of the habitus of the
birds.   We do not know whether the kidney secretion of marine
birds is more antidipsic than that of other birds.   The osmotic
pressure of the blood of birds is higher than that of mammals.
Pigeon blood has an osmosity of 0.171 M. sodium chloride; hen

---

[64] Many animals (all insects) which excrete uric acid instead of urea never have
access to free water and live on air dried food usually containing less than 10%
water (clothes moths, grain weevils).   Water from the oxidation of fat and carbohydrate is more than enough to replace respiratory and surface loss since no
poisonous metabolic products are formed.

The osmotic pressure of insect blood (expressed as per cent sodium chloride) is
rather high (834).   Instead of the 0.9% of mammals, that of bee larvae is 1.5%;
ephemerid nymphs, 0.69 to 1.0%; mealworm (*Tenebrio*) larvae, 2.12%.   It tends
to be higher in insects from dry environments, some of which, unlike frogs, take
up water from sufficiently humid air, e.g., clothes moth larvae (*Tineola*), meal
worm (*Tenebrio*), and the grasshopper (*Chortophaga*).   The osmotic pressure of
clear urine of the bug, *Rhodnius*, is equivalent to 1.0% salt but fluid accumulating
in the rectum by 48 hours may be 2.2%.   Urine of some insects is a "dry" solid.

blood is isosmotic with 0.175 M. sodium chloride (215).

Schmidt-Nielsen *et al.* (688) have recently discovered a curious phenomenon in the cormorant (*Phalacrocorax auritus*). Young birds, during experimental salt loading, secrete a hypertonic fluid from the nose, the secretion dripping out from the internal nares and collecting at the tip of the beak, from which the drops are shaken with a sudden jerk of the head. Concentration (500 to 600 mEq./L. of sodium chloride, both ions in nearly equivalent amounts) and flow (up to 0.15 cc./min. in a 1.5 Kg. bird) are so high that with continuous secretion the entire sodium chloride content might be eliminated in roughly 10 hours. The production of nasal secretion follows from osmotic loading with sucrose and may reflect a response to general osmotic stimulation.

Whether such a mechanism straightens the account of mariposia in sea birds (or even marine reptiles), and whether the production of this hypertonic secretion has roots in comparative physiology and anatomy (such as connect it with the hypertonic secretion of the gills of marine fish) remain to be seen.

Unpublished observations of McDowell and Wolf in the course of studies of osmotic volumes of distribution (530) revealed that in anesthetized dogs with large osmotic loads of sodium salts (chloride, sulfate) there is frequently produced a "nasal" secretion, copious at times and dripping from the external nares, which is hypertonic to the concurrent plasma. Concentrations as high as 247, 199, 18, and 160 mEq./L. for sodium, chloride, potassium, and sulfate, respectively, were noted (the two latter following infusions of sodium sulfate); in one sample, the osmotic pressure of the nasal drip was 415 mOs./L.

Fishes

Cannon (156, 158), in drawing the possible consequences of his dry mouth theory, thought it improbable that thirst would arise in fish because of the stream of water moving through the mouth and gills. No one can say, although numerous birds which have dry mouths (p. 52) because of lack of salivary glands are not notably pollakiposic. Yet fish, particularly marine teleosts, are known to drink. Smith's studies (734) on the catadromous eel (*Anguilla rostrata* = *A. chrysypa*) and the marine sculpin (*Myoxocephalus octodecimspinosus*) showed that these fish swallow

50 to 200 cc. of sea water per Kg. per day, of which they absorb about 75% of the water. Of the absorbed water, as much as 90% may be excreted extrarenally.

Smith's findings were based in part upon tests with phenol red which was added to aquarium water. This dye is not absorbed by the skin or gills, yet is concentrated in the intestine. Marine fish invariably drink within 2 to 3 hours after being placed in tinctured water.[65] Marine teleosts absorb most of the ingested water, sodium, potassium, and chloride from the intestine, leaving a residue relatively rich in magnesium and sulfate and approximately isotonic with their blood.

However, fresh water fish may not swallow water within 24 to 48 hours. In spite of failure to ingest water, their urine flow is larger than that of marine forms which excrete 2 to 5 cc./Kg./day (739). Some fresh water fish such as the goldfish (*Carassius auratus*) have been found to drink considerable quantities of water readily (30). In *Anguilla* (which lives in both sea and fresh water), the fresh water carp (*Cyprinus carpio*), and *Carassius*, the urine flow was 60 to 400 cc./Kg./day. In the gar pike (*Lepisosteus*), flows of 200 to 400 cc./Kg./day of dilute urine ($\Delta = 0.08°$ C.) are reported.

The osmotic pressure and chloride concentration of the plasma of marine teleosts varies, among other things, with the conditions of capture. Caught on a long line or by net, or bled after a delay and rough handling, values tend to be higher than in hook and line material or in fish long acclimated to life in a tank and obtainable for prompt bleeding (302). The relation of these elevations to the muscular exercise of struggling has been suggested, and the elevation of serum chloride and sodium with the violent muscular exercise of electroshock convulsions in man (818) is called to mind. Supposedly normal plasma values, relatively uncomplicated by muscular activity, are given by Grafflin (302) for fish which had been living for a long time in a tank: pollack (*Gadus pollachius*), $\Delta = 0.643°$ C. and chloride 151.8 mM./L.; conger eel (*Conger vulgaris*), $\Delta = 0.760°$ C. and chloride 171.8 mM./L. It is also stated (630) that the blood of marine and fresh water teleosts are osmotically similar ($\Delta = $ ca. $0.57°$ C.) but the

---

[65] After capture, marine teleosts are said to drink copiously of sea water as a result of which they sustain a diuresis in which, however, the concentration ratio of chloride is less than 1 (266).

former may be considerably higher (735, 736); the blood of the conger eel has been reported with $\Delta = 1.03°$ C. (735).

Scholander *et al.* (698) studied some curious phenomena in certain arctic fishes. *Lycodes, Liparis,* and *Gymnacanthus,* living at the bottom all year in sea water at $-1.73°$ C., are permanently supercooled by almost $1°$ C. If experimentally seeded with ice at their normal habitat temperature, most of them freeze and die, but ice cannot reach them at the bottom and in the absence of seeding they maintain physical metastability. Shallow water fishes such as the Fjord cod (*Gadus ogac*) and the sculpin (*Myoxocephalus scorpius*) swim about under the ice in winter, also at a temperature of $-1.73°$ C., but they are protected because the freezing point depression of their body fluids in that season rises as high as $1.6°$, almost isosmotic with sea water and freeze proof. In summer, in water at $5°$ C. their body fluids show $\Delta = 0.8°$. The large rise in osmoconcentration in the winter in these fishes is a unique adaptation induced by temperature, which protects them from the catastrophe of assuming the stable frozen state.

Smith (734) deduced that the large urine flow of the fresh water forms resulted from absorption of water through the gills, since the body fluids of these animals were osmotically superior to their environment. While a substantial contribution to the urine of fresh water fish by drinking is not ruled out, this inference was confirmed by Keys (418, 419). The latter developed an isolated heart-gill preparation of the common eel (*Anguilla vulgaris*), consisting of a double perfusion system, with sea or fresh water cycling through the mouth and out the branchial apertures, and a buffered perfusion medium (internal) which entered the heart and was collected from the dorsal aorta after traversing the gills. With fresh water in the external medium, analyses of the internal medium showed that water diffused into it, diluting chloride. When sea water was used, chloride fell in the internal medium even faster, showing that this ion was secreted into the external medium.

The euryhaline teleost, exemplified by the eel which tolerates a wide salt concentration in its external medium, may be considered a typical fresh water fish in fresh water and a typical marine fish in sea water (420). With the stenohaline fresh water fishes, they share renal salt conservation and elimination of water;

with the stenohaline marine teleosts, they share the method of eliminating excess salt and conserving water by the gills. Mullins (566) has shown through measurements of radioactive sodium and potassium exchange, that the rate of drinking of sticklebacks (*Gasterosteus aculeatus*) transferred from tap water to Baltic sea water of salinity about half that of normal sea water (Table XIII) was about 4% of the body weight per hour.

Smith (735, 736, 738, 739) has treated in detail the interesting case of the elasmobranchs (sharks, rays, skates, chimerae). In these forms, particularly the marine, there is a reduced excretion of urea with a resultant "physiological uremia" in which blood levels of 2.0 to 2.5% urea are found. The osmotic pressure of this urea, along with other substances, is effective to a degree that the body fluids of these forms are hypertonic to sea water.[66] Water is absorbed from the environment for the formation of urine in relatively large volumes (20 cc./Kg./day). The marine elasmobranch thus resembles the fresh water teleost, not needing to drink. The urine of marine elasmobranchs and teleosts approaches the tonicity of their blood, but does not exceed it. The osmotic pressure, however, of the blood of the elasmobranch exceeds that of its medium.

In fresh water elasmobranchs, the urine is distinctly hypotonic to the blood ($\overline{\Delta} < 0.1°$ C.) and the osmotic pressure of the blood is lower than in marine forms (about half). They form an abundant hypotonic urine. In the fresh water sawfish (*Pristis microdon*), a shark, urine flow averages 250 cc./Kg./day (741). Krogh (445) should be consulted for a critique of these points.

---

[66] The freezing point of sea water varies considerably with locality as may be seen from Table XIII. In general, the freezing point depression of elasmobranch serum exceeds that of the fluid of its habitat. Where for sea water $\Delta = 1.87°$ C. (Table XII), the serum $\Delta = $ ca. $2°$ C. It should be noted that the chloride of the blood plasma of fresh water elasmobranchs is typically about 170 mM./L. (as in marine teleosts, p. 366); that of marine forms is about 230 mM./L. (378). The osmosity of the electrolytes of these fish bloods thus exceeds that of mammals.

PART II

My thirst was the tallest tree in a forest of pain.
—Richard Evelyn Byrd

FOREWORD

Laboratory and field studies, and even clinical observations, generally fall short of revealing the full power and circumstance of the thirst sensation. But there are, elsewhere, striking recitals of such details. Some of these contain a wealth of raw material for the physiologist which, used carefully, can substantially forward scientific dissection of the problems of thirst. As a supplement to the formal treatment of Part I, therefore, several valuable accounts have been reprinted in Part II. All but the last are complete. They were chosen for interest and potential scientific and practical value; and some weight was given also to the possible difficulty one might experience in obtaining them and the usefulness of having these references at hand in one volume.

Atkinson's description (58), presumably of diabetes insipidus, lacks precision but not much else. The accounts of King (422) and McGee (533–535) are classics, widely mentioned in physiologic literature but generally quoted in insignificant fragments. They are worth perusal in the whole. McGee has also written of the Seri Indians (532), dealing with the peculiarly developed water-sense of desert peoples (Locale: 29° parallel, Mexico, Sierra Seri, Encinas Desert). We read there:

> . . . . for among folk habituated to thirst through terrible (albeit occasional) experience, water is the central nucleus of thought about which all other ideas revolve in appropriate orbits—it is an ultimate standard of things incomparably more stable and exalted than the gold of civilized commerce, the constantly remembered basis of life itself.

Pujo's notes (632) on thirst in the desert regions of French Equatorial Africa—the rock plateaus of Borkou—seem not to have been noticed by dipsologists. Their detailed and often unexplained observations take not a little of their importance from having been made by a medical officer.

Of all the horrible stories of the castaway at sea, of which *The Mariner's Chronicle* (217) or Edgar Allen Poe's fictive *Narrative of A. Gordon Pym* seem the adumbration, and the wreck of the *Medusa* (p. 246) or Gibson's *The Boat* (290) the real quintessence, few are so detailed as that of Rickenbacker (655). The latter is paralleled by the account of the same misfortune written by Whittaker (831), co-pilot of the ill-fated plane which carried Rickenbacker and the others. Coupled with Commander Haynes' report (338) of survivors of the sinking of the USS *Indianapolis,* and the extracts in Chapter V dealing with shipwreck survivors, these accounts leave little to be added to the subjectivity of thirst at sea.

CHAPTER VI

A REMARKABLE CASE OF INTEMPERATE DRINKING*

BE NOT startled, Messrs. Editors, by the apprehension that I am about to bore you and your readers with a disquisition on the evils resulting from the improper or excessive use of ardent spirits. Were I a professed lecturer on temperance, physicians are the last persons to whom I would address myself on that subject, since to none are those evils so apparent as to them. My purpose is to give you an account of a remarkable *water drinker,* and to inquire if you have ever seen or heard of a parallel case.

The *Boston Medical Journal* tells of a Mr. James Webb, of Fairhaven, (Mass.,) aged fifty-eight years, for whom, "under ordinary circumstances, *three gallons* of water is rather a short daily allowance," and who, "it would seem impossible, could live through the night with less than a pailful." The Journal adds, that "with this immense amount of cold water poured into the stomach, Mr. Webb has been in good health and spirits."

I remember to have seen, some years ago, in the Richmond Enquirer, an account given by the then Editor, (the lamented Thomas Ritchie, Sr.,) of some experiments which he had recently witnessed in *animal magnetism,* by which he had been convinced of the truth of that so-called science, and which he said were of so astounding a character as to be wholly incredible by all who had not seen them.

Now, Messrs. Editors, whilst I regard the case which I am about to communicate, as a most extraordinary one, and altogether without a parallel, so far as I am informed; and whilst it may be rejected as exaggerated, or altogether apocryphal, by those to whom I am personally unknown, I, nevertheless, vouch for its accuracy,

* By Thomas P. Atkinson, M.D. (58).

as it occurred under my own observation, and there are many persons yet living to whom an appeal might be had, were it necessary to sustain a statement made by one whose sole authority, he flatters himself, is sufficient to inspire confidence in any representation which he may make.

The case to which I allude, is that of Mr. J. H., who was my neighbor during my residence in the county of Halifax. He was a young man, below medium size, of sallow complexion, and more abdominous than is usual in persons of his age, presenting the appearance of one who, in his childhood, had been a *dirt-eater*. He was active and industrious, and enjoyed good health. He complained of nothing but *excessive thirst*. To such a degree did he suffer from this cause, that it was hard to resist the conviction that he had been bitten by the "Dipsas," a serpent known among the ancient Greeks, whose sting produced a mortal thirst.

Although a sober man, he was the most intemperate drinker I ever knew, from *four to six gallons* of water being required to keep him comfortable during the night, while his daily ration of this, to him literal *"aqua vitae,"* amounted to not less than from *eight to twelve gallons*. He always placed a *large tubful* near his bed, on retiring for the night, which often proving insufficient, he was forced to hurry to the spring to obtain relief from the intense suffering occasioned by the scanty supply. He has frequently driven the hogs from mud-holes in the road, and slaked his thirst with the *semi-liquid* element in which they had been rolling, himself *luxuriating* in that which had afforded only a moderate degree of enjoyment to the swine.

He married quite a good-looking and respectable girl, and, in the year 1829, left Halifax for the Western District of Tennessee, whither several of his neighbors had emigrated a short time before; but arriving at a *first rate spring*, on the top of the Cumberland mountain, he "squatted" near it; where, at the last account which I had of him, (in 1854,) he was quaffing his nectar as in days of yore, surrounded by his children, who had attained the age and arrived at the stature of full grown men.

Whether the excessive thirst of this individual be regarded as only a symptom of disease, or as *"ipse morbus,"* I think the case deserves to be recorded as one altogether anomalous in its character. I, therefore, forward it to you, again vouching for its accuracy in every particular.

CHAPTER VII

BRIEF ACCOUNT OF THE SUFFERINGS OF A DETACHMENT OF UNITED STATES CAVALRY, FROM DEPRIVATION OF WATER, DURING A PERIOD OF EIGHTY-SIX HOURS, WHILE SCOUTING ON THE "LLANO ESTACADO" OR "STAKED PLAINS," TEXAS*

IT SHOULD be stated that the following report is not based upon personal observation. The writer was one of the relieving party sent in quest of the lost men, and shortly after meeting them noted down the substance of this paper, which he gleaned while the events were still vividly impressed on their memories. It is feared that some of the details may, at first sight, appear scarcely worthy of notice; but any particulars concerning human beings deprived of water for such a long period, and under such circumstances, apart from bearing in a measure upon physiological science, are not totally devoid of interest.

On the evening of August 4th, 1877, two non-commissioned officers and one private belonging to company "A," tenth calvary, came into Fort Concho, Texas, reporting that Capt. Nolan and Lieut. Cooper, with twenty-six soldiers, while in pursuit of marauding Indians, had wandered amongst the sand-hills on the Staked Plains; that no water could be found, and that, when last seen, the whole command was exhausted and dying of thirst.

A relieving party, to which the writer was attached, was organized at once, and left immediately in search of the missing men. After a rapid march of sixty-two hours we reached Capt. Nolan's supply camp, situated seven miles northeast of the Muchakoway Mountain and 140 miles from Concho, where we

* By J. H. King, M.D., Captain and Assistant Surgeon U.S.A. (422).

learned that Capt. Nolan, Lieut. Cooper, and all the men except four had just come in safely one hour previously.

As the lost men advanced towards us, we remarked their changed appearance since we had last seen them, a few weeks before; their aged and careworn faces portrayed the hardships they had undergone, while additional gray locks and other indications of suffering were visible. The following is the painful history which they narrated.

Capt. Nolan, Lieut. C. L. Cooper, and forty troopers of Co. A, 10th Cav., with eight pack-mules, had for some days been scouting in the region of "Double Lakes" and "Cedar Lake," looking for Indians. On the 26th of July, 1877, rumour was brought into camp at "Double Lakes" that a band of hostile Indians had recently been seen passing "Dry Lake." Capt. Nolan forthwith prepared to follow them, and broke up camp at 1 P.M., July 26th.

The Indian trail was struck west of Dry Lake, and pursued until dark, being then no longer discernible. The guide, in his anxiety to keep the Indian trail, had neglected his landmarks, and was unable to find water when the halt was sounded. The party were compelled, therefore, to make a dry camp and so pass the night. On leaving "Double Lake," each man's canteen had been filled, but in consequence of the intense heat they were emptied in the early part of the march, and what little water "Dry Lake" contained was so strongly alkaline that neither man nor beast could drink it.

At dawn the trail was again taken up and followed perseveringly, not only with a view of capturing the Indians, but also with hopes that it might conduct them to some lake or water-hole. Their course lay over a gently undulating country; the soil dry, mostly of a reddish colour, covered with bunches of short grass, here and there a stunted mesquite-bush ten or fifteen inches high, and occasional twigs of scrub-oak of similar size. The heat was excessive—"coup de soleil" had prostrated two men, and all were suffering severely from thirst.

Towards sunset the trail commenced to spread, breaking into a multitude of ill-defined tracks, rendering further pursuit useless, and the chase was given up. Men had been thrown out on the flanks all day to seek for water, and for the same purpose the guide explored every valley and depression within view. Matters were assuming a grave aspect; many were faint and exhausted; some fell from their saddles. The horses needed water equally with their riders. After adopting all customary methods to extricate his command from this critical position, Capt. Nolan finally mounted the guide on his private horse, a tough animal, and ordered him to traverse the country, ranging wherever he thought it possible to find water. This guide was never seen afterwards. Capt. Nolan for a time awaited his return, and then determined to fall back upon "Double Lakes," which were supposed to be 75 or 100 miles distant, where he felt confident of obtaining water.

Another day was drawing to a close, and, as night came on, advantage was taken of the cooler atmosphere, and every nerve was strained to reach "Double Lakes."

The next day found them still marching onwards, and the midday tropical heat causing great suffering. The desire for water now became uncontrollable. The most loathsome fluid would now have been accepted to moisten their swollen tongues and supply their inward craving. The salivary and mucous secretions had long been absent; their mouths and throats were so parched that they could not swallow the government hard-bread; after being masticated it accumulated between the teeth and in the palate, from whence it had to be extracted with the fingers; the same occurred with mesquite-beans and whatever else they attempted to eat. The sensibility of the lingual and buccal mucous membranes was so much impaired that they could not perceive when anything was in their mouths. The condition of the "primae viae" may in a degree be realized, when it is explained that brown sugar would not dissolve in their mouths, and that it was impossible for them to swallow it. Vertigo and dimness of vision affected all; they had difficulty in speaking, voices weak and strange-sounding; and they were troubled with deafness, appearing stupid to each other, questions having to be repeated several times before they could be understood; they were also very feeble and had a tottering gait. Many were delirious. What little sleep they were able to get was disturbed with ever-recurring dreams of banquets, feasts, and similar scenes, in which they were enjoying every kind of dainty food and delicious drink.

At this stage they would in all likelihood have perished had they not resorted to the use of horse-blood. As the animals gave out they cut them open and drank their blood. The horses had been so long deprived of every kind of fluid that their blood was thick, and coagulated instantly on exposure; nevertheless, at the time it appeared more delicious than anything they had ever tasted; in fact, every one was so eager to obtain it that discipline alone prevented them from struggling for more than the stinted share allowable to each. The heart and other viscera were grasped and sucked as if to secure even the semblance of moisture. At first they could not swallow the clotted blood, but had to hold it in their mouths, moving it to and fro between the teeth, until it became somewhat broken up, after which they were enabled to force it down their parched throats. The horse-blood quickly developed diarrhoea, passing through the bowels almost as soon as taken. Their own urine, which was very scanty and deep coloured, they drank thankfully, first sweetening it with sugar.*
The inclination to urinate was absent, and micturition performed with difficulty. A few drank the horses' urine, although at times it was caught in cups and given to the animals themselves. They became oppressed with dyspnoea, and a feeling of suffocation as though the sides of the trachea were adhering, to relieve which they closed the lips and breathed through the nose, prolonging the intervals between each inspiration as much as possible. Gazing on each other, their lips thus closed were observed to be covered with a whitish, dry froth, and had a ghastly, pale, lifeless appearance, as thought they would never be opened again. Their fingers and the palms of their hands looked shrivelled and pale; some who had removed their boots suffered from swollen feet and legs.

---

* The men of Hedin's caravan (339) were driven to hemoposia and uriposia. They drank rooster blood but were unable to take sheep blood, it being too repulsive; even the dog of the party licked it and went his way. The men turned to camel urine to which had been added some vinegar and sugar. Not all the men were able to drink this abominable concoction, the mere smell of which was nauseating; those who drank it were seized with violent and painful vomiting which completely prostrated them.

The situation was now desperate, and feelings akin to despair took possession of them—suspicious ideas towards each other came over them, and they lost confidence in each other. They again saw the sun set, and another night was spent on these untrodden wastes, without alleviation of their misery. Persistent wakefulness now aggravated their mental anguish, and in vain at every halt they lay down and tried to sleep.

Their deplorable condition continued to gradually grow worse, until 5 A.M., July 30th, 1877, when, providentially, part of the command succeeded in making "Double Lakes." At this time a number of men were missing, some having been unable to keep up with the main column, while others had strayed after water.

Both officers and men were almost helpless on reaching "Double Lakes," and the wished-for water did not greatly benefit any of them this day. Canteens of water were at once strapped to the horses, and two or three men sent with them on the back trail to succor and help on the stragglers.

Fortunately, the following morning, Capt. Lee, 10th Cavalry, with a detachment of Youkoway scouts, touched at "Double Lakes" and rendered most valuable assistance to Capt. Nolan's party, despatching his scouts on all sides to hunt for men and horses, and furnishing rations and some delicacies which the sufferers were in absolute need of.

The demands of their systems were so imperative that the inclination to drink was irresistible; it seemed impossible to refrain from pouring down water, notwithstanding that their stomachs would not retain it. As they kept filling themselves with water, it was vomited up; the same thing occurred when they endeavoured to eat dry food. Warm coffee was the only thing they had that revived them at all, until after Capt. Lee met them.

Although water was imbibed again and again, even to repletion of the stomach, it did not assuage their insatiable thirst, thus demonstrating that the sense of thirst is, like the sense of hunger, located in the general system, and that it could not be relieved until the remote tissues were supplied. Moreover, the activity of this regenerating process was prevented by the deficiency of water in the absorbent vessels themselves. The same cause is competent to explain the overpowering dyspnoea, which threatened the existence of these men; for only moist membranes allow the free passage of gases which must take place in respiration. The lungs of these men were filled with the purest air, yet they appreciated an almost overwhelming sense of suffocation. Another point worthy of our attention is the loss these men must have sustained by integumentary and pulmonary exhalations. The mean daily exhalation of watery vapour in expired air Valentin estimates at $1^1/_5$ lbs. av., and the daily loss by cutaneous transpiration at about 2 lbs.; in the case before us the quantities were influenced and increased by the conditions of temperature, exercise, etc.

The superior endurance of the mule over the horse was obviously manifested on this scout. The horses' tongues were swollen, mouths and systems generally affected much in the same manner as the men's; they could not chew or swallow grass; many gave out completely. On the other hand, the mules, comparatively unfatigued, would crop the grass and graze at every halt.

It is essential to remember that the sensations of thirst, to which these cavalrymen almost succumbed, were intensified by the dry state of the atmosphere; they were toiling over arid plains and elevated plateaus in a climate noted for its lack of moisture.

On August 1st, 1877, Capt. Nolan heard that fourteen of his followers had managed to get all right as far as the Supply Camp. His total loss, therefore, after this disastrous scout, only consisted of two men dead and two missing, supposed to be dead. Capt. Nolan remained five or six days at "Double Lakes" to recuperate, and then retraced his steps to the Supply Camp, arriving there on August 7th, 1877.

FORT CLARK, TEXAS, Jan. 21st, 1878.

CHAPTER VIII

DESERT THIRST AS DISEASE*

I. A CASE OF THIRST

T HE PRINCIPAL scene of the case is a typical auguaje (i.e., "water") of southwestern Arizona, known since the days of Padre Kino (who apparently passed that way in the expedition of 1701 which proved that California is not an island, and located the "Tinaxa" on his map of 1702) as Tinajas Altas, or "high tanks." The water lies in a number of potholes or water-pockets in a gorge cleaving the northeastern side of Sierra Gila; it is chiefly a residuum of the light midsummer or midwinter rains, though the deeper pools are partly supplied by seepage from the granite ledges and precipices rising ruggedly several hundred feet above the gorge-bottom. The locality is about 75 miles southeast of Yuma, 40 miles south of Gila River, and three or four miles north of the Mexican boundary at a point 50 miles east of the mouth of Rio Colorado. The nearest house—the Southern Pacific station at Wellton—is some 30 miles northward in an air line, over broad sandwastes with scattered sierritas and buttes; water is obtainable at the Fortuna mine, 35 miles northwestward in Sierra Gila, and sometimes in other waterholes in the granites seven miles southward and twenty miles eastward; the abandoned Tule Well is 23 miles eastward, and the nearest certain water in that direction is in Rio Sonoyta sandwash at Agua Salada, some 80 miles away, or Agua Dulce, ten miles further. The region was never permanently inhabited by the aborigines, though temporarily occupied by the Papago Indians at the times of the cactus-fruit harvests, and apparently by the Cocopa and Maricopa Indians as a waystation on a severe and secret route of intercommunication; and hundreds of mortars are ground into the granites about the tinajas, while other

* By W. J. McGee, LL.D., Director Saint Louis Public Museum (535).

381

relics occur. For the two half-centuries (1750–1848) during which California was a flourishing Mexican province, Tinajas Altas was reputed the sole sure "water" between Rio Sonoyta at Santo Domingo or Quitobaquito and Rio Colorado at Yuma on that desperately hard overland route known as El Camino del Diablo, which joined the royal roads of Sonora and Sinaloa with the easier El Camino Real along which the old missions of southern California were strung; and during the days of the Argonauts, from '49 to the middle '50s, the same route was the hardest part of the Old Yuma Trail trod by American Pioneers in their long trek to the land of gold. From the single-house settlement of Quitobaquito to the town of Yuma the way is houseless, and apparently never had a fixed habitation save a small adobe at Tule Well; yet the passage of pioneers over the desert stretches was so steady and long-continued that hardly a mile of the 200 from Santo Domingo to Yuma remains unmarked by one or more cruciform stone-heaps attesting death by the wayside; death commonly in its cruelest form—by the torture of thirst. Most of the movement was westward, and the worst reach lay between Tule Well and Tinajas Altas; along this way the cross-shape stone-heaps, each telling its mute tale of tragedy, thicken until within gunshot of the nearly perennial water, where are over 60 marked graves—and how many unmarked none know—lie mostly on a single little mesa in plain sight of the pools; for again and again exhausted strugglers fell at the foot of the gentle up-slope, or failed to find water in the lowest pool and were unable to climb the rocks to the higher reservoirs: when, if the next followers were pious folk—as were most of the Mexican pioneers—the stark bodies were laid in shallow graves laboriously sealed with the sign of the cross.

Such was the site of my camp from May 20 to August 28, 1905 —a tentless camp, with a living population of one when Papago Jose was gone for a week or less at a time, of two when either he or the young histrion Harrison Ford was present (during the few weeks of his stay), and three with both; or of half a dozen for a few hours at a time when, as happened twice or thrice, prospecting parties passed that way: a camp devoted to meteorologic observation and study of the effects of light on desert life.

Just before noon of Monday, August 14, Pablo Valencia and Jesus Rios drifted into camp horseback en route to the "lost mines" rediscovered by the former some months before.   They were supplied with pinole (parched-wheat meal), bread, cheese, sugar, coffee, and tobacco for a week's subsistence, with two 2-gallon and two 1-gallon canteens, and had also a dozen pounds of pressed alfalfa and twice as much rolled barley for the horses.[2]   Jesus is 65, a former vaquero and nearly typical Mexican, claiming familiarity with the country, but erratic and inconsequent and little dependable in statements of fact or in any other way; he rode his own grass-fed horse, which shrank, bronco-like, from barley.   Pablo is about 40, of remarkably fine and vigorous physique—indeed, one of the best-built Mexicans known to me.   In earlier life he was a sailor on Pacific vessels and afterward a wandering prospector and miner; he was tiding over the summer of 1905 by growing watermelons on a ranchita near Gila City.   He measures about 5 feet 7 inches, weighs normally some 155 pounds, and is notably deep-chested and round-bodied, with—for a Mexican—exceptionally robust limbs; he is reputed a large eater and heavy sleeper, and is of phlegmatic disposition, given to drowsing in the shade rather than working in the sun—yet between periods of repose he is of energetic and pertinacious habit, walking barefoot or in sandals (in preference to riding) with a quick and strong upspringing gait carrying him by all but the best horses, openly scorning hunger and thirst and boasting ability to withstand far beyond ordinary men these habitual inconveniences of the range. In a word, he is a particularly fine type of the animal genus *Homo* —a most matter-of-fact man of action in his little world, albeit lightly burdened with acute sensibility, imagination, or other mentality; indeed, an ideal man to endure stressful experience.   He

---

[2] They were outfitted at Yuma by Jim Tucker, miner and rancher; they left there in the saddle after noon on August 12, having shipped a bale of hay and a bag of barley with some of their food and canteens to Wellton: camping on the banks of the Gila north of Blaisdell, they started early Sunday morning and reached Wellton about midafternoon, where they took their freight and fed and watered freely, leaving part of the feed for the return. They started for Tinajas Altas Monday morning "at the time of the morning star" (say three o'clock) and covered the thirty-odd miles in a little over eight hours.

rode Jim Tucker's best horse—an animal of exceptional bottom, well inured to desert work.

While their horses ate, Pablo and Jesus lunched with Jose and me, feasting on jerked cimarron (mountain-sheep meat), in addition to their own comestibles. Against my advice (which was to leave at 1 A.M. Tuesday, the moon being about the full), they set out for their El Dorado about five o'clock; but in half an hour they returned, having decided to wait until morning on the ostensible ground that the horses had drank but little, though in reality because my judgment had finally worked in. Next morning Jose stirred up Jesus, and the two pulled Pablo from his saddle-blanket for breakfast; and they got off at day-light. This was the real beginning of the journey—about 3:45 Tuesday morning, August 15.

Soon after midnight Jesus came in alone, with both horses, reporting that Pablo had sent him back from a point about 35 miles southeastward to re-water, he himself going forward on foot with a 2-gallon canteen and a stock of pinole, under an agreement —an inane if not insane one in desert life—to rendezvous 24 to 30 hours later not on the trail but on the farther side of a nearby sierra. Jesus drank, ate, watered, fed, and struck the trail again (with five gallons of water, taking one of my canteens) about 3:30 A.M. on the 16th. Next morning about 7 he again came in alone with both horses, reporting that his own animal had broken down after a short distance and that he had ridden the Tucker horse by a better route both to the rendezvous and to where he had left Pablo at the edge of the sand-hills; and that he had been unable to find either the lost man or his trail. He explained that Pablo had probably gone on to Agua Salada (as he had advised all along, misstating the distance, etc.), and proposed after resting to return to Wellton and Yuma. He was indeed exhausted, having ridden some 150 miles in about 52 consecutive hours; while his horse was practically broken down, and the Tucker animal tired. On putting together all statements from both Pablo and Jesus, I was in doubt as to whether or not Pablo had gone on toward Rio Sonoyta, though this seemed probable; yet I thought he ought to have another chance for his life, and so held Jesus at Tinajas Altas and sent Jose (an expert trailer among his tribe of trailers) out on the Tucker horse to find Pablo's track, giving him full instructions as to routes, places for smoke signals, etc. (for I knew the region better than he), and directing him to go to the limit of his horse's endurance and then to his own limit beyond. Jose carried a feed of barley, a couple of pounds of pinole and dates for himself, and two extra canteens; he got off about 10 o'clock Thursday, August 17. Stopping only to send up smokes, he followed old Jesus' ill-chosen trails and easily located the point at which Pablo had left him on the 15th; thence he followed the foot-trail with difficulty in the darkness of the early night. Reaching the sandhills about moonrise, he left the horse and labored through the dunes seven miles further—then returned as he came, making signal fires here and there. Picking up the horse in the dawn and giving him a half-gallon of water from his hat, he arrived at camp in speechless exhaustion just before noon Friday, the 18th. I was convinced that further effort would be bootless, since it seemed probable that even if Pablo had not gone on to Agua Salada en route to Santo Domingo he could hardly still survive, for he had already been out over three days with only one day's water—and most of those who die from desert thirst expire in less time; so although Jesus and his horse were still unrestored and the Tucker animal had been moving almost steadily for 80 hours and over 225 miles, I packed Jesus off toward Wellton and Yuma to report his virtual abandonment of the man he had undertaken to guide and protect—supplementing his prospective oral report with a special delivery letter to El Padron (Jim Tucker), to be mailed at Wellton in time for the 2 o'clock train Saturday morning.[3]

So ended the first episode in the Pablo Valencia event, in the afternoon of August 18. I remained uneasy a day or two longer, and next day and the day after climbed a neighboring peak 750 feet high and walked out a few miles on the trail to seek for sign; then Jose and I fell into normal camp routine.

In the graying dawn of Wednesday, August 23, the grasp of sleep on me relaxed in a vivid dream recalling a picture often

---

[3] Jesus started about four o'clock P.M. on August 18 and should have reached Wellton between one and two, thus getting the letter into Tucker's hands early the next morning, and he should have himself arrived in Yuma early Sunday morning, August 20; but he slumped characteristically on the Wellton stretch, and made a needless camp beyond, so that he and the letter arrived about the same time on Monday afternoon.

presented in the ganaderos (half-wild cattle ranges) of western Sonora—the picture of an orderly file of stock, led by a stalwart bull and trailing down to yearlings in the rear, the leader iterating his grave grumbling roar of assurance to the herd which at last— as on the range—rose in quick crescendo into the ear-piercing bellow of challenge and defiance to all other kine. I awoke at the dream-sound to realize its actuality, and turned my head half expecting to see the herd; instead, there stood Jose, just arisen from his blanket, looking down the arroyo. Seeing my movement, he asked: "What is it? I thought it was one of them roaring, lions, like in the Zoo." Now fully awake, I replied: "It must be Pablo; take the canteen." Though wholly incredulous, he mechanically seized a canteen and a strip of manta which with his coat made a pillow, and, after a call in reply, ran down the trail. I soon followed, carrying another canteen and a medicine case; and on the arroyo sands, under an ironwood tree, at the foot of the Mesita de los Muertos with its two-score cross-marked graves, came on the wreck of Pablo, with Jose already ministering unto him.

Pablo was stark naked; his formerly full-muscled legs and arms were shrunken and scrawny; his ribs ridged out like those of a starveling horse; his habitually plethoric abdomen was drawn in almost against his vertebral column; his lips had disappeared as if amputated, leaving low edges of blackened tissue; his teeth and gums projected like those of a skinned animal, but the flesh was black and dry as a hank of jerky; his nose was withered and shrunken to half its length, the nostril-lining showing black; his eyes were set in a winkless stare, with surrounding skin so contracted as to expose the conjunctiva, itself black as the gums; his face was dark as a negro, and his skin generally turned a ghastly purplish yet ashen gray, with great livid blotches and streaks; his lower legs and feet, with forearms and hands, were torn and scratched by contact with thorns and sharp rocks, yet even the freshest cuts were as so many scratches in dry leather, without trace of blood or serum; his joints and bones stood out like those of a wasted sickling, though the skin clung to them in a way suggesting shrunken rawhide used in repairing a broken wheel. From inspection and handling, I estimated his weight at 115 to

120 pounds. We soon found him deaf to all but loud sounds, and so blind as to distinguish nothing save light and dark. The mucus membrane lining mouth and throat was shriveled, cracked, and blackened, and his tongue shrunken to a mere bunch of black integument. His respiration was slow, spasmodic, and accompanied by a deep guttural moaning or roaring—the sound that had awakened us a quarter of a mile away.[4] His extremities were cold as the surrounding air; no pulsation could be detected at wrists, and there was apparently little if any circulation beyond the knees and elbows; the heartbeat was slow, irregular, fluttering, and almost ceasing in the longer intervals between the stertorous breathings.

The victim was, of course, unable to articulate or to swallow. Water was slushed over his face, head, chest, and abdomen, and rubbed into his limbs and extremities, the skin first shedding and then absorbing it greedily as a dry sponge—or more exactly, as this-season's rawhide; dilute whiskey was forced into his mouth and rubbed on his chest with prompt effect (doubtless the greater because Pablo was a habitual tee-totaler); and when in half an hour swallowing motions began feebly, both whiskey and a powerful heart stimulant (digitalis-nitroglycerin-belladonna tabloid triturates) were administered internally. In an hour he drank, though most of the water was immediately expelled from the stomach; in two hours he began to partake of food—a bird fricassee with rice and shredded bacon; in some three hours (soon after sunrise) he was able with some help to walk into camp. By this time he had ingested and retained about $2^{1}/_{2}$ ounces of whisky, with 5 ounces of water, and 2 or 3 ounces of food; his external tissues were saturated and softened, circulation was restored sluggishly in his extremities, and his numerous wounds begun to inflame or exude blood and serum. Articulation slowly returned, and in a cracked voice, breaking involuntarily from bass to falsetto, he began to beg pathetically for "agua, agua," and to protest against the "dust" which we were compelling him to sip;

[4] The distance to which the moaning carried was doubtless due partly to the funnel-shape gorge in which the sound was concentrated, while the audibility was, of course, enhanced by our habitude to the desert stillness, seldom broken save by chattering of ravens, cooing of pigeons, or whistling of quails, all beginning later in the day.

he even failed to recognize coffee, which was given in small quantities.

As Pablo's strength returned in the course of the day, two abnormal conditions developed: the more disturbing at the outset began with local inflammation about the cuts, scratches and bruises suffered in creeping the last seven miles over a cactus-dotted and often stony plain, and extended into a general feverish and irritable state doubtless intensified by the long-continued nerve-strain; it was accompanied by pains and inflammation in wrists and hands, feet and ankles, and at one stage I feared loss of nails and sloughing of phalanges, which might have ensued in a less pure and invigorating air. The other disturbing condition was the passing of the hoarse, stertorous breathing into a sort of spasm, apparently affecting stomach, diaphragm, intercostal muscles, and the upper part of the body generally—a combined retching and hiccoughing so severe as to rack the victim from head to foot and induce violent vomiting. A preparation of bismuth in tablets gave some relief, and pepsin-pancreatin tablets taken with food were beneficial; yet the spasms were so severe and persistent as to threaten fatal exhaustion. Toward evening urinary excretion began feebly, at first accompanied by blood and mucus; it was over two days before movement of the bowels began. The camp dietary was then reduced, but the birds (California quail and Sonora pigeons, shot fresh every morning) fricasseed with rice and minced bacon were nutritious and easily digested: though we longed for watermelon for him. On the third day (Saturday, August 26) vision and audition became normal, and Pablo began to notice things in an infantile way, as if the power of apperception were awakening; he stared at and evidently recognized shrubs and rocks about the camp, scrutinized and curiously felt of his own hands and feet, and also clearly recognized water; while his mind began to place Jose and me in his fabric of definite cognition—for we had been mere shadow-objects before. He surprisedly examined his wounds, which were then healing satisfactorily, and described the spasmodic retching as due to the forming of a "ball" in his stomach. On the second day he had muttered, half to himself, the events of his journey; on the third, he recounted them spontaneously and in reply to inquiries in such manner as to yield a definite and doubtless fairly trustworthy itinerary.

On Sunday, August 27, came in Jim Tucker with four-horse wagon and extra saddle animals, accompanied by two or three men (all friends of Pablo) to search for trails and remains; at first the patient hardly knew them, and shrank from them as creatures of a nightmare; but they showered him with attentions and forced on him heaping plates of stew, frijoles, fried bacon, and whole loaves of soggy Dutch-oven bread, with the result that the spasms were intensified and accompanied by effusions of biliary matter streaked with blood. For a day Tucker planned going on to the "lost mine," leaving Pablo with me; but the relapse was so serious and the recurrent spasms so severe that by Monday noon I felt compelled to prescribe a return to Wellton. About 4 o'clock the spasm-racked wreck was bedded in the wagon; about 11 P.M., when a halt was made to rest the team—for the nearly trackless sands dragged heavily—I judged there was an equal chance of getting the patient alive to Wellton; at 2 we were moving again, and about 7 we drew into the clean sand-wash in the rear of the station. Twenty minutes later we had raw eggs, and Pablo's crisis was past. Later in the day some watermelons were secured; and next morning we were in Yuma. Pablo was guarded for a few hours, but spent practically the whole of August 31 deliberately and methodically devouring watermelons, with occasional lapses into slumber; and in a week he was well and cheerful, weighing 135 pounds or more—though his stiff and bristly hair, which had hardly a streak of gray a fortnight before, had lost half its mass and turned iron-gray.

The nature of the case and the severity of the stress successfully encountered by Pablo Valencia cannot fully be understood without considering the utterly desert character of the region—than which there is none worse in North America save Death Valley and a few other basins not opening toward the sea—and the torridity of the climate and season. The 100-day record (May 21 to August 28) of temperature and humidity at Tinajas Altas served to define a vapor-zone about Gulf of California in which a large part of our storm-centers find origin; and although most of Pablo's route lay outside this zone and in a hotter and drier belt, the record from

TEMPERATURE AND MOISTURE

Dates	Temperature — Self-Registering Thermometers				Psychrometer				Moisture — Humidity	Moisture	
	Maximum	Minimum	Range	Mean	Dry Bulb	Wet Bulb	De-pres'n	Dew Point	Relative Humidity	Rain (in.)	Cloudiness (tenths of sky)
August 14. 8 p.m.	99.1°	85.1°	14.0°	92.1°	91.0°	65.0°	26.0°	48.0°	23.0%	0	0.1—
August 15. 8 a.m.	91.8	76.8	13	85.3	90.5	62.5	28	41	18	0	.1—
8 p.m.	98.9	90.9	8	94.9	92	66.5	25.5	51	25	0	.1—
August 16. 8 a.m.	92	81	11	86.5	86	69	17	60	42	0	.1—
8 p.m.	99.5	85	14.5	92.2	91.5	71.5	20	61.5	38	0	.2—
August 17. 8 a.m.	94	79.7	14.3	86.8	93	68	25	54	26.5	0	.1—
8 p.m.	103.2	93.2	10	98.2	95	69	26	54	25.5	0	.1—
August 18. 8 a.m.	95	83	12	89	87	76	11	72	60.5	0	.1—
8 p.m.	96	86.6	9.4	91.3	88.5	73	15.5	66	48	0	.8—
August 19. 8 a.m.	88.5	80.5	8	84.5	87	74	13	69	54.5	0	.1—
8 p.m.	98.4	85.4	13	91.9	90	73	17	65	44	0	.0—
August 20. 8 a.m.	90	81	9	85.5	87.5	73	14.5	66.5	50	0	.1—
8 p.m.	99.1	87.3	11.8	93.2	89	71.5	17.5	63	42.5	0	.1—
August 21. 8 a.m.	89.9	78.4	11.5	84.2	88	74	14	68	52	0	.6—
8 p.m.	91	87	4	89	90	71	19	62	39	0	.6—
August 22. 8 a.m.	92.1	81	11.1	86.7	91	69	22	57	32.5	0	.2—
8 p.m.	100	90	10	95	91	71	20	61	37.5	0	.7—
August 23. 8 a.m.	91.8	82.1	9.7	86.9	91	69	22	57	32.5	0	.2—
Means, August 14–23	95	84.2	10.8	89.6	89.9	70.3	19.6	59.8	38.4		.12—
Average, August 1–28	101.8	81.7	20.1	91.7	92.3	69.7	22.6	56	32.9	.004	.067—
Average, 100-day period	99.3	77	22.3	88.2	88.9	64.5		46.5	27.1	.0012	

the evening of August 14 to the morning of August 23 approximately indicates the attendant climatal conditions. This record, with the means for the 9-day period and also the averages for both August 1–28 and for the 100-day period, is appended—from which it will appear that Pablo was favored by exceptionally low temperature and high humidity; yet the maximum temperatures ranged from 88.5 to 103.2 (averaging 95), and the minimum night temperatures from 78.4 to 93.2 (averaging 84.2), i.e., were always above that somewhat variable yet most important physiologic value which may be termed the *perspiration-point:* the point at which the burden of elimination is transferred either from kidneys and lymphatics to the skin, or from the epidermal to the internal eliminative structures, as the temperature-measure is passed. Pablo was also exceptionally favored by clouds; for although the sky was never wholly overcast, the average of morning and evening cloudiness reached two-tenths of the total sky. He was fortunate, too, in the high relative humidity for a desert range; at Tinajas Altas the percentage of aqueous vapor ranged from 18 to over 60 (averaging 38), indicating that along his route it probably oscillated between 15 and 55.

Pablo's itinerary, taken partly from his nearly meaningless maunderings as speech returned, but chiefly from connected statements largely in reply to inquiries, runs thus:

Tuesday, August 15: Left Tinajas Altas at 3:45, horseback, with Jesus; rode some 35 miles, reaching "sand-hills" about one o'clock; thence afoot with 2-gallon canteen (full at starting), pinole, tobacco, serape, duck coat, prospector's hammer, canvas specimen-bag, cigarette papers, and matches, faring some ten miles through the sands before stopping to sleep. Drank three or four times, and took pinole twice.

Wednesday, August 16: Starting with the rise of the morning-star, reached the ledge of which he was in quest about midforenoon; after collecting specimens, erected monuments and posted notices for a mineral claim, finishing this work before midday. Ate a little pinole and drank sparingly (as he had done before starting), for the canteen was nearly empty. Starting northward, began search for a road described (falsely) by Jesus, and straggled rather aimlessly over the sands, moistening his mouth occasionally but not swallowing water, until the canteen was empty; at nightfall reached an arroyo in which he fancied signs of water. In the darkness of the early night (before moonrise) abandoned his nuggets, and soon after threw away his stock of pinole and his coat and serape. Failing to find water, he sought sleep in the sands; and when awakened by mouth-dryness obtained some relief—after the fashion of all Mexicans and most Americans in like cases—by occasionally filling his mouth and gargling his throat with urine.

Thursday, August 17: Set out early, seeking trails and tinajas, and working northward; unable to withstand the heat of midday, he lay down in an arroyo and ate calabasitas (wild gourds of intense bitterness), which his stomach rejected. Arising as the sun declined, he threw away shoes and trousers (with money, knife, and tobacco in the pockets), and wandered on northward, finding occasionally old trails which either faded away in a few miles or else led into sands or impassable rocks—trails mostly figments of disordered fancy. One led to an immense tinaja; but it was dry. During the day he had frequent recourse to urine, though he nearly lost the power to swallow; during the night he saved every drop of the excretion in the canteen, which he still carried.

Friday, August 18: In early morning he walked a few miles, but was overcome by the torrid heat and crept under the shade of a paloverde overhanging an arroyo; toward evening he arose, and chewed paloverde twigs with little effect save to irritate mouth and throat. Setting out northward before sunset he found a mescal (a variety of agave) and chewed the stipes, extracting a little moisture; at sunset he caught a few flies and spiders, which he chewed and tried to swallow. Still he wandered northwardly, having in mind first the rendezvous with Jesus, then the Old Yuma Trail he had traversed years before. Toward morning he became convinced that Jesus had deliberately misled and abandoned him with murderous intent in the plan of thus securing his El Dorado; and his wrath spurred him on with the aim of knifing his deceiver —a potent incentive which carried him miles and doubtless saved his life. He continued to relieve mouth-thirst with urine.

Saturday, August 19: In early morning he found mule-wagon

tracks and recognized the Old Yuma Trail,[5] which he followed, but soon fell under the heat and lay all day in an arroyo. In the afternoon he saw one of the large light-green scorpions of the region; it looked luscious, and he captured it, ground off its sting with a stone, and devoured it. As before he used urine, swallowing a part with great difficulty. Toward evening he resumed journeying northward, often falling; near morning he found (or thought he found) Jesus' trail where he had wandered in search of the hopeless rendezvous set for the 16th. Throughout the night he caught occasional glimpses of a coyote trailing him. During all of Saturday and throughout this night on the trail he was buoyed by a new incentive—the hope of reaching Tule Well and casting himself into the moist mud at its bottom and at the worst dying in the dampness and coolness 37 feet below ground; he felt the notion half insane and the hope wholly hopeless, yet unto them he clung as to an inspiration. Meantime, he constantly sought insects to chew, and continued using his urine, now "mucho malo" (very bad).

Sunday, August 20: In early morning he pushed on westward, often sitting down, sometimes falling, and tried crawling—with little success. His vision was vague; the mountains danced, and the cactus and chapparal clumps moved to and fro before his eyes; and before full day he passed the first Tule Well guidepost unseen (Tule Well is a mile or two north of the main line of the trail) and kept on westward to the second one, west of the well—where the sun was growing strong, and he was too weak to work back along the side trial. Regarding his passing of the well as an omen of speedy relief, he hung his hat on the guidepost, and, after creeping to one or two tinajas—known to him of old—which he found dry, he lay all day in the shade of the rocks, utilizing every drop of urine, which now dripped scantily and involuntarily. Toward evening he again bethought himself of Jesus and the pleasure of knifing him, and was inspired to further effort; but he

---

[5] Here I first locate him. Apparently he was then just west of Tule Playa and east of the adjacent sandhill-malpais ridge—i.e., about 27 miles east of Tule well and 50 miles from Tinaja Altas. This trail coincides closely with the International Boundary; Colonel D. Du B. Gaillard gave a good account of it in the *Cosmopolitan Magazine* (October, 1896, pages 592–603) about the time the last Boundary Survey was completed; and I described it, with illustrations of Tinajas Altas and the graves on the neighboring mesita, in "The Old Yuma Trail," *National Geographic Magazine,* Volume XII, 1901, pages 103–107, 129–143.

fell so often as he struggled forward that he was only at a remembered camp-site $3^1/_2$ miles west of Tule Well when day
broke again.

Monday, August 21: On reaching at dawn the camp-site, only
19 miles from Tinajas Altas, he felt sure of relief and stretched
himself across the trail so as not to be missed by rescuers—there he
dozed and slept, starting up frequently at fancied sounds of wheels
and hoofs; the buzzards, which had followed him for two days,
now came almost within hand-reach. The sleep and coolness
(only 91 degrees) of the day and the short distance traversed the
night before had their effect; he felt stronger, and toward sunset
he set out again westward along the trail, buoyed by the certainty
of at least finding full canteens (of which Jesus had indeed left
two, at impossible places). The course was down grade, along
the arroyo and across the black malpais mesita on which the
ancient graves lie thick; and his hope was strong, though the mountains were no longer seen in their places and he had to feel the
trail with his hands every few yards to be sure he went aright. He
often thought he saw Tinajas Altas with abundant water and food
just before him, yet was not wholly cast-down on feeling a land-
mark he knew to be miles away; so he made, with many rests and
naps, twelve miles.

Tuesday, August 22: In early dawn his mind was reaching out
buoyantly to Tinajas Altas as but a few steps away, when he half
saw, and then fully felt all over, the six-mile guidepost (about
seven miles from camp), and awoke to the sad certainty that no
canteen hung there, and the still more crushing realization that he
could not cover the remaining miles of sand—for his urine had
ceased to flow hours before, and he felt his last recourse gone.[6]
As the sun rose he sought the shade of a shrub and there knelt in
final prayer for the dying; then he laid himself down with feet and
face to the eastward, made the sign of the cross with a pang over
the absence of consecrated water, and composed himself for the
end. There—and this was his clearest concept, unreal though it

---

[6] Pablo thought he left at the six-mile guidepost his hat and underclothes, though
they were not found on subsequent search; it is more probable they were left at
the western Tule Well guidepost, where he remembered hanging his hat as a
signal. His trail here showed that he seldom walked, and then but for a few steps,
only to fall again, and mostly crept wanderingly amid the thorny clumps, though
sticking fairly to the trail.

be—with the rising of the sun he died, and his body lay lifeless under the burning rays, though his innermost self hovered about, loth to leave the material husk about which the buzzards waited patiently. The sun swung across the shimmering vault, and darkness fell; in the chill of evening (fortunately an exceptionally cool night—just above 82 degrees) some vague shadow external to his Ego stirred and then struggled aimlessly against chapparal and cactus along the most trying stretch of El Camino del Diablo. Sometimes he felt half alive and wrung by agony of severing spirit and flesh; oftener he felt that the naked body was pushed and dragged and belabored and tortured by something outside; he knew its voice tried to cry out in protest or call for rescue, but did not feel the voice his own. So the night dragged on and on, until at early dawn the vague consciousness knew itself near the camp with the certainty of relief, and was dimly surprised at the bellowing break in a final call.

Wednesday, August 23: After uttering this call, he crawled some 50 yards down the last descent to the arroyo below the Mesa of the Forty Graves. Of this day, with its physical shock and psychical break, Pablo remembered nothing clearly.

Summarily: Pablo was in the desert just eight days (and nights), with one day's water; he rode in the saddle 35 miles and walked or crept between 100 and 150 miles. For nearly seven days, or fully 160 consecutive hours, he was wholly without water from sources exterior to his system, save the few drops extracted from the scorpion, agave stipes, and insects—a desert record without parallel known to me: for half the victims of desert thirst die within 36 hours of deprivation, another quarter within 48 or 50 hours, and nearly all known to survivors within 70 to 80 hours (three days and nights), or hardly half of Pablo's stress. For some five days (August 16–21) he consumed his urine; ordinarily, the reconversion of excreted liquid is hardly helpful if not wholly harmful, yet in Pablo's case it seems to have materially prolonged vitality. For nearly nine days (August 17–26) his bowels were inactive, and for two days his kidneys failed to function. The eight-day siege lost him 35 or 40 pounds (or 25 per cent.) of his weight, chiefly through evaporation from skin and membrane; he also suffered fully two-score cuts, scratches, and bruises, each of sufficient severity to give some shock to the system; and his mouth, esophagus, and stomach were seriously deranged by his desperate efforts to relieve the thirst-torture. The most striking feature of the case was the absence of wholly insane delirium; he was, indeed, affected by the revulsion against gold, as shown by the abandonment of his nuggets and the casting away of his money; he was possessed of hallucinations as to the wetness of sands, the moisture of articulates and shrubs, and the nearness of Tinajas Altas; he was obsessed by the desire for vengeance against Jesus, the dream of casting himself in Tule Well, and the delusion of death—yet he never lost his trail-sense, and apparently squandered little vitality in those aimless movements that commonly hasten and harden the end of the thirst-victim.

II. THIRST IN GENERAL

In viewing thirst as a pathologic condition, it is needful to review the role of water in normal physiology. The average human body is about one-fifth solid matter and four-fifths liquid, i.e., H_2O or water. This liquid forms the chief distributing or circulating agency of the organism; it is no less essential to assimilation and metabolism than to circulation in the artero-venous and lymphatic systems; it forms the bulk of the softer tissues and enters into the composition of the harder, and permeates or flows through all structures either by osmosis or through specialized vessels. As an agency connecting the individual with the external, i.e., with environment, water is far more important than "food," more important even than air; water streams through the entire organism, entering chiefly through the alimentary system and escaping through the skin and membranes as well as through the main excretory channels; water as liquid and vapor in connection with the lungs and skin affords the chief means of equalizing and controlling the temperature required for organic existence; and water is undoubtedly the primary requisite for that ionization to which it is customary of late to reduce the chemistry of vital existence and growth. It is in harmony with the essential and distinctive role of water in the normal organism that the average human dietary embraces 4 to 12 (averaging about 6) parts of liquid to one part of solid matter—a mean ration for adults of, say, six pounds of liquid and one pound of dry food; it is in harmony, too, with the demonstrations of Dr. Tanner and others that with water a fast of forty days is feasible but without liquid is fatal in far less time: indeed, water is to be regarded not so much a mere solvent of food-matter as an actual aliment—and by far the most important aliment in the animal economy.[7] Accordingly, in this view of the role of water in the normal body, thirst, in extreme stages at least, is seen to constitute and express a general and fundamental derangement of the vital system.

It may be convenient to define three types of thirst, i.e., (1) the Ordinary Thirst, experienced in humid lands, caves, mines, etc., in which the air is charged with aqueous vapor and the tissues little affected by salts external to the system; (2) the Thirst of the Sea, experienced where the air is heavily charged with vapor and non-potable liquid abounds, while the tissues are subjected to the action of salts; and (3) the Desert Thirst experienced where water is lacking both as liquid and as vapor, and where free salts external to the system are (commonly) absent. The third of these types is, of course, the most distinctive; and it is this alone which I have had opportunity to study in sufficient detail to warrant discussion. My data embrace personal observation on a score or more of thirsty men at divers times and in sundry places; reminiscences gathered personally from a dozen or more survivors of extreme thirst, and from a considerably larger number of men who have chanced to succor the thirsty; portions of the abounding thirst-lore in the arid districts of Arizona, California, Nevada, New Mexico, and Sonora; numerous newspaper and magazine accounts—all more or less pointless and inaccurate; a few unwittingly faithful records like that of Manley in "Death Valley in '49"; conferences with men like artist Lungren, naturalist Merriam, litterateur Lummis, *et al.*, who have both seen and felt; and—

---

[7] The role of water in the human system and its place among food-substances are discussed more fully in "Potable Waters of Eastern United States," Fourteenth Annual Report of the U. S. Geological Survey (1894), pages 5–8; and incidentally in "The Seri Indians," Seventeenth Annual Report of the Bureau of American Ethnology (1898), pages 180–182. The reckoning of ratios of solids to liquids both in body and in food varies with modes of analysis, the interpretation of hydrates, etc., so that the values given above are to be regarded as illustrative and merely approximate rather than definitely quantitative.

safest of all—several personal experiences, one extending over half way through the successive stages.[8]

It is convenient to recognize five phases of desert thirst, falling into three successive stages; the first phase and stage may be considered *normal,* while the remaining stages, each comprising two phases, are distinctively abnormal or *pathologic*—the earlier being marked by *functional derangement* and the later by *structural degeneration.* The phases ensue in fixed order though the rate of progress is variable, ranging—according to heat, air-dryness, stress of exercise, and (more than all else) inurement of the sufferer to desert life—from, say, six hours to several days; while certain features of the later phases may be more or less masked when the progress is retarded either by favorable physical conditions or by special fitness of the organism.

1. The Stage of Normal Dryness—a. The normal system deprived of water reacts mechanically with a sensation of dryness in mouth and throat, and instinctively in the general craving for liquid denoted as thirst; in conditions of extreme aridity and heat the sensation of dryness and the instinct of thirst frequently arise without actual deprivation in persons not inured to desert life. If not relieved, the initial condition passes into general uneasiness, discomfort, or irritation, accompanied by rise of temperature and other febrile symptoms. Commonly the condition is alleviated by a moderate quantity of water; sometimes fruit acids and other sapid substances exciting flow of saliva are requisite for relief; and in the practical life of the range a pebble or nail carried in the mouth is often efficacious. This stage—and phase—may be of little consequence save as the beginning of a series; it is experienced again and again by all men of arid regions, and excites annoyance rather than apprehension on the part of the patient, hilarity rather than pity among the company—it is the *clamorous* phase, or the stage of complaining.

---

[8] A considerable part of the data were summarized in 1898 in an article entitled "Thirst in the Desert" in the *Atlantic Monthly* (Volume LXXXI, pages 483–488), originally designed as a contribution to the physiology of thirst to be presented before the Medical Society of the District of Columbia (in recognition of the honor of election as a "Member by Invitation"), and only through chance diverted to a purely literary medium; the quoted extracts beyond are from this paper.

2. *The Stage of Functional Derangement—b.* In the incipient phase of pathologic dryness a general febrile condition becomes marked and is accompanied by special local symptoms; saliva and mucus in mouth, throat, and nostrils become scant and sticky, and there is a feeling of dry deadness of membranes extending to the epiglottis and even into the lungs—the sensation of inbreathed air changing from one of refreshing coolness (the chief physical pleasure of life in the desert) to one of oven-like heat; the tongue may cling irritatingly to the teeth, or stick to the roof of the mouth; a lump seems to rise in the throat and starts endless swallowing motions to dislodge it; discomfort and pain run from throat to ears along the eustachian tubes and through the tissues; the tympana may snap and drum annoyingly, while the ear-openings itch and the eyes smart. There is a feeling of fullness in face and head (doubtless due to shrinking of the skin), usually accompanied by headache and throbbing pains in the nape and down the upper spine; the hearing is disturbed and seeing capricious, so that illusions and hallucinations—especially the delectable pictures engendered by the desert mirage—spring constantly unless checked by connected effort; irascibility arises, and companions quarrel and separate, perhaps to reunite for the very satisfaction of further dispute; the solitary sufferer may soliloquize, largely in impassioned invective—though the voice becomes cracked, husky or hoarse, and given to unexpected breaking into high tenor or dropping into an absurd whisper. The intellections are insensibly distorted more and more as the phase advances; prejudices are intensified, unreasoned revulsions arise against persons and things, while water and wetness are subconsciously exalted as the end of all excellence; the victim may gravely, after deliberate discussion in his quavering and ill-controlled voice, discard hat or shoes— for it is in this stage that Mexicans generally and Americans frequently begin to strip themselves of clothing*—or spurn the gold which he has been seeking or the tobacco which has been his solace, or perhaps burden himself with a heavy cask or fragile demijohn. The face grows pinched and care-marked, the eyes

---

* "This discarding of clothing is a bad sign with a man suffering from thirst; many a dead man had been found in the dunes, stark naked, his boots and clothing scattered along his staggering trail" (181).

bloodshot and perhaps tearful, the movements ill-aimed, the
utterances capricious, while the temperature rises and the pulse
quickens: the sufferer is a walking fever patient, passing or
passed into a delirium usually wild and paralyzing in the tenderfoot, but concentrated on a central instinct in the desert habitue—
the instinct of the trail, or the way to water. The disordered state
of body and brain is often revealed by ceaseless talk: the sufferer
strains tongue and throat to "talk and talk and talk, without pre-
vision of the next sentence or memory of the last—and all the
talk is of water in some of its inexpressibly captivating aspects.
A group of ranchmen, tricked by an earthquake-dried spring,
craked* and croaked of rivers they had forded in '49, of the ver-
dure of the bluegrass region in which one of them was born, of a
great freshet in the Hassayamp' which drowned the family of a
friend and irrigated the valley from mountain to mesa, of the acre-
inches of water required to irrigate a field seeded to alfalfa, of the
lay of the land with respect to flowing wells, of the coyote's cunning in 'sensing' water five feet down in the sand, of the fine watermelons grown on Hank Wilson's ranch in Salado valley; now and
then articulation ceased and lips and tongue moved on in silent
mockery of speech for a sentence or two before the sound was
missed, when with painful effort the organs were whipped and
spurred into action and the talk rambled on and on—all talking
slowly, seriously, with appropriate look and gesture, not one consciously hearing a word. When I was deceived into dependence
on the brine of a barranca in Encinas Desert, thirst came, . . . and
some of the party babbled continuously of portable apparatus for
well-boring, of keeping kine by means of the bisnaga—a savagely
spined cactus yielding poisonless water—and reveling in milk,
of the memory of certain mint juleps in famous metropolitan
hostelries on the farther border of the continent, of the best form
of canteen (which should hold at least two gallons—three would
be better); they were bright men, clear and straight and forceful
thinkers when fully sane: yet they knew not that their brilliant
ideas and grandiloquent phrases were but the ebullition of incipient delirium, and seriously contracted for five gallons of ice-
cream to be consumed by three persons on arriving at Hermosillo,

* "creaked" (533).

and this merely as dessert!" This phase is well known on the range, where many survive it and some delude themselves with the notion that it marks all there is of thirst; and scores of survivors have hit on the same expression to denote it: it is the *cotton-mouth* phase.

Thirst in this phase is best relieved by water—water swallowed in quarts, preferably a gill at a gulp with time for breathing between, and snuffed anon into the nostrils—water also slushed over face, head, neck, and chest: and where conditions permit, hot coffee or soup, the nearer the scalding point the better. Some desert rovers limit the quantity—wisely when the water is salt-charged or microbe-laden—though there is little risk to the habitue if the water be pure; the tenderfoot may overcharge his system and so burden his heart and invite collapse next day. When water is scant (as always on the range and often in camp) it may be economized by a method well known in all arid regions—that of alleviating local dryness of the buccal and other membranes by sipping and sniffing a few drops at a time, and allowing the general condition to take care of itself. Many vaqueros and prospectors become artists in mouth-moistening and carry canteens only for this purpose (depending on lavish draughts at camp to supply the general needs of the system), and unwittingly follow the example of desert plants in habituating their external tissues to conservation rather than evaporation of the organic water; the sipped liquid lubricates the membranes, permeates both cavities and tissues, facilitates automatic swallowing of saliva and spitting of effete mucus, and compensates that evaporation accompanying respiration which most effectively controls the body-temperature—as demonstrated by the sweatless but panting dog. On the empirical practice of the range even expert medicine may hardly improve; and unless complications arise, dry medicaments are useless—or worse.

c. The later phase of functional derangement is an intensification of the earlier; saliva ceases, and membrane-mucus dries into a collodion-like film which compresses and retracts the lips, tightens on the tongue until it numbs and deadens, shrivels the gums and starts them from the teeth, and shrinks linings of nostrils and eyelids giving irritating sensations of dust and grit; tears fall until they are gone, when the eyelids stiffen and the eyeballs set themselves in a winkless stare; the distal tongue hardens into a senseless weight, swinging on the still-soft root and striking foreignly against the teeth with the movement of riding or walking; articulate speech ends,[†] though hoarse moanings or weirdly unhuman bellowings may issue from the throat. Gradually the shrinking extends from membrane to skin; numbness creeps over the face, then over the hands and under the clothes, imparting a dry, rattling, hush-like sensation so nerve-trying that few longer resist the impulse to cast off clothing in automatic outreaching for relief; the feeling of fullness in the head increases and extends to the chest; the sufferer spasmodically snatches at hat and hair and tears the scalp with his nails, while breathing becomes labored and gasping; the heartbeat grows slow and heavy, and each pulsation brings kaleidoscopic gleams before the eyes and crackling and tearing noises in the ears, perhaps passing into singing sounds simulating—and sometimes mistaken for—sweet music from some unseen source; the head throbs painfully, and excruciating twinges shoot from the nape down the spine and through neck and shoulders; the hearing is more and more disturbed and the seeing distorted by the desiccation of the tissues, and hallucinations arise constantly to pass quickly into complete delirium in all but the best-inured, and even in these unto insanity of all senses save that of the trail. When Doctor Merriam was caught on the threshold of this phase of thirst he was impressed by the labored beating of his heart, and gained a sense of the gradual thickening of his blood as its liquid portion evaporated; "he was unable to see, or saw in mirage-like distortion when they were pointed out to him, the familiar birds and mammals of which he was in search. A prospector, later in the stage, tore away his sleeve when the puzzling numbness was first felt; afterward, seeing dimly a luscious-looking arm near by, he seized it

---

[†] Coleridge's ancient Mariner, at a dear ransom, freed his speech from the bonds of thirst:

> "With throats unslaked, with black lips baked,
> We could nor laugh nor wail;
> Through utter drought all dumb we stood!
> I bit my arm, I sucked the blood,
> And cried, A sail! a sail!"

and mumbled it with his mouth, and greedily sought to suck the blood; he had a vague sense of protest by the owner of the arm, who seemed a long way off, and was astounded two days later to find that the wounds were inflicted on himself. Deceived by a leaky canteen on the plateau of the Book Cliffs of Utah, I held myself in the real world by constant effort, aided by a bit of mirror an inch across whereby forgotten members could be connected with the distorted face in which motionless eyes were set; yet I was rent with regret (keen, quivering, crazy remorse) at the memory of wantonly wasting—actually throwing away on the ground!—certain cups of water in boyhood, and gloried in the sudden discovery of a new standard of value destined to revolutionize the commerce of the world—the beneficent unit being the rational and every-ready drop of water.* I collected half a dozen double-eagles from each of four pockets, tossed them in my hand, scorned their heavy clumsiness and paltry worthlessness in comparison with my precious unit, and barely missed (through a chance gleam of worldly wisdom) casting them away on the equally worthless sand." With the advancement of this phase, fever burns more and more fiercely; yet several observers have concurred in denoting it by perhaps the most distinctive local condition: it is the phase of the *shriveled tongue*.

In this phase, too, the thirst is relieved only by water—water in gallons, applied inside and out, but with caution as to rate lest the desiccated tissues be saturated so suddenly as to set up dangerous disorganization. Save in cases of the strongest contitution, the water should be supplemented either by some febrifuge (perhaps aconite) or, if the sufferer is so inured that his tissues are toughened, by a heart-tonic to hold up the circulation despite the dilution of the blood as the alleviating water finds its way into veins and arteries. In the absence of water little can

---

* Stott (769) described effects of heat and dehydration on the crew of the airship "Horsa," forced to land in the Arabian desert. After rescue, in his host's house at Bahrein, he was about to "pour water from a large jug into a basin to wash my hands—when suddenly my raised hand stopped. I could not pour out this fluid, each drop of which was so precious, in such quantity and for so wanton a purpose! And it took a real effort to pour out that water." See Critchley (190) for other instances of the "queer craving for the sight and feel of fresh water" among survivors.

be done: heart-stimulants or nerve-sedatives might be beneficial if available, though alcohol usually does more harm than good; the experiment of moistening membranes of mouth and throat (and of nostrils and windpipe and bronchia by inhalation) with glycerine—perhaps dilute—would be worth trying; while unguents applied to the tightening skin of chest, neck and head might be beneficial. The over-stressed system seems to respond sluggishly and slightly to ordinary drugs; when I left my party in Seriland in the closing days of 1895 and trudged over the sierritas and sand-wastes 55 miles to the ranch of San Francisco de Costa Rica for water and less essential supplies, all liquids in the medicine case (except laudanum and castor-oil) were consumed; a brandy and blackberry compound, listerine, extract of witch-hazel, sweet oil, cascara extract, eye-water, *et al;* but no effects were reported— or detected. It is in this phase if not before that most sufferers are led, either by aimless instinct or the reasoned desire of keeping membranes moist, to have recourse to urine—either their own or the still saltier stale of their stock: a desperate device which some-times saves life at the cost of some poisoning of the system, but doubtless hastens the end of the inured.

3. *The Stage of Structural Degeneration—d.* The passage of the thirst-patient into the earlier phase of this stage depends largely on his physical condition, especially his inurement to heat and dryness (as well illustrated by the case of Pablo Valencia); the tenderfoot makes the transition quickly and completely, while the well-inured victim whose membranes and skin are toughened and habituated to conservation of organic water may resist the tissue-disorganization up to and even beyond dissolution when the air is dry enough and the heat high enough—the dissolution in this case being a progressive mummification of the initially living body, beginning with the extremities and slowly approach-ing the vital organs. In the ordinary case the fourth phase be-gins with an acceleration of the drying process due to disorganiza-tion of external tissues: the collodion-like coating on the lips cracks open and curls up, and the clefts push into membrane and flesh beneath so that thickened blood and serum exude; "this ooze evaporates fast as formed, and the residuum dries on the deadened surface to extend and hasten the cracking; each cleft is a wound

which excites inflammation, and the fissuring and fevering proceed cumulatively until the lips are everted, swollen, shapeless masses of raw and festering flesh. The gums and tongue soon become similarly affected, and the oasis in the desert appears in delirium when the exuding liquid trickles in mouth and throat; the shrunken tongue swells quickly, pressing against the teeth, then forcing the jaws asunder and squeezing out beyond them, a reeking fungus on which flies—coming unexpectedly, no one knows whence—love to gather and dig busily with a harsh grating sound, while an occasional wasp plunks down with a dizzying shock to seize or scatter them; and stray drops of blood escape the flies and dribble down the chin and neck with a searing sensation penetrating the numbness: for the withered skin is ready to chap and exude fresh ooze, which ever extends the extravasation. Then the eyelids crack and the eyeballs are suffused and fissured well up to the cornea and weep tears of blood; and as the gory drops trickle down the shrunken cheeks are welted with raw flesh. The sluggishly exuding ooze seems infectious; wherever it touches there is a remote, unreal prickling, and lo, the skin is chapped and dark red blood dappled with serum wells slowly forth. The agony at the nape continues, the burden of the heart-throb increases, but as the skin opens the pain passes away; the fingers wander mechanically over the tumid tongue and lips, producing no sensation save an ill-located stress, when they, too, begin to chap and swell and change to useless swinging weights. . . . The throat is as if plugged with a hot and heavy mass, which gradually checks the involuntary swallowing motion, causing anon a horrible drowning sensation, followed by a dreamy gratification that the trouble is over. The lightning in the eyes glances and the thunder in the ears rolls, and the pressing brow-bands tighten. The thoughts are but vague flashes of intelligence, though a threadlike clue may be kept in sight by constant attention —the trail, the trail, the elusive, writhing, twisting trail that ever seeks to escape and needs the closest watching; all else is gone until water is "sensed" in some way which only dumb brutes know. . . . Rice remembered hearing his horse (which, startled by a rattlesnake, had escaped him twenty hours before, and which he had trailed in half-blind desperation) battering at the

cover of a locked watering-trough with fierce pawing like that
of a dog digging to fresh scent; the vaqueros, awakened by the
horse, found the man wallowing, half-drowned in the trough; he
always ascribed the bursting of his lips and tongue to his earlier
effort to get moisture by chewing stray blades of grass (supplemented by urine), and he never consciously recognized the
normal symptoms of the fourth phase. When my deer-path
trail on the Utah plateau turned out of the gorge over a slope too
steep for the fixed eyes to trace, I followed the ravine to stumble
into a chance water-pocket with a submerged ledge and there
soaked an hour before a drop of water could be swallowed; then,
despite a half-inch cream of flies and wasps, squirming and buzz-
ing above and macerated into slime below, I tasted ambrosia!*
A poor devil on the Mohave desert reached a neglected water-hole
early in this stage; creeping over debris in the twilight, he paid no
attention to turgid toads and a sodden snake and the seething
scum of drowned insects until a soggy, noisome mass turned under
his weight, and a half-fleshed skeleton, still clad in flannel shirt and
chaparejos, leered in his face with vacant sockets and fallen jaw:
he fled, only to turn back later, as his trail showed, seeking the
same water-hole, and during his days of delirium in the hands of
rescuers raved unremitting repentance of his folly in passing the
'last water.'" A bronco-thrown vaquero picked up by Don
Pascual Encinas after three days of deprivation was expressively
described by the strenuous old "Conquerer of the Seri" as "sweating blood and fighting buzzards"; and his phrase may fitly be
applied to the phase of desert thirst in which the external tissues
inflame and begin to break down in a *blood-sweat;* the phase is
not in the books, but it is indelibly burned into some brains.

In this phase there can be little alleviation: for water, however
judiciously administered, brings hurt rather than healing; and
even if the degenerated tissues are reorganized, the cerebral and
neural structures may scarce recover from the shock—the sufferer,

---

* A story, possibly apocryphal but appearing in older thirst literature (150, 494),
tells of Darius, King of the Persians. That hero, lacking in martial zeal because of
thirst became grateful for being able to refresh himself with a pleasurable draft of
blood stained water which had been defiled by corpses, although previously he had
quenched thirst only with wine. See King's account (p. 378) of hemoposia and
uriposia.

like the Encinas foundling, or like press-reported Hoffman, sole
survivor of the ill-outfitted Grindell expedition of 1905, remains
little more than a gibbering imbecile for months if not for life.

e. In the final phase of desert thirst the external symptoms are
little changed: "The benumbing and chapping and suffusion of
the periphery and extremities continue, and in this way the blood
and serum and other liquids of the body are conveyed to the
surface and cast out on the thirsty air, so that the desiccation of
the organism is hastened; perhaps the tumid tongue and livid lips
dry again as the final spurts from the capillaries are evaporated;
thirsty insects gather to feast on the increasing waste, and the
unclean blow-fly hastes to plant its foul seed in eyes and ears and
nostrils, while the greedy vulture soars low and the ravening
coyote licks his chops." The internal or subjective symptoms may
be inferred only through extension of the knowledge of earlier
stages and from movements inscribed in the trail of the victim—
for in the desert perception is sharpened and scarce-visible features in the track of man or beast open a faithful panorama to the
trained vision of the trailer: "the wanderer, striving to loosen the
tormenting brow-bands, tears his scalp with his nails and scatters
stray locks of hair over the sand; the forbidding cholla, spiniest of
the cruelly spined cacti, is vaguely seen as a huge carafe surrounded by crystal goblets, and the flesh-piercing joints are
greedily grasped and pressed against the face to cling like beggar-
ticks to woolen garments, with the spines penetrating cheeks and
perhaps tapping arteries; the shadow of shrub or rock is a Tantalus'
pool in which the senseless automaton digs desperately amid the
gravel until nails and even phalanges are torn off; then the face
is forced into the cavity, driving the thorns further into the flesh,
breaking the teeth and bruising the bones, until the half-stark
and already festering carcass arises to totter toward fresh torment. . . . A child in a single garment wandered out on Mohave
desert and was lost before the distracted mother thought of
trailers; his tracks for thirty hours were traced, and showed that
the infant had aged to the acuteness of maturity in husbanding
strength and noting signs of water, and had then slowly descended
into the darkness and automatic death of the fifth phase of thirst—
had at last dug the shadow-cooled sands with tender baby fingers,

and then courted and kissed the siren cactus even unto the final embrace in which he was held by a hundred thorns too strong for his feeble strength to break."

In this final phase there is no alleviation, no relief save the end; for it is the ghastly yet possibly painless phase of *living death,* in which senses cease and men die from without inward—as dies the desert shrub whose twigs and branches wither and blow away long before bole and root yield vitality.

As I passed through Yuma, August 31, 1905, press dispatches were announcing a fatality from thirst in Death Valley, incidentally noting that it was the *thirty-fifth* of the season in that valley alone; unnumbered others occurred elsewhere during the same season, including a straggler whose remains were found two months later by the Jim Tucker and Pablo Valencia above mentioned.   Does it not behoove the makers of medical science to assume seriously the duty of devising preventive and remedial measures against a death-cause so frequent, so widespread, so distressful, and so intimately connected with those organic functions and structures on which they speak with authority; and does not the behoof rest especially on the medical men of the Key City of the Southwest — Saint Louis?

CHAPTER IX

NOTES ON THIRST IN A DESERT REGION*

In the few notes which follow, we present three observations of the group of phenomena we call "attack of thirst."

These phenomena are always produced in desert regions by lack of water. A recent tour in the region of the stony desert plateaus of Borkou, permitted us to observe the evolution of the signs that lack of water brings in some individuals of different races.

We call the group of phenomena which spring from this absence of water "attack of thirst" for, as we shall see, the sensation of thirst and the subjective phenomena which accompany it do not always have the same intensity. They are intimately linked with the course of the sun, increasing in proportion as it rises above the horizon and following a declining course toward the end of the day.

In the course of these observations we were able to observe the treatment of attack of thirst by the natives of the region. At the end of this study, we shall give an outline of these methods.

The three observations which follow have as subjects three men belonging to different races: a Sara M'Baye infantryman, a native boy from Bossangoa (Ubangi) and, finally, a European (self-observation).

OBSERVATION I

N'G . . .; age 23; infantryman; race, Sara M'Baye.

The observation began the 26th of August 1934. On that day the infantryman, water becoming scarce, received about a quarter of a liter for all drinking. Due to the scarcity of water he was

---

* By Dr. Pujo, Captain, Medical Corps (632).

unable to eat and, with the exception of a few dried dates, ate nothing more until the first of September.

The next day, August 27th, a fresh ration of a quarter of a liter of water was quickly drunk as on the day before. N'G . . . had to make part of the trip on foot. Although usually his strong constitution permitted him to make very long marches without apparent fatigue, on the evening of the 27th, on arrival at the halting place, he fell to the ground.

On the 28th, at the rationing of water (the last to be made), he received only an eighth of a liter of water. Since morning, the features of the infantryman were drawn, his lips dried, the mucosa greatly stretched and ready to crack, his tongue was saburral, and salivation produced on expectoration a thick, sticky, whitish and excessively adherent saliva. The conjunctivas were inflamed and red, the movement of the eyelids caused a slight burning. Constipation was present since the day before. The urine was reddish and slightly increased in volume.*

The evening of August 28th, fatigue was extreme and walking became more and more painful. The sensation of thirst, intolerable during the day, diminished slightly at night. During the night, the march toward the uncertain water source was resumed and N'G . . . marched always afoot, but with more and more difficulty. The dried soles of his feet were covered with cracks, painless at rest, but which marching made very painful.

The morning of the 29th, a halt was made at 8 o'clock. The heat was, or seemed, unbearable; the infantryman spoke with difficulty, his walk had become hesitant. After a few moments of rest, we noticed his blank expression, his mouth open, lips swollen, the labial mucosa dried and scaly, showing raw areas covered with a very sticky yellowish white coating, uniting by threads the two half-open lips. His tongue was dried and its appearance had changed since the previous day: its rim was red, bounding a surface covered with a thick whitish coating about a half centimeter wide; the central portion of the tongue was yellow brown and seemed varnished. The tongue itself was increased in size; the whole mouth was dry and the infantryman

---

* This observation is repeated in the third case (p. 413).

declared he could feel no sensation in the buccal mucosa except an intense dryness.

The same day, at 10 o'clock in the morning, nervous symptoms made their appearance. First dizziness, his walk became hesitant, wavering, with a sensation of loss of equilibrium, a violent headache. A little later, delirium appeared, a euphoric delirium. The infantryman thought he was at his own funeral in Sara country and uttered the usual lamentations. Then, the military obsession appeared and, for more than an hour, he issued orders (those he had already heard at drill). This military obsession pursued him until the moment a veritable epileptic fit seized him. Uttering inarticulate cries, he shook violently, rolling on the ground, the whole thing accompanied by unrestrained movements (the witnesses' condition did not allow them to help the sick man). About 2 P.M. the attack reached its crisis. The phenomena continued with less intensity until 5 P.M. when sleep suppressed the apparent nervous symptoms. As on every day, sundown brought a diminution of the phenomena. With short periods of sleep, which he left only to crawl to another position, the infantryman spent part of the night.

On awakening, it was impossible for him to walk, or stand and he was completely unconscious; raised onto a camel, he followed slowly for a few hours uttering hoarse cries and laments. A little before sunrise he became calm. Since the previous evening constipation had disappeared and had given away to a loss of fecal matter; urine was always the same volume and very reddish.

The forenoon of August 30th was very painful for the footsoldier. At 7 A.M., his sensation of heat becoming intense, he insisted on a stop in the shade, unable to remain on the camel. Shortly after the halt, the nervous phenomena reappeared with greater intensity than on the preceding day. The paroxysms were separated by periods of subcoma which became more and more frequent. Cutaneous anesthesia was complete, the unrestrained tossing of the sick man on the ground covered with sharp acacia thorns causing no reaction, although he was very often pricked.

At noon on August 30th, the natives searching for the party brought water. N'G . . . in a moment of consciousness understood. He cried simply: "Water! Water!" But taking a few drops of water was painful, he experienced a strong sensation of constriction of the pharynx. After having been treated as we shall see later, he was raised onto a camel and in 18 hrs. marching brought back to the well.

His dazed condition and unconsciousness persisted and it was a veritable human rag which arrived at the water source on August 31st.

His lips had lost their yellowish coating, his whitish tongue was no longer varnished, but the sensation of tightness of the pharynx persisted. About every hour an insistent need to drink seized the sick man. Dejection and profuse diarrhea set in. After two days, food and water intake having been restored, the nervous phenomena receded, consciousness returned, and his walk was steadier. Dullness and fatigue alone persisted. By the 3rd of September, all phenomena had disappeared except these two signs.

OBSERVATION II

J . . . age 28, boy, race, Kaba (Bossangoa—Ubangi).

On the 26th, 27th, and 28th of August, he received the same amounts of water as the soldier in Case I. The phenomena he presented were less in intensity.

From the 26th, there was a stoppage of feces. Urine increased in volume, reddish.

The sensation of thirst appeared gradually, his mouth became progressively dry. Any food intake from the 26th on, even if available, seemed to the boy as if it would not be tolerated by his stomach.

His tongue, which the first two days was saburral, assumed a new appearance: it was slightly swollen, the red edge bordered a yellowish, thick, dry surface; within this line the surface of the tongue was blackish and the boy declared he couldn't touch the roof of his mouth without its feeling like a brush.

His mouth felt so dry the native dared not speak, nor open his mouth, so as not to suffer too much, he said. Besides, speech, as well as any attempt to swallow, speedily caused nausea.

The nervous phenomena we met in the preceding observation

appeared only during the heat of the day and with much less intensity: they exhibited only a slight euphoria unaccompanied by delirium. At night, calm returned and permitted rest, his sensation of thirst was less and his mouth was moistened by a thick and whitish saliva.

The next day his tongue regained its "wooden" appearance and consistency. His lips were less dried than those of N'G. . . However, if his thirst was more easily borne, dizziness and difficulty in standing persisted longer.

Treatment brought marked relief, restoration of food and water intake caused the disappearance within twenty-four hours of all signs of these minor attacks of thirst.

OBSERVATION III

This personal observation, less complete than the preceding two, will show, however, the development of "the attack of thirst" in direct relation with the course of the sun during the day.

The 26th and 27th of August, the water intake was a quarter of a liter per day. From the evening of the 25th all food intake ceased and was not resumed until the evening of September 2nd. From the beginning the lack of food had no effect, and a hearty appetite of preceding days was replaced by a complete lack of appetite.

The first two days, outside of the lack of appetite already mentioned, the sole phenomena which appeared were: a slight increase in the volume of urine and the color of the urine became a redder and redder hue. Finally, a complete halt of defecation was noted.

Starting from August 27th, about noon, the heat seemed unbearable and a sensation of extreme fatigue appears, accompanied, on moving about or standing up, by dizziness and loss of equilibrium.

From the first day, the tongue was saburral, although the sensation of thirst was quite endurable and until the evening of August 27th it was possible to smoke without too great a sensation of dryness. But the 28th the intake of only an eighth of a liter of water changed the state of affairs. Dizziness and weakness only increased and a slight persistent headache commenced. At noon the sensation of dryness of the mouth was at its maximum, the tongue was bordered with a thick, yellowish, adhesive coating, this area surrounding a dark gray zone in the middle of which the anatomical details of the tongue stood out, the lingual V being greatly hypertrophied. The motion of swallowing had become impossible and provoked nausea.

The 28th, shortly before sunset, march was resumed, but weakness was such that at sundown a halt was necessary. The dryness of the mouth decreased in intensity and a refreshing sleep restored calm.

On awakening, dizziness persisted, but with less intensity than on the preceding day and the march could be resumed. During the day of August 29th, the phenomena reappeared and about 8 A.M. the forward march had to be halted. The headache and dizziness increased and thirst became more and more painful to bear. The least attempt to swallow produced violent nausea. Weakness was such that shade was not even sought. A true cutaneous insensibility set in; the very numerous pricks of acacia thorns (the ground was strewn with thorns) were only noticed when we had reached the water-hole and a more normal life. Prostration was extreme and the day passed in a state of unconsciousness and somnolence left only occasionally to attempt an impossible swallowing.

During the night of the 29th to 30th, a painful and difficult forward march took place, but our state did not allow us to go very far and at 7 A.M. a halt was made, necessitated by the condition of the members of the convoy. Thirst increased as usual with the heat, nausea became more frequent and considerable willpower was required to refrain from swallowing. A sharp pain in the pharynx began. The intensity of thirst was so great that we caught our urine in cupped hands and drank it eagerly. The drowsiness of the preceding day returned, accompanied by dreams, which persisted all the forenoon. At times, all consciousness was lost, and it is impossible to recall our reactions at that time; it was at the end of one of these periods of subcoma that a cry recalled us to reality and we saw the arrival of the native rescuers with the water we lacked so much.

As we have seen, the reactions of three members of the party were noticeably different. The strangest reactions were noted in the Sara infantryman. The natives of Sara country, a desert region, need great quantities of water daily even when in camp at sedentary work.

We believe we can call the group of phenomena provoked by thirst "attack of thirst," for, as we saw, these signs had their paroxysm linked to the height of the sun above the horizon and were, moreover, more intense as the sun was nearer its zenith. It was impossible for us to record the thermal reactions of the members of the party; however, we believe some elevation in temperature must have occurred and was also in direct relation to the course of the sun. One fact is certain, there was a marked diminution in the phenomena starting at sunset and continuing throughout the night.

TREATMENT OF THE ATTACK OF THIRST BY THE GORANES

The first thought which occurs to a man who had been about to die of thirst, after he has been rescued, is to throw himself eagerly on the water container offered him. This method would have serious consequences, so the thirsty man is allowed to take only a very small amount of water; then the proffered container is removed.

The thirsty man being laid down, he is divested of his clothing and carefully, drop by drop, water is poured first in the supra- and subclavicular hollows, the axillae, the bend of the elbow, the epigastric hollow and the inguinal folds. These different areas being well moistened, they are patted lightly with a damp hand for a moment. Then following the same method, the same gestures are repeated over the head and face. Finally, to finish, the legs are carefully sprinkled. For a few minutes, the body of the thirsty man is covered with his dampened clothes. Immediately afterward the man falls into a light sleep, from which he soon rouses to ask for a drink. Then the same procedure is followed; after drinking a little water the body of the patient is sprinkled anew, and so on, until a refreshing sleep overtakes him. On awakening, after many hours of rest, thirst is less and gradually every-thing returns to normal. As we saw, this very simple treatment, immediately applied by the natives who were used to dealing with men suffering from lack of water, produces good results, since the members of our party, treated in this fashion, were able to reach the nearest water source and this adventure is no more to them than a bad memory.

CHAPTER X

PACIFIC MISSION*

I. IN WHICH EIGHT MEN ARE CAST ADRIFT IN MID-PACIFIC ON RUBBER RAFTS

By way of preface, I wish one point to be understood: what follows is almost all out of memory. I made no notes during our 21 days of drifting on the Pacific, and even if I had had paper for making them, the salt water and sweat which dissolved everything dissolvable would have left nothing but a pulp. Therefore the sequence of events may be rather uncertain. What I may remember as happening on one day or another may, by my companions' recollections, have happened earlier or later. But such discrepancies, if they exist, are unimportant. My instinct then was not to remember but to live.

Again, men place different values on experiences shared together. What stirred or depressed me may have seemed inconsequential to the others. While I sit in a Rockefeller Plaza office which I have all to myself and where a push on a buzzer will summon nearly anything I need, much of what I went through on that ridiculously small raft now seems almost irrelevant. It is like trying to remember being dead.

The beginnings of this episode on the Pacific go back to last March when Lieut. General Henry H. Arnold, Chief of the Army Air Forces and an old friend, asked me to visit the various combat units being assembled in this country for overseas action. It was his idea that the new generation of American air fighters would profit from the knowledge of combat psychology that had come to me in the last war. This I was honored to do. The results were

* By Edward V. Rickenbacker (655). Reprinted from *Life* Magazine. An almost identical account appeared in book form, *Seven Came Through: Rickenbacker's Full Story* (see (831) also).

evidently useful enough to induce Secretary of War Stimson to offer me a worldwide mission to inspect U. S. air combat groups, both fighter and bomber, in all theaters of war. The assignment called for a report on the comparative values of U. S. aircraft and those of the enemy, together with my own opinions on air-fighting techniques. I was to be paid $1 a day, and at the request of Mr. Stimson I was appointed special consultant to him. This gave me the independence I wanted. In a way, I was the people's representative on American airpower.

The European mission carried me to England, Ireland and Iceland. It was kept secret until I returned to Washington, early in October, to make my report. Five or six days later, I headed into the Pacific. Here, as in the Atlantic area, my assignment was to visit the combat air bases, question the commanding officers, pilots and ground crews, and make up my mind as to the good and bad. It was on this trip that I ran into trouble.

Flight to Hawaii

Accompanying me as aide, besides providing the necessary amount of gold braid to satisfy protocol, was an old friend—Colonel Hans Adamson. I have known him since he was aide to F. Trubee Davison, Assistant Secretary of War for Air in Hoover's Cabinet.

Adamson and I flew from New York to Los Angeles on the night of Oct. 17, where I stopped only long enough to visit my mother, now in her 80th year. Next evening I continued to San Francisco and 24 hours later we met again aboard a Pan American Clipper, bound for Hawaii. It was a fine flight, putting us down in Honolulu on the morning of Oct. 20, in the record time of 15 hours.

My principal destinations were Australia, New Guinea and Guadalcanal. I wanted to go on that same night. Lieut. General Delos C. Emmons, commander of the Hawaiian Department, had been advised by Mr. Stimson of my coming. I talked with his staff and they showed me the Air Force units, and by evening I was ready to leave. Brig. General William L. Lynd, commanding officer of Hickam Field, promised to have a ship ready by 10:30 P.M. I had hoped for a converted B-24 bomber, because it is roomier, but the only long-range four-engine plane available was a tactically obsolete Boeing Flying Fortress which had been earmarked for return to the U. S. for training uses.

I asked General Lynd about the crew. He assured me they were experienced men, all members of the Army Air Transport Command, several with airline experience.

That night General Lynd drove Colonel Adamson and myself to Hickam Field. Our bags went into the cabin, followed by a dozen sacks of high-priority mail for the different headquarters enroute. I was told there would be an extra passenger—Sergeant Alexander Kaczmarczyk, a ground crew chief. He had been taken off a transport because he had yellow jaundice, and while recovering from this, had come down with appendicitis. Now he was enroute to Australia to rejoin his unit.

We got going. The plane was making 80 m.p.h. on the flat when I felt it lunge to the left, and saw the dark shadows of the hangars rushing up. The thought crossed my mind: "Hickam gets another blitz and Rickenbacker's part of it." The pilot, by clever manipulation of the engines, managed to swing back onto the runway. By the time he reached the end of the field, the speed had worn off enough for him to risk a violent ground loop, which saved us from plunging into the bay.

A broken hydraulic line on the starboard brake system was at fault. Captain Cherry, the pilot, was too young to walk when I commanded the pursuit squadron on the Western Front. But he was happy-go-lucky like so many Texans are. He brushed off the accident, saying: "We got more of these, Captain. The crew and I will stand by until another plane is ready." I thought: "Well, it had better not be like the first."

General Lynd drove me back to his quarters and shortly after midnight word came that another ship, also a Flying Fortress, was ready. The baggage and mail were already aboard and General Lynd had thoughtfully added a cot for Adamson and myself. I asked Captain Cherry about the weather ahead. High scattered clouds, he answered, but clear—"an uneventful flight," was the forecast.

And so it was—through the first nine hours. Off at 1:30 A.M., Oct. 21, we squared away on the course for Island X, 1,800 miles or so to the southwest. The night was beautiful—high, thin clouds, a three-quarter moon. I sat for an hour in the cockpit, enjoying the night and the small talk, then walked aft to the tail for a few hours' sleep, Col. Adamson joining me. By then we were at 10,000 ft. and although I had a blanket around me, and a trench coat, I was cold and slept only in snatches.

At 6:30 daylight broke. I had orange juice and coffee from the thermos jugs, and a sweet roll. Forward in the cockpit everything seemed serene. Captain Cherry said we were due to make our land-fall at 9:30 A.M.

An hour before that time Cherry started downhill, gliding from 9,000 to 1,000 ft. That was when we started to look for our island. We kept on looking and I, for one, have yet to see it.

How We Lost Our Way

The sun climbed high in the port quarter, and while the clouds were heavier, huge stretches of blue sky showed between. At 10:15 A.M., three-quarters of an hour beyond the expected arrival time, Captain Cherry was still holding to the original course. I asked how much gas he had. "A little over four hours," he said. I was sitting directly behind him. In fact, I was glued there, because a wholly unreasonable premonition that we were in trouble had lodged in my mind. In a little while I asked how much tail-wind we were supposed to have. The answer was about ten miles.

Call it hindsight, if you want, since I certainly had no way of telling, but I was sure we had been flying faster than we knew. Inside me the feeling grew that we had overshot the mark and were moving away from it, into the open Pacific. One daybreak weeks later, in the cockpit of another bomber bound for Brisbane, Australia, I was to learn how it happened. The officer beside me then mentioned casually that he had been navigator on an airplane that had left Hickam Field, bound for the same Island X, just an hour before we did. He too had been given the same tailwind forecast, but a check on his speed had convinced him it was three times as strong and he had corrected accordingly.

It was our bad luck not to be aware of this. At the speed we were making, the airplane must have been beyond Island X before

Captain Cherry started downhill. All this time the radio operator was in routine contact with Island X, and the navigator, in the astro-hatch, was trying to shoot the sun. About 10:30 o'clock I suggested to the pilot that he ask Island X for bearings. Island X replied it couldn't give us a bearing—it had no equipment. So we tried Island Y, another U. S. outpost, some distance east and north of the first. Island Y instructed us to climb to 5,000 ft. and circle for 30 minutes, sending out a radio signal, while they took a bearing. This we did. They supplied us with a compass course, which meant nothing; we could be on it, yet a thousand miles below or above the island. Nevertheless, we let down through the cloud layer and lined up on the new course which took us west. We flew on, at better than three miles a minute, but all we saw was water and more water.

It was plain now that we were lost, and the first slight signs of nervousness appeared in the crew. The young navigator, after half a dozen first-class Pacific crossings, was baffled by his failure. Then the only possible explanation occurred to him: his octant, which had been on the navigation table, must have been badly jarred when the first airplane ground-looped at Hickam Field. This alone could have thrown his observations off—perhaps by several degrees. So it is probable that the positions subsequently obtained were erroneous. It is easy then to understand how we could have passed the island far to the left or right.

I present these facts not in criticism but in explanation. Whoever travels in wartime must expect risks. Weather and radio aids that are commonplace in commercial airline operations do not yet exist in the Pacific; nor is there always time for thorough inspection. If the Army had waited for prissy safeguards there would be no American airpower in the Pacific today.

We Get "Island Eyes"

There was nothing to do but fall back on the last resort of the lost and box the compass. I shall not dwell on the next few hours. We turned every which way. We even asked Island X to fire their anti-aircraft guns, setting the shells to burst at 7,000 ft., well above the cloud level. We also asked them to send out planes, on the chance they might see us, or we them. Both were done, but although we rose to 8,000 ft. and circled we saw nothing.

In due time, like all others lost on the Pacific, we got what airmen call "island eyes." You see land because you want to see it and have to see it, and with all of us at the windows, every cloud shadow momentarily held the promise of land.

Captain Cherry, coming down low over the sea, leaned the mixture, but our time and gasoline were running out. The radio operator kept calling for bearings, hoping that someone would be able to take a cross bearing on us. At 1:30 P.M. Captain Cherry turned east, doubling back on his tracks. The clouds were thinning out and he climbed back to 5,000 ft. to see better, and to save gasoline he cut out the two outboard engines. The only hope now was to find a ship. After talking to Captain Cherry I wrote out a radio message saying one hour's fuel remained—the last message heard by anyone. The operator started to pound out SOS and he did not stop until a second or two before the plane hit. No one heard it.

The fact that the SOS went unacknowledged meant that in addition to our not knowing where we were, none of the islands from which a search might be started knew, either. And that, I remarked to Adamson, was a hell of a fine basis for rescue operations.

Realizing what we were in for, I found myself studying my companions. Other than Adamson, they were strangers. Adamson was three months older than I, and I had had my 52nd birthday in Scotland, a few weeks before. In his youth Hans had been an explorer, but like me he had become a desk man and paper shuffler. Too old to fight but familiar with war, he and I were not expected to face hardships or risks; these were for younger men.

In the moments before the crash, Hans, too, must have been thinking hard, because he said, with a grim smile, "Rick, I hope you like the sea. I think we're going to spend a long time on it."

A Look At The Crew

As for the crew, the oldest man was the co-pilot, Lieut.

Whittaker, a heavy-set, self-assured fellow of about 40. All that I knew about him came from a few remarks he had dropped—that he had been a contractor and promoter in civilian life, and before joining the Air Force had done most of his flying in private airplanes. The navigator, Lieutenant De Angelis, was only 23; he was a short, wiry, thoughtful kid, with black curly hair. Private Bartek, the flight engineer, was the same age. Sergeant Reynolds, the radioman, was a tall, skinny chap, several years older, with an air of quiet competence.

Then there was the extra man—Sergeant Alex. He had had little to say, and studying him I thought he looked frail. As for Captain Cherry, I knew nothing about him either, except that he had been a copilot on American Airlines. Only 27, he had the gay and buoyant disposition of most airman. In the cynical way of an older man who had had his share of trouble, I thought, "Well, my young friend, your cowboy boots and goatee are going to look pretty damn funny in the middle of the Pacific."

The last minutes ran out fast. The instant Cherry wheeled east all of us accepted the inevitability of a crash landing. We made ready to throw overboard everything that was movable. I helped Sergeant Alex pry open the bottom hatch in the tail and between us we dumped all that high-priority mail into the blue Pacific. Then the tool box, the cots, the blankets, the empty thermos bottles, a brand-new Burberry coat I had bought only a few weeks before in London, and all the baggage, including a beautiful suitcase that the boys and girls of Eastern Air Lines had given me for Christmas two years before. I had frugally removed a spare bridge that my dentist had just made for me, but after a second's deliberation I threw that away too. After it went my briefcase, bulging with papers of which no copies existed—papers that I had considered important. Let the moment come when nothing is left but life and you will find that you do not hesitate over the fate of material possessions, however deeply they may have been cherished.

Make Ready to Crash

We made all possible preparations for the crash. The remaining thermos bottles were filled with water and coffee. With the emergency rations, which were stowed in a small metal box, they were piled on the deck in the radio compartment, just below the hatch from which we planned to leave. Sergeant Alex dumped half a can of condensed milk into a thermos jug, saying, "I've got to have cream in my coffee." Poor Alex, he had already had his last coffee and cream that morning. Adamson suggested maybe we'd better drink our fill of water, but I advised against it, thinking we might need it more later on. As Adamson was later to remind me, that was probably the worst advice he had ever been given.

Before dumping the suitcase, I had snatched out a handful of handkerchiefs, including three handsome ones—a blue, a gray and a brown—that Mrs. Rickenbacker had bought for me some years ago in Paris. I had a hunch then they might be useful in protecting us from the sun. I also broke open a couple of cartons of cigarets, passing the packages around, keeping two or three for myself. Adamson, Sergeant Alex and De Angelis had meanwhile propped the mattresses against the bulkheads, to cushion the shock if we were thrown forward. All of us, by then, had put on Mae West life-jackets.

Lean as the mixture was, the two engines ran sweetly, but our ears were listening for the first dry splutter. There were eight of us, and if the plane survived the crash, we could count on three life rafts. Two were so-called five-man rafts in compartments on opposite sides of the plane, which Bartek was to expel by pulling levers in the cockpit. There was also a two-man raft rolled up in the radio compartment. This was placed with the little pile of sea-going rations.

We had worked out a plan for abandoning ship, even to the point of assigning stations on the rafts. The Fortress is, of course, a land plane, weighing about 25 tons. Many have been force-landed at sea in this war, and while a few had stayed afloat longer, Cherry could not safely count on more than 30 to 60 seconds. So we'd have to be quick. Unwilling to burden myself, yet fearful of leaving something indispensable behind, I rummaged through my remaining possessions. I stuffed the map inside my shirt; my passport and the official papers that Mr.

Stimson had given me I stowed in an inside pocket. A frugal instinct caused me to pocket a chocolate bar, and to salvage a 60-ft. length of line, which I wound around my body. The last thing I did before sitting down was to help Sergeant Alex loosen the hatch, lest it be jammed in the crash.

Somebody brought back word that Cherry was starting down. The plane dipped into a long glide. Adamson was sitting on the deck, his back braced against one of the mattresses. De Angelis was lying on the floor, pressed against the other. Sergeant Reynolds was at his little desk, watching the busy dials on the panel, while his fingers played out the SOS that no one ever heard. Squatting behind him was Sergeant Alex. I was on the right-hand side, strapped in the seat, holding a parachute to protect my face. From the window I could see the ocean coming closer. For the first time I realized that it was quite rough, with a long, heavy swell.

The others kept asking "How much longer?" and I kept answering "Not yet, not yet." The pilots, Cherry and Whittaker, were, of course, forward and Bartek was standing behind the latter, with his hand on the levers for springing the big rafts. Somebody across from me said, "Only 50 ft. left." And an instant later one engine cleared its throat, choked and died. "Hold on," I shouted. "Here it comes." Reynolds bent his head, but he did not take his hand off the key.

The crash was a violent jumble of sounds and motions. Only once before had I ever heard such sounds: that was when I crashed at Atlanta. Pieces of the radio equipment bolted to the bulkhead flew about like shrapnel. A moment later, while we were still stunned from the first crash, a second one came and with that the plane lost motion. I doubt if from where the belly first grazed the water to where we stopped dead was more than 50 ft. As I struggled to unfasten myself, green water was pouring over my legs and down my back. The window beside me had been broken and the topside hatch had carried away. The whole Pacific Ocean seemed to be rushing in.

But it was a wonderful landing, timed to the second. Young Cherry laid his airplane down in the middle of a trough, and killed her off against the waning slope of a swell. Had he miscalculated by two seconds and hit the crest, I would not be telling this now. The Fortress would have gone straight on to the bottom of the sea.

Adamson staggered to his feet, moaning about his back. Sergeant Alex and De Angelis looked all right, but Sergeant Reynolds had his hands to his face and blood was running through his fingers. He had been jerked against the radio panel. When he took his hands away I saw a bloody gaping slash across his nose. I heard Bartek yell that the rafts were free. Then the two pilots splashed aft to give us a hand.

All of us were badly shaken up and it seemed to take forever for us to clear out. Adamson and I being super-cargo, the crew insisted we go first. I stood on the arm of the seat and hauled myself through the hatch, while the others shoved from below. Once on the wing I was able to give them a hand. Bartek, who had escaped through the forward hatch, was already on the wing, which was barely awash. The two rafts, which had automatically inflated themselves when expelled, were buoyant on the swell, one on each side of the plane. But the line holding mine had become fouled, and in trying to free it, Bartek had cut his fingers to the bone. Blood reddened everything he touched.

All Aboard the Rafts

"So this," I thought, "is the placid Pacific." The swells were twice as high as I am tall, which is tall enough, and with the submerged plane surging and heaving from crest to trough, it was hard to keep a footing. With Bartek's help, I managed to free my raft and work it alongside the wing so that Adamson, who was in great pain from his hurt back, could slide down. Bartek crawled in next. When I tried to coil my 185-lb. frame in the stern, there wasn't enough room left for a midget.

Cherry, Whittaker and Sergeant Reynolds were already clear in the other big raft; but the two-man affair was upside down, and Alex and De Angelis were splashing wildly in the water, trying to push it back to the wing. It had tipped over when Alex stepped in, throwing both him and the other man overboard.

They managed to right it and get aboard. By that time I was in difficulty. Before I could break out the two little aluminum oars secured to the inside of my raft, a swell had washed us against the tail of the Fortress and we just missed being overturned. As it was, the raft filled with water.

I really don't know how long it took us to do all these things, but we were quicker than we thought. Although deep down, the Fortress was still afloat. A good deal of shouting was going on between the rafts, and after we had drifted 50 yards or so downwind, somebody called out: "Who has the water?"

No one had it. No one had the rations, either.

I am quite sure that none of us wholly understood, then, what this meant. Life by itself seemed the most adequate of rations. If it seems odd that we should have left the food and water after all the careful preparations, I can only say that the shock and confusion, the hurt men, the rough seas, the trouble with the rafts, drove the thought of them out of mind. By the time the last man got out, the water was feet deep inside the plane; the pile of things we had collected was somewhere underneath, scattered by the crash. After arguing back and forth, we decided not to re-enter the plane, lest somebody get caught inside when it sank. This was another mistake. The Fortress stayed afloat nearly six minutes. I was bailing with my hat when I heard a shout: "There she goes." The tail swung upright, in true ship's fashion, hesitated, then slid quickly out of sight.

By my watch it was 2:36 P.M. on the afternoon of Oct. 21.

The line around my waist was now put to good use. Because the wind and seas were fast sweeping the rafts apart, I called the others in and, fastening the rope to the hand lines around the rafts, we formed a line astern, 20 ft. or so apart. Cherry being captain, his raft was first, mine was second and the two-man raft brought up the rear. The arrangement had its drawbacks. In the heavy swell, as the rafts rose and fell at their different intervals, the interminable uneven shocks on the line made rest impossible. But I shall always believe that had we separated, few if any of us would now be alive. A strong man may last a long time alone but men together somehow manage to last longer.

My memory of that first afternoon is not wholly clear. The spray and the green water coming over the roll of the raft kept us soaked, and I bailed for hours with my hat—my wonderful old hat. This gave me exercise, besides keeping me from thinking too much.

Food Supply: Four Oranges

Some time during the afternoon we totted up our possessions. The only food was four oranges that Cherry had stuffed in his pocket just before the crash, together with the chocolate bar that I had and a half a dozen more that Alex had, which an Army doctor had given him the day before. The chocolate was never eaten. Alex's was ruined by his thrashing around in the water and he had to throw it away. Next day, when I felt in the pocket for mine, it had become a green mush, which neither I nor my companions would touch.

So, except for the oranges, we started with nothing. But knowing that a man can live a long time without food or water, I was more worried over the shortage of clothing. Only Adamson and I were fully dressed. He had his uniform and cap and I had on a blue summer-weight business suit, complete with necktie, pocket handkerchief, and refillable pencil. The others, expecting to swim, had taken off their shoes and hats before abandoning ship. None had hats or sweaters, but the two pilots had their leather jackets. Several had even thrown their socks away. Bartek, in fact, was naked except for a one-piece jumper.

I may have forgotten an item or two, but these were our total possessions: a first-aid kit, 18 flares and one Very pistol for firing them; two hand pumps for both bailing and renewing the air in the rafts; two service sheath knives; a pair of pliers; a small pocket compass; two revolvers belonging to Cherry and Adamson; two collapsible rubber bailing buckets; three sets of patching gear, one for each raft; several pencils; and my map of the Pacific. We all had cigarets, but the salt water got to these immediately, and they were thrown away. And, finally, Reynolds produced two fish lines, with hooks attached, which he had snatched from a parachute bag after the crash. But there was no bait, and unless we managed to shoot down a gull, our chances of "living off the country" were decidedly thin.

But that first afternoon no one was conscious of our poverty; we were too exhausted to care. Three or four of the boys were violently seasick and I didn't feel any too comfortable myself, although I never reached the point of vomiting. Adamson was in agony from his wrenched back; every jerk of the boat, he said, felt as if someone was kicking him in the kidneys. But I was more worried about Sergeant Alex, in the little raft astern. Long after the others had stopped, he continued to retch. "What's the matter with him?" I called to De Angelis. "I don't know," answered De Angelis, "he must have swallowed a lot of salt water when we tipped over."

The sun went down swiftly, a cold mist gathered on the sea, and the moon came up—a three-quarter moon—beautiful to see. The wisecracks and the small talk, which sounded pretty silly in the immensity of the night, petered out and we were beginning to realize that we were in for hard times.

Sharks Bump Us All Night

Of course, we set a watch—what we called an alert—relieving one another in turn every two hours. It seems pretty silly now, but I offered $100 to the first man to see land, a ship, or airplane. But nobody slept that night. We were wet and miserable. Although the swell moderated just before midnight, the waves kept slopping into the rafts. Both air and water were warm, yet with each splash I felt as if I was being doused with buckets of ice water. Bartek and I changed positions every hour or so, to share the comfort of the other's lee. But I was never warm, and put in most of the night bailing. Sharks followed us from the plane; the water seemed full of them. Every now and then one would bump his back against the bottom. You could feel his hard body through the thin canvas bottom. The force of the blow was enough to lift you three or four inches.

The second day came on slowly, first a gray mist and then the sun breaking through clear. It took hours to get warm, for the night mist penetrated to the bone. As I have said, we had those four oranges, but we decided to save them against the future. By popular vote I was made their custodian, and Cherry generously handed them over. We agreed to divide the first that morning, and the others on alternate days. That way, they would last eight days.

I cut the orange in half, then halved the haves, then halved the quarters, giving each man one-eighth. With seven men watching, you can be sure I made an exact division. In fact, I studied the fruit a full minute before I cut. Some sucked and ate the peel, but Cherry and I saved ours for bait.

Men have been lost at sea before; others have spent more days on rafts than we did. A good deal of what we went through was what you might expect—hunger, thirst, heat, cold and a slow rotting away. In some respects, the period from the second to the eighth day was the worst. A glassy calm fell upon the sea; the sun beat down fiercely all day; the rafts stood still, with the lines slack between; I even imagined I smelled flesh burning, and the sweet stink of hot rubber.

Face, neck, hands, wrists, legs and ankles burned, blistered, turned raw, and burned again. In time, De Angelis and Whittaker, having darker skins, developed a protecting tan, but the rest of us cooked day after day. My hands swelled and blistered: when the salt water got into the flesh, it burned and cracked and dried and burned again. Three months later the scars still show on the knuckles. Our mouths became covered with ugly running sores. Reynolds, having no covering for his legs, turned into a sodden red mass of hurt. Even the soles of his feet were burned raw.

These first five or six days were the worst I have ever known. The night I lay in a wrecked plane near Atlanta, with a dead man half-crushed under my chest, had produced its own kind of suffering. But then the pain had been dulled by delirium, and after a while I could hear people moving around in the dark. But on the Pacific I was something being turned on a spit. Without my hat, I would have been badly off. I would fill it with water, then jam it down over my ears. Before our rescue, the brim was half torn away from the crown.

Some of the others, to escape the terrible heat, paddled for hours in the water. But they paid a stiff price for the relief because their flesh burned again as it dried, and the salt brine stung. Without my handkerchiefs we would have had a much harder time. I passed them around and, folded bandit-fashion across the nose, they protected the lower part of the face. But there was no sparing the eyes. The sea sent back billions of sharp splinters of light; no matter where one looked it was painful. A stupor descended upon the rafts. Men simply sat or sprawled, heads rolling on the chest, mouths half open, gasping. Reynolds, from the cut on his nose, was a horrible sight. The sun would not let the wound heal. He washed the blood off with salt water, but it soon oozed again, spreading over his face, drying in a red crust. Bartek, too, was in agony from his cut fingers. He splashed them with iodine from the first-aid kit, but the salt water ate it away.

Daytimes we prayed for the coolness of the nights; nights we craved the sun. But I really came to hate the nights. Daytimes, I could see my fellow men, the play of the water, the gulls, all the signs of life. But the night brought us all close to fear. A cold dense mist always rose around us. The damp soaked our clothes and we pressed together for warmth. Sometimes, when the mist was very heavy, the other rafts would be hidden. If the sea was calm and the line had fallen slack, I would sometimes come out of a nightmare, and pull in the tow lines until they fetched up hard, and I knew the others were still there. Other times, I would hear moans or groans, or a cry and often a prayer. Or I would see a shadow move and twist as a man tried to ease his torture.

Like Two Men in a Bathtub

What made the night hardest was that we could never stretch out. Some day I shall meet the man who decided these rafts could hold two men and five men each. When I do, he is either going to revise his opinions or prove them on a long voyage, under conditions I shall be happy to outline. Adamson weighed over 200 lb. and I was not much lighter. On our five-man raft, he and Bartek and I shared an inside room measuring 6 ft. 9 in. by 2 ft. 4 in. Counting the narrow inflated roll, on which a man could stretch out for an hour or so with his feet dangling in the water, the dimensions were 9 ft. by 5.

Because Adamson was in such pain, Bartek and I gave him one end to himself. He lay with his bumpus on the bottom, his head against the carbon dioxide bottle, his feet across the roll. Bartek and I lay facing each other, or back to back, with our legs crooked over the roll. This was the way it was in Cherry's boat. But Alex and De Angelis in the two-man raft, although the smallest men, were much worse off. They had to sit facing each other, one with his legs over the other man's shoulders, while he took the legs of the other under his armpits, or they sat back to back, dangling their legs in the water. And sometimes De Angelis lay sprawled out, with Alex on his chest. Imagine two men in a small, shallow bathtub, and you will have a reasonably good idea of how much room they had.

Whenever you turned or twisted, you forced the others to turn or twist. It took days to learn how to make the most of the space, at an incalculable price in misery. A foot or hand or shoulder, moved in sleep or restlessness, was bound to rake the raw flesh of a companion. With the flesh, tempers turned raw and many things said in the night had best be forgotten.

Yet, it would be wrong to give the impression the night was empty of blessings. I was awake a good part of the time, hoping to catch the loom of a ship. In those first nights of utter calm, staring up through the mist, I saw cloud shapes in the moonlight that were the most authentic imitations of living things I have ever seen—elephants, birds, castles, beautiful women, a wild boar. I thought my mind was playing tricks but on the third night I roused Adamson and pointed them out. He recognized the shapes too, and said he had never imagined that cloud structures could be so positive. Adamson, until his strength ebbed, used to tell me about the stars of the Southern Hemisphere, about which he knew a good deal.

How Not To Lure Fish

On the fourth morning the second orange was divided. Except for the orange on the second morning, we had then been 72 hours without food or liquid. Fish were all around; I could see hundreds swimming idly just below the raft. Cherry and I fished for hours with pieces of orange peel. I even borrowed Adamson's key ring, which was shiny, and tried to manipulate it as a spinner. The fish would nose the hook, fan their tails in curiosity, but they never struck.

For six days on the glassy, sizzling sea, the rafts did not seem to move. But by our watches we knew we were drifting; each morning the sun rose just a little bit later. This meant the rafts were inching west and south. We argued interminably over where we were, but it turned out only Cherry and I were right. We were positive of having overshot our island and, if our guess was true, we could count on no land nearer than certain Japanese-held islands 400–500 miles away. I studied the map two or three times a day, always returning it to my inside coat pocket, to protect it against the water. But the colors were already beginning to run.

Commencing the second night, Cherry sent up a flare every night. Having 18, we first decided to use three a night, the first after sundown, the second around midnight, the last before dawn. But of the first three sent aloft, one was a complete dud and the second flickered for only a few seconds. The third, swinging on its parachute, gave a scary, blinding red light, lasting perhaps a minute and a half. Next night, cutting down the expenditure to two good ones, we had another dud; this decided us to reduce the nightly allotment to a single good one.

Always, after the light had exhausted itself, my eyes strained into the darkness, hoping to catch a responding gleam—a gleam which would not settle into the steadiness of a star. It was plain that unless we soon had food or water or the terrible hot calm relented, some of us were bound to die. Adamson, being portly, felt the heat worse than the rest. Reynolds, thin anyway, was fading to skin and bones. Alex, though, was really in a bad way. His mouth was dry and frothing, he cried continually for water. He was only a boy—barely 22—and thinking he was quitting, I pulled his raft in close and asked why the hell he couldn't take it? It was a brutal thing to do, yet I was determined to shock him back to his senses. I found out then what was wrong. He was only three weeks out of the hospital. In addition, he had contracted a lip disease, something like trench mouth, with a scientific name I do not remember. All this had left him with less strength than the rest from the start, and the salt water he swallowed when his raft capsized had helped to do him in.

Unfortunately for him that wasn't the only salt water Alex had had. De Angelis woke one night to find him half out of the raft, gulping salt water. Alex admitted he had been doing this persistently. It explained the cries for water we didn't have. "I tried not to," Alex said, "but I had to. I just had to have water."

So it was only a question of time for poor Alex. He sank deeper into delirium, murmuring his "Hail Mary" and other Catholic prayers. In his wallet was a photograph of a young girl to whom he was engaged: he talked to it, prayed over it. Finally he could neither sleep nor lie down. De Angelis tried to keep the sun off him, but there was no shadow anywhere. So he burned and burned. At night in the moonlight I could see him sitting on the raft shaking as if with ague. He literally vibrated, he was so horribly cold. Yet, except to cry for water, he never really complained.

We Start Reading the Bible

Bartek had a New Testament in his jumper pocket. Watching him read it, the thought came to me that we might all profit by his example. I am not a religious man, but I was taught the Lord's Prayer at my mother's knee and I had gone to Sunday School. If I had any religion in my later life, it was based on the Golden Rule. Yet I have always been conscious of God.

With the New Testament as an inspiration, we held morning and evening prayers. The rafts were pulled together, making a rough triangle. Then, each in turn, one of us would read a passage. None of us, I must confess, showed himself to be very familiar with them, but thumbing the book we found one that more than any other bespoke our needs. This we never failed to read:

> Therefore take no thought, saying, What shall we eat? or What shall we drink? or, Wherewithal shall we be clothed? . . . For

your heavenly Father knoweth that ye have need of all these things.
But seek ye first the kingdom of God, and his righteousness; and all
these things shall be added unto you. Take therefore no thought
for the morrow: for the morrow shall take thought for the things of
itself. Sufficient unto the day is the evil thereof.

(MATTHEW 6:31–34)

One or two turned scornful and bitter because the answer was
slow in coming, but the rest went on praying with deep-felt hope.
Yet we did not neglect anything that might help us to help ourselves. Whittaker tried to make a spear from one of the aluminum
oars, tearing the flat corners away with the pliers. He drove it
into the back of a shark which rubbed alongside, but the hide was
tougher than the point. After several tries it was so blunted as
to be useless. Whittaker threw it angrily into the bottom of the
raft. He had gained nothing and wasted an oar.

Also, Cherry sat all day long with a loaded revolver in his lap,
hoping to knock down a gull. But none came close enough for
a shot. He broke the revolver open two or three times a day
and rubbed the moving parts with oil from his nose and the back
of his ears, but he could not halt the sea-water corrosion. When
the parts froze solid he threw the gun into the Pacific.

To keep the sick men alive, we finished the oranges faster than
we had intended. We had the third on the morning of the fifth
day, the last on the sixth. The last two were shrunken, much of
the juice appeared to have evaporated, and the last one was
beginning to rot. So long as there was that sliver of orange to
anticipate, no one complained of hunger. Now, memories of food
and drink began to haunt us.

Visions of Chocolate Malted Milk

Reynolds talked about how much soda pop he was going to
drink the rest of his life. Cherry couldn't think about anything
but chocolate ice cream. As I listened to the thirsty talk between
the rafts, my own mind slowly filled with visions of chocolate
malted milk. I could actually taste it, to the point where my
tongue worked convulsively. The strange part is that I hadn't
had a chocolate malted milk in nearly 25 years.

The eighth day was another hot, flat calm. It did not help our stomachs any to look down and see dolphin and mackerel, sleek and fat and twelve to eighteen inches long, and thousands of smaller fish swimming in the depths. That afternoon Cherry read the service, with the usual quotation from Matthew. About an hour later, when I was dozing with my hat pulled down over my eyes, a gull appeared from nowhere and landed on my hat.

I don't remember how it happened or how I knew he was there. But I knew it instantly, and I knew that if I missed this one, I'd never find another to sit on my hat. I reached up for him with my right hand—gradually. The whole Pacific seemed to be shaking from the agitation in my body, but I could tell he was still there from the hungry, famished, almost insane eyes in the other rafts. Slowly and surely my hand got up there; I didn't clutch, but just closed my fingers, sensing his nearness, then closing my fingers hard.

I wrung his neck, defeathered him, carved up the body, divided the meat into equal shares, holding back only the intestines for bait. Even the bones were chewed and swallowed. No one hesitated because the meat was raw and stringy and fishy. It tasted fine. After Cherry had finished his piece, I baited a hook and passed it over to him. The hook, weighted with Whittaker's ring, had hardly got wet before a small mackerel hit it, and was jerked into the raft. I dropped the other line, with the same miraculous result, except that mine was a small sea bass.

All this food in the space of a few minutes bolstered us beyond words. We ate one of the fish before dark, put the other aside for the next day. Even the craving for water seemed to abate, perhaps from chewing the cool,wet flesh while grinding the bones to a pulp. Alex and Adamson ate their shares, and I was optimistic enough to believe they were immediately better. I say in all truth that at no time did I ever doubt we would be saved, but as that eighth night rose around us I was sure we could last forever. The ocean was full of fish, and we could catch them.

As the sun went down, the sky clouded over, the air turned cool, a soft uncertain wind made cat's-paws on the water, all portents of rain. I tried to stay awake to have everything in readiness if it came, but I finally dozed off with my head across Adamson's knees.

My next recollection is of being jolted awake, as if from a blow. The raft was slamming up and down on a heavy irregular swell. It was pitch black—so black that I could scarcely make out the other rafts, except when they were thrown up on a swell. Gusts of wind came at us from every quarter. And I knew, if I ever knew anything, that rain was near.

Rain!

From midnight we were on the watch for the rushing shadows of rain squalls. About 3 o'clock in the morning I heard the cry, "Rain." Drops splattered against my face and mouth, clean and sweet to taste. After the first few drops there was nothing more, but far off I could see the squall. The wind had a new sound as if it were no longer empty. We paddled toward the squall and I prayed to God to put us in its path. We had a plan all worked out—bailing buckets ready and the empty canvas covers for the Very light cartridges. We took our shirts and socks off to spread over our head and shoulders. The handkerchiefs were to be laid on the inflated roll until they became soaked. Adamson had even taken off his shorts to wring.

It was one hell of a night—all wind, waves, noise, lightning and big black shadows. We paddled into it, shouting at the top of our lungs. Out of that uproar came a cry for help. The little raft, with De Angelis and Alex, had broken loose. Bartek and I, with an oar to the side, set out after them, Cherry's raft following in our wake. I was afraid we'd lost them, but we sighted the raft against the white rush of a breaking wave, overtook it and made it fast. A moment later the squall enveloped us.

Rain fell as from a waterfall. I spread the handkerchiefs on the roll of the raft, where they would catch the water and fluffed my shirt over my head. Adamson, roused by the cool water on his body, draped his underpants over his chest to catch more water. I appointed myself wringer, and as fast as the others passed over the soaked pieces of cloth, I would twist them hard, forcing the water out, to rid the cloth of salt rime. I had done this several times with each piece, always tasting the last drippings for salt.

I had finished rinsing out the bucket and cartridge covers, and was ready to collect the first water when a sharp pull came on the bowline, twisting the raft around. Out of the corner of my eye I saw Cherry's raft being rolled over on its beam ends by a wave.

All three men were thrown out, and with Reynolds so weak I was sure he was going to drown. But in the next flash of lightning I counted three heads bobbing around the sides. While they clung to the hand line around the sides, we pulled in the line, bringing them in on our lee side, holding the raft steady while they helped each other in. Reynolds, gasping, mustered the strength to haul himself back. I shall never stop marveling at the hidden resources of men whose minds never give up. Cherry and Whittaker saved the oars, but they saved little else. The Very pistol and the last of the cartridges were lost. So were the bailing bucket and the little water they had collected.

All this—from the breaking away of the little raft to the righting of Cherry's—took no more than ten minutes, perhaps as little as five. But rather than wearing us down the exertions seemed to fill us with strength. I passed Cherry the bailing bucket, and while he bailed I watched anxiously for any let up in the rain. Adamson and Bartek sucked at the wet clothes, filling their mouths with the first water in eight days. To make up for his lost bucket, we gave Cherry the cartridge cover.

When they finally pulled away, I fell to wringing the sopping garments Bartek and Adamson had ready for me. Lightning flashed, the sea rumbled, the raft tossed wildly, but I was not really aware of them. I was gauging matters by just one thing— the water level in the bailing bucket.

Quite suddenly the wind died down and the rain stopped. The squall could not have lasted more than 20 minutes. But I had nearly a quart and a half of water in the bucket. Cherry in his boat, had about a quart, but De Angelis and Alex, who had nothing to catch water in, had none. They had simply sucked their shirts.

In the calm that followed, the rafts were pulled in close. The round-table decision was that we'd better try to go on with as little water as possible—a half jigger per man per day. In the dark I poured what I guessed to be that much into one of the empty Very cartridge cases, and passed it seven times down the line of hands. It was the sweetest water I ever tasted. And the rain that had drenched our bodies, washing away the salt rime and cleansing the sores, had refreshed us quite as much.

On the ninth morning we shared the second mackerel, and another half-jigger of water. From this point on my memory may be hazy. Alex got no better, and on the tenth day, for his safety and Adamson's, we increased the water ration to two jiggers a day, one in the morning and one at sundown. On the following day we added another one at noon.

Death of Sergeant Alex

It was on the tenth evening, I think, that I asked Bartek to change rafts with Sergeant Alex, thinking that Alex, might rest better. It took the combined strength of Bartek, De Angelis and myself to move him. I stretched him on the lee side on the bottom of the boat and put my arm around him, as a mother cuddles a child, hoping in that way to transfer the heat of my body to him during the night. In an hour or so his shivering stopped and sleep came—a shallow sleep in which Alex mumbled intermittently in Polish—phrases about his mother and his girl "Snooks."

I kept Alex there all night, the next day and night, and the twelfth day. He was weaker, although more rational. When evening came, after the customary prayer, he asked to be put back in the little boat with De Angelis. I knew he couldn't last many hours longer, and so we pulled the other boat up and changed around again. We had to lift him like a baby. A strong wind came up and I slept fitfully that night, worrying about that little raft bouncing on the rough sea. Yet I must have dozed off, because my next recollection is of the sound of a long sigh.

I called to De Angelis: "Has he died?"

De Angelis said, after a pause, "I think so."

Sharks Sense the Presence of Death

It was about 3:00 A.M. and very dark and although it was hard on De Angelis to wait for dawn with a dead man across his body, I did not want to make a decision until there was light to see by. The other men stirred, woke up, and understood, almost without being told, what had happened. I remember someone saying, "Well, his sufferings are over." I think we were all a little frightened, with the wind blowing and clouds rushing across the sky, and Alex dead in that plunging raft. Somewhere I have read that sharks can sense the coming of death. That night there seemed twice as many as we had seen before.

At daybreak Bartek hauled Alex's little raft alongside, and Cherry paddled up in his. The body was already stiff, but I checked the heart, the pulse, checked in every way I knew. And I asked Cherry and Whittaker to do so, not wishing to accept the responsibility alone. We agreed Alex was dead. We removed his wallet and identification disc, which Captain Cherry has since returned to the family, and we saved the jacket. De Angelis murmured what he remembered of the Catholic burial service. Then we rolled the body over the side. It did not sink at once but rather floated off face down a little while.

This was the 13th morning.

II. IN WHICH THE NAVY RESCUES SEVEN CASTAWAYS AFTER 21 DAYS' DRIFTING

As I said, Sergeant Alex died and was buried during the early morning of our 13th day in the rafts. It had been my habit, as soon as it was light enough to see, to count heads in the rafts. Seven (not including myself) was the number fixed in my mind. For the first few days, as I counted automatically, I would discover with a kind of shock that there were only six. Then I would remember. Alex was the seventh.

Alex's death left Lieutenant De Angelis, the navigator, alone in the two-man raft at the end of the line. With me in the middle raft were Colonel Adamson and Private Bartek, both very weak. Captain Cherry, the pilot, Lieutenant Whittaker, the co-pilot, and Sergeant Reynolds were in the leading raft. Bartek now asked De Angelis to change places with him. De Angelis was willing, but he preferred to be with his fellow officers at the head of the rafts. So Sergeant Reynolds came back with me and Adamson, and Bartek shifted to the little raft alone.

Before daylight a morning or two later, I woke up to find the little raft gone. The connecting rope was trailing in the water and, having tied the knot myself, I knew it could not have pulled loose.

At daybreak we saw his raft only a half a mile away, bobbing up and down on a gentle swell. We waved and yelled. Finally Bartek heard us and paddled back, almost reluctantly. I asked what happened. He admitted having untied the line during the night. I have never been able to understand why and, although I asked him directly, he offered no explanation.

My memory may be a little off, but I think we finished the last of the rainwater the evening before Alex died. Another calm spell settled over our piece of the Pacific. The rafts, scarcely moving, lay bunched together, and the sun started to burn our guts out all over again.

We went another 48 hours or so without water. After the last drop had gone, several men were almost raving wild in their thirstiness. There is really no limit to what men will try in their extremity. In the first terrible week we had saved our urine in the empty Very cartridge shells and let it stand for several days, hoping that the sun and air would work a beneficial chemical change. That was my idea. It was a bad one.

A Taste of Shark Meat

We had been without food since we ate the last mackerel on the ninth day. Cherry, who had been fishing patiently, lost the second and last line and hook on a big shark. But before this happened, he had actually hooked a two-foot shark. With Whittaker's help, he managed to hoist it into the raft, where he stabbed it with a knife. Cherry cut the carcass into two pieces, keeping the smaller one for his raft and passing the other back to me, for Adamson, Reynolds and myself, and for Bartek in the little raft.

I cut off equal pieces for the four. The meat was rubbery and tough; it took all my strength to force the rusty blade through it. Maybe we were more pernickety than some other castaways, but hungry as we were, no one had stomach for shark meat. It had a foul rancid taste and the two or three of us who chewed and sucked the meat, mostly for the liquid in it, soon spit out the pieces, gagging as we did so. I kept my piece in the boat all day, hoping the sun would cure it and make it palatable, but I simply could not down it. When I offered them another piece, Adamson and Bartek shook their heads. The flesh was beginning to stink, so I threw it overboard, without regret. In a little while I heard a splash—Cherry's half had followed ours.

While trying to stab the shark in the raft, Cherry had driven his knife through the rubberized canvas floor, making a quarter-inch tear, through which water seeped. Because the day was calm, Cherry decided to try to make a patch with the repair kit. In the kit were a tube of glue, a piece of sandpaper, and a small roll of patching material. The problem was to dry the raft bottom so the patch would hold. Cherry and the other two got out of their raft and turned it bottom side up, so that it floated on the inflated roll, leaving an air space underneath. Then they hauled themselves back on the bottom, resting there while the canvas dried.

The patch was a failure—perhaps because the patching material was ruined by salt water. It pulled loose soon after they righted the raft. They never tried another. The rent didn't let in enough water to cause danger, but enough to make them miserable. Unless they bailed frequently, there was always two or three inches of water in the bottom.

Our bodies, our minds, the few things we had with us were slowly rotting away. All the watches except Whittaker's stopped running, as salt-water corrosion froze the works. The compass needle ceased to point and finally rusted hard in the direction in which it had set. The silver coins in my pockets took on a discolored look. The secret orders that Mr. Stimson had given me faded and became unintelligible. The colors and the print came off our only map, which finally stuck together at the folds and could not be opened. But by then I had memorized the position of every island or bit of land of any possible use to us.

Career of a Crucifix

In the breast pocket of my coat I have carried, for many years, a little leather case containing a crucifix and three St. Christopher medals. The crucifix was given to me in 1917 when I left with the A. E. F. by a 10-year-old girl, the daughter of a friend. Whenever

I flew on the Western front, I always had that case in my flying suit. As the case wore out, I had it replaced—half a dozen times, I'd say. It was with me the night I flew into a hill near Atlanta. And it was with me again on the Pacific. Like all the other metal things, the crucifix and the medals started to corrode and disintegrate. I am not a Catholic and, aside from the sentiment connected with such things, I was certainly under no illusions as to what they could do for me. Yet after all the years, and the good fortune associated with them, I found myself believing, as men will when everything else is going to pieces, that my fate was somehow involved with them.

The watch I had was a gift from the city of Detroit after the other war. It was a fine, expensive timepiece; I valued it for that and other reasons. Yet not to be able to tell the time turned out to be no particular loss. Time, merely as something to keep track of, ceased to be any real concern of ours. One of the men who had a small notebook kept a diary through the first week but as far as I could see he never wrote afterward.

Adamson used to pencil terse notes on the side of the raft, with the date. But by the second week he was satisfied merely to scratch the day. His last note I remember clearly: "Fourteenth day. Rick and I still alive."

Either the 14th night, or the night before, an unexpected and depressing event occurred. After Alex died, I began to despair of Adamson. The nagging pain in his back, aggravated by salt-water sores, gave him no peace. To my knowledge he never slept deeply. He just slipped off into a permanent semiconsciousness, occasionally broken by feeble gusts of fury and intolerable pain. His feet, legs, arms, wrists and face had been burned to a red pulp and any movement in the raft, however slight, was certain to communicate itself to his back.

Hans Adamson is an old and dear friend. It was a terrible responsibility to sit there and watch the strength go out of him. His clothes were rotting on his back. The colonel's eagles on his tunic were corroded. His uniform shirt and pants were water-stained and coming to pieces. A gray stubble covered his face and his eyes were bloodshot and swollen.

On this particular night I felt the raft give a violent lurch. My first thought was that a shark was attacking. Adamson's body was no longer against mine. His end of the raft was empty. I saw something struggling in the water close by and my hand gripped Adamson's shoulder. He was too heavy for me to hold up alone, but my yells for help brought Cherry and Whittaker up in their raft. We were a long time at it, but we managed to haul him back into the raft.

In the morning Hans had a long lucid interval. We talked about many things, familiar and pleasant things done together, the mission we were on. But from that day on he seldom spoke or asked for anything.

It does us no dishonor to say that we were all becoming a little unhinged. We were unreasonable, at times, in our demands upon one another. Wrathful and profane words were exchanged over nothing at all. Every night the rafts were drawn together for prayer meeting. We continued to read from Bartek's New Testament, now yellowed and stained by salt water. But one or two, who had been most fervent, became backsliders. Because their prayers were not answered within 24 or 48 hours, they condemned the Lord for His failure to save them.

As commander I had final responsibility for the party and the only weapon I had was to brutalize and jar those whose chins sagged too far down on their chests. One man said to me across 20 ft. of water: "Rickenbacker, you are the meanest, most cantankerous so-and-so that ever lived." Some of the things I said could have been a heavy weight on my conscience. But I felt better after we reached land. Several of the boys confessed that they once swore an oath to live for the sheer pleasure of burying me at sea.

There were occasions when I myself was pretty hard-pressed; when my private store of aches and pains reduced me to something less than a good companion. My legs and hip were rather severely torn in the Atlanta crash. Right up to the time of the Pacific trip I was under regular diathermic and physiotherapeutic treatment. If anyone had told me I could live for 21 days with two other men in a space approximately nine feet by five, I would have said he was crazy.

As I got thinner and thinner, my teeth began to give trouble. The gums seemed to shrink in proportion to the rest of me, and the new front bridgework which my dentist finished a few days before I left turned loose and uncomfortable. My mouth dried out, and under the bridge the saliva formed an evil-tasting cottony substance that felt like mush. However, by washing the bridge four and five times a day in the ocean, and forcing salt water against the gums with my tongue, I found some relief. Knowing the fix I'd be in if the bridge ever slipped out of my hand, I was extremely cautious about this ceremony—overcautious, in fact. One time it did slip from my hand, but I had it back before it had sunk six inches. For me that was the most frightening moment in the 21 days.

Thus, like the others, I had my difficulties and, I might add, my particular delusions. One was a dream that repeated itself endlessly. It always began with my sighting an island occupied by an old friend with a fine home who was happy to welcome us. There would be breakfast, with an abundance of the fruit juices that I craved, and a telephone with a direct line to Mr. Stimson, who was waiting to hear where we were, so that he could send a plane to pick us up. Then I would wake up in horror, to find myself on the Pacific, with the raft rocking on the swell and the gray mist around.

Both Cherry and I were convinced we were well to the north and west of the convoy and air ferry routes. We tried from time to time to paddle in a southeasterly direction, but the effort taxed us and we gave up. It seemed much more important to conserve our strength.

On the 14th night or so we got a wonderful break. A series of squalls, one behind the other, passed over the rafts. It was a wild night. I doubt if I ever worked so hard, or to such good effect. When I finished wringing the last shirt and sock dry at dawn, there was a gallon of water in my bailing bucket. Cherry had nearly as much in the Mae West. In the morning and again at noon we had a jigger around. This, with what we had sucked from the clothes before we squeezed the water out, refreshed and heartened us.

But because our last resources were plainly running out, we held council the next afternoon and decided to chance a course that I had steadily held to be risky. Ever since leaving the airplane I had insisted that the rafts stay together. But now I had come to believe that our only hope was for one raft, manned by the strongest three, to try to beat across the current to the southeast. In that direction they stood a better chance to fall in with a transport plane or a ship; and if they were lucky enough to be picked up alive, they would direct the search for us. Cherry agreed to go, and Whittaker and De Angelis, who were in better shape than any of the others, also volunteered. I gave them most of the water, and the last oar in the little raft.

They set out in the early afternoon. Or I should say they tried to set out. They untied the line and paddled off. The sea was flat, but there was a slight headwind. Hours later they were still in sight, not more than a mile away, perhaps less. Watching, I could see two men paddling while the third rested. Long after the sun had set, I saw their shadows rising on the swell. Then I lost them in the night mist.

When day came and I hauled myself over Reynolds' back for a look around I saw they were only a short distance away, sleeping. Presently they paddled back, exhausted. Cherry said it was a physical impossibility to force the raft against the current and that little breeze. This was a heavy disappointment to all of us, but in an odd way the incident marked a turning point in our fortunes. Thereafter we were never without water. The skies clouded over, and there were few hours during the day or night when rain squalls were not chasing across the horizon.

We also invented a storage system for water. I hated to leave it in the bailing bucket on the bottom of the raft because there was always the risk of knocking it over. And the loss by evaporation during the heat of the day could be very heavy. The idea of using the Mae West lifejacket, which I wore, occurred to me. This had two double compartments, filled with carbon dioxide, each closed by a bicycle valve.

I let out the gas and, taking a mouthful at a time from the bailing bucket, forced the water down a narrow tube past the valve into the compartment. This took a long time—perhaps 15 to 20 minutes to transfer a quart. All the while the boys had their eyes fixed on my Adam's apple, watching for a convulsive jerk. The honor system has seldom been put to a more severe test, and I can't blame the others for being suspicious. One night I heard one man muttering to a companion that while it only took a count of three for Rickenbacker to fill his mouth from the bucket, it took a count of 16 for him to transfer the mouthful to the jacket.

The three used Very shells that we had saved served as drinking cups. They were about six inches long and perhaps an inch and a quarter wide. There was one in each raft. Proving how far men will go in adapting themselves to hard conditions, we also urinated in them since we dared not stand up in the raft. (Throughout the 21 days, even when we were without water, our kidneys functioned almost normally. On the other hand, I do not recall that anyone had a single bowel movement.)

Mackerel Jump into the Boats

With water we also gained a little food, by a great stroke of luck. One night in the third week, there was a tremendous splashing all around the boat. It was pitch dark, but the water blazed with zigzagging phosphorescent streaks. We could hear heavy bodies hitting the water terrific smacks.

A pack of sharks had hit a school of mackerel with the rafts in the middle of the slaughter. The terrified mackerel shot out of the water like star shells. One landed in my raft and I fell on him before he could flop out. Simultaneously another landed in Cherry's boat and was bagged. They provided food for two days. It was our first in nearly a week.

Cherry was the only one who could claim to have been hurt by a shark; and this was by mistake. One night we were all aroused by a blood-curdling shriek. There was a God-awful thrashing around in the forward raft and finally I heard Cherry yelling, "A damn shark came up and hit me and broke my nose."

We pulled the boats together and from Cherry's misery it was plain that he had been hit a hard wallop. Blood was streaming down his face and shirt. Whittaker made him lie down while he heaped wet handkerchiefs over his nose. This stopped the bleeding and, after the pain eased, Cherry decided that his nose hadn't been broken after all. He had only the foggiest idea how it happened. He was stretched across the raft, with the upper half of his body across the inflated bulge, and while asleep he must have rolled out, just far enough for a shark to reach him with a flick of the tail.

The 17th day brought the first tantalizing hint that we had finally drifted within the reach of assistance. We had been through several days and nights of squally weather which blew us in all directions. The rafts had taken a pounding and the interminable slap-slap of the waves, the everlasting pitching and swaying, had left us sleepless, exhausted and miserable. I would wring rainwater from clothes until my fingers turned stiff and useless. Then I would rest and wring some more. The reserve in the Mae West grew steadily; it had a fine heft when I lifted it. And we were drinking three jiggers a day per man.

This particular afternoon was heavily overcast; the sea was quite rough, with whitecaps, and I was worrying about the strain on the connecting lines. I saw Cherry in the raft ahead sit up, cock his head. Then he shouted back, "I hear a plane. Listen!"

In a few minutes we all saw an airplane off to the left. It came out of a squall, flying low and fast, about five miles away. Bartek was back in my raft that day. He stood up while I held him, and waved his arms and shouted until he slid out of my arms and fell exhausted across the raft.

The seven of us yelled our lungs out. The plane came no nearer. It was a single-engine pontoon job. I doubt that we had it in sight more than three or four minutes. It was too far off for us to make out its markings. A squall moved in between and we did not see it again. The yelling stopped and for a long time no one talked. My throat hurt from shouting so much.

Yet just to see that airplane was a terrific stimulus. It was the first outside sign of human life visible to us in two and a half weeks. Here at last was proof that land was close by, or at least a ship capable of catapulting such an airplane. Only the sick men slept that night. Cherry, Whittaker, De Angelis and I talked steadily across the rafts.

On the 18th day, again in the afternoon, we saw two more airplanes of the same type, flying close together, perhaps six miles away. We waved our shirts but did not shout, knowing it was useless. On the 19th day, in the morning, there were four more airplanes, first a pair to the north, then another to the south, perhaps 4,000 ft. high. First the strong resonant note of the engines came from below the horizon; then we saw the planes themselves; then we watched them disappear. The sound lingered after they had gone.

That afternoon no airplanes appeared and somehow the fear took hold of us that perhaps we had gone past the land, perhaps we had drifted through a string of islands and were moving into the open Pacific. Being picked up, quite obviously, was going to be a chance in a million. We had assumed that an airplane with a vigilant crew could not miss the bright yellow rafts. Now we knew otherwise. In a rough sea the rafts must be just flecks against the whitecaps.

Yet this should have been our best time. We had water in reserve and we also had food. In the early morning, in the gray half-light before dawn, hundreds and hundreds of finger-length fish, resembling sardines, collected around the rafts. With practice and diligence, we learned how to scoop them up. The trick was to bring your hand from behind and pin them with a quick move against the raft. But for every one landed, a hundred were lost. Through the last three days we must have caught between 20 and 30. They were divided, share and share alike, and the fishes were still wriggling when we bit into them. I crunched them and downed them whole.

Cherry Goes Off Alone

We come to the evening of the 20th day—about 6 o'clock. Cherry and De Angelis were arguing. I paid no attention until a phrase, louder than the others, came across the little stretch of water. It was the first inkling of what was afoot. Captain Cherry wanted De Angelis to give up his place in the little raft. "Why do you want it, Cherry?" I asked. He answered, "I'm going to try to make land. Staying together is no good. They'll never see us this way."

I told Cherry then he was wrong, and I still think he was wrong, despite the fact he was the first to be picked up. We argued back and forth between the rafts for at least an hour. My point was that he had no way of telling which was the best direction to take. The various airplanes had appeared in the north, south, east and west. And if they couldn't see three rafts bunched together, what chance did they have of seeing one? But Cherry was insistent. He argued that our only chance was to scatter. Yet he left the decision to me, saying: "I won't go unless you agree it is all right for me to."

I realized that no good would come out of prolonging the argument. De Angelis paddled past us in the little raft, transferred to the lead raft, and Cherry took his place. I wished Captain Cherry well and said so long. He had some water in his Mae West so I was not worried on that account. He drifted off alone, carried by the swell and a slight breeze.

Whittaker and De Angelis watched the receding raft with increasing nervousness. I heard them saying that maybe Cherry was right and there was nothing to be gained by staying together. They too decided to go off. I remonstrated with them as I had with Cherry. I was angry now. "What about Reynolds?" I said. "You haven't asked him." They couldn't ask him, Reynolds was too sick, too weak, to understand.

I gave in again. The talk had worn me down.

Cherry was almost out of sight when Whittaker cast off the line. Both rafts were out of sight before night fell. Now there were three of us—Adamson, Bartek and myself. Adamson and Bartek were more dead than alive. They hadn't been drawn into the arguments of the afternoon. I doubt that they even heard what was said. They were crunched up at opposite ends of the raft.

I was terribly worried that night. If we had indeed drifted past land, our chances of holding out much longer were damn poor. I had perhaps two quarts and a pint of water in the Mae West. Half of this, in one compartment, was good sweet water. The rest was dubious, being from the first wringing of the soaked rags. To be sure of getting rid of all the salt in the rags, we had at first thrown away the first pint or so, after using it to rinse out the bailing bucket and the Very "cups." However, a sip convinced me this water was drinkable and thereafter I frugally transferred the first water of a rain to the inside compartment of the Mae West. This became the emergency supply. The product of subsequent wringings went into what I called the "sweet water" chamber. This provided the regular ration.

On the 21st morning I woke from a particularly pleasant version of my usual dream. I issued the morning jigger of water, but Adamson and Bartek were almost too weak to raise their heads to drink. As I measured the water into the shell, my hand trembled so much I spilled some. Part of Bartek's ration ran down his chin, and I had to give him more to make up for it. After two hours of scooping, I caught several more of the little fishes. But I was nervous and impatient and my hand moved with exasperating clumsiness.

The sky had cleared during the night and after the sun got up it turned terribly hot. I watched for seaweed and debris—anything suggestive of land. But the ocean was bare. Even the gulls were absent. Some time during the morning Bartek emerged briefly from his coma and asked: "Have the planes come back?"

I said, "No, there haven't been any since day before yesterday."

He seemed to have difficulty understanding this. Then he mumbled "They won't come back. I know. They won't come back." He said that over and over again.

"Listen, Captain—planes!"

Yet it was Bartek who first heard the planes when they returned late in the afternoon. I am quite sure that I was awake, but my senses must have been dulled, because Bartek pulled at my shirt and whispered, "Listen, Captain—planes! They're back. They're very near."

There were two airplanes approaching from the southeast. Adamson and Bartek were too weak to stand themselves, or to hold me up. Sitting down, I waved as hard as I could with my old hat. The planes, only a few hundred yards off the water, passed within a couple of miles and disappeared into the setting sun. My first elation was swallowed up in despair. Night was only a few hours away. This was our last chance.

Half an hour later we heard them again, much closer. They came directly out of the sun, straight for us. The first dived right

over the raft. We yelled like maniacs. The plane was so low
that I could see the pilot's expression. He was smiling and wav-
ing. Not until then did I look at the insignia. It was the U. S.
Navy and gratitude and happiness filled me. I waved and waved,
out of a half-crazy notion that the pilot must be made to understand we were not three dead men on a raft.

The first airplane made a full circle around the raft, then set
off after the other. They disappeared into the direction from
which they first had come. Like the others, they were single-
engine pontoon jobs.

Bartek kept asking, "Are they coming back? Are they coming
back?" I said yes, they know where we are and they are certainly
coming back. My idea was that they returned to some island base
to report and a PBY flying boat would be sent to pick us up. In
fact, I worked out half a dozen reasons to account for their leaving us. But, as it turned out, I overlooked the obvious one—they
were short of gas.

As the minutes dragged, my confidence weakened. The sun
was going down fast, and a dangerous-looking squall was making
up in the south. About three-quarters of an hour later the same
two airplanes reappeared, skirting the squall. While still a mile or
so off, they veered off into a low cloud and vanished. Obviously
they had lost us again. But a few minutes later they burst out of
the heart of the squall, headed directly for the raft. They must
have seen us instantly, because they glided down and circled.
Then one plane went off, while the other stayed overhead.

He circled, circled, circled. I waved and waved and waved.
Never have I known myself to possess such strength, showing
what mind can do over matter.

The eastern horizon was already quite dark. I wondered what
program the pilot had in mind, whether he was waiting for someone else, or planned to land and pick us up himself. The sun
finally set, but he just went on circling and the fear took hold
that now he would have to return to his base and we would be in
for another night on the raft, and if this squall caught us, God
knows where we would be blown by morning. I couldn't understand why he didn't land.

Only a little light was left in the western sky when a white flare flamed below the plane. A minute later the pilot fired another—a red one. The reason for the circling now became clear. The pilot was waiting for a boat. Far off on the southern horizon two lights blinked a code signal.

The Plane Lands Beside Us

The plane straightened out and made a cautious landing on the darkened sea. Fortunately, it was smooth, except for a long swell. After taxiing within a few yards, the pilot shut off the engine. I paddled up and caught hold of the pontoon. The radioman climbed down to help me. The pilot joined him and I remember thinking how clean and handsome they were, how proud I was to have them as countrymen.

They introduced themselves—Lieutenant Eadie (W. F. Eadie of Evanston, Ill.) and Radioman Boutte (L. H. Boutte of Abbeville, La.). Eadie said a PT boat was on its way to take us in. But he went on to say that he didn't want to show another light, since there might be Japs in the vicinity. So rather than wait, he proposed that we taxi into the base, which he said was 40 miles away.

I told the lieutenant that first we had to dispose of a piece of unfinished business. The afternoon before, after the others had gone off, I had made this deal with Bartek and Adamson: the moment we knew we were safe, all the water in the Mae West was to be divided. They were to have all the sweet water and I the "tainted." This would give me twice as much water, but they were all for it.

I opened the valve in the Mae West and poured the sweet water into the bailing bucket for Adamson and Bartek. There was enough to give each a pint. While they were drinking, I unscrewed the other valve, lifted the tube to my lips and drank to the last drop. I must have had nearly a quart. It was salty all right, but if there had been a gallon I would have taken it.

Lieut. Eadie meanwhile gave us the good news about the others. Captain Cherry had been sighted the afternoon before about 25 miles away by a Navy plane on routine evening patrol, piloted by Lieutenant Frederick E. Woodward of Davenport,

Iowa. With him was the same radioman who was with Eadie, and he was first to sight the raft.

Luckily for Cherry, a PT boat was nearby. Cherry, not knowing where we had drifted during the night, was able to give only vague directions as to our likely position. Every available plane was put in the air and in the midst of the search a radio call from a nearby island informed the base that natives had seen three castaways on the beach of an uninhabited island several miles away. This news was supplied by an English missionary who had a small radio transmitter, and presumably it accounted for Whittaker, De Angelis and Reynolds. A doctor had already been dispatched to them in an airplane.

We were really the lucky ones. Our raft, during the night, drifted through the chain of islands, into the open sea. The next landfall was hundreds of miles away. There is, of course, no way of telling how far we drifted during the 21 days. My guess is between 400 and 500 miles. Unknowingly, we had drifted across the International Date Line, losing a day. By our calendar we were picked up Wednesday, Nov. 11—or Thursday, Nov. 12 by the pilot's. We were then a few hours into our 22nd day.

After we had finished the water, Eadie and Boutte hoisted Adamson 8 ft. into the cockpit. The plane had room for only one passenger and I took it for granted that Eadie would leave Bartek and me behind. So I said to Lieutenant Eadie, "Would you mind waiting until the PT does come up? I don't want them to miss us in the dark."

Eadie said calmly, "Why, Captain Eddie, you fellows are going too."

I looked at the cockpit. "Where?" He smiled and said, "On the wing."

Eadie had the strength of Hercules. With Boutte's help, he hauled Bartek to the wing, lifted him over the cockpit and sat him on the right wing with his legs hanging over the leading edge. In that position he was tied securely to the wing and cockpit. I was boosted to the left wing and tied in the same way. I was deeply impressed by these two young Navy fliers. They knew their business, they asked no foolish questions. All that we could say was "This is heaven" and "Thank God" and "God bless the Navy."

I don't know how long we taxied—perhaps half an hour. It was pitch-dark and with the propeller wash battering my eyelids I couldn't see much anyway. Presently the shadow of a PT boat loomed up ahead. Eadie cut the engine and drifted within hailing distance. After a three-cornered argument involving him, the skipper of the PT and myself, it was arranged that Bartek and I be transferred and that Adamson continue in the plane, rather than be put to the discomfort of another change.

It was no hardship for me to change. I knew there'd be water and food—but water, above all—on the boat. They lowered Bartek and me back into the raft, and I paddled across to the boat. Planting my feet upon an American deck was the next-best thing to being home. The crew gave us a cheer. It bucked us up no end, but we hardly deserved it. There's no great honor attached to saving your own skin.

Bed rolls and blankets were laid out. Bartek fell asleep instantly, but all the excitement made me wakeful. Moreover, the salty water I had drunk stimulated a bowel action that took me to the toilet. My legs were rusty after days and nights of just sitting. Nevertheless, by holding on to things I managed to get to the washroom.

Enough Water at Last

Water was the only thing on my mind. One of the men led me into a cabin where I downed four China mugs of water in quick succession. The skipper, who was barely half my age, became alarmed. "Aren't you overdoing it?" he asked. I said yes, maybe too much water would be bad. So I had a couple of mugs of pineapple juice and a mug of hot beef broth, one after the other.

By this time we were at the base, and a beaching boat had come alongside. A Colonel Fuller, the ranking doctor, appeared with several pharmacist's mates. They had two stretchers, on which they lowered Bartek and me to the other boat. A few minutes later the keel crunched on the beach. We were carried across the beach and down a road, under the most beautiful palm trees

I have ever seen. The moon was shining through the clouds, the air was warm—it was a lovely evening.

They took us into a little one-story hospital, with eight or ten cots in a single room. Colonel Fuller said proudly it had just been built and we were the first patients. My clothes literally came apart as they undressed me. As soon as they put me to bed, I demanded water. The colonel turned to the pharmacist's mate and directed him to give me two ounces every two hours. I said I wanted it in a bucket, not a medicine dropper. "If you drink too much," the colonel said, "the after-effects could be quite serious." I told him what I had had on the PT boat. "All the more reason," he said severely. "Two ounces every two hours."

That was all I got and that night I was literally afire. I thirsted as I never had the worst day on the raft. The salt in the water I had drunk was doubtless responsible.*

I slept badly. The burns on my wrists, neck and face, the loathsome sores that covered my legs, thighs and bumpus were plastered with healing compounds, but they hurt now as they never hurt on the raft. My old dream repeated itself, but with a nightmarish twist at the end. I was again in the fine house, eating and drinking with gluttonous pleasure. Then the dream dissolved and I woke almost in terror, imagining the raft was rocking and swinging under me, and mistaking the moonlight through the windows for the ocean mist.

In the morning I was aroused by a fearful hammering and pounding. I was told that a new and bigger hospital was being built a short distance away. Cherry was brought in that day and on the following day, Whittaker and De Angelis arrived. After being picked up, they had all been taken aboard a Navy tender. Poor Reynolds, however, had to be left behind. In his weakened condition the doctors were afraid to move him. I found I had lost 40 lb. on the raft. Adamson and Cherry, both heavier than I to start with, had each lost 55 lb.

* When Gibson (290) and his companions finally obtained fresh water after severe deprivation it "seemed as if we would never stop drinking. We were too far gone to remember all the old precepts about sipping small quantities, but it seemed to do us no harm.

"As fast as we drank the water came through us—just as if we had been pouring it in at one end of a funnel for it to run out of the other." (See p. 248.)

Whittaker and De Angelis had a hair-raising tale to tell. The morning after they left us, they saw palm trees a long way off to the north. Whittaker said he rowed for hours. Every approach to the island was guarded by reefs, over which the surf broke heavily, but they took a chance and rode the breakers to the beach. Too weak to walk, Whittaker and De Angelis crawled on their hands and knees, dragging Reynolds between them.

After propping Reynolds against a palm tree, they searched the underbrush for food and water. A short distance away they found a partly finished hut and the half-finished hull of a canoe, carved from the trunk of a coconut tree. The canoe had collected considerable rainwater. They skimmed off the dead bugs and drank to their bellies' content. The rubbish was infested with rats. They got close enough to one to club it to death, and devoured it raw. Afterward some natives arrived in a canoe and took them to an island several miles away. Here they were cared for by the English missionary until the Navy doctor arrived.

That same afternoon a flying boat brought two doctors in from Samoa—a Captain Jacobs of the Marine Corps and a Lieut. Commander Durkin of the Navy. They gave us a careful going over and decided that all of us, except Bartek, should fly back with them to Samoa. Bartek was still too sick to be moved. As for Reynolds, the last word was that it would be best for him to remain on the tender. Adamson had failed to bounce back as rapidly as the rest and the doctors deliberated some time over the wisdom of moving him. They finally decided to chance it, since the base hospital at Samoa was much better equipped to take care of him. It was a good thing they did. Had they left Hans there, I am sure he would have died before another week was out.

In three flying boats we took off early Monday morning. I was mighty glad to be on my way, but I was also sorry to leave my friends on the island. My affection went beyond the fact they had done so many wonderful things for us. I liked their spirit, the conscientious way they went about their patrols, and I liked the way they put up that hospital. College men for the most part, pharmacist's mates by Navy grade, few of them knew anything about carpentry. But they put up that hospital in three days. They were up before dawn and they worked until dark. There's no 40-hour week on that island.

CHAPTER XI

AN ACCOUNT OF SURVIVORS FOLLOWING THE SINKING OF THE USS INDIANAPOLIS*

. . . . Following the sinking of the U.S.S. *Indianapolis* shortly after midnight on 30 July 1945, I found myself with a large group of men, between 300 and 400, grouped together and swimming in the heavy fuel oil. At no time during the abandoning of the ship and in the momentary confusion following it, did I witness any acts of panic or hysteria. The men were calm and quiet and I look back with pride at their behavior. Lieutenant Jack Orr, USNR, who had abandoned ship once before shouted for all hands to lock arms and form in a group and not to swim. Discipline was immediately established and a large group was formed. There were a large number of casualties in the group, I would estimate about 50. The majority had severe flash burns of the face, trunk and arms. There were several compounded fractures and in some who died I could discern no injuries. The wounded men were all being supported by shipmates and we tried to get them together. Those with life jackets supported those without and the morale was excellent. The men cussed their plight and the fact that we were unescorted but were good natured and cooperative. The majority of the fracture and burn cases died during the first few hours in the water from shock and there was little I could do for them. No supplies of any kind were available. When a man died, we would remove his life jacket and give it to those without jackets. All hands appeared to be nauseated from the heavy fuel oil.

At daybreak on 30 July it was obvious that we had become divided into three groups. One large group of about 200 men, a group of about 100 and a smaller group of about 50 men. The groups were several hundred yards apart. I was with the large

* By Comdr. Lewis L. Haynes USN. Abridged from (338).

group which had as its leader, Capt. Ed Parke, USMC who was outstanding in his energy, leadership, and selfsacrifice. On several occasions, he gave his life jacket to others whose rubber rings had become deflated and swam without a jacket until one became available. Early in the morning, a patrol plane flew over at about 1500 feet altitude and we all splashed our feet trying to attract his attention. Ens. Park, an aviator, had some green marker dye in his jacket which he spread in the water, but we were not detected. Several other planes flew over during the day, but at a high altitude. The men were discouraged but would rally quickly and made good natured cracks about blind aviators. In the morning, I visited all three groups and cautioned the men about drinking salt water and tried to find some first aid supplies. The groups would merge and break apart during the day and were constantly changing. Capt. Parke then found a cork life ring with about 100 feet of attached line. To prevent drifting he strung the line out and each man grabbed a piece of it and took up the slack. In this way, we formed a long line of men which curled on itself as a safety line. The wounded were tied to the life ring with their jacket string. There was no confusion during the day and the men stayed well grouped together. From about 1000 on we all suffered from intense photophobia and headache probably as a result of the glare of the sun. The ocular pain was severe and was not relieved until the sun went down that night. We had the men tear up clothing which they used to cover their eyes and their discomfort was eased. The seas that day were choppy with large swells. The wounded did quite well and only a few died. Several had to be constantly supported and whenever I called for volunteers as reliefs, men always came forward. Comdr. Lipski had to be supported constantly as did several others who died toward evening. Two men were outstanding in cooperation, and cheerfulness. They were Maday Anthony, F, [sic] Amm 1/c 300-37-21 who supported Comdr. Lipski almost constantly for two days and three nights in spite of his own exhaustion and Rich, Sk3/c who did the same with others and was constantly cheerful and helpful until he died of exhaustion. Rich helped me support Father Conway for several hours while the Father was delirious, in spite of being completely exhausted himself. Until Rich died on the third night, the men constantly called to him for help and he always responded.

Monday night 30 July was very choppy and the group had difficulty in staying together. Capt. Parke would take the free end of the line and swim around the group and then we would take up the slack. This prevented drifting. At sundown, we sighted what appeared to be a ship's running lights, but these were probably flares from the life raft group. Because of the choppy seas, sleep was impossible, and at dawn the condition of the men was, in general, not good and the group seemed smaller.

Tuesday 31 July the seas became more calm and the sun was very hot. The men were very exhausted and complained a lot of thirst. Delirium became evident and many began to talk incoherently and to drink salt water. As they became acutely dehydrated, they would become maniacal and thrash around in the water exhibiting considerable energy in comparison to the rest of us who were very tired. These frenzied spells would continue until the man would accidently drown or would become comatose. Several men drowned trying to hold or support these maniacal cases, particularly if they were wearing a rubber life ring and it became deflated during the struggle. In the evening, all the stragglers were rounded up and the group kept the sicker ones in the center. Our Kapoks had by then lost so much buoyancy that the feeling of security was gone. Shortly after sundown, we all experienced severe chills which lasted for at least an hour and were followed by high fever as most of the group became delirious and got out of control. The men fought with one another thinking there were Japs in the group and disorganization and disintegration of the group rapidly occurred. Capt. Parke worked until he collapsed and I was so exhausted that I drifted away from the group. I was alone most of the night and slightly delirious but was able to join another group during the night by the noise of the delirious members and once near I called for help and Chief Phm. John Schmuek 2238755 swam out and helped me in and supported me for several hours so that I could rest. Ensign Moynelo was in charge of this group and had kept it well organized. Someone in the group had suggested using the leg straps on the Kapok jackets to snap the men together. This was a very satisfactory arrangement and prevented drifting. The men in this group did not show the exhaustion the first group had exhibited.

Wednesday 1 August the sea was mirror calm and the condition of the men was rapidly becoming critical. It was difficult to think clearly and most of the men talked incoherently and had frank hallucinations. The Kapok jacket would just keep one's head out of the water and the sun was very intense. Early in the day, the group imagined that an island was near and a number of men broke off all day trying to reach the imaginary islands. They also imagined the ship was just beneath the surface and dove to drink from the scuttlebutts removing jackets to do so. Many were drowned in this manner and the group was much smaller by sundown. Chief Schmuek, Dr. Modisher and others rounded up the stragglers and we locked the men together with leg straps. That night was particularly difficult and most of us suffered from chills, fever and delirium and when morning arrived, we were scattered. The men formed around Chief Gunner Harrison and through his efforts, we managed to keep together. His morale was high and his cheerful exhortations kept everyone united.

The morning of 2 August 1945 the condition of most of the men was critical. Many were comatose and could be aroused only with difficulty and the group separated with the men just drifting and dying one by one.

Early in the morning a group of about 25 headed by a Quartermaster decided to swim to Leyte. They figured there was a two-knot current and by swimming one knot they would make Leyte in a day and a half. Chief Gunner Harrison and myself along with Chief Pharmacist's Mate Schmuek tried to argue them out of it to no avail and about 20 of them swam away till out of sight. About 11:30 another plane came over, but this one after passing by reversed his course and came back low over the water; we knew then we had been sighted.

. . . .

. . . . Two factors, other than lack of water, contributed greatly to the high mortality. Namely the heat from the tropical sun and the ingestion of salt water. For the most part, the ingestion of the salt water in our group was not deliberate but occurred during delirium or from the accidental swallowing of water in the choppy seas. The constant breaking of waves over one's head the first two days, particularly if you tried to rest, caused most of us to develop a mechanical sinusitis and the swallowing of small amounts of sea water and fuel oil could not be avoided. The sun caused intense headache and photophobia and these factors combined, resulted in many deaths.

GLOSSARY

Absolute Dehydration. Actual water deficit as measured by a difference from the normal or from a given water content. See **Hydropenia.**

Absolute Hydration. Actual water excess as measured by difference from the normal or from a given water content.

Adipsa. Remedies to allay thirst; foods which do not produce thirst.

Adipsia, Adipsy. Absence of thirst. See **Hydro-adipsia.**

Adipsous. Quenching thirst, as certain fruits.

Anadipsia. Intense thirst. See **Hyperdipsia.**

Antidipsia. Antipathy to water or other potable liquids.

Antidipticum. A remedy that lessens thirst. See **Adipsa.**

Antiposia. Antipathy to drinking.

Aposia. Absence of or abnormal avoidance of drinking.

Apote. An individual that does not drink. See **Oligopote.**

Aptyalia, Aptyalism. Deficiency or absence of saliva; asialia.

Asialia. Aptyalia.

Balance. Equality of intake and output per unit time, usually 24 hours; gain minus loss.

Dehydration. Water deficit; negative water load; removal of water. See **Absolute D., Relative D.,** and **Voluntary D.**

Dipsesis. Morbid thirst.

Dipsetic. Producing thirst; a dipsogen.

Dipsia. Thirst.

Dipsic. Thirsty.

Dipsogen. A thirst provoking agent or agency.

Dipsogenic. Engendering thirst.

Dipsology. The study of thirst.

Dipsomania. Uncontrollable desire for spirituous liquor.

Dipsopathy. A condition characterized by dipsomania; pathologic thirst.

Dipsosis. Morbid thirst.

Dipsotherapy. Thirst cure; treatment by strict limitation of the amount of water to be drunk.

Draft. Drink.

Draft Frequency. The number of separate drinks taken per unit time.

Drink. A quantity of liquid taken in one or a series of successive swallows; to take a drink. See **Sham D.**

Ecuresis. A condition in which urinary excretion and intake of water act to produce an absolute dehydration of the body. See **Emuresis.**

Effective Osmotic Pressure. That part of the total osmotic pressure of a solution which governs the tendency of its solvent to pass across a boundary, usually a semipermeable bounding membrane. It is commonly represented by the product of the total osmotic pressure of the solution and the ratio (corrected for activities) of the number of dissolved particles which do not permeate the bounding membrane to the total number of particles in the solution; equivalent in meaning to tonicity; commonly expressed in equivalent units of osmolality rather than pressure per se.

Emuresis. A condition in which urinary excretion and intake of water act to produce an absolute hydration of the body. See **Ecuresis.**

Eudipsia. Ordinary mild thirst.

Euhydration. Normal state of body water content. Absence of absolute or relative hydration or dehydration.

Euvolia. Normal water content or volume of a given compartment, e.g., extracellular euvolia.

Facultative Urine Volume. Urine volume in excess of the obligatory urine volume and, in water balance, equal to the **Facultative Water (Intake).**

Facultative Water (Intake). Water intake in excess of need and, in water balance, equal to the **Facultative Urine Volume.**

False Thirst. Thirst which is not satisfied by drinking or taking water; thirst associated with a dry mouth but not with a bodily need for water; pseudodipsia.

Free Water. Water of an aquiferous intake not obligated to urinary excretion of solute.

Fugacity. The tendency of a fluid, as a resultant of all forces acting on it, to leave a given site in the body; escaping tendency of a fluid.

Hemodipsia. Blood thirst. Desire to drink blood to assuage thirst.

Hemoposia. Blood drinking.

Homaluria. Normal urine flow.

Hydro-adipsia. Absence of thirst for water.

Hydrodipsia. Water thirst, characterizing animals that ordinarily drink water.

Hydropenia. Water deficit; absolute dehydration, generally associated with relative dehydration.

Hydroposia. Water drinking, characterizing animals that ordinarily drink water.

Hyperdipsia. Intense thirst; thirst which is relatively temporary. See **Polydipsia.**

Hyperposia. Intense or forced drinking; drinking which is relatively temporary. See **Polyposia.**

Hypersalemia. Increased salt concentration in blood and body fluids; hypertonia.

Hypertonia, Hypertonicity. An increased effective osmotic pressure of body fluids.

Hypervolia. Augmented water content or volume of a given compartment, e.g., cellular hypervolia.

Hypodipsia. Insensible, twilight, or subliminal thirst; a physiologic condition, perhaps of hypertonicity of body fluids, insufficient to initiate drinking but at times sufficient to sustain drinking once started; loosely oligodipsia.

Hypoposia. Hypodipsia, with emphasis on latent tendency to drink rather than on the latent sensation of thirst.

Hyposalemia. Decreased salt concentration in blood and body fluids; hypotonia.

Hypotonia, Hypotonicity. A decreased effective osmotic pressure of body fluids.

Hypovolia. Diminished water content or volume of a given compartment, e.g., extracellular hypovolia.

Insensible Thirst. See **Hypodipsia.**

Isorrhea. Steady state equality of intake and output of water and/or solute; the isorrheic state.

Isorrheic Water. Any total water intake consistent with isorrhea of water and solutes.

Isosmotic. A term denoting equality of osmotic pressures of solutions; loosely, isotonic.

Isotonic. A term denoting equality of effective osmotic pressures of solutions; loosely, isosmotic.

Limiting Isorrheic Concentration (LIC). The upper limit of urinary concentration at which a steady state consistent with effective physiologic regulation of solute and water balances can be maintained.

Load. A departure from normal body content, as of water, salt, or heat. Positive loads are quantities in excess of the normal; negative loads are quantities in deficit.

Mariposia. Sea water drinking. Thalassoposia.

Maximum Urinary Concentration (MUC). The highest attainable concentration of a solute or of the collective solutes of the urine.

Minimal Isorrheic Concentration. The lower limit of urinary concentration at which a steady state consistent with effective physiologic regulation of solute and water balances can be maintained.

Nimiety. That degree of repletion or excess of water which, beyond satiety, elicits antidipsia.

Obligatory Urine Volume. The minimal volume of urine consistent with the excretion of its solute.

Oligodipsia. Abnormal diminution of thirst.

Oligoposia, Oligoposy, Oligopotism. Abnormal diminution of drinking; disordered state resulting from too little drinking.

Oligopote. An individual that drinks little.

Osmolality. Osmotic concentration, defined as the number of osmols ($= \phi n$ mols, where ϕ is the osmotic coefficient, and n is the number of particles or ions formed upon dissociation of a solute in solution; e.g., $n = 2$ for sodium chloride and $n = 1$ for glucose) of a solute per kilogram of solvent (water). Thus osmolality is given by ϕnc, where c is the molal concentration of solute. The osmolality of a given solution is numerically equal to the molality of an ideal solution of a nonelectrolyte having the same freezing point. It is approximated by the quotient of the freezing point depression of an aqueous solution below that of water (Δ °C.) and the molal freezing point depression for water (ca. 1.86° C. per mol of undissociated solute per kilogram of water), i.e., osmolality $= \Delta/1.86$.

Osmolarity. Loose term for osmolality (which see).

Osmometric. Pertaining to osmometers.

Osmosity. That measure of the osmotic pressure of a solution given numerically by the molarity (or, loosely, by the millimolarity) of a sodium chloride solution having the same osmotic pressure; approximated by the quotient $\Delta/3.46$. See **Osmolality.**

Osmotic Coefficient. A factor, ϕ, which corrects for the deviation in the behavior of a solute in question from ideal behavior defined by the ideal gas equation as applied to osmotic pressure.

Paradipsia. Perverted appetite for fluids ingested without relation to bodily need.

Pollakidipsia. Unduly frequent thirst.

Polydipsia. Sustained, excessive thirst. See **Hyperdipsia, Primary Polydipsia.**

Polyposia. Sustained, excessive drinking. See **Hyperposia.**

Potable. Drinkable; applied to water fit to drink (i.e., respecting taste, pathogenicity, etc.) or to solutions containing sufficient free water to sustain life.

Potification. The process of making water potable. Applied to sea water, it is the process of removing sufficient salts to render the remaining fluid safe for drinking. Potifying.

Potogenic. Engendering drinking.

Potomania. An abnormal desire to drink; delirium tremens.

Primary Polydipsia. Polydipsia preceding polyuria in onset.

Pseudodipsia. See **False Thirst.**

Relative Dehydration. Water deficit relative to content of solutes contributing effective osmotic pressure; state of increased effective osmotic pressure of body fluids; hypertonia; hypersalemia.

Satiety. Lack of desire to drink following full gratification of thirst; physiologic adipsia or aposia; satisfaction of thirst. See **Nimiety.**

Sham Drink. Drink, as by esophagostomized dog, in which swallowed water fails to be ingested or retained in the stomach.

Thalassoposia. See **Mariposia.**

Thirst. A sensation, often referred to the mouth and throat, associated with a craving for drink; dipsia; urge to drink; appetite for water; water deficit. See **False T., True T.**

Tonicity. See **Effective Osmotic Pressure.**

True Thirst. Thirst which can be satisfied by drinking water; "real thirst."

Twilight Thirst. See **Hypodipsia.**

Uriposia. Urine drinking.

Voluntary Dehydration. That physiologic lag or deficit in water intake which results when sensations of thirst are not strong enough to bring about complete replacement of water loss, as in rapid sweating.

Xerostomia. Dryness of the mouth from lack of the normal secretion.

BIBLIOGRAPHY

1. Abrahams, A.: Thirst. *Practitioner, 146*:400–403, 1941.
2. Abrams, M., DeFriez, A. I. C., Tosteson, D. C., and Landis, E. M.: Self-selection of salt solutions and water by normal and hypertensive rats. *Am. J. Physiol., 156*:233–247, 1949.
3. Achard, C., and Ramond, L.: Potomanie chez un enfant. *Bull. et mém. Soc. méd. d. hôp. de Paris, 12*:380–390, 1905.
4. Adolph, E. F.: The regulation of the water content of the human organism. *J. Physiol., 55*:114–132, 1921.
5. Adolph, E. F.: *The Regulation of Size as Illustrated in Unicellular Organisms.* Springfield, Thomas, 1931.
6. Adolph, E. F.: The metabolism and distribution of water in body and tissues. *Physiol. Rev., 13*:336–371, 1933.
7. Adolph, E. F.: Measurements of water drinking in dogs. *Am. J. Physiol., 123*:3, 1938.
8. Adolph, E. F.: Measurements of water drinking in dogs. *Am. J. Physiol., 125*:75–86, 1939.
9. Adolph, E. F: *Physiological Regulations.* Lancaster, Jaques Cattell Press, 1943.
10. Adolph, E. F.: Do rats thrive when drinking sea water? *Am. J. Physiol., 140*:25–32, 1943.
11. Adolph, E. F.: Urges to eat and drink in rats. *Am. J. Physiol., 151*:110–125, 1947.
12. Adolph, E. F.: Tolerance to heat and dehydration in several species of mammals. *Am. J. Physiol., 151*:564–575, 1947.
13. Adolph, E. F.: Water metabolism. *Ann. Rev. Physiol., 9*:381–408, 1947.
14. Adolph, E. F.: Water ingestion and excretion in rats under some chemical influences. *Am. J. Physiol., 155*:309–316, 1948.
15. Adolph, E. F.: Quantitative relations in the physiological constitutions of mammals. *Science, 109*:579–585, 1949.
16. Adolph, E. F.: Thirst and its inhibition in the stomach. *Am. J. Physiol., 161*:374–386, 1950.
16a. Adolph, E. F.: Principles of water and salt balance. *Activities Report, Research and Development Assoc., Food and Container Institute for U. S. Armed Forces,* n.s. 3:143–146, 1951 (October).
17. Adolph, E. F.: Personal communication, 1956.
17a. Adolph, E. F.: Ontogeny of physiological regulations in the rat. *Quart. Rev. Biol., 32*: 89–137, 1957.
18. Adolph, E. F., and Associates: *Physiology of Man in the Desert.* New York, Interscience, 1947.
19. Adolph, E. F., Barker, J. P., and Hoy, P. A.: Multiple factors in thirst. *Am. J. Physiol., 178*:538–562, 1954.
20. Adolph, E. F., and Dill, D. B.: Observations on water metabolism in the desert. *Am. J. Physiol., 123*:369–378, 1938.

21. Adolph, E. F., and Molnar, G. W: Exchanges of heat and tolerances to cold in men exposed to outdoor weather. *Am. J. Physiol., 146*:507–537, 1946.

22. Adolph, E. F., and Northrop, J. P.: Physiological adaptations to body-water excesses in rats. *Am. J. Physiol., 168*:320–334, 1952.

23. Adolph, E. F., and Parmington, S. L.: Partial nephrectomy and the water exchanges of rats. *Am. J. Physiol., 155*:317–326, 1948.

24. Adolph, E. F., Wolf, A. V., and Kelly, J. J.: Unpublished observations, 1942.

25. Ahlman, K. L., Eränkö, O., Karvonen, M. J., and Leppänen, V.: Effects of hard competitive muscular work on electrolyte content of thermal sweat. *J. Appl. Physiol., 4*:911–915, 1952.

26. Ahlman, K. L., Eränkö, O., Karvonen, M. J., and Leppänen, V.: Effects of prehydration and repeated or prolonged thermal stress on the electrolyte content of thermal sweat. *Acta Endocrinol., 12*:140–146, 1953.

27. Albrecht, C. B.: Toxicity of sea water in mammals. *Am. J. Physiol., 163*: 370–385, 1950.

28. Aldrich, C. A., and McClure, W. B.: The intradermal salt solution test. II. Its prognostic value in "nephritis" with generalized edema. *J.A.M.A., 82*:1425–1428, 1924.

29. Allard, H. A.: How some birds satisfy thirst. *Science, 80*:116–117, 1934.

30. Allee, W. C., and Frank, P.: Ingestion of colloidal material and water by goldfish. *Physiol. Zoöl., 21*:381–390, 1948.

31. Allen, W. H.: Thirst. *Natural History, 65*:513–518, 555, 1956.

32. Allison, I. S.: The problem of saline drinking waters. *Science, 71*:559–560, 1930.

33. Allison, R. S., and Critchley, M.: Observations on thirst. *J. Roy. Nav. M. Serv., 29*:258–266, 1943.

34. Allott, E. N.: Sodium and chlorine retention without renal disease. *Lancet, 1*:1035–1037, 1939.

35. Ambard, L., and Papin, E.: Étude sur les concentrations urinaires. *Arch. internat. physiol., 8*:437–488, 1909.

36. Anand, B. K., and Brobeck, J. R.: Hypothalamic control of food intake in rats and cats. *Yale J. Biol. & Med., 24*:123–140, 1951.

37. Anand, B. K., Dua, S., and Shoenberg, K.: Hypothalamic control of food intake in cats and monkeys. *J. Physiol., 127*:143–152, 1955.

38. Andersson, B.: The effect and localisation of electrical stimulation of certain parts of the brain stem in sheep and goats. *Acta physiol. Scandinav., 23*:1–16, 1951.

39. Andersson, B.: Polydipsia caused by intrahypothalamic injections of hypertonic NaCl-solutions. *Experientia, 8*:157–158, 1952.

40. Andersson, B.: Polydipsi som följd av injektioner av hypertonisk NaCl-lösning i hypotalamus. *Nord. med., 47*:663–665, 1952.

41. Andersson, B.: The effect of injections of hypertonic NaCl-solutions into different parts of the hypothalamus of goats. *Acta physiol. Scandinav., 28*:188–201, 1953.

42. Andersson, B.: Om vattenomsättningen och törstens fysiologi. Meddelande Nr. 7, *Institutet för Maltdrycksforskning*, Stockholm, 1955.

43. Andersson, B.: Polydipsia, antidiuresis and milk ejection caused by hypothalamic stimulation, in *The Neurohypophysis*, Ed., H. Heller. Proc. 8th

Symposium of the Colston Research Society, 1956. New York, Acad. Press, 1957, pp. 131–140.

44. Andersson, B., and Larsson, S.: Water and food intake and the inhibitory effect of amphetamine on drinking and eating before and after "prefrontal lobotomy" in dogs. *Acta physiol. Scandinav., 38:*22–30, 1956.

45. Andersson, B., and McCann, S. M.: Hypothalamic control of water intake. *J. Physiol., 129:*44P, 1955.

46. Andersson, B., and McCann, S. M.: A further study of polydipsia evoked by hypothalamic stimulation in the goat. *Acta physiol. Scandinav., 33:*333–346, 1955.

47. Andersson, B., and McCann, S. M.: Drinking, antidiuresis and milk ejection from electrical stimulation within the hypothalamus of the goat. *Acta physiol. Scandinav., 35:*191–201, 1955.

48. Andersson, B., and McCann, S. M.: The effect of hypothalamic lesions on the water intake of the dog. *Acta physiol. Scandinav., 35:*312–320, 1956.

49. Andersson, B., and Zotterman, Y.: The water taste in the frog. *Acta physiol. Scandinav., 20:*95–100, 1950.

50. Andrews, R. C.: Living animals of the Gobi desert. *Natural History, 24:* 150–159, 1924.

51. Anthonisen, P., Hilden, T., and Thomsen, A. C.: Electrolyte disturbances in cerebral lesions. *Acta med. Scandinav., 150:*355–367, 1954.

52. Archdeacon, J. W., and Allen, R. S.: Some factors involved in food and water ingestion in the dog. *Am. J. Physiol., 153:*27–30, 1948.

53. Archdeacon, J. W., Presnell, M. W., and Walton, C. J.: Effects of atropine on food ingestion and water drinking in dogs. *Am. J. Physiol., 157:*149–152, 1949.

54. Arden, F.: Experimental observations upon thirst and on potassium over-dosage. *Australian J. Exper. Biol. & M. Sc., 12:*121–122, 1934.

55. Aretæus, The Cappadocian: *The Extant Works of Aretæus, The Cappadocian.* Edited and translated by Francis Adams. London, Sydenham Society, 1856.

56. Armsby, H. P., and Moulton, C. R.: *The Animal as a Converter of Matter and Energy.* Am. Chem. Soc. Monograph. New York, Chemical Catalog Co., 1925.

57. Asher, D. W., and Hodes, H. L.: Studies in experimental dehydration. *Am. J. M. Technol., 5:*216–234, 1939.

58. Atkinson, T. P.: A remarkable case of intemperate drinking. *Month. Stethoscope & M. Reporter, 1:*157–158, 1856.

59. Atwood, W. H.: *Comparative Anatomy.* St. Louis, Mosby, 1955, p. 285.

60. Aury, G.: L'eau de mer, boisson des naufragés. Résultats d'expériences récentes dans l'Aéronautique Navale Française. Report of Section Scientifique de l'Etat-Major-Général de la Marine, June 1, 1954. See also translation in *Gt. Britain Royal Naval Personnel Research Committee,* Report SS 61, June 1954; and Rapport de mission à Brest a/s de l'expérience de survie en mer. Report of Section Scientifique de l'Etat-Major Général, Division Navires-Armes, Flotte en Service, Paris, May 1955. Various French newspapers carried accounts describing further similar experiments in the Brest roadstead, March 22–28, 1955.

60a. Aury, G.: L'eau de mer, boisson des naufragés. Résultats d'expériences récentes dans l'Aéronautique Navale Française. *Rev. méd. nav., Par.,* 9:7–44, 1954.

60b. Aury, G.: *Opération Survie.* Paris, France-Empire, 1955.

61. Austin, V. T., and Steggerda, F. R.: Congenital dysfunction of the salivary glands with observations on the physiology of thirst. *Illinois M. J.,* 69:124–127, 1936.

62. Babbitt, J. D.: Osmotic pressure. *Science,* 122:285–287, 1955.

63. Babcock, S. M.: Metabolic water: its production and role in vital phenomena. *Univ. Wisconsin Agricultural Exper. Station. Research Bull.* No. 22, 1912.

64. Babineau, L. M., and Pagé, E.: On body fat and body water in rats. *Canad. J. Biochem. & Physiol.,* 33:970–979, 1955.

65. Babkin, B. P.: *Secretory Mechanism of the Digestive Glands.* New York, Hoeber, 1950.

66. Bailey, V.: Sources of water supply for desert animals. *Scient. Monthly,* 17:66–86, 1923.

67. Baldes, E. J., and Smirk, F. H.: The effect of water drinking, mineral starvation and salt administration on the total osmotic pressure of the blood in man, chiefly in relation to the problems of water absorption and water diuresis. *J. Physiol.,* 82:62–74, 1934.

68. Baldwin, H. W.: *Sea Fights and Shipwrecks.* True Tales of the Seven Seas. New York, Hanover House, 1955.

69. Barber, T. X.: Experiments in hypnosis. *Scient. Am., 196:*54–61, 1957, (April).

70. Barbero, G. J., Katz, S., Kraus, H., and Leedham, C. L.: Clinical and laboratory study of thirty-one patients with hemorrhagic fever. *Arch. Int. Med.,* 91:177–196, 1953.

71. Bardier, E.: Faim. *Charles Richet's Dict. d. Physiologie,* 6:1–29, 1904.

72. Bare, J. K.: The specific hunger for sodium chloride in normal and adrenalectomized white rats. *J. Comp. & Physiol. Psychol.,* 42:242–253, 1949.

73. Barker, J. P., and Adolph, E. F.: Survival of rats without water and given seawater. *Am. J. Physiol.,* 173:495–502, 1953.

74. Barker, J. P., Adolph, E. F., and Keller, A. D.: Thirst tests in dogs and modifications of thirst with experimental lesions of the neurohypophysis. *Am. J. Physiol.,* 173:233–245, 1953.

75. Barnes, H.: Some tables for the ionic composition of sea water. *J. Exper. Biol.,* 31:582–588, 1954.

76. Barnes, H.: The analysis of sea water. A review. *Analyst: J. Soc. Anal. Chem.,* 80:573–592, 1955.

77. Bartter, F. C.: The role of aldosterone in normal homeostasis and in certain disease states. *Metabolism,* 5:369–383, 1956.

78. Bartter, F. C., Liddle, G. W., Duncan, L. E., Jr., Barber, J. K., and Delea, C.: The regulation of aldosterone secretion in man: the role of fluid volume. *J. Clin. Investigation,* 35:1306–1315, 1956.

79. Bayliss, W. M.: *Principles of General Physiology.* London, Longmans, 1931.

80. Bean, W. B.: Discussion. *Tr. Am. Clin. & Climatol. A.* (1952), 64:102–103, 1953.

81. Beaumont, W.: *Experiments and Observations on the Gastric Juice and the Physiology of Digestion.* Plattsburgh, Allen, 1833. Facsimile of the original edition, Cambridge, Harvard, 1929.

82. Bellows, R. T.:   Relationship of polydipsia and polyuria in diabetes insipidus. *Am. J. Physiol., 123*:14p, 1938.

83. Bellows, R. T.:   Time factors in water drinking in dogs.   *Am. J. Physiol., 125*:87–97, 1939.

84. Bellows, R. T., and Van Wagenen, W. P.:   Experimental diabetes insipidus. *Science, 86*:447, 1937.

85. Bellows, R. T., and Van Wagenen, W. P.:   The relationship of polydipsia and polyuria in diabetes insipidus.   A study of experimental diabetes insipidus in dogs with and without esophageal fistulae.   *J. Nerv. & Ment. Dis., 88*:417–473, 1938.

86. Bellows, R. T., and Van Wagenen, W. P.:   The effect of resection of the olfactory, gustatory and trigeminal nerves on water drinking in dogs without and with diabetes insipidus.   *Am. J. Physiol., 126*:13–19, 1939.

87. Benedict, F. G.:   *A Study of Prolonged Fasting.*   Washington, Carnegie Inst., 1915.

88. Bentley, P. J.:   Some aspects of the water metabolism of an Australian marsupial *Setonyx brachyurus.   J. Physiol., 127*:1–10, 1955.

89. Bernard, C.:   *Leçons de Physiologie expérimentale appliquée a la Médecine.* Cours du semestre d'été, 1855, Vol. 2, Paris, Baillière, 1856, pp. 49–52.

90. Bernard, C.:   *Leçons sur les Phénomènes de la Vie en Communs aux Animaux et aux Végétaux.*   Vol. 1.   Paris, Baillère, 1878.

91. Bernard, C.:   *An Introduction to the Study of Experimental Medicine.* Translated by Henry Copley Greene.   New York, Schuman, 1949.

92. Bernard, E.:   Recherches cliniques et physiopathalogiques sur la saignée. Les rapports du plasma et des liquides interstitiels.   Paris, Thèse No. 61, 1925, 208 pp.

93. Berryhill, F. M.:   Acceptability and thirst during water deprivation.   *Defence Research Medical Laboratories (Toronto)*, DRML Project No. 104-35-9, Report No. 104-1, January, 1955.

94. v. Bezold, A.:   Untersuchungen über die Vertheilung von Wasser, organischer Materie und anorganischen Verbindungen im Thierreiche.   *Ztschr. f. wiss. Zoöl., 8*:487–524, 1857.

95. Bickel, A.:   Wüstenklima-Durst-Kochsalzstoffwechsel.   *Arch. f. path. Anat., 227*:108–113, 1920.

96. Bidder, F., and Schmidt, C.:   *Die Verdauungssaefte und der Stoffwechsel.* Mittau u. Leipzig, Reyher, 1852, pp. 3–4.

97. Binet, L.:   La soif.   *Presse méd., 34*:676–678, 1926.

98. Binet, L.:   La soif.   *Traité de physiol. normale et pathol.*, eds. G. H. Roger and L. Binet.   *2*:89–98, 1931, Paris.

99. Bing, F. C., and Mendel, L. B.:   The relationship between food and water intakes in mice.   *Am. J. Physiol., 98*:169–179, 1931.

100. Birchard, W. H., Rosenbaum, J. D., and Strauss, M. B.:   Renal excretion of salt and water consequent to hypertonic saline infusion followed by water ingestion.   *J. Appl. Physiol., 6*:22–26, 1953.

101. Birchard, W. H., and Strauss, M. B.:   Factors influencing the diuretic response of seated subjects to the ingestion of isotonic saline solution.   *J. Clin. Investigation, 32*:807–812, 1953.

102. Bischoff, E.:   Einige Gewichts- und Trockenbestimmungen der Organe des menschlichen Körpers.   *Ztschr. f. rat. Med., 20*:75–118, 1863.

103. Biske, V.: Thirst at sea. *Brit. M. J.*, 2:211, 1941.
104. Black, D. A. K.: Renal factors in volume control. *The Kidney*, Ciba Foundation Symposium. Boston, Little, 1954, pp. 309–316.
105. Black, D. A. K., McCance, R. A., and Young, W. F.: A study of dehydration by means of balance experiments. *J. Physiol.*, 102:406–414, 1944.
106. Black, D. A. K., and Milne, M. D.: Experimental potassium depletion in man. *Clin. Sc.*, 11:397–415, 1952.
107. Black, D. A. K., and Thomson, A. E.: Day-to-day changes in sodium and water output with and without posterior pituitary extract. *Clin. Sc.*, 10:511–520, 1951.
108. Blair, H. A.: The time-intensity curve and latent addition in the mechanical stimulation of nerve. *Am. J. Physiol.*, 114:586–593, 1936.
109. Block, R. J., and Bolling, D.: *The Amino Acid Composition of Proteins and Foods. Analytical Methods and Results.* Springfield, Thomas, 1951.
110. Blomhert, G., Gerbrandy, J., Borst, J. G. G., Molhuysen, J. A., and deVries, L. A.: Diuretic effect of isotonic saline solution compared with that of water. Influence of diurnal rhythm. *Lancet*, 2:1011–1015, 1951.
111. Blumenbach, J. F.: *The Institutions of Physiology.* Translated from Latin by John Elliotson. London, Burgess and Hill, 1820.
112. Bombard, A.: *The Bombard Story.* London, Andre Deutsch, 1953. Also *The Voyage of the Heretique.* New York, Simon and Schuster, Inc., 1953, 1954.
113. Bombard, A.: La survie prolongée en mer. Rapport technique de l'expérience de survie prolongée en mer à bord de l'*Hérétique*, en 1952. Paris, Éditions de Paris, 1954.
114. Bonnier, P.: La soif et les centres hygrostatiques. *Compt. rend. Soc. de biol.*, 76:240–242, 1914.
115. Boring, E. G.: Processes referred to the alimentary and urinary tracts: a qualitative analysis. *Psychol. Rev.*, 22:306–331, 1915.
116. Boring, E. G.: *Sensation and Perception in the History of Experimental Psychology.* New York, Appleton, 1942.
117. Borst, J. G. G.: The cause of hyperchloremia and hyperazotemia in patients with recurrent massive hemorrhage from peptic ulcer. *Acta med. Scandinav.*, 97:68–88, 1938.
118. Borst, J. G. G.: The maintenance of an adequate cardiac output by the regulation of the urinary excretion of water and sodium chloride; an essential factor in the genesis of oedema. *Acta med. Scandinav.*, 130 (Suppl. 207), 1948.
119. Borst, J. G. G.: The characteristic renal excretion patterns associated with excessive or inadequate circulation. *The Kidney*, Ciba Foundation Symposium. Boston, Little, 1954, pp. 255–284.
120. Borst, J. G. G., and deVries, L. A.: The three types of "natural" diuresis. *Lancet*, 2:1–6, 1950.
121. Bottazzi, F.: Osmotischer Druck und elektrische Leitfähigkeit der Flüssigkeiten der einzelligen, pflanzlichen und tierischen Organismen. *Ergebn. Physiol.*, 7:161–402, 1908.
122. Bouffard, M.–A.: Quelques considérations sur la soif. Paris, Thèse No. 437, 1805.
123. Bowman, W.: On the structure and use of the Malpighian bodies of the

kidney, with observations on the circulation through that gland. *Phil. Tr. Roy. Soc., London, 132*:57–80, 1842.

123a. Boyarsky, S., and Smith, H. W.: Renal concentrating operation at low urine flows. *J. Urol., 78*:511–524, 1957.

124. Bradish, R. F., Everhart, M. W., McCord, W. M., and Witt, W. J.: Some physiologic aspects of the use of sea water to relieve dehydration. *J. A. M. A., 120*:683–685, 1942.

125. Bradley, S. E., Mudge, G. H., and Blake, W. D.: The renal excretion of sodium, potassium, and water by the harbor seal (*Phoca vitulina* L.): effect of apnea; sodium, potassium, and water loading; pitressin; and mercurial diuresis. *J. Cell. & Comp. Physiol., 43*:1–22, 1954.

126. Brady, J. V.: Personal communication, 1955.

126a. Breton, E. J., Jr.: Water and ion flow through imperfect osmotic membranes. *Office of Saline Water Research and Development* Progress Report No. 16, U. S. Dept. of Interior, April 1957.

127. Brobeck, J. R., Larsson, S., and Reyes, E.: A study of the electrical activity of the hypothalamic feeding mechanism. *J. Physiol., 132*:358–364, 1956.

128. Brobeck, J. R., Tepperman, J., and Long, C. N. H.: Experimental hypothalamic hyperphagia in the albino rat. *Yale J. Biol. & Med., 15*:831–853, 1943.

129. Broch, O. J.: The base-binding power of serum proteins and their function as osmoregulators in body fluids. *Scandinav. J. Clin. & Lab. Invest., 5*:9–17, 1953.

130. Brocklehurst, H. C.: *Game Animals of the Sudan.* London, Gurney and Jackson, 1931.

131. Brocq-Rousseu, and Roussel, G.: La soif après la saignée. *Sang, 3*:44–50, 1929.

132. Brodsky, W. A., Rapoport, S., and West, C. D.: The mechanism of glycosuric diuresis in diabetic man. *J. Clin. Investigation, 29*:1021–1032, 1950.

133. Brokaw, A.: Renal hypertrophy and polydipsia in potassium-deficient rats. *Am. J. Physiol., 172*:333–346, 1953.

134. Brooks, S. C., and Brooks, M. M.: *The Permeability of Living Cells.* Berlin, Borntraeger, 1941.

135. Bruce, H. M., and Kennedy, G. C.: The central nervous control of food and water intake. *Proc. Roy. Soc., London, s. B., 138*:528–544, 1951.

136. Bruce, R. H.: An experimental investigation of the thirst drive in rats with especial reference to the goal gradient hypothesis. *J. Gen. Psychol., 17*:49–62, 1937.

137. Brun, C., Knudsen, E. O. E., and Raaschou, F.: The influence of posture on the kidney function. I. The fall of the diuresis in the erect posture. *Acta med. Scandinav., 122*:315–331, 1945.

138. Brun, C., Knudsen, E. O. E., and Raaschou, F.: The influence of posture on the kidney function. II. Glomerular dynamics in the passive erect posture. *Acta med. Scandinav., 122*:332–341, 1945.

139. Brun, C., Knudsen, E. O. E., and Raaschou, F.: On the cause of post-syncopal oliguria. *Acta med. Scandinav., 122*:486–500, 1945.

140. Brun, C., Knudsen, E. O. E., and Raaschou, F.: Kidney function and circulatory collapse. Post-syncopal oliguria. *J. Clin. Investigation, 25*:568–574, 1946.

141. Brunn, F.: The sensation of thirst. *J. A. M. A., 85*:234–235, 1925.

141a. Buettner, K.: Diffusion of water and water vapor through human skin. *J. Applied Physiol.*, *6*:229–242, 1953.

142. Bull, G. M.: The relation of the renal blood flow to the general circulation. *Visceral Circulation*, Ciba Foundation Symposium. Boston, Little, 1953, pp. 242–255.

143. Burgen, A. S. V.: Osmotic work of salivary secretion. *Am. J. Physiol.*, *179*: 623–624, 1954.

143a. Burggraf, E. J.: Personal communication, 1957.

144. Burns, T. W.: Endocrine factors in the water metabolism of the desert mammal, *G. gerbillus*. *Endocrinology*, *58*:243–254, 1956.

145. Burns, T. W.: Some physiological observations on the 'Ababda tribespeople of the eastern desert of Egypt. *J. Appl. Physiol.*, *9*:287–290, 1956.

146. Burton, A. C.: On the physical equilibrium of small blood vessels. *Am. J. Physiol.*, *164*:319–329, 1951.

147. Butler, A. M.: Fish juice, emergency lifeboat ration and castaway's extrarenal water loss. Committee on Medical Research of the OSRD, Monthly Progress Report No. 1 (July 26, 1943) and Summary (December 7, 1943).

148. Byrd, R. E.: *Alone*. New York, Putnam's, 1938.

149. Caldwell, G. T.: Studies in water metabolism of the cat. The influence of dehydration on blood concentration, thermoregulation, respiratory exchange, and metabolic-water production. *Physiol. Zoöl.*, *4*:324–359, 1931.

150. Callenfels, G. T.: *De Fame et Siti*. Gandavi, 1824.

151. Calvery, H. O., Draize, J. H., and Laug, E. P.: The metabolism and permeability of normal skin. *Physiol. Rev.*, *26*:495–540, 1946.

152. Calvin, A. D., and Behan, R. A.: The effect of hunger upon drinking patterns in the rat. *Brit. J. Psychol.*, *45*:294–298, 1954.

153. Cannon, W. B.: A consideration of the nature of hunger. *Harvey Lect.*, *7*:130–152, 1911–12.

154. Cannon, W. B.: The physiological basis of thirst. *Proc. Roy. Soc., London, s. B.*, *90*:283–301, 1918.

155. Cannon, W. B.: Les bases physiologiques de la soif. *Rev. gén. d. sc. pures et appliq.*, *30*:69–79, 1919.

156. Cannon, W. B.: Some modern extensions of Beaumont's studies on Alexis St. Martin. *J. Michigan M. Soc.*, *32*:155–164, 1933.

157. Cannon, W. B.: *Bodily Changes in Pain, Hunger, Fear and Rage*. New York, Appleton, 1929.

158. Cannon, W. B.: Hunger and thirst. Chapter V of *A Handbook of General Experimental Psychology*, edited by Carl Murchison. Worcester, Clark Univ. Press, 1934, pp. 247–263.

159. Cannon, W. B.: *The Way of An Investigator*. A scientist's experiences in medical research. New York, Norton, 1945.

160. Cannon, W. B., and Washburn, A. L.: An explanation of hunger. *Am. J. Physiol.*, *29*:441–454, 1912.

161. Carlson, A. J.: *The Control of Hunger in Health and Disease*. Chicago, Univ. of Chicago Press, 1916.

162. Carlson, A. J.: Hunger and thirst. *Hygeia*, *7*:684–687, 1929.

163. Casby, J. U.: Personal communication, 1954.

164. Chadwick, J., and Mann, W. N.: Airs, waters, places, in *The Medical Works of Hippocrates*. Oxford, Blackwell, 1950, pp. 90–111.

165. Chalfant, W. A.: *Death Valley. The Facts.* Stanford University, California, Stanford Univ. Press, 1936.
166. Chapman, T. T.: Exposure and water balance test (Three men cast adrift for one week). *Gt. Britain Royal Naval Personnel Research Committee,* RNP 48/490, SS 22, November 1948.
167. Chapman, T. T.: Drinking sea-water. *Brit. M. J.,* 2:246, 1954.
168. Chase, J. S.: *California Desert Trails.* Boston: Houghton, 1919, pp. 197, 277, 284.
169. Chinard, F. P.: The definition of osmotic pressure. *J. Chem. Ed.,* 31:66–69, 1954.
170. Chinard, F. P., and Enns, T.: Osmotic pressure. *Science, 124*:472–474, 1956.
171. Cizek, L. J.: Total water content of laboratory animals with special reference to volume of fluid within the lumen of the gastrointestinal tract. *Am. J. Physiol., 179*:104–110, 1954.
172. Cizek, L. J., Semple, R. E., Huang, K. C., and Gregersen, M. I.: Effect of extracellular electrolyte depletion on water intake in dogs. *Am. J. Physiol., 164*:415–422, 1951.
173. Clarke, G. L., and Bishop, D. W.: The nutritional value of marine zooplankton with a consideration of its use as an emergency food. *Ecology, 29*:54–71, 1948.
174. Clarke, R. W.: Water distribution and sexual skin of the baboon. *Am. J. Physiol., 131*:325–330, 1940.
175. Coats, D. A., Denton, D. A., Goding, J. R., and Wright, R. D.: Secretion by the parotid gland of the sheep. *J. Physiol., 131*:13–31, 1956.
176. Colin, G.: *Traité de Physiologie Comparée des Animaux,* Vol. 1. Paris, Baillière, 1871, pp. 558–562.
177. Consolazio, W. V., and Pace, N.: Minimal water and salt requirements in fasting men. *Naval Medical Research Institute (Bethesda, Md.),* Project No. X-100 (General 15), Report No. 6, 1943.
177a. Consolazio, W. V., and Pace, N.: An appraisal of some devices for obtaining drinking water from the sea under actual conditions on inflatable life rafts. *Naval Medical Research Institute (Bethesda, Md.),* Project No. X-127, Report No. 2, 1943.
178. Consolazio, W. V., Pace, N., and Ivy, A. C.: Drinking water from sea water. *U. S. Naval Institute Proc., 70*:971–979, 1944.
179. Conway, E. J., Geoghegan, H., and McCormack, J. I.: Autolytic changes at zero centigrade in ground mammalian tissues. *J. Physiol., 130*:427–437, 1955.
180. Conway, E. J., and McCormack, J. I.: The total intracellular concentration of mammalian tissues compared with that of the extracellular fluid. *J. Physiol., 120*:1–14, 1953.
181. Cornell, F. C.: *The Glamour of Prospecting.* London, T. Fisher Unwin Ltd., 1920, p. 258.
182. Cort, J. H.: The renal response to extrarenal depletion of the blood volume. *J. Physiol., 116*:307–319, 1952.
183. Cort, R. L.: The interrelationship of hunger and thirst in normal rats and rats with hypothalamic lesions. Thesis for degree of Doctor of Medicine, Yale University School of Medicine, New Haven, 1951.
184. Cotlove, E., Holliday, M. A., Schwartz, R., and Wallace, W. M.: Effects of

electrolyte depletion and acid-base disturbance on muscle cations. *Am. J. Physiol.*, *167*:665–675, 1951.

185. Crafts, A. S., Currier, H. B., and Stocking, C. R.: *Water in the Physiology of Plants.* Waltham, Chronica Botanica Co., 1949.

186. Crandon, J. H., Lund, C. C., and Dill, D. B.: Experimental human scurvy. *New England J. Med.*, *223*:353–369, 1940.

187. Crawford, B., and Ludemann, H.: The renal response to intravenous injection of sodium chloride solutions in man. *J. Clin. Investigation*, *30*:1456–1462, 1951.

188. Creac'h, P. V.: Composition et utilisation des aliments protidiques liquides retirés du poisson. *Congrès international d'étude sur le rôle du poisson dans l'alimentation.* Paris, Institut Océanographique, 1950, pp. 225–248.

189. Crisler, G.: The effect of withdrawal of water on the salivary conditioned reflex induced by morphine. *Am. J. Physiol.*, *85*:324–331, 1928.

190. Critchley, M.: *Shipwreck-Survivors: A Medical Study.* London, Churchill, 1943.

191. Cullumbine, H.: Personal communication, 1955.

192. Cullumbine, H., McKee, W. H. E., and Creasey, N. H.: The effects of atropine sulphate upon healthy male subjects. *Quart. J. Exper. Physiol.*, *40*: 309–319, 1955.

193. Cullumbine, H., and Miles, S.: The effect of atropine sulphate on men exposed to warm environments. *Quart. J. Exper. Physiol.*, *41*:162–179, 1956.

194. Curtis, G. M.: The production of experimental diabetes insipidus. *Arch. Int. Med.*, *34*:801–826, 1924.

195. Czerny, A.: Versuche über Bluteindickung und ihre Folgen. *Arch. exper. Path. u. Pharmakol.*, *34*:268–280, 1894.

196. Danowski, T. S., Elkinton, J. R., and Winkler, A. W.: The deleterious effect in dogs of a dry protein ration. *J. Clin. Investigation*, *23*:816–823, 1944.

197. Danowski, T. S., Fergus, E. B., and Mateer, F. M.: The low salt syndromes. *Ann. Int. Med.*, *43*:643–657, 1955.

198. Darley, W., and Doan, C. A.: Primary pulmonary arteriosclerosis with polycythemia: associated with the chronic ingestion of abnormally large quantities of sodium chlorid (halophagia). *Am. J. M. Sc.*, *191*:633–647, 1936.

199. Darragh, J. H., Welt, L. G., Goodyer, A. V. N., and Abele, W. A.: Influence of the tonicity of body fluids on rate of excretion of electrolytes. *J. Appl. Physiol.*, *5*:658–664, 1953.

200. Darrow, D. C., and Yannet, H.: The changes in the distribution of body water accompanying increase and decrease in extracellular electrolyte. *J. Clin. Investigation*, *14*:266–275, 1935.

201. Darwin, E.: *Zoonomia; or, the Laws of Organic Life.* London, Johnson, 1801.

202. Davis, M.: Personal communication, 1954.

203. Dawson, W. R.: Temperature regulation and water requirements of the brown and Abert towhees, *Pipilo fuscus* and *Pipilo aberti. Univ. California Publ., Zoöl.*, *59*:81–124, 1954.

204. Delaunay, H.: Hémorragies. In *Traité de physiologie normale et pathologique*, Vol. 7. Paris, Masson, 1926, p. 172.

205. De Morgan, A.: *A Budget of Paradoxes.* Vol. I. New York, Dover, 1954.

206. Deneufbourg, E.-F.: Quelques considérations sur la soif. Paris, Thèse No. 117, 1813, p. 39.

207. Deyrup, I.: A study of the fluid uptake of rat kidney slices in vitro. *J. Gen. Physiol.*, 36:739–749, 1953.

208. Dill, D. B.: *Life, Heat and Altitude.* Cambridge, Harvard, 1938.

209. Dill, D. B., Jones, B. F., Edwards, H. T., and Oberg, S. A.: Salt economy in extreme dry heat. *J. Biol. Chem.*, 100:755–767, 1933.

210. Di Salvo, N. A.: Drinking responses to intravenous hypertonic sodium chloride solutions injected into unrestrained dogs. *Am. J. Physiol.*, 180:133–138, 1955.

211. Di Salvo, N. A.: Factors which alter drinking responses of dogs to intravenous injections of hypertonic sodium chloride solutions. *Am. J. Physiol.*, 180: 139–145, 1955.

212. Dontas, S.: Über den Mechanismus der Wärmeregulation. *Arch. ges. Physiol.*, 241:612–629, 1939.

213. Dreser, H.: Ueber Diurese und ihre Beeinflussung durch pharmakologische Mittel. *Arch. exper. Path u. Pharmakol.*, 29:303–319, 1892.

214. Drury, D. R., Henry, J. P., and Goodman, J.: The effects of continuous pressure breathing on kidney function. *J. Clin. Investigation*, 26:945–951, 1947.

215. Dukes, H. H.: *The Physiology of Domestic Animals.* Ithaca, Comstock, 1947.

216. Dumas, C.-L.: *Principes de Physiologie.* Vol. 4. Paris, Déterville, 1803.

217. Duncan, A.: *The Mariner's Chronicle.* Vol. 1. London, Cundee, 1804.

218. Durig, A.: Durst. *Die Umschau*, 45:49–52, 1941.

219. Edelman, I. S., Haley, H. B., Schloerb, P. R., Sheldon, D. B., Friis-Hansen, B. J., Stoll, G., and Moore, F. D.: Further observations on total body water. I. Normal values throughout the life span. *Surg., Gynec. & Obst.*, 95: 1–12, 1952.

220. Edelman, I. S., Olney, J. M., James, A. H., Brooks, L., and Moore, F. D.: Body composition: studies in the human being by the dilution principle. *Science*, 115:447–454, 1952.

221. Edelmann, A., and Eversole, W. J.: Changes in antidiuretic activity of rat serum after X-irradiation. *Am. J. Physiol.*, 163:709, 1950.

222. Editorial: Qu'est-ce que la soif? *Gaz. des hôp. civ. et mil.*, 73:1431–1434, 1900.

223. Editorial: The prevention of thirst at sea. *New York Med. J.*, 107:848, 1918.

224. Editorial: In open boats. *Brit. M. J.*, 2:869–870, 1924.

225. Editorial: Thirst at sea. *Brit. M. J.*, 2:126, 1941.

226. Editorial: Thirst at sea. *Lancet*, 2:127–128, 1942.

227. Editorial: Sea water enemas. *J. A. M. A.*, 119:307, 1942.

228. Editorial: Survival at sea. *Brit. M. J.*, 2:1044, 1045, 1956.

229. Eichna, L. W., Bean, W. B., Ashe, W. F., Jr., and Nelson, N.: Performance in relation to environmental temperature. *Bull. Johns Hopkins Hosp.*, 76:25–58, 1945.

230. Elkinton, J. R., and Danowski, T. S.: *The Body Fluids.* Basic physiology and practical therapeutics. Baltimore, Williams and Wilkins, 1955.

231. Elkinton, J. R., and Squires, R. D.: The distribution of body fluids in congestive heart failure. I. Theoretic considerations. *Circulation*, 4:679–696, 1951.

232. Elkinton, J. R., and Taffel, M.: Prolonged water deprivation in the dog. *J. Clin. Investigation*, 21:787–794, 1942.

233. Elkinton, J. R., and Winkler, A. W.: Transfers of intracellular potassium in experimental dehydration. *J. Clin. Investigation, 23*:93–101, 1944.

234. Elkinton, J. R., and Winkler, A. W.: Physiologic effects of drinking undiluted sea water. *War Med., 6*:241–246, 1944.

235. Elkinton, J. R., Winkler, A. W., and Danowski, T. S.: Inactive cell base and the measurement of changes in cell water. *Yale J. Biol. & Med., 17*:383–393, 1944.

236. Elliot, A.: Hyperchloremia, azotemia and pulmonary edema of cerebral origin. *Acta med. Scandinav., 150*:467–476, 1955.

237. Ellis, C. B.: *Fresh Water from the Ocean.* New York, Ronald, 1954.

238. Engstrom, W. W., and Liebman, A.: Chronic hyperosmolarity of the body fluids with a cerebral lesion causing diabetes insipidus and anterior pituitary insufficiency. *Am. J. Med., 15*:180–186, 1953.

239. Epstein, A. N., and Stellar, E.: The control of salt preference in the adrenal-ectomized rat. *J. Comp. & Physiol. Psychol., 48*:167–172, 1955.

240. Epstein, F. H.: Personal communications, 1953, 1955.

241. Epstein, F. H.: Renal excretion of sodium and the concept of a volume receptor. *Yale J. Biol. & Med., 29*:282–298, 1956.

242. Epstein, F. H., Goodyer, A. V. N., Lawrason, F. D., and Relman, A. S.: Studies of the antidiuresis of quiet standing: the importance of changes in plasma volume and glomerular filtration rate. *J. Clin. Investigation, 30*: 63–72, 1951.

243. Epstein, F. H., Kleeman, C. R., and Hendrikx, A.: The influence of bodily hydration on the renal concentrating process. *J. Clin. Investigation, 36*: 629–634, 1957.

244. Epstein, F. H., Kleeman, C. R., Pursel, S., and Hendrikx, A.: The effect of feeding protein and urea on the renal concentrating process. *J. Clin. Investigation, 36*:635–641, 1957.

245. Epstein, F. H., Post, R. S., and McDowell, M.: The effect of an arteriovenous fistula on renal hemodynamics and electrolyte excretion. *J. Clin. Investigation, 32*:233–241, 1953.

246. Von Euler, C.: A preliminary note on slow hypothalamic "osmo-potentials." *Acta physiol. Scandinav., 29*:133–136, 1953.

247. Fabre, P.: L'hypodipsie et les oligopotes. *Gaz. méd. de Paris, 83*:215–216, 1912.

248. Fabre, P.: L'hypodipsie et les oligopotes. *Rev. de thérap. méd.-chir., 79*: 253–258, 1912.

249. Falls, W. E.: Diary of last days on a Mexican desert. Account published in *The San Diego Union,* San Diego, California, October 13, 1955. Also, A desert tale, *Time, 66*:20, 1955.

250. Farez, P.: La psychologie de l'adipsie. *Rev. de psychothérap., 26*:174–181, 1911.

251. Farrell, A. (Ed.): *John Cameron's Odyssey.* New York, Macmillan, 1928.

252. Fehr, C.: Ueber die Exstirpation sämmtlicher Speicheldrüsen bei dem Hunde *Arch. path. Anat., 25*:186–188, 1862.

252a. Feldman, S. E., Larsson, S., Dimick, M. K., and Lepkovsky, S.: Aphagia in chickens. *Am. J. Physiol., 191*:259–261, 1957.

253. Fenn, W. O.: The role of tissue spaces in the osmotic equilibrium of frog muscles in hypotonic and hypertonic solutions. *J. Cell. & Comp. Physiol., 9*:93–103, 1936.

254. Fenn, W. O.: Oxygen. *Lectures at the Army Medical Service Graduate School*, September 25–27, 1952.

255. Fetcher, E. S.: The water balance in marine mammals. *Quart. Rev. Biol.*, 14:451–459, 1939.

256. Fetcher, E. S., Jr., and Fetcher, G. W.: Experiments on the osmotic regulation of dolphins. *J. Cell. & Comp. Physiol.*, 19:123–130, 1942.

257. Finch, G.: Salivary conditioning in atropinized dogs. *Am. J. Physiol.*, 124:136–141, 1938.

258. Findlay, A.: *Osmotic Pressure*. London, Longmans, 1919.

259. Finger, F. W., and Reid, L. S.: The effect of water deprivation and subsequent satiation upon general activity in the rat. *J. Comp. & Physiol. Psychol.*, 45:368–372, 1952.

260. Fiori-Ratti, L.: Ricerche sulla sete. I. Tasso idremico nella sete provocata. *Margin. otolaryng., Fir.*, 6:114–128, 1948.

261. Fisher, J., and Lockley, R. M.: *Sea-Birds*. An introduction to the natural history of the sea-birds of the North Atlantic. Boston, Houghton, 1954.

262. Fishman, R. A.: The failure of intracranial pressure-volume change to influence renal function. *J. Clin. Investigation*, 32:847–850, 1953.

263. Fodéré, F. E.: *Essai de Physiologie Positive, Appliqué Spécialement a la Médecine Pratique*, Vol. 3. Avignon, Séguin et fils, 1806, pp. 10–11.

264. Forbes, G. B., and Perley, A.: Estimation of total body sodium by isotopic dilution. II. Studies on infants and children: an example of a constant differential growth ratio. *J. Clin. Investigation*, 30:566–574, 1951.

265. Foreign Letters: Enemas of sea water unsuccessful for quenching thirst. *J. A. M. A.*, 119:962, 1942.

266. Forster, R. P.: A comparative study of renal function in marine teleosts. *J. Cell. & Comp. Physiol.*, 42:487–509, 1953.

267. Foster, C.: *1700 Miles in Open Boats*. The story of the loss of the S. S. *Trevessa* in the Indian Ocean, and the voyage of her boats to safety. London, Hopkinson, 1924.

268. Fourman, P.: Depletion of potassium induced in man with an exchange resin. *Clin. Sc.*, 13:93–110, 1954.

269. Fowler, R., Jr.: Some long-term effects of anaesthesia, mercurial diuresis, or alteration of blood volume on the control of body water content. *Australasian Ann. Med.*, 4:224–229, 1955.

270. Foy, H., Altmann, A., and Kondi, A.: Thirst at sea—sea-water enemas. *South African M. J.*, 16:113–115, 1942.

271. Frank, M. N., Dreifus, L. S., Rarick, F., and Bellet, S.: Urinary osmolar concentration in the hydropenic state as a measure of renal tubular function: a test for early renal impairment: preliminary report. *Am. J. M. Sc.*, 233:121–125, 1957.

272. Friis-Hansen, B. J., Holiday, M., Stapleton, T., and Wallace, W. M.: Total body water in children. *Pediatrics*, 7:321–327, 1951.

272a. Futcher, P. H.: Don't drink sea water! *Bureau of Naval Personnel Information Bull.* (U.S.) No. 324, March 1944, pp. 28–29, 46.

273. Futcher, P. H., Consolazio, W. V., and Pace, N.: The effects of drinking unmodified sea water, and a comparison with the effects of drinking D-S (Goetz) water and a limited supply of "fresh water." *Naval Medical Research Institute (Bethesda, Md.)*, Project No. X-100 (General 15), Report No. 5, May 1943.

274. Futcher, P. H., Consolazio, W. V., and Pace, N.: Water balance of survivors of shipwreck in tropical waters. *War Med.*, 5:203–206, 1944.

275. Futcher, T. B.: A clinical report of nine cases of diabetes insipidus. *Tr. A. Am. Physicians, 19*:247–286, 1904.

276. Gamble, J. L.: The water requirements of castaways. *Proc. Am. Philos. Soc.*, 88:151–158, 1944.

277. Gamble, J. L.: Physiological information from studies on the life raft ration. *Harvey Lect.*, 42:247–273, 1946–47.

278. Gamble, J. L., and Butler, A. M.: Measurement of the renal water requirement. *Tr. A. Am. Physicians, 58*:157–161, 1944.

279. Gamble, J. L., McKhann, C. F., Butler, A. M., and Tuthill, E.: An economy of water in renal function referable to urea. *Am. J. Physiol., 109*:139–154, 1934.

280. Gamble, J. L., Putnam, M. C., and McKhann, C. F.: The optimal water requirement in renal function. I. Measurements of water drinking by rats according to increments of urea and of several salts in the food. *Am. J. Physiol., 88*:571–580, 1929.

281. Gamble, J. L., Ross, G. S., and Tisdall, F. F.: The metabolism of fixed base during fasting. *J. Biol. Chem., 57*:633–695, 1923.

282. Gantt, W. H.: Salivary secretion and the intake of fluid. *Am. J. Dis. Child.*, 37:1125–1127, 1929.

283. Garofeanu, M., and Derevici, M.: Sur les modifications histologiques des divers organes pendant la soif. *Compt. rend. Soc. de biol., 91*:1230–1232, 1924.

284. Gärtner, W.: Morphologische Beiträge zur Wirkung der Bromide sowie der Zufuhr grosser Salzmengen auf das Zentralnervensystem. *Ztschr. ges. exper. Med., 51*:98–111, 1926.

285. Gasnier, A., Gompel, M., Haman, F., and Mayer, A.: Régulation automatique de l'ingestion et de l'absorption des aliments en fonction de la teneur en eau du régime. *Ann. physiol., 8*:870–890, 1932.

286. Gauer, O. H., and Henry, J. P.: Beitrag zur Homöostase des extraarteriellen Kreislaufs. Volumenregulation als unabhängiger physiologischer Parameter. *Klin. Wchnschr., 34*:356–366, 1956.

287. Gauer, O. H., Henry, J. P., Sieker, H. O., and Wendt, W. E.: Heart and lungs as a receptor region controlling blood volume. *Am. J. Physiol., 167*:786–787, 1951.

288. Gauer, O. H., Henry, J. P., Sieker, H. O., and Wendt, W. E.: The effect of negative pressure breathing on urine flow. *J. Clin. Investigation, 33*:287–296, 1954.

289. Gautier, E. F.: *Sahara, the Great Desert.* New York, Columbia Univ. Press, 1935.

290. Gibson, W.: *The Boat.* London, Allen, 1952. Also Boston, Houghton, 1953.

291. Gilbert, G. J.: The subcommissural organ. *Anat. Rec., 126*:253–265, 1956.

291a. Gilbert, G. J.: The subcommissural organ: a regulator of thirst. *Am. J. Physiol., 191*:243–247, 1957.

292. Gilman, A.: The relation between blood osmotic pressure, fluid distribution and voluntary water intake. *Am. J. Physiol., 120*:323–328, 1937.

293. Gilman, A., and Goodman, L.: The secretory response of the posterior pituitary to the need for water conservation. *J. Physiol., 90*:113–123, 1937.

294. Glaser, E. M., and Hervey, G. R.: First report on survival trials in the tropics. *Gt. Britain Royal Naval Personnel Research Committee,* RNP 50/631, SS 36, 1950.

295. Glaser, E. M., and McCance, R. A.: Survival at sea in the cold. *Gt. Britain Royal Naval Personnel Research Committee,* RNP 49/542, SS 27, 1949.

295a. Glax, J.: Seebad. Die therapeutische Verwertung der Heilkräfte des Meeres. In *Handbuch der Balneologie medizinischen Klimatologie und Balneographie,* Vol. 4, Ed. Dietrich und Kaminer, Leipzig, Thieme, 1924, pp. 110–171.

296. Good, H. S.: Fifteen days adrift on a raft. A clinical evaluation of five survivors. *U. S. Naval Med. Bull., 41*:367–373, 1943.

297. Goodyer, A. V. N., and Glenn, W. W. L.: Excretion of solutes injected into the renal artery of the dog. *Am. J. Physiol., 168*:66–76, 1952.

298. Goodyer, A. V. N., Relman, A. S., Lawrason, F. D., and Epstein, F. H.: Salt retention in cirrhosis of the liver. *J. Clin. Investigation, 29*:973–981, 1950.

299. Gorham, L. W., Lester, D. E., Wolf, A. V., and Shultz, H. H.: The relative importance of dietary sodium chloride and water intake in cardiac edema. *Ann. Int. Med., 27*:575–583, 1947.

300. Gotch, F., Nadell, J., and Edelman, I. S.: Gastrointestinal water and electrolytes. IV. The equilibration of deuterium oxide (D_2O) in gastrointestinal contents and the proportion of total body water (T. B. W.) in the gastrointestinal tract. *J. Clin. Investigation, 36*:289–296, 1957.

301. Govaerts, P., and Bernard, J.: Sur l'interprétation du test d'Aldrich et McClure. *Compt. rend. Soc. biol., 97*:183–186, 1927.

302. Grafflin, A. L.: Chloride and total osmotic pressure in the blood of marine teleosts. *Biol. Bull., 69*:245–258, 1935.

302a. Grande, F., Anderson, J. T., and Taylor, H. L.: Effect of restricted water intake on urine nitrogen output in man on a low calorie diet devoid of protein. *J. Appl. Physiol., 10*:430–435, 1957.

303. Green, D. M., and Farah, A.: Influence of sodium load on sodium excretion. *Am. J. Physiol., 158*:444–456, 1949.

304. Greer, M. A.: Personal communication, 1954.

305. Greer, M. A.: Suggestive evidence of a primary "drinking center" in hypothalamus of the rat. *Proc. Soc. Exper. Biol. & Med., 89*:59–62, 1955.

306. Gregersen, M. I.: A method for uniform stimulation of the salivary glands in the unanesthetized dog by exposure to a warm environment, with some observations on the quantitative changes in salivary flow during dehydration. *Am. J. Physiol., 97*:107–116, 1931.

307. Gregersen, M. I.: The physiological mechanism of thirst. *Am. J. Physiol., 101*:44–45, 1932.

308. Gregersen, M. I.: Studies on the regulation of water intake. II. Conditions affecting the daily water intake of dogs as registered continuously by a potometer. *Am. J. Physiol., 102*:344–349, 1932.

309. Gregersen, M. I., and Bullock, L. T.: Observations on thirst in man in relation to changes in salivary flow and plasma volume. *Am. J. Physiol., 105*:39–40, 1933.

310. Gregersen, M. I., and Cannon, W. B.: Studies on the regulation of water intake. I. The effect of extirpation of the salivary glands on the water intake of dogs while panting. *Am. J. Physiol., 102*:336–343, 1932.

311. Gregersen, M. I., and Cizek, L. J.: Total water balance; thirst, fluid deficits, and excesses. Ch. 50 in *Medical Physiology*, Philip Bard, ed., St. Louis, Mosby, 1956, pp. 763–779.

312. Greiner, A., and Podhradszky, L.: Kidney function in diabetes insipidus. *Lancet*, 2:498–501, 1947.

313. Grossman, J.: Volume factors in body fluid regulation. *A. M. A. Arch. Int. Med.*, 99:93–128, 1957.

314. Grossman, M. I.: Integration of current views on the regulation of hunger and appetite. *Ann. New York Acad. Sc.*, 63:76–91, 1955.

315. Grossman, M. I., and Stein, I. F., Jr.: Vagotomy and the hunger-producing action of insulin in man. *J. Appl. Physiol.*, 1:263–269, 1948.

316. Grünwald, H. F.: Beiträge zur Physiologie und Pharmakologie der Niere. *Naunyn-Schmiedeberg's Arch. exper. Path. u. Pharmakol.*, 60:360–383, 1909.

317. Guggenheim, K., and Hegsted, D. M.: Effect of desoxycorticosterone and posterior pituitary hormone on water and electrolyte metabolism in protein deficiency. *Am. J. Physiol.*, 172:23–28, 1953.

318. Guttmann, P.: Experimentelle Untersuchungen über die Wirkungen der Kali-und Natronsalze. *Berl. klin. Wchnschr.*, 2:344–348; 355–358; 367–371, 1865.

319. Hall, F. G.: The vital limit of exsiccation of certain animals. *Biol. Bull.*, 42: 31–51, 1922.

320. Hall, W. H.: Suggestions regarding a proposed standardization of osmotic pressure as a term. *Science*, 92:334, 1940.

321. Hallay, L. I.: Diadermic drinking of water. *Virginia M. Monthly*, 69:496–498, 1942.

322. Haller, A.: *Primae Lineae Physiologiae*. Gottingae, Vandenhoeck, 1747, p. 314, DLXXXIII.

323. Haller, A.: *First Lines of Physiology*. Translated from the correct Latin edition of 1766. Edinburgh, Elliot, 1779.

324. Hamburger, J., and Mathé, G.: Sur un phénomène inédit du rupture de l'équilibre hydrique au cours de l'anoxie. *Presse méd.*, 59:265–267, 1951.

325. Hamburger, J., and Mathé, G.: *Physiologie Normale et Pathologique du Métabolisme de l'Eau*. Paris, Editions Médicales Flammarion, 1952.

326. Hamilton, B., and Schwartz, R.: The composition of tissues in dehydration. *J. Biol. Chem.*, 109:745–753, 1935.

327. Hamilton, G.: *A Voyage Round the World in His Majesty's Frigate* Pandora. Berwick, Phorson, 1793.

328. Hamoir, G.: Fish proteins. *Advances in Protein Chemistry*, 10:227–288, 1955.

329. Hancock, W., Whitehouse, A. G. R., and Haldane, J. S.: The loss of water and salts through the skin, and the corresponding physiological adjustments. *Proc. Roy. Soc., London, s. B.*, 105:43–59, 1929.

330. Handley, C. A., and Keller, A. D.: Changes in renal functions associated with diabetes insipidus precipitated by anterior hypothalamic lesions. *Am. J. Physiol.*, 160:321–324, 1950.

331. Harby, S. F.: They survived at sea. *National Geographic Magazine*, 87: 617–640, 1945.

332. Hardy, R.: Thirst at sea. *Brit. M. J.*, 2:286, 1941.

333. Hare, K.: Water metabolism: neurogenic factors. Ch. XIII in The Hypothalamus and Central Levels of Autonomic Function. *A. Research Nerv. & Ment. Dis., Proc. (1939), 20*:416–435, 1940.

334. Harvey, E. N.: A determination of the tension at the surface of eggs of the annelid, *Chætopterus. Biol. Bull., 60*:67–71, 1931.

335. Harvey, E. N.: The tension at the surface of marine eggs, especially those of the sea urchin, *Arbacia. Biol. Bull., 61*:273–279, 1931.

336. Harvey, H. W.: *Recent Advances in the Chemistry and Biology of Sea Water.* Cambridge, University Press, 1945.

337. Hawkins, D. M.: Atlantic torpedo. *Britain, 3* (6):16–21, 1944 (April). Also published London, Victor Gollancz, 1943.

338. Haynes, L. L.: An account of survivors following the sinking of the USS *Indianapolis* with recommended changes in life saving equipment. From the files of the Research Division, Bureau of Medicine and Surgery, Navy Department, Washington, D. C., November 1945.

339. Hedin, S.: *Through Asia.* Vol. I, II. New York and London, Harper, 1899.

340. Heilbrunn, L. V.: *An Outline of General Physiology.* 3rd ed. Philadelphia, Saunders, 1952.

341. Heller, H.: Discussion in *The Kidney,* Ciba Foundation Symposium. Boston, Little, 1954, p. 317.

342. Heller, V. G.: Saline and alkaline drinking waters. *J. Nutrition, 5*:421–429, 1932.

343. Heller, V. G., and Haddad, M.: Paths of excretion and mineral balance in animals drinking saline and alkaline waters. *J. Biol. Chem., 113*:439–447, 1936.

344. Heller, V. G., and Larwood, C. H.: Saline drinking water. *Science, 71*: 223–224, 1930.

345. Henderson, L. J.: On volume in biology. *Proc. Nat. Acad. Sc., 2*:654–658, 1916.

346. Heppel, L. A.: The electrolytes of muscle and liver in potassium-depleted rats. *Am. J. Physiol., 127*:385–392, 1939.

347. Hervey, G. R.: Drinking sea-water. *Brit. M. J., 1*:1494, 1954.

348. Hervey, G. R.: Drinking sea-water. *Brit. M. J., 2*:359, 1954.

349. Hervey, G. R.: Notes to accompany report RNP 54/811 SS 62 "The production, yield and composition of fish lymph," by C. G. Hunter and C. O. Hughes. *Gt. Britain Royal Naval Personnel Research Committee,* SS 67, November 1954. [See ref. 388]

350. Hervey, G. R.: Fish fluid as a source of water for castaways. *Gt. Britain Royal Naval Personnel Research Committee,* RNP 56/859, SS 79, February 1956.

351. Hervey, G. R.: Drinking sea-water. *Lancet, 1*:533–534, 1957.

352. Hervey, G. R., and McCance, R. A.: The effects of carbohydrate and sea water on the metabolism of men without food or sufficient water. *Proc. Roy. Soc., London, s. B., 139*:527–545, 1952.

353. Hervey, G. R., and McCance, R. A.: The provisioning of expeditions in the field. *Proc. Nutrition Soc., 13*:41–45, 1954.

354. Hess, W. R.: *Diencephalon. Autonomic and Extrapyramidal Functions.* New York, Grune & Stratton, 1954.

355. von Hevesy, G., and Hofer, E.: Elimination of water from the human body. *Nature, London, 134*:879, 1934.

356. von Hevesy, G., and Hofer, E.: Der Austausch des Wassers im Fischkörper. *Ztschr. f. physiol. Chem.*, *225*:28–34, 1934.

357. Heyerdahl, T.: Our four months on an ocean raft. *Reader's Digest*, *51*:102–108, 1947.

358. Heyerdahl, T.: *Kon-Tiki: Across the Pacific by Raft.* Chicago, Rand McNally, 1950, pp. 132–133.

359. Hiatt, E. P., and Hiatt, R. B.: The effect of food on the glomerular filtration rate and renal blood flow in the harbor seal (*Phoca vitulina* L.). *J. Cell. & Comp. Physiol.*, *19*:221–227, 1942.

360. Higginbotham, A. C., and Koon, W. E.: Temperature regulation in the Virginia opossum. *Am. J. Physiol.*, *181*:69–71, 1955.

361. Hildebrand, J. H.: Osmotic pressure. *Science*, *121*:116–119, 1955.

362. Hildes, J. A., and Ferguson, M. H.: The concentration of electrolytes in normal human saliva. *Canad. J. Biochem. & Physiol.*, *33*:217–225, 1955.

363. Hill, A. V.: The state of water in muscle and blood and the osmotic behaviour of muscle. *Proc. Roy. Soc., London, s. B.*, *106*:477–505, 1930.

364. Hill, J. H., and Stellar, E.: An electronic drinkometer. *Science*, *114*:43–44, 1951.

365. Hillarp, N.-Å.: Cell reactions in the hypothalamus following overloading of the antidiuretic function. *Acta Endocrinol.*, *2*:33–43, 1949.

366. Himwich, W. A., and Himwich, H. E.: Brain composition during the whole life span. *Geriatrics*, *12*:19–27, 1957.

367. Hirschfelder, A. D., and Bieter, R. N.: Local anesthetics. *Physiol. Rev.*, *12*:190–282, 1932.

368. Holmes, J. H.: Further observations on drinking induced in dogs by hypertonic saline solutions. *Am. J. Physiol.*, *163*:721–722, 1950.

369. Holmes, J. H.: Thirst as a symptom. *Tr. Am. Clin. & Climatol. A.*, *64*:94–104, 1952.

370. Holmes, J. H.: Unpublished observations, 1954.

370a. Holmes, J. H.: *Thirst: Clinical Pathology and Medical Aspects.* Springfield, Thomas, in preparation.

371. Holmes, J. H., and Behan, M.: Thirst with thyroid feeding. *Federation Proc.*, *10*:66, 1951.

372. Holmes, J. H., and Cizek, L. J.: Observations on sodium chloride depletion in the dog. *Am. J. Physiol.*, *164*:407–414, 1951.

373. Holmes, J. H., and Gregersen, M. I.: A study of the character and the mechanism of the thirst induced by the intravenous injection of hypertonic salt solution. *Am. J. Physiol.*, *126*:P537–P538, 1939.

374. Holmes, J. H., and Gregersen, M. I.: Relation of the salivary flow to the thirst produced in man by intravenous injection of hypertonic salt solution. *Am. J. Physiol.*, *151*:252–257, 1947.

375. Holmes, J. H., and Gregersen, M. I.: Origin of thirst in diabetes insipidus. *Am. J. Med.*, *4*:503–510, 1948.

376. Holmes, J. H., and Gregersen, M. I.: Observations on drinking induced by hypertonic solutions. *Am. J. Physiol.*, *162*:326–337, 1950.

377. Holmes, J. H., and Gregersen, M. I.: Role of sodium and chloride in thirst. *Am. J. Physiol.*, *162*:338–347, 1950.

378. Holmes, J. H., and Montgomery, A. V.: Physiological changes induced by high fluid intakes. *Federation Proc. 10*:66, 1951.

379. Holmes, J. H., and Montgomery, A. V.: Observations on relation of hemorrhage to thirst. *Am. J. Physiol.*, 167:796, 1951.

380. Holmes, J. H., and Montgomery, A. V.: Salivary electrolyte excretion in man. *Federation Proc.*, 11:73, 1952.

381. Holmes, J. H., and Montgomery, A. V.: Thirst as a symptom. *Am. J. M. Sc.*, 225:281–286, 1953.

382. Howard, H. J.: *Ten Weeks with Chinese Bandits.* New York, Dodd, 1926.

382a. Howard, R. A.: *Sun-Sand and Survival.* An analysis of survival experience in desert areas. ADTIC Publ. No. D-102, Maxwell Air Force Base, Alabama, Air University, 1953.

382b. Howe, E. D.: Utilization of sea water. Arid Zone Programme No. 4, *Reviews of Research on Problems of Utilization of Saline Water*, UNESCO, Paris, 1954, pp. 73–91.

383. Howe, P. E., Mattill, H. A., and Hawk, P. B.: Fasting studies: V. (Studies on water drinking: XI.) The influence of an excessive water ingestion on a dog after a prolonged fast. *J. Biol. Chem.*, 10:417–432, 1911.

384. Howe, P. E., Mattill, H. A., and Hawk, P. B.: Fasting studies: VI. Distribution of nitrogen during a fast of one hundred and seventeen days. *J. Biol. Chem.*, 11:103–127, 1912.

385. Huang, K. C.: Effect of salt depletion and fasting on water exchange in the rabbit. *Am. J. Physiol.*, 181:609–615, 1955.

386. Hunt, E. H.: The regulation of body temperature in extremes of dry heat. *J. Hyg.*, 12:479–488, 1912.

387. Hunter, C. G.: The value of fish muscle juice as a source of water in dehydrated fasting men. *Gt. Britain Royal Naval Personnel Research Committee*, SS 76, September 1955.

388. Hunter, C. G., and Hughes, C. O. LeC.: The production, yield and composition of fish lymph. *Gt. Britain Royal Naval Personnel Research Committee*, RNP 54/811, SS 62, September 1954. Also Addenda, RNP 54/819, SS 68, November 1954.

389. Hunter, J. H.: *Adrift.* The story of twenty days on a raft in the South Atlantic. New York, Evangelical, 1943.

390. Hurran, W. J.: Thirst at sea. *Brit. M. J.*, 2:528, 1941.

391. Hutchings, S. S.: Drive the water to the sheep. *National Wool Grower*, 36 (No. 4):10–11, 48, 1946.

392. Hutchinson, J.: On the influence of age on the sensation of thirst. *Arch. Surg., Lond.*, 6:180–181, 1895.

393. Huxley, J. S.: Constant differential growth-ratios and their significance. *Nature, London*, 114:895–896, 1924.

394. Huxley, J. S.: *Problems of Relative Growth.* London, Methuen, 1932.

395. Hyde, W. W.: The ascent of Mont Blanc. *National Geographic Magazine*, 24:861–942, 1913.

396. Irving, L., Fisher, K. C., and McIntosh, F. C.: The water balance of a marine mammal, the seal. *J. Cell. & Comp. Physiol.*, 6:387–391, 1935.

396a. Ivy, A. C., Futcher, P. H., Consolazio, W. V., and Pace, N.: Potability of sea water after de-salination. *Naval Medical Research Institute (Bethesda, Md.)*, Project X-100 (General 15), Report No. 1, 1943.

397. Janowitz, H. D., and Grossman, M. I.: Hunger and appetite: some definitions and concepts. *J. Mt. Sinai Hosp.*, 16:231–240, 1949.

398. Janssen, S.: Pharmakologische Beeinflussung des Durstes. *Arch. f. exper. Path. u. Pharmakol., 181*:126–127, 1936.
399. Jenkins, D. S.: Fresh water from salt. *Scient. Am., 196*:37–45, 1957.
400. Jessen, P. C.: *De Siti.* Jenae, 1751.
401. Johnson, R. E.: Nutritional standards for men in tropical climates. *Gastroenterology, 1*:832–840, 1943.
402. Jones, G. P.: *Two Survived.* The story of Tapscott and Widdicombe, who were torpedoed in mid-Atlantic and survived seventy days in an open boat. London, Hamish Hamilton, 1941.
403. Judson, W. E., Epstein, F. H., Tinsley, C. M. Burrows, B. A., and Wilkins, R. W.: The hemodynamic and renal functional effects of venous congestion of the limbs in patients with diabetes insipidus. *J. Clin. Investigation, 29*:826–827, 1950.
404. Judson, W. E., Hatcher, J. D., Hollander, W., Halperin, M. H., and Wilkins, R. W.: The effects of venous congestion of the limbs and phlebotomy upon renal clearances and the excretion of water and salt. II. Studies in patients with congestive failure. *J. Clin. Investigation, 34*:1591–1599, 1955.
405. Kanter, G. S.: Excretion and drinking after salt loading in dogs. *Am. J. Physiol., 174*:87–94, 1953.
406. Kanter, G. S.: Heat and hydropenia; their effects on thirst and chloride regulation in dogs. *Am. J. Physiol., 174*:95–105, 1953.
407. Kanter, G. S.: Effect of heat on regulation of body fluids and electrolytes in dogs. *Am. J. Physiol., 178*:259–262, 1954.
407a. Kaunitz, H., Slanetz, C. A., Johnson, R. E., and Guilmain, J.: Influence of diet composition on caloric requirements, water intake and organ weights of rats during restricted food intake. *J. Nutrition, 60*:221–228, 1956.
407b. Kellogg, R.: Adaptation of structure to function in whales. *Cooperation in Research,* Publication 501. Washington, Carnegie Inst. of Washington, 1938, p. 655.
408. Kellogg, R. H., and Burack, W. R.: Effect of adrenalectomy upon the diuresis produced by isotonic saline solutions in rats. *Am. J. Physiol., 177*:38–43, 1954.
409. Kellogg, R. H., Burack, W. R., and Isselbacher, K. J.: Comparison of diuresis produced by isotonic saline solutions and by water in rats studied by a "steady state" method. *Am. J. Physiol., 177*:27–37, 1954.
410. Kennedy, M. J.: On the brink. A personal experience with hemorrhagic fever. *Mil. Surgeon, 114*:421–424, 1954.
411. Kenney, R. A.: The effect of the drinking pattern on water economy in hot, humid environments. *Brit. J. Indust. Med. 11*:38–39, 1954.
412. Kenney, R. A., and Miller, D. H.: The effect of environmental temperature on water output and the pattern of chloride excretion. *Acta med. Scandinav., 135*:87–90, 1949.
413. Kerpel-Fronius, E.: Über die Beziehungen zwischen Salz-und Wasserhaushalt bei experimentellen Wasserverlusten. *Ztschr. Kinderh., 57*:489–504, 1935.
414. Kerpel-Fronius, E.: Durstexsikkose und Salzmangelexsikkose. *Acta paediat., 22*:143–145, 1937.
415. Kerpel-Fronius, E.: Die Durstexsikkose. *Paediat. danub., 1*:33–40, 1947.
416. Kerpel-Fronius, E., and Leövey, F.: Über die Störung der Osmo-regulation bei der experimentellen Exsikkose. *Arch. Kinderheilkunde, 94*:9–15, 1931.

417. Kessler, E., Nelson, W. P. III, Rosano, C. L., and Lansing, P. F.: Studies on the volume factor in the regulation of excretion of sodium. *Clin. Res. Proc.*, 2:95–96, 1954.

418. Keys, A. B.: The heart-gill preparation of the eel and its perfusion for the study of a natural membrane in situ. *Ztschr. f. vergl. Physiol.*, 15:352–363, 1931.

419. Keys, A. B.: Chloride and water secretion and absorption by the gills of the eel. *Ztschr. vergl. Physiol.*, 15:364–388, 1931.

420. Keys, A. B.: The mechanism of adaptation to varying salinity in the common eel and the general problem of osmotic regulation in fishes. *Proc. Roy. Soc., London, s. B.*, 112:184–199, 1933.

421. Keys, A., Brožek, J., Henschel, A., Mickelsen, O., and Taylor, H. L.: *The Biology of Human Starvation*. Minneapolis, University of Minnesota Press, 1950, p. 934.

422. King, J. H.: Brief account of the sufferings of a detachment of United States Cavalry, from deprivation of water, during a period of eighty-six hours, while scouting on the "Llano Estacado" or "Staked Plains," Texas. *Am. J. M. Sc.*, 75:404–408, 1878.

423. Kinsey, A. C., Pomeroy, W. B., Martin, C. E., and Gebhard, P. H.: *Sexual Behavior in the Human Female*. Philadelphia, Saunders, 1953.

424. Kionka, H.: Die Bekämpfung des Durstes. *Arzt und Sport*, 12:53–54, 1936, Suppl. to *Deutsche med. Wchnschr.*, vol. 62.

425. Kitching, J. A.: The physiology of contractile vacuoles. I. Osmotic relations. *J. Exper. Biol.*, 11:364–381, 1934.

426. Kitching, J. A.: The physiology of contractile vacuoles. II. The control of body volume in marine Peritricha. *J. Exper. Biol.*, 13:11–27, 1936.

427. Kitching, J. A.: The physiology of contractile vacuoles. III. The water balance of fresh-water Peritricha. *J. Exper. Biol.*, 15:143–151, 1938.

428. Kitching, J. A.: Osmoregulation and ionic regulation in animals without kidneys. Symposia of the Society for Experimental Biology, No. 8, *Active Transport and Secretion*. Cambridge, University Press, 1954, pp. 63–75.

429. Kleeman, C. R., and Maxwell, M.: Functional hyposthenuria: a reversible tubular defect probably secondary to chronic polydipsia. *Clin. Res. Proc.*, 5:43, 1957.

430. Kleitman, N.: The effect of starvation on the daily consumption of water by the dog. *Am. J. Physiol.*, 81:336–340, 1927.

431. Klippel, M.: De la soif pathologique en général et en particulier de la soif Brightique. *Arch. gén. de méd*, 3:415–420, 1900.

432. Klisiecki, A., Pickford, M., Rothschild, P., and Verney, E. B.: The absorption and excretion of water by the mammal. Part I. The relation between absorption of water and its excretion by the innervated and denervated kidney. *Proc. Roy. Soc., London, s. B.*, 112:496–521, 1933.

433. Klisiecki, A., Pickford, M., Rothschild, P., and Verney, E. B.: The absorption and excretion of water by the mammal. Part II. Factors influencing the response of the kidney to water-ingestion. *Proc. Roy. Soc., London, s. B.*: 112:521–547, 1933.

434. Knowles, H. C., Jr.: Hypernatremia. *Metabolism*, 5:508–518, 1956.

435. Kourilsky, R.: Le role de la soif. *Presse méd.*, 50:535–536, 1942.

436. Kourilsky, R.: Diabetes insipidus. *Proc. Roy. Soc. Med.*, 43:842–844, 1950.

437. Kourilsky, R., David, M., Sicard, J., and Galey, J. J.: Diabète insipide post-traumatique—cessation subite de la soif au cours de l'ouverture d'un kyste arachnoïdien de la région optochiasmatique—guérison. *Rev. neurol., 74:* 264–280, 1942.

438. Kourilsky, R., Hinglais, H., and Welti: Un cas de diabète insipide avec dissociation extrême de la soif et de la polyurie. *Bull. et mém. Soc. méd. d. hôp. de Paris, 61:*273–279, 1945.

439. Kourilsky, R., Kourilsky, S., Laudat, M., and Regaud, J.: La physiologie du diabète insipide humain doit-être conçue en fonction de la soif beaucoup plus que de la polyurie. *Bull. et mém. Soc. méd. d. hôp. de Paris, 58:* 104–109, 1942.

440. Kourilsky, R., Kourilsky, S., Laudat, M., and Regaud, J.: Action des diurétiques mercuriels dans un cas de diabète insipide. *Bull. et mém. Soc. méd. d. hôp. de Paris, 58:*58–61, 1942.

441. Kourilsky, R., Kourilsky, S., Sicard, J., and Galey, J.-J.: Une nouvelle observation de diabète insipide à précession polydipsique. Etude de la soif. *Bull. et mém. Soc. méd. d. hôp. de Paris, 58:*115–121, 1942.

442. Kourilsky, R., and Larget, P.: Polyurie permanente isotée sans polydipsie. *Bull. et mém. Soc. méd. d. hôp. de Paris, 61:*279–285, 1945.

443. Kourilsky, R., Laudat, M., and Lartat-Jacob, E.: La cause de la soif dans le diabète insipide. *Bull. et mém. Soc. méd. d. hôp. de Paris, 58:*166–168, 1942.

444. Kourilsky, R., and Sicard, J.: L'importance clinique de la soif dans le diabète insipide. *Bull. et mém. Soc. méd. d. hôp. de Paris, 58:*168–170, 1942.

445. Krogh, A.: *Osmotic Regulation in Aquatic Animals.* Cambridge, University Press, 1939.

446. Kudo, T.: Studies on the effects of thirst. I. Effects of thirst on the weights of the various organs and systems of adult albino rats. *Am. J. Anat., 28:* 399–430, 1921.

447. Kudo, T.: Studies on the effects of thirst. II. Effects of thirst upon the growth of the body and of the various organs in young albino rats. *J. Exper. Zool., 33:*435–461, 1921.

448. Kuhlmann, D., Ragan, C., Ferrebee, J. W., Atchley, D. W., and Loeb, R. F.: Toxic effects of desoxycorticosterone esters in dogs. *Science, 90:*496–497, 1939.

449. Kunde, M. M.: The after effects of prolonged fasting on the basal metabolic rate. *J. Metab. Research, 3:*399–449, 1923.

450. Kunin, R., and Myers, R. J.: *Ion Exchange Resins.* New York, Wiley, 1950.

451. Kuno, Y.: *Human Perspiration.* Springfield, Thomas, 1956.

452. Kunstmann: Über die Wirkung der Zufuhr grosser Wassermengen auf den Organismus. *Arch. exper. Path. u. Pharmakol., 170:*701–718, 1933.

453. Kyle, L. H.: Personal communication, 1957.

454. Ladd, M.: Effect of prehydration on the response to saline infusion in man. *J. Appl. Physiol., 3:*379–387, 1951.

455. Ladd, M., and Raisz, L. G.: Response of the normal dog to dietary sodium chloride. *Am. J. Physiol., 159:*149–152, 1949.

456. Ladell, W. S. S.: Effects of drinking small quantities of sea-water. *Lancet,* 2:441–444, 1943.

457. Ladell, W. S. S.: Oesophageal activity in men during water privation. *J. Physiol., 104:*43P–44P, 1946.

458. Ladell, W. S. S.: Effects on man of restricted water-supply. *Brit. M. Bull.*, 5:9–13, 1947.

459. Ladell, W. S. S.: Heat cramps. *Lancet*, 2:836–839, 1949.

460. Ladell, W. S. S.: Drinking sea-water. *Brit. M. J.*, 2:359–360, 1954.

461. Ladell, W. S. S.: The effects of water and salt intake upon the performance of men working in hot and humid environments. *J. Physiol.*, 127:11–46, 1955.

462. Ladell, W. S. S.: The influence of environment in arid regions on the biology of man. Arid Zone Research Report No. 8, *Human and Animal Ecology*, Reviews of Research, UNESCO, Paris, 1957, pp. 43–99.

463. Lamdin, E., Kleeman, C. R., Rubini, M., and Epstein, F. H.: Studies on alcohol diuresis. III. The response to ethyl alcohol in certain disease states characterized by impaired water tolerance. *J. Clin. Investigation*, 35:386–393, 1956.

464. Laragh, J. H., Van Dyke, H. B., Jacobson, J., Adamsons, K., Jr., and Engel, S. L.: The experimental production of ascites in the dog with diabetes insipidus. *J. Clin. Investigation*, 35:897–903, 1956.

465. Larrey, D.-J.: *Relation historique et chirurgicale de l'Expédition de l'Armée d'Orient en Égypte et en Syrie.* Paris, Demonville, 1803.

466. Lavietes, P. H., D'Esopo, L. M., and Harrison, H. E.: The water and base balance of the body. *J. Clin. Investigation*, 14:251–265, 1935.

467. Lawson, H.: The physiology of hunger and thirst. *Kentucky M. J.*, 36:432–435, 1938.

468. Leaf, A., Bartter, F. C., Santos, R. F., and Wrong, O.: Evidence in man that urinary electrolyte loss induced by pitressin is a function of water retention. *J. Clin. Investigation*, 32:868–878, 1953.

469. Leaf, A., and Mamby, A. R.: An antidiuretic mechanism not regulated by extracellular fluid tonicity. *J. Clin. Investigation*, 31:60–71, 1952.

470. Leitch, I., and Thomson, J. S.: The water economy of farm animals. *Nutrition Abstr. & Rev.*, 14:197–223, 1944.

471. Le Magnen, J.: La prise d'eau du Rat en inanition prolongée. *J. physiol., Par.*, 48:608–612, 1956.

472. Lepidi-Chioti, G., and Fubini: Influenza delle penellazioni faringee di cloridrato di cocaina nella sensazione della sete e nella secrezione della saliva parotidea umana. *Gior. d. r. Accad. di med. di Torino*, 33:905–906, 1885.

473. Lepkovsky, S., Lyman, R., Fleming, D., Nagumo, M., and Dimick, M. M.: Gastrointestinal regulation of water and its effect on food intake and rate of digestion. *Am. J. Physiol.*, 188:327–331, 1957.

474. Leschke, E.: Ueber die Durstempfindung. *Arch. f. Psychiat.*, 59:773–781, 1918.

474a. Levenson, S. M.: Personal communication, 1956.

475. Levkoff, A. H., Demunbrun, T. W., and Keller, A. D.: Disparity between fluid intake and renal concentrating deficit in dogs with diabetes insipidus. *Am. J. Physiol.*, 176:25–32, 1954.

476. Lewis, G. N.: The osmotic pressure of concentrated solutions, and the laws of the perfect solution. *J. Am. Chem. Soc.*, 30:668–683, 1908.

477. Lewis, J. M., Jr., Buie, R. M., Sevier, S. M., and Harrison, T. R.: The effect of posture and of congestion of the head on sodium excretion in normal subjects. *Circulation*, 2:822–827, 1950.

478. Lewy, F. H., and Gassmann, F. K.: Experiments on the hypothalamic nuclei in the regulation of chloride and sugar metabolism. *Am. J. Physiol., 112*: 504–510, 1935.

479. Lifson, N.: Note on the total osmotic activity of human plasma or serum. *J. Biol. Chem., 152*:659–663, 1944.

480. Lifson, N., Varco, R. L., and Visscher, M. B.: Relationship between osmotic activity and sodium content of gastric juice. *Proc. Soc. Exper. Biol. & Med., 47*:422–425, 1941.

481. Liljestrand, G., and Zotterman, Y.: The water taste in mammals. *Acta physiol. Scandinav., 32*:291–303, 1954.

482. Linazasoro, J. M., Jiménez Diaz, C., and Castro Mendoza, H.: The kidney and thirst regulation. *Bull. Inst. M. Res. Malaya, 7*:53–61, 1954.

482a. Lindemann, H.: Alone at sea for 72 days. *Life, 43*:93–108, 1957.

483. Llano, G. A.: *Airmen against the Sea.* An analysis of sea survival experiences. ADTIC Publ. No. G-104, Maxwell Air Force Base, Alabama, Air University, 1955.

483a. Llano, G. A.: Personal communication, 1957.

484. Lockhart, J. G.: *Peril of the Sea.* A book of shipwrecks and escapes. London, Allan, 1924, pp. 187–222.

485. Lockley, R. M.: The seabird as an individual: results of ringing experiments. *Proc. Roy. Inst. of Great Britain, 30*:434–454, 1938.

486. Lolli, G., Rubin, M., and Greenberg, L. A.: The effect of ethyl alcohol on the volume of extracellular water. *Quart. J. Stud. on Alcohol, 5*:1–4, 1944.

487. Lombardo, T. A., and Harrison, T. R.: Effect of neck compression on sodium excretion in subjects with congestive heart failure. *Circulation, 7*:88–90, 1953.

488. Longet, F.-A.: *Traité de Physiologie.* Vol. 1. Paris, Baillère, 1868, pp. 21–38.

488a. Longuet, D.-M.: Contribution a l'étude des problèmes du sauvetage maritime. L'eau de mer, boisson du naufragé. Thèse No. 89, Université de Bordeaux. Bordeaux, Drouillard, 1955.

489. Lowe, T. E.: Fluid balance in congestive cardiac failure. Two mechanisms in diuresis. *Lancet, 2*:851–856, 1951.

490. Lowe, T. E.: Influence of a mercurial diuretic on the mechanism of diuresis in congestive cardiac failure. *Lancet, 2*:1238–1241, 1952.

491. Lowe, T. E.: Intake and output of water in the control of body water content. *Australasian Ann. Med., 2*:136–143, 1953.

491a. Lowe, T. E.: Control of body fluid volume. Some observations and a hypothesis. *Am. Heart J., 53*:265–276, 1957.

492. Lowe, T. E., and Sayers, B. McA.: Control of the water content of the body. *Australasian Ann. Med., 1*:51–57, 1952.

493. Luciani, L.: Sulla genesi delle sensazioni della fame e della sete. *Arch. fisiol., 3*:541–546, 1906.

494. Ludeman, P. C.: *De Siti.* Lugd. Bat., Luchtmans, 1745.

495. Ludwig, C.: *Lehrbuch der Physiologie des Menschen.* Vol. 2. Leipzig u. Heidelberg, Winter, 1861, p. 586.

496. Luetscher, J. A., Jr., and Blackman, S. S., Jr.: Severe injury to kidneys and brain following sulfathiazole administration: high serum sodium and chloride levels and persistent cerebral damage. *Ann. Int. Med., 18*:741–756, 1943.

497. Lusk, J. A., Viar, W. N., and Harrison, T. R.: Further studies on the effects of changes in the distribution of extracellular fluid on sodium excretion. *Circulation*, 6:911–918, 1952.

498. Lyman, J.: Personal communication, 1955.

499. Lyman, J., and Fleming, R. H.: Composition of sea water. *J. Marine Research*, 3:134–146, 1940.

500. MacCarty, C. S., and Cooper, I. S.: Neurologic and metabolic effects of bilateral ligation of the anterior cerebral arteries in man. *Proc. Staff Meet., Mayo Clin.*, 26:185–190, 1951.

501. Macdonald, T. C.: Drinking sea-water. *Brit. M. J.*, 1:1035, 1954.

502. MacDougal, D. T.: *Botanical Features of North American Deserts.* Washington, Carnegie Institution Publication No. 99, 1908.

503. Mach, R. S.: *Les Troubles du Métabolisme du Sel et de l'Eau.* Paris, Masson, 1946.

504. Macnamara, C.: How some birds satisfy thirst. *Science*, 80:164, 1934.

505. MacNeill, A. E., and Doyle, J. E.: Personal communication, 1956.

506. Madden, P.: *Survivor.* Milwaukee, Bruce, 1944.

507. Magee, H. E.: The daily water consumption of adults. *J. Hyg.*, 37:30–35, 1937.

508. Magendie, F.: *A Summary of Physiology.* Translated from the French by John Revere. Baltimore, Coale, 1822.

509. Mahler, R. F., and Stanbury, S. W.: Potassium-losing renal disease. *Quart. J. Med.*, 25:21–52, 1956.

510. Marchal, F.-J.: Sur la soif, considerée dans l'état de santé et dans celui de maladie. Paris, Thèse No. 133, 1815.

510a. Margaria, R.: Irrazionalità dell'ingestione di acqua di mare per il mantenimento del ricambio idrico. *Riv. Med. Aeron.*, 20:210–223, 1957.

511. Marie, J.: Application de l'épreuve de l'eau à l'étude de la polyurie du diabète insipide: l'épreuve mixte (épreuves de l'eau et de la soif associées). *Bull. et mém. Soc. méd. d. hôp. de Paris*, 58:230–232, 1942.

512. Marriott, W. McK.: Anhydremia. *Physiol. Rev.*, 3:275–294, 1923.

513. Mattill, H. A., and Hawk, P. B.: Studies on water drinking: IX. The distribution of bacterial and other forms of fecal nitrogen and the utilization of ingested protein under the influence of copious and moderate water drinking with meals. *J. Am. Chem. Soc.*, 33:1999–2019, 1911.

514. Mattill, H. A., and Hawk, P. B.: Studies on water drinking: X. Fecal output and its carbohydrate content under the influence of copious and moderate water drinking with meals. *J. Am. Chem. Soc.*, 33:2019–2032, 1911.

515. Mayer, A.: Variations de la tension osmotique du sang chez les animaux privés de liquides. *Compt. rend. Soc. de biol.*, 52:153–155, 1900.

516. Mayer, A.: Note sur la soif d'origine gastrique. *Compt. rend. Soc. de biol.*, 52:523–524, 1900.

517. Mayer, A.: *Essai sur la Soif.* Ses causes et son mécanisme. Travail du laboratoire de pathologie expérimentale et comparée de la Faculté de Médecine de Paris. Paris, Félix Alcan, 1901.

518. Mayer, J.: Genetic, traumatic and environmental factors in the etiology of obesity. *Physiol. Rev.*, 33:472–508, 1953.

519. McCance, R. A.: Experimental sodium chloride deficiency in man. *Proc. Roy. Soc., London, s. B.*, 119:245–268, 1936.

520. McCance, R. A.: Medical problems in mineral metabolism. III. Experimental human salt deficiency. *Lancet, 1*:823–830, 1936.
521. McCance, R. A.: The effect of salt deficiency in man on the volume of the extracellular fluids, and on the composition of sweat, saliva, gastric juice and cerebrospinal fluid. *J. Physiol., 92*:208–218, 1938.
522. McCance, R. A., and Morrison, A. B.: The effects of equal and limited rations of water, and of 1, 2 and 3 per cent solutions of sodium chloride on partially nephrectomized and normal rats. *Quart. J. Exper. Physiol., 41*:365–386, 1956.
522a. McCance, R. A., Naylor, N. J. B., and Widdowson, E. M.: The response of infants to a large dose of water. *Arch. Dis. Childh., Lond., 29*:104–109, 1954.
523. McCance, R. A., Ungley, C. C., Crosfill, J. W. L., and Widdowson, E. M.: The hazards to men in ships lost at sea, 1940–44. *Spec. Rep. M. Res. Counc., Lond.*, No. 291, 1956.
524. McCance, R. A., and Widdowson, E. M.: The secretion of urine in man during experimental salt deficiency. *J. Physiol., 91*:222–231, 1937.
525. McCance, R. A., and Widdowson, E. M.: A method of breaking down the body weights of living persons into terms of extracellular fluid, cell mass and fat, and some applications of it to physiology and medicine. *Proc. Roy. Soc., London, s. B., 138*:115–130, 1951.
526. McCance, R. A., and Young, W. F.: The secretion of urine during dehydration and rehydration. *J. Physiol., 102*:415–428, 1944.
527. McCance, R. A., and Young, W. F.: Observations on water metabolism. *Brit. M. Bull., 2*:219–220, 1944.
528. McCay, C. M., and Eaton, E. M.: The quality of the diet and the consumption of sucrose solutions. *J. Nutrition, 34*:351–362, 1947.
529. McClure, W. B., and Aldrich, C. A.: Time required for disappearance of intradermally injected salt solution. *J. A. M. A., 81*:293–294, 1923.
530. McDowell, M. E., Wolf, A. V., and Steer, A.: Osmotic volumes of distribution. Idiogenic changes in osmotic pressure associated with administration of hypertonic solutions. *Am. J. Physiol., 180*:545–558, 1955.
531. McEvoy, J. P.: Survive at sea by eating and drinking fish! *Reader's Digest, 42*:27–30, 1943.
532. McGee, W. J.: The Seri Indians. *Report of the U. S. Bureau of American Ethnology, 17*:9–344, 1895–96. Washington, Government Printing Office, 1898, pp. 181–182.
533. McGee, W. J.: Thirst in the desert. *Atlantic Month., 81*:483–488, 1898.
534. McGee, W. J.: A case of thirst. *J. Missouri M. A., 2*:827–842, 1906.
535. McGee, W. J.: Desert thirst as disease. *Interstate M. J., 13*:279–300, 1906.
536. McIlrath, R. A.: Drinking sea water. *Brit. M. J., 1*:1264, 1954.
537. McLean, F. C.: Edema as a problem in physiological regulation. *Physiol. Rev., 5*:618–640, 1925.
538. Medical Research Council: A guide to the preservation of life at sea after shipwreck. *M. R. C. War Memorandum* No. 8, London, His Majesty's Stationery Office, 1943.
539. Medical Research Council: Naval emergency rations. Rations and water for life rafts (-survival rations). *Gt. Britain Royal Naval Personnel Research Committee*, RNP 47/390, SS 9, 1947.
540. Medical Research Council: High altitude research: the Everest expedition.

Report of the Medical Research Council for the year 1952–1953. London, Her Majesty's Stationery Office, 1954, pp. 9–16.

541. Meigs, J. F.: *On the Internal Use of Water for the Sick, and on Thirst.* Philadelphia, Lindsay & Blakiston, 1880.

542. Mellanby, K.: Metabolic water and desiccation. *Nature, London, 150:*21, 1942.

543. Mellor, J. W.: *Modern Inorganic Chemistry.* New York, Longmans, 1912.

544. Meroney, W. H.: Activities report of the renal insufficiency center, Wonju, Korea, for the period 25 Feb.–6 Aug., 1953. Washington, Army Medical Service Graduate School, 1953, Section II, pp. 2–3.

545. Meroney, W. H.: Personal communication, 1954.

546. Meroney, W. H., and Herndon, R. F.: The management of acute renal insufficiency. *J. A. M. A., 155:*877–883, 1954.

547. Meyer, J. H., Weir, W. C., and Smith, J. D.: A study of sheep during starvation and water deprivation. *J. Animal Science, 14:*160–172, 1955.

548. Mickelsen, O., and Keys, A.: The composition of sweat, with special reference to the vitamins. *J. Biol. Chem., 149:*479–490, 1943.

548a. Miller, N. E.: Experiments on motivation. *Science, 126:*1271–1278, 1957.

549. Miller, N. E., Richter, M. L., Bailey, C. J., Southwick, J. B., Lacy, G. M., and Jensen, D. D.: Learning and performance motivated by direct stimulation of the brain. Personal communication from N. E. Miller, 1957.

550. Miller, N. E., Sampliner, R. I., and Woodrow, P.: Thirst-reducing effects of water by stomach fistula vs. water by mouth measured by both a consummatory and an instrumental response. *J. Comp. & Physiol. Psychol., 50:*1–5, 1957.

550a. Minard, D., and Schlang, H. A.: Navy Trials. Effects of simulated survival conditions on water balance and metabolism in human volunteers. *Activities Report, Research & Development Assoc., Food and Container Institute for U. S. Armed Forces,* n. s., 3:160–165, 1951 (October).

551. Mitscherlich, A., and Mielke, F.: *Doctors of Infamy.* The story of the Nazi medical crimes. New York, Schuman, 1949.

552. Moncrieff, R. W.: *The Chemical Senses.* New York, Wiley, 1946.

553. Montgomery, A. V., and Holmes, J. H.: Role of gastrointestinal tract in satisfaction of thirst. *Am. J. Physiol., 167:*811, 1951.

554. Montgomery, A. V., and Holmes, J. H.: Gastric inhibition of the drinking response. *Am. J. Physiol., 182:*227–231, 1955.

555. Montgomery, M. F.: The rôle of the salivary glands in the thirst mechanism. *Am. J. Physiol., 96:*221–227, 1931.

556. Montgomery, M. F.: The influence of atropin and pilocarpin on thirst (voluntary ingestion of water). *Am. J. Physiol., 98:*35–41, 1931.

557. Montgomery, M. F.: Effect of pilocarpine, atropine, morphine, and epinephrine upon oral and pharyngeal mucous secretion. *Proc. Soc. Exper. Biol. & Med., 31:*913–915, 1934.

558. Moore, F. D., McMurrey, J. D., Parker, H. V., and Magnus, I. C.: Body composition. Total body water and electrolytes: intravascular and extravascular phase volumes. *Metabolism, 5:*447–467, 1956.

559. Morgan, C. T., and Stellar, E.: *Physiological Psychology.* New York, McGraw-Hill, 1950.

560. Morgulis, S.: *Fasting and Undernutrition.* New York, Dutton, 1923.

560a. Morrison, S. D., and Mayer, J.: Adipsia and aphagia in rats after lateral subthalamic lesions. *Am. J. Physiol., 191*:248–254, 1957.

560b. Morrison, S. D., and Mayer, J.: Effect of sham operations in the hypothalamus on food and water intake of the rat. *Am. J. Physiol., 191*:255–258, 1957.

561. Moss, K. N.: Some effects of high air temperatures and muscular exertion upon colliers. *Proc. Roy. Soc., London, s. B., 95*:181–200, 1923.

562. Moulton, C. R.: Age and chemical development in mammals. *J. Biol. Chem., 57*:79–97, 1923.

563. Müller, L. R.: Über die Durstempfindung. *Neurol. Centralbl., 38*:721–723, 1919.

564. Müller, L. R.: Ueber den Durst und über die Durstempfinding. *Deutsche med. Wchnschr., 46*:113–116, 1920.

565. Müller, L. R.: *Die Lebensnerven.* Berlin, Springer, 1924, pp. 530–537.

566. Mullins, L. J.: Osmotic regulation in fish as studied with radioisotopes. *Acta physiol. Scandinav., 21*:303–314, 1951.

567. Murphy, M.: *83 Days.* The survival of Seaman Izzi. New York, Dutton, 1943. Also: A reporter at large. *New Yorker, Aug. 21*:26–32; *Aug. 28*: 27–35; *Sept. 4*:42–57, 1943.

568. Nadal, J. W., Pedersen, S., and Maddock, W. G.: A comparison between dehydration from salt loss and from water deprivation. *J. Clin. Investigation, 20*:691–703, 1941.

569. Navy Department, (U. S.): Seaman who survived 83 days on life raft makes tour of war production plants. Press and Radio Release, March 26, 1943.

570. Navy Department, (U. S.): *Survival on Land and Sea.* Publications branch, Office of Naval Intelligence, 1944.

571. Navy Department, (U. S.): *Survival in the Water.* Navy training courses, NAVPERS 10080, Washington, U. S. Gov't. Printing Office, 1952.

571a. Navy Department, (U. S.): *How to Survive on Land and Sea.* Revised by Craighead, F. C., Jr., Craighead, J. J., and Carmi, O. P. Annapolis, U. S. Naval Institute, 1956.

572. Needham, J.: Chemical heterogony and the ground-plan of animal growth. *Biol. Rev., 9*:79–109, 1934.

573. Needham, J., and Lerner, I. M.: Terminology of relative growth-rates. *Nature, London, 146*:618, 1940.

574. Nelson, D.: Do rats select more sodium chloride than they need? *Federation Proc., 6*:169, 1947.

575. Nelson, K. H., and Thompson, T. G.: Desalting of seawater by freezing processes. Bibliography on snow, ice and permafrost with abstracts. (Corps of Engineers, U. S. Army) Sipre Report 12, No. 8894, *7*:65–66, 1955.

576. Nelson, W. P., III.: Personal communication, 1953.

577. Nelson, W. P., III, Rosenbaum, J. D., and Strauss, M. B.: Hyponatremia in hepatic cirrhosis following paracentesis. *J. Clin. Investigation, 30*:738–744, 1951.

578. Netravisesh, V.: Effects of posture and of neck compression on outputs of water, sodium and creatinine. *J. Appl. Physiol., 5*:544–548, 1953.

579. Newburgh, L. H., and Johnston, M. W.: *The Exchange of Energy between Man and the Environment.* Springfield, Thomas, 1930.

580. Nicholson, W. M., and Taylor, H. M.: The effect of alcohol on the water and electrolyte balance in man. *J. Clin. Investigation, 17*:279–285, 1938.
581. Nicholson, W. M., and Taylor, H. M.: Blood volume studies in acute alcoholism. *Quart. J. Stud. on Alcohol, 1*:472–482, 1940.
582. Nims, L. F., and Sutton, E.: Weight changes and water consumption of rats exposed to whole-body x-irradiation. *Am. J. Physiol., 171*:17–21, 1952.
583. Nonnenbruch, W.: Pathologie und Pharmakologie des Wasserhaushaltes einschliesslich Ödem und Entzundung. *Handbuch norm. path. Physiol., 17*:223–286, 1926.
584. Nothnagel, H.: Durst und Polydipsie. *Arch. path. Anat., 86*:435–447, 1881.
585. Oehme: Die Entstehung der Durstempfindung und die Regulation der Wasserzufuhr. *Deutsche med. Wchnschr., 48*:277, 1922.
585a. Olivecrona, H.: Paraventricular nucleus and pituitary gland. *Acta physiol. Scandinav., 40*:(Suppl. 136), 1957.
586. Osborne, W. A.: Some new aspects of the function of the skin in temperature regulation. *J. Physiol., 57*:xxvi–xxvii, 1923.
587. Oster, K. A., and Martinez, O.: Water metabolism in hypertensive rats. *J. Exper. Med., 78*:477–487, 1943.
588. Oswald, R. J. W.: Saline drink in industrial fatigue. *Lancet, 1*:1369–1370, 1925.
589. Pack, G. T.: New experiments on the nature of the sensation of thirst. *Am. J. Physiol., 65*:346–349, 1923.
590. Page, L. B., and Reem, G. H.: Urinary concentrating mechanism in the dog. *Am. J. Physiol., 171*:572–577, 1952.
591. Paintal, A. S.: A study of gastric stretch receptors. Their role in the peripheral mechanism of satiation of hunger and thirst. *J. Physiol., 126*:225–270, 1954.
592. Paintal, A. S.: The response of gastric stretch receptors and certain other abdominal and thoracic vagal receptors to some drugs. *J. Physiol., 126*:271–285, 1954.
593. Pappenheimer, J. R.: Passage of molecules through capillary walls. *Physiol. Rev., 33*:387–423, 1953.
594. Pappenheimer, J. R., Renkin, E. M., and Borrero, L. M.: Filtration, diffusion and molecular sieving through peripheral capillary membranes. A contribution to the pore theory of capillary permeability. *Am. J. Physiol., 167*:13–46, 1951.
595. Papper, S., Saxon, L., Rosenbaum, J. D., and Cohen, H. W.: The effects of isotonic and hypertonic salt solutions on the renal excretion of sodium. *J. Lab. & Clin. Med., 47*:776–782, 1956.
596. Parker, A.: Potable water from sea-water. *Nature, London, 149*:184–186, 1942.
597. Pasqualini, R. Q.: El problema de la sed. *Medicina, Buenos Aires, 3*:221–234, 1943.
598. Pasqualini, R. Q., and Avogadro, A.: Acción de la pitresina sobre la sed en la diabetes insípida. *Rev. Soc. argent. de biol., 18*:88–92, 1942.
599. Patton, H. D.: Physiology of smell and taste. *Ann. Rev. Physiol., 12*:469–484, 1950.
600. Patton, H. D., and Ruch, T. C.: Preference thresholds for quinine hydrochloride in chimpanzee, monkey and rat. *J. Comp. Psychol., 37*:35–49, 1944.

601. Pavlov, I. P.: *The Work of the Digestive Glands.* London, Griffin, 1910, pp. 70–71, 82.

602. Pearce, M. L., and Newman, E. V.: Some postural adjustments of salt and water excretion. *J. Clin. Investigation, 33*:1089–1094, 1954.

603. Pearson, J. S.: The inability of sea water to prevent dehydration. *Contact,* 2:43–45, 1942. Pensacola, U. S. School of Aviation Med.

604. Pernice, B., and Scagliosi, G.: Ueber die Wirkung der Wasserentziehung auf Thiere. *Virchows Arch. f. path. Anat., 139*:155–184, 1895.

605. Peters, J. P.: *Body Water.* Springfield, Thomas, 1935.

606. Peters, J. P.: The role of sodium in the production of edema. *New England J. Med., 239*:353–362, 1948.

607. Peters, J. P.: Personal communication, 1950.

608. Peters, J. P.: Fluid regulation in health and in disease. *Medical Basic Science Notes, 1*:105–216, 1951, Washington, Army Medical Service Graduate School, Walter Reed Army Medical Center.

609. Peters, J. P.: The problem of cardiac edema. *Am. J. Med., 12*:66–76, 1952.

610. Petersdorf, R. G., and Welt, L. G.: The effect of an infusion of hyperoncotic albumin on the excretion of water and solutes. *J. Clin. Investigation, 32*: 283–291, 1953.

611. Pfaffmann, C., and Bare, J. K.: Gustatory nerve discharges in normal and adrenalectomized rats. *J. Comp. & Physiol. Psychol., 43*:320–324, 1950.

612. Pfeiffer, L.: Ueber den Fettgehalt des Körpers und verschiedener Theile desselben bei mageren und fetten Thieren. *Ztschr. Biol., 23*:340–380, 1886.

613. Pick, E. P.: The regulation of water metabolism. *Harvey Lect., 25*:25–55, 1929–30.

614. Pincoffs, M. B.: Discussion. *Tr. Am. Clin. & Climatol. A., 64*:103, 1952.

615. Pinson, E. A.: Water exchanges and barriers as studied by the use of hydrogen isotopes. *Physiol. Rev., 32*:123–134, 1952.

616. Pittard, K.: Dehydration combatted with sea water. *Contact, 1*:11–13, 1942. Pensacola, U. S. School of Aviation Med.

617. Pitts, G. C., Johnson, R. E., and Consolazio, F. C.: Work in the heat as affected by intake of water, salt and glucose. *Am. J. Physiol., 142*:253–259, 1944.

618. Platt, R.: Structural and functional adaptation in renal failure. *Brit. M. J., 1*:1372–1377, 1952.

619. Poincaré, H.: *The Foundations of Science.* New York, Science Pr., 1913, pp. 299–300.

620. Pond, A. W.: *Afoot in the Desert.* A contribution to basic survival. ADTIC Publ. No. D-100, Maxwell Air Force Base, Alabama, Air University, 1956.

620a. Pond, A. W.: Personal communication, 1956.

621. Ponder, E.: *The Mammalian Red Cell and the Properties of Haemolytic Systems, Protoplasma-Monographien,* Vol. 6. Berlin, Borntraeger, 1934, p. 122.

622. Portier, P.: Pression osmotique des liquides des oiseaux et mammifères marins. *J. de physiol. et de path. gén., 12*:202–208, 1910.

623. Potts, W. T. W.: The energetics of osmotic regulation in brackish- and fresh-water animals. *J. Exper. Biol., 31*:618–630, 1954.

624. Powell, G. M.: Hemorrhagic fever: a study of 300 cases. *Medicine, 33*: 97–153, 1954.

625. Prentice, T. C., Berlin, N. I., Hyde, G. M., Parsons, R. J., Lawrence, J. H.,

and Port, S.: Total red cell volume, plasma volume, and sodium space in congestive heart failure. *J. Clin. Investigation, 30*:1471–1482, 1951.

626. Prentiss, P. G., Wolf, A. V., and Eddy, H. A.: Hydropenia in cat and dog: ability of the cat to meet its water requirements solely from a diet of fish or meat. In preparation.

627. Pribor, H. C.: Alterations in autonomic ganglion cells in fever, dehydration, and inanition. *A. M. A. Arch. Path., 61*:91–96, 1956.

628. Priestley, J. G.: The regulation of excretion of water by the kidneys. II. *J. Physiol., 50*:304–311, 1916.

629. Prosser, C. L.: The clinical sequence of physiological effects of ionizing radiation in animals. *Radiology, 49*:299–313, 1947.

630. Prosser, C. L. (Editor): *Comparative Animal Physiology.* Philadelphia, Saunders, 1950.

631. Prudden, J. F., Danzig, L. E., and Stirman, J. A.: The effect of acute potassium depletion on the functional compartmentalization of water. *Surg., Gynec. & Obst., 102*:553–564, 1956.

632. Pujo: Notes sur la soif en région désertique. *Ann. de méd. et de pharm. colon., 33*:146–154, 1935.

633. Quashnock, J. M.: Water requirements of life raft survivors. Memorandum Report Aero Medical Lab., U. S. Army Air Force Engineering Division, Serial No. ENG-49-696-39E, August 21, 1943.

634. Quinton, R.: *L'Eau de Mer. Milieu Organique.* Paris, Masson, 1904.

635. Rabbeno, A.: Ricerche sull' azione farmacologica dell' acqua di mare. Nota I. Tossicità dell' acqua di mare introdotta per vena. *Arch. di sc. biol., 12*:469–477, 1928.

636. Rabbeno, A.: Ricerche sull' azione farmacologica dell' acqua di mare. Nota V. Riassunto generale e commento critico. *Arch. di sc. biol., 14*:58–75, 1929.

637. Ragan, C., Ferrebee, J. W., Phyfe, P., Atchley, D. W., and Loeb, R. F.: A syndrome of polydipsia and polyuria induced in normal animals by desoxycorticosterone acetate. *Am. J. Physiol., 131*:73–78, 1940.

638. Randoin, L., Causeret, J., and Gavrel-Szymanski, M.: Comportement du jeune rat normal auquel on donne le choix entre de l'eau pure et une solution peu concentrée de chlorure de sodium. *J. physiol., Paris, 42*: 447–450, 1950.

639. Rausse, J. H.: *The Water-Cure, Applied to Every Known Disease.* Translated by C. H. Meeker. New York, Fowlers and Wells, 1852, pp. 113–114.

640. Regnier, A.: Ueber den Einfluss diätetischer Massnahmen auf das osmotische Gleichgewicht des Blutes beim normalen Menschen. *Ztschr. exper. Path. u. Therap., 18*:139–164, 1916.

641. Reid, C. E.: Research investigation of synthetic osmotic membranes for use in desalting sea and other saline waters; and Process development of a desalting method using synthetic osmotic membranes. *Third Ann. Rep. of the Sec'y. of Interior (U. S.) on Saline Water Conversion,* January 1955, pp. 94–97.

642. Reifenstein, E. C., Jr., Albright, F., and Wells, S. L.: The accumulation, interpretation, and presentation of data pertaining to metabolic balances, notably those of calcium, phosphorus, and nitrogen. *J. Clin. Endocrinol., 5*:367–395, 1945.

643. Reignier, A.: Un cas d'oligopotisme. *Centre Méd. et Pharm., Gannat.,* 17:324, 1911–12.
644. Remington, J. W.: Personal communication, 1950.
645. Remington, J. W., Parkins, W. M., and Hays, H. W.: Influence of prolonged electrolyte deprivation and final restoration on fluid intake, balance and distribution. *Proc. Soc. Exper. Biol. & Med.,* 47:183–187, 1941.
646. Reuters (dispatch), Marsala, Sicily, Feb. 11, 1957: Seawater diet saves 3 men adrift 6 days. *Washington Post and Times Herald,* February 12, 1957, p. B-12.
647. Reymond, J.-C.: Note physiologique sur la soif. *J. prat., Paris,* 65:314–315, 1951.
648. Richet, C.: La mort par la soif. *Presse méd.,* 55:597, 1947.
649. Richter, C. P.: Thirst: a function of body-surface. *Ninth International Congress of Psychology (1929),* Princeton, Psychological Review Co., 1930, pp. 358–359.
650. Richter, C. P.: Factors determining voluntary ingestion of water in normals and in individuals with maximum diabetes insipidus. *Am. J. Physiol.,* 122:668–675, 1938.
651. Richter, C. P.: Salt taste thresholds of normal and adrenalectomized rats. *Endocrinology,* 24:367–371, 1939.
652. Richter, C. P.: Total self regulatory functions in animals and human beings. *Harvey Lect.,* 38:63–103, 1942–43.
653. Richter, C. P., and Brailey, M. E.: Water-intake and its relation to the surface area of the body. *Proc. Nat. Acad. Sc.,* 15:570–578, 1929.
654. Richter, C. P., and Mosier, H. D., Jr.: Maximum sodium chloride intake and thirst in domesticated and wild Norway rats. *Am. J. Physiol.,* 176:213–222, 1954.
655. Rickenbacker, E. V.: Pacific mission. *Life, 14:*21 (Jan. 25), 78 (Feb. 1), 95 (Feb. 8), 1943. Also *Seven Came Through.* Rickenbacker's full story. New York, Doubleday, Doran, 1943.
656. Rieser, P.: The resistance of cell membranes to internal pressure. *Physiol. Zoöl.,* 23:199–208, 1950.
657. Roberts, M.: Thirst at sea. *Brit. M. J.,* 1:220, 1918.
658. Robinson, E. A., and Adolph, E. F.: Pattern of normal water drinking in dogs. *Am. J. Physiol.,* 139:39–44, 1943.
659. Robinson, J. R.: Osmoregulation in surviving slices from the kidneys of adult rats. *Proc. Roy. Soc., London, s. B.,* 137:378–402, 1950.
660. Robinson, J. R.: The active transport of water in living systems. *Biol. Rev.,* 28:158–194, 1953.
661. Robinson, J. R.: Secretion and transport of water. Symposia of the Society for Experimental Biology, No. 8, *Active Transport and Secretion.* Cambridge, University Press, 1954, pp. 42–62.
662. Robinson, K., and Lee, D. H. K.: Reactions of the pig to hot atmospheres. *Proc. Roy. Soc. Queensland,* 53:145–158, 1941.
663. Robinson, S., Kincaid, R. K., and Rhamy, R. K.: Effect of salt deficiency on the salt concentration in sweat. *J. Appl. Physiol.,* 3:55–62, 1950.
663a. Robinson, S., Nichols, J. R., Smith, J. H., Daly, W. J., and Pearcy, M.: Time relation of renal and sweat gland adjustments to salt deficiency in men. *J. Appl. Physiol.,* 8:159–165, 1955.
664. Rogers, L.: Thirst at sea. *Brit. M. J.,* 2:211, 1941.

665. Rothman, S.: *Physiology and Biochemistry of the Skin.* Chicago, University Chicago Press, 1954.

666. Rowntree, L. G.: Diabetes insipidus. *Oxford Medicine.* Vol. 4, Chapter VI. New York, Oxford, 1921, pp. 179–193.

667. Rowntree, L. G.: The water balance of the body. *Physiol. Rev.,* 2:116–169, 1922.

668. Rowntree, L. G.: Water intoxication. *Am. J. Physiol.,* 59:451–452, 1922.

669. Royer, P.-H.: Psycho-physiologie de la soif. *Hyg. ment.,* 42:1–14, 1953.

670. Rubini, M. E., and Wolf, A. V.: Refractometric determination of total solids and water of serum and urine. *J. Biol. Chem.,* 225:869–876, 1957.

671. Rubini, M. E., Wolf, A. V., and Meroney, W. H.: Effects of sea water on the metabolism of men without food or sufficient water. Research Report WRAIR-190-56, November 1956, Walter Reed Army Institute of Research, Walter Reed Army Medical Center, Washington, D. C.

672. Rubner, M.: *Lehrbuch der Hygiene.* Leipzig und Wien, Deuticke, 1907, p. 325.

673. Rullier: Soif. *Dict. d. Sc. méd., Par.,* 51:448–490, 1821.

674. Sargent, F., Robinson, P., and Johnson, R. E.: Water-soluble vitamins in sweat. *J. Biol. Chem.,* 153:285–294, 1944.

675. Savigny, J. B. H., and Corréard, A.: *Naufrage de la Frégate la Méduse.* Paris, Hocquet, 1817.

676. Sawyer, C. H., and Gernandt, B. E.: Effects of intracarotid and intraventricular injections of hypertonic solutions on electrical activity of the rabbit brain. *Am. J. Physiol.,* 185:209–216, 1956.

677. Sawyer, W. H.: and Schisgall, R. M.: Increased permeability of the frog bladder to water in response to dehydration and neurohypophysial extracts. *Am. J. Physiol.,* 187:312–314, 1956.

678. Schemm, F. R., and Camara, A. A.: The relief of resistant edema by utilization of a sump phenomenon. *Circulation,* 11:411–421, 1955.

679. Schiff, M.: *Leçons sur la physiologie de la digestion, faites au muséum d'histoire naturelle de Florence.* Vol. 1, edited by Emile Levier, Florence and Turin, Loescher, 1867, pp. 41–42.

680. Schloerb, R. P., Friis-Hansen, B. J., Edelman, I. S., Solomon, A. K., and Moore, F. D.: The measurement of total body water in the human subject by deuterium oxide dilution. *J. Clin. Investigation,* 29:1296–1309, 1950.

681. Schmidt-Nielsen, B.: Water conservation in small desert rodents. In *Biology of Deserts,* Edited by J. L. Cloudsley-Thompson. London, Institute of Biology, 1954, pp. 173–181.

682. Schmidt-Nielsen, B., and Schmidt-Nielsen, K.: Do kangaroo rats thrive when drinking sea water? *Am. J. Physiol.,* 160:291–294, 1950.

683. Schmidt-Nielsen, B., and Schmidt-Nielsen, K.: Pulmonary water loss in desert rodents. *Am. J. Physiol.,* 162:31–36, 1950.

684. Schmidt-Nielsen, B., and Schmidt-Nielsen, K.: A complete account of the water metabolism in kangaroo rats and an experimental verification. *J. Cell. & Comp. Physiol.,* 38:165–181, 1951.

684a. Schmidt-Nielsen, B., and Schmidt-Nielsen, K.: The camel—facts and fables. *UNESCO Courier,* No. 8–9: 28–32, 63, 1955.

685. Schmidt-Nielsen, B., Schmidt-Nielsen, K., Brokaw, A., and Schneiderman, H.: Water conservation in desert rodents. *J. Cell. & Comp. Physiol.,* 32:331–360, 1948.

686. Schmidt-Nielsen, B., Schmidt-Nielsen, K., Houpt, T. R., and Jarnum, S. A.: Water balance of the camel. *Am. J. Physiol., 185*:185–194, 1956.

686a. Schmidt-Nielsen, B., Schmidt-Nielsen, K., Jarnum, S. A., and Houpt, T. R.: Dehydration and rehydration in the camel. *Federation Proc., 14*:132–133, 1955.

687. Schmidt-Nielsen, K.: Water storage in the camel. *Federation Proc., 15*:164, 1956.

688. Schmidt-Nielsen, K., Jörgensen, C. B., and Osaki, H.: Secretion of hypertonic solutions in marine birds. *Federation Proc., 16*:113–114, 1957.

689. Schmidt-Nielsen, K., and Schmidt-Nielsen, B.: Water metabolism of desert mammals. *Physiol. Rev., 32*:135–166, 1952.

690. Schmidt-Nielsen, K., Schmidt-Nielsen, B., Houpt, T. R., and Jarnum, S. A.: Body temperature of the camel. *Federation Proc., 14*:133, 1955.

691. (Omitted)

692. Schmidt-Nielsen, K., Schmidt-Nielsen, B., and Schneiderman, H.: Salt excretion in desert mammals. *Am. J. Physiol., 154*:163–166, 1948.

693. Schmidt-Nielsen, S., and Holmsen, J.: Sur la composition de l'urine des baleines. *Arch. internat. de physiol., 18*:128–132, 1921.

694. Schmidt-Nielsen, S., and Schmidt-Nielsen, S.: Orientierende Fütterungsversuche mit Deuteriumoxyd an Ratten. *K. norske vidensk. Selsk. Forh., Trondheim., 8* (Nr. 8): 27–28, 1935.

695. Schneider, O.: Über Behandlung von Durstzuständen mit Cesol. *Med. Klin., 18*:1583–1585, 1922.

696. Schneyer, L. H.: Method for the collection of separate submaxillary and sublingual salivas in man. *J. Dent. Research, 34*:257–261, 1955.

697. Schneyer, L. H., and Levin, L. K.: Rate of secretion by individual salivary gland pairs of man under conditions of reduced exogenous stimulation. *J. Appl. Physiol., 7*:508–512, 1955.

698. Scholander, P. F., van Dam, L., Kanwisher, J. W., Hammel, H. T., and Gordon, M. S.: Supercooling and osmoregulation in arctic fish. *J. Cell. & Comp. Physiol., 49*:5–24, 1957.

699. Schreinemakers, F. A. H.: *Lectures on Osmosis.* The Hague, G. Naeff, 1938.

700. Schroeder, H. A.: Renal failure associated with low extracellular sodium chloride. The low salt syndrome. *J. A. M. A., 141*:117–124, 1949.

701. Schwimmer, D., and McGavack, T. H.: Protein metabolism on reduced caloric and water intakes. *Quartermaster Food and Container Inst. for the Armed Forces,* Chicago, Illinois. (Committee on Food Research), Report No. 5 (7-84-12-08), 1948.

702. Schwimmer, D., and McGavack, T. H.: Some newer aspects of protein metabolism. I. Résumé of experimental data. *New York State J. Med., 48*:1797–1799, 1948.

703. Scott, E. M.: Self selection of diet. I. Selection of purified components. *J. Nutrition, 31*:397–406, 1946.

704. Scott, E. M., and Quint, E.: Self selection of diet. II. The effect of flavor. *J. Nutrition, 32*:113–119, 1946.

705. Scott, E. M., and Quint, E.: Self selection of diet. IV. Appetite for protein. *J. Nutrition, 32*:293–301, 1946.

706. Scott, E. M., and Verney, E. L.: Self selection of diet. V. Appetite for carbohydrates. *J. Nutrition, 34*:401–407, 1947.

707. Scott, E. M., and Verney, E. L.: Self selection of diet. VI. The nature of appetites for B vitamins. *J. Nutrition, 34*:471–480, 1947.

708. Scott, E. M., and Verney, E. L.: Self selection of diet. VIII. Appetite for fats. *J. Nutrition, 36*:91–98, 1948.

709. Scott, R. F.: *The Voyage of the "Discovery."* Vol. 1. New York, Scribner's, 1905, pp. 292–293.

710. Scott, R., Jr.: Personal communication, 1954.

711. Secretan, W. B.: Rectal injections of sea-water for thirst. *Brit. M. J., 2*:928, 1924.

712. Seldin, D. W., and Tarail, R.: Effect of hypertonic solutions on metabolism and excretion of electrolytes. *Am. J. Physiol., 159*:160–174, 1949.

713. Semple, R. E.: Compensatory changes in the rat following removal of electrolytes by intraperitoneal dialysis. *Am. J. Physiol., 168*:55–65, 1952.

714. Shackleton, E.: *South.* The story of Shackleton's last expedition 1914–1917. London, Heinemann, 1919.

715. Sherman, H. C.: *Chemistry of Food and Nutrition.* New York, Macmillan, 1933.

716. Sherman, H. C.: *Chemistry of Food and Nutrition.* New York, Macmillan, 1952.

717. Sherrington, C. S.: *The Integrative Action of the Nervous System.* New York, Scribner's Sons, 1906.

718. Shock, N. W., Yiengst, M. J., and Watkin, D. M.: Age change in body water and its relationship to basal oxygen consumption in males. *J. Gerontol., 8*:388, 1953.

719. Shohl, A. T.: *Mineral Metabolism.* New York, Reinhold, 1939.

720. Sholl, D.: The quantitative investigation of the vertebrate brain and the applicability of allometric formulae to its study. *Proc. Roy. Soc., London, s. B., 135*:243–258, 1948.

721. Shotton, F. W.: The availability of underground water in hot deserts. In *Biology of Deserts*, Edited by J. L. Cloudsley-Thompson. London, Institute of Biology, 1954, pp. 13–17.

722. Siegel, P. S.: The relationship between voluntary water intake, body weight loss, and number of hours of water privation in the rat. *J. Comp. & Physiol. Psychol., 40*:231–238, 1947.

723. Siegel, P. S., and Stuckey, H. L.: An examination of some factors relating to the voluntary water intake of the rat. *J. Comp. & Physiol. Psychol., 40*: 271–274, 1947.

724. Siegel, P. S., and Stuckey, H. L.: The diurnal course of water and food intake in the normal mature rat. *J. Comp. & Physiol. Psychol., 40*:365–370, 1947.

725. Siegel, P. S., and Talantis, B. S.: Water intake as a function of privation interval when food is withheld. *J. Comp. & Physiol. Psychol., 43*:62–65, 1950.

726. Sieker, H. O., Gauer, O. H., and Henry, J. P.: The effect of continuous negative pressure breathing on water and electrolyte excretion by the human kidney. *J. Clin. Investigation, 33*:572–577, 1954.

727. Skattebol, L.: *The Last Voyage of the* Quien Sabe. New York, Harper, 1944.

728. Skelton, H.: The storage of water by various tissues of the body. *Arch. Int. Med., 40*:140–152, 1927.

729. Slevin, J. R.: Log of the schooner "Academy" on a voyage of scientific re-

search to the Galapagos Islands 1905–1906. *Occasional Papers of the California Academy of Sciences* 17, February 14, 1931, Plate 4.

730. Smiley, D. F., and Gould, A. G.: *Your Health.* New York, Macmillan, 1951, p. 129.

731. Smirk, F. H.: The rate of water absorption in man and the relationship of the water load in tissues to diuresis. *J. Physiol.,* 78:113–126, 1933.

732. Smith, D. E., and Tyree, E. B.: Influence of x-irradiation upon water consumption by the rat. *Am. J. Physiol.,* 184:127–133, 1956.

733. Smith, E. A.: Salivary secretion during thirst. *Am. J. Physiol.,* 113:123, 1935.

733a. Smith, G. H.: Survival in the South Seas. *Bureau of Naval Personnel Information Bull.* (*U.S.*) No. 323, February 1944, pp. 32–35.

734. Smith, H. W.: The absorption and excretion of water and salts by marine teleosts. *Am. J. Physiol.,* 93:480–505, 1930.

735. Smith, H. W.: Water regulation and its evolution in the fishes. *Quart. Rev. Biol.,* 7:1–26, 1932.

736. Smith, H. W.: The functional and structural evolution of the vertebrate kidney. *Sigma Xi Quarterly,* 21:141–151, 1933.

737. Smith, H. W.: The composition of urine in the seal. *J. Cell. & Comp. Physiol.,* 7:465–474, 1936.

738. Smith, H. W.: The retention and physiological role of urea in the Elasmobranchii. *Biol. Rev.,* 11:49–82, 1936.

739. Smith, H. W.: *The Kidney. Structure and Function in Health and Disease.* New York, Oxford, 1951.

740. Smith, H. W.: Renal excretion of sodium and water. *Federation Proc.,* 11:701–705, 1952.

741. Smith, H. W.: *From Fish to Philosopher.* Boston, Little, 1953.

741a. Smith, H. W.: *Principles of Renal Physiology.* New York, Oxford, 1956.

741b. Smith, H. W.: Salt and water volume receptors. An exercise in physiologic apologetics. *Am. J. Med.,* 23:623–652, 1957.

742. Smith, J. A. B.: Energy value of food. *Nature, London,* 176:152–153, 1955.

743. Smith, M. F., and Smith, K. U.: Thirst-motivated activity and its extinction in the cat. *J. Gen. Psychol.,* 21:89–98, 1939.

744. Smith, S. G., and Lasater, T. E.: A diabetes insipidus-like condition produced in dogs by a potassium deficient diet. *Proc. Soc. Exper. Biol. & Med.,* 74:427–431, 1950.

745. Snow, E. R.: *The Vengeful Sea.* New York, Dodd, 1956, pp. 83–84.

746. Soberman, R. J.: A comparison of total body water as determined by antipyrine and desiccation in rabbits. *Proc. Soc. Exper. Biol. & Med.,* 71:172–173, 1949.

747. Soberman, R. J.: Use of antipyrine in measurement of total body water in animals. *Proc. Soc. Exper. Biol. & Med.,* 74:789–792, 1950.

748. Soldier's Letter: Quotation from a letter from the Crimea. *Scient. Am.,* 194:18, 1956.

749. Soloff, L. A., and Zatuchni, J.: Syndrome of salt depletion induced by a regimen of sodium restriction and sodium diuresis. *J.A.M.A.,* 139:1136–1139, 1949.

750. Spealman, C. R.: The chemical removal of salts from sea water to produce potable water. *Science,* 99:184–185, 1944.

751. Squires, R. D., and Elkinton, J. R.: The significance of hyponatremia in congestive heart failure. *J. Clin. Investigation,* 30:675, 1951.

752. Stamler, J., Brostoff, P., Levinson, I., and Ellis, A.: Response to rapid intravascular infusion of dogs with isotonic expansion of plasma–extracellular fluid volume. *Federation Proc., 14*:143–144, 1955.

753. Stanbury, S. W., and Thomson, A. E.: Diurnal variation in electrolyte excretion. *Clin. Sc., 10*:267–293, 1951.

754. Starkenstein, E.: Wasserhaushalt und Durststillung. *Klin. Wchnschr., 6*: 147–152, 1927.

755. Starling, E. H.: *The Fluids of the Body.* London, Constable, 1909.

756. Steer, A.: Personal communication, 1955.

757. Stefansson, V.: *The Friendly Arctic.* New York, Macmillan, 1922, pp. 31, 166, 167, 351, 352.

758. Stefansson, V.: *Arctic Manual.* New York, Macmillan, 1944.

759. Steggerda, F. R.: The relation of dry mouth to thirst in the human. *Am. J. Physiol., 126*:P635, 1939.

760. Steggerda, F. R.: Observations on the water intake in an adult man with dysfunctioning salivary glands. *Am. J. Physiol., 132*:517–521, 1941.

761. Steggerda, F. R., and Bouten, V.: Further studies on a case of dysfunctioning salivary glands in man. *Am. J. Physiol., 119*:409, 1937.

762. Stellar, E.: The physiology of motivation. *Psychol. Rev., 61*:5–22, 1954.

763. Stellar, E., and Hill, J. H.: The rat's rate of drinking as a function of water deprivation. *J. Comp. & Physiol. Psychol., 45*:96–102, 1952.

764. Stellar, E., Hyman, R., and Samet, S.: Gastric factors controlling water- and salt-solution-drinking. *J. Comp. & Physiol Psychol., 47*:220–226, 1954.

765. Stevenson, J. A. F.: Effects of hypothalamic lesions on water and energy metabolism in the rat. *Recent Progress in Hormone Research, 4*:363–394, 1949.

766. Stevenson, J. A. F., Welt, L. G., and Orloff, J.: Abnormalities of water and electrolyte metabolism in rats with hypothalamic lesions. *Am. J. Physiol., 161*:35–39, 1950.

767. Stewart, J. D., and Rourke, G. M.: Intracellular fluid loss in hemorrhage. *J. Clin. Investigation, 15*:697–702, 1936.

768. Stewart, J. D., and Rourke, G. M.: The effects of large intravenous infusions on body fluid. *J. Clin. Investigation, 21*:197–205, 1942.

769. Stott, H.: Heat exhaustion and dehydration in the Arabian desert. *Indian M. Gaz., 71*:712–714, 1936.

770. Straub, W.: Ueber den Einfluss der Wasserentziehung auf den Stoffwechsel und Kreislauf. *Ztschr. f. Biol., 38*:537–566, 1899.

771. Strauss, H.: Über die Wirkung der Aufnahme grosser Wassermengen auf den Organismus. *Klin. Wchnschr., 1*:1302–1305, 1922.

771a. Strauss, M. B.: *Body Water in Man. The Acquisition and Maintenance of the Body Fluids.* Boston, Little, 1957.

772. Strauss, M. B., Davis, R. K., Rosenbaum, J. D., and Rossmeisl, E. C.: "Water diuresis" produced during recumbency by the intravenous infusion of isotonic saline solution. *J. Clin. Investigation, 30*:862–868, 1951.

773. Strauss, M. B., Davis, R. K., Rosenbaum, J. D., and Rossmeisl, E. C.: Production of increased renal sodium excretion by the hypotonic expansion of extracellular fluid volume in recumbent subjects. *J. Clin. Investigation, 31*:80–86, 1952.

774. Strauss, M. B., Rosenbaum, J. D., and Nelson, W. P., III: The effect of

alcohol on the renal excretion of water and electrolyte. *J. Clin. Investigation, 29*:1053–1058, 1950.

775. Strominger, J. L.: The relation between water intake and food intake in normal rats and in rats with hypothalamic hyperphagia. *Yale J. Biol. & Med., 19*:279–288, 1947.

776. Summers, T. O.: Hunger and thirst. *Nashville J. Med. & Surg.*, n. s. *15*: 144–155, 1875.

777. Surtshin, A., Hoeltzenbein, J., and White, H. L.: Some effects of negative pressure breathing on urine excretion. *Am. J. Physiol., 180*:612–616, 1955.

778. Sverdrup, H. U., Johnson, M. W., and Fleming, R. H.: *The Oceans.* Their physics, chemistry, and general biology. New York, Prentice-Hall, 1942.

779. Sweet, W. H., Cotzias, G. C., Seed, J., and Yakovlev, P. I.: Gastrointestinal hemorrhages, hyperglycemia, azotemia, hyperchloremia and hypernatremia following lesions of the frontal lobe in man. *A. Research Nerv. & Ment. Dis., Proc.* (*1947*), *27*:795–822, 1948.

780. Tancredi, L.: *Da Fame et Siti*, Lib. 3. Venetiis, 1607.

781. Tanner, J. M.: Fallacy of per-weight and per-surface area standards, and their relation to spurious correlation. *J. Appl. Physiol., 2*:1–15, 1949.

782. Taylor, H. L., Grande, F., Buskirk, E., Anderson, J. T., and Keys, A.: Water exchange in man in the presence of a restricted water intake and a low calorie carbohydrate diet. *Federation Proc., 15*:185, 1956.

783. Thomas, L.: *The Wreck of the* Dumaru. A story of cannibalism in an open boat. New York, Doubleday, Doran, 1930.

784. Thompson, D. W.: *On Growth and Form.* New York, Macmillan, 1943.

785. Tiedemann, F.: *Physiologie des Menschen.* Vol. 3. Darmstadt, C. W. Leske, 1836, pp. 57–73.

786. Tiira, E.: *Raft of Despair.* London, Hutchinson, 1954.

787. Tosteson, D. C., DeFriez, A. I. C., Abrams, M., Gottschalk, C. W., and Landis, E. M.: Effects of adrenalectomy, desoxycorticosterone acetate and increased fluid intake on intake of sodium chloride and bicarbonate by hypertensive and normal rats. *Am. J. Physiol., 164*:369–379, 1951.

788. Towbin, E. J.: Gastric distention as a factor in the satiation of thirst in esophagostomized dogs. *Am. J. Physiol., 159*:533–541, 1949.

789. Towbin, E. J.: Thirst and hunger behavior in normal dogs and the effects of vagotomy and sympathectomy. *Am. J. Physiol., 182*:377–382, 1955.

790. Trousseau, A.: *Lectures on Clinical Medicine.* Vol. 3. Philadelphia, Lindsay & Blakiston, 1870, p. 530.

791. Trumbull, R.: *The Raft.* New York, Holt, 1942.

792. Underhill, F. P., and Roth, S. C.: The influence of water deprivation, pilocarpin, and histamine upon changes in blood concentration in the rabbit. *J. Biol. Chem., 54*:607–616, 1922.

793. Ussing, H. H.: Some aspects of the application of tracers in permeability studies. *Advances Enzymol., 13*:21–65, 1952.

794. Valenti, A.: Sulla genesi delle sensazioni di fame e di sete. *Arch. di farmacol. sper. e Scienze affini, 8*:285–296, 1909.

795. Valenti, A.: Sur la genèse des sensations de faim et de soif. *Arch. ital. de biol., 53*:94–104, 1910.

796. Veil, W. H.: Über die Wirkung gesteigerter Wasserzufuhr auf Blutzusammensetzung und Wasserbilanz. *Deutsches Arch. klin. Med., 119*:376–436, 1916.

797. Veil, W. H.: Physiologie und Pathologie des Wasserhaushaltes. *Ergebn. inn. Med. u. Kinderh.*, *23*:648–784, 1923.

798. Verney, E. B.: The antidiuretic hormone and the factors which determine its release. *Proc. Roy. Soc., London, s. B.*, *135*:25–106, 1947.

799. Vinogradov, A. P.: *The Elementary Chemical Composition of Marine Organisms.* Memoir No. II. New Haven, Sears Foundation for Marine Research, Yale University, 1953.

800. von Voit, C.: Durstgefühl. In *Hermann's Handbuch der Physiologie*, Vol. 6, Leipzig, Vogel, 1881, pp. 566–568.

801. Volhardt, F., and Schütte, E.: Über die Verträglichkeit von Meerwasser. *Deutsche med. Wchnschr.*, *75*:1425–1427, 1950.

802. Wall, C. B.: Torpedoed in the Arctic. *Liberty*, 28–29, 1944 (June 24).

803. Walter, H. E.: *Biology of the Vertebrates.* New York, Macmillan, 1935.

804. War Department (U. S.): *Desert Operations.* Basic field manual, FM 31-25. Washington, U. S. Government Printing Office, 1942, p. 13. See also edition of 1955 (Department of the Army), pp. 50, 54–55.

805. Warbasse, J. P., and Smyth, C. M., Jr.: *Surgical Treatment: A Practical Treatise on the Therapy of Surgical Diseases.* Vol. 3, Philadelphia, Saunders, 1937, p. 33.

806. Warner L. H.: A study of thirst behavior in the white rat by means of the obstruction method. *J. Genet. Psychol.*, *35*:178–192, 1928.

807. Washburn, B.: Mount McKinley conquered by new route. *National Geographic Magazine*, *104*:219–248, 1953.

808. Waterlow, D. J.: Water requirements for men adrift in the tropics. *Gt. Britain Royal Naval Personnel Research Committee*, RNP 47/392, SS 12, 1947.

809. Watson, L. S., Gullixson, K. S., Rennie, D. W., and Youmans, W. B.: Effect of hemorrhage on renal handling of sodium in normal and adrenalectomized dogs. *Am. J. Physiol.*, *181*:140–148, 1955.

810. Watt, B. K., and Merrill, A. L.: *Composition of Foods — Raw, Processed, Prepared.* Agriculture Handbook No. 8, Washington, U. S. Dept. of Agriculture, 1950.

811. Weber, E. H.: Der Tastsinn und das Gemeingefühl. In *Wagner's Handwörterbuch der Physiologie*, Vol. 3. Braunschweig, Vieweg, 1846, p. 586.

812. Weech, A. A.: The significance of the albumin fraction of serum. *Harvey Lect.*, *34*:57–87, 1938–39.

813. Wehmeyer, P.: Variations in the composition of the blood in cows during thirst, after intake of water, and on hungering. *Acta path. et microbiol. Scandinav.*, *34*:518–520, 1954.

814. Weiner, I. H., and Stellar, E.: Salt preference of the rat determined by a single-stimulus method. *J. Comp. & Physiol. Psychol.*, *44*:394–401, 1951.

815. Weir, J. F., Larson, E. E., and Rowntree, L. G.: Studies in diabetes insipidus, water balance, and water intoxication. Study I. *Arch. Int. Med.*, *29*:306–330, 1922.

816. Welt, L. G., and Nelson, W. P., III: Excretion of water by normal subjects. *J. Appl. Physiol.*, *4*:709–714, 1952.

817. Welt, L. G., and Orloff, J.: The effects of an increase in plasma volume on the metabolism and excretion of water and electrolytes by normal subjects. *J. Clin. Investigation*, *30*:751–761, 1951.

818. Welt, L. G., Orloff, J., Kydd, D. M., and Oltman, J. E.: An example of cellular hyperosmolarity. *J. Clin. Investigation, 29*:935–939, 1950.

819. Welt, L. G., Seldin, D. W., Nelson, W. P., III, German, W. J., and Peters, J. P.: Role of the central nervous system in metabolism of electrolytes and water. *Arch. Int. Med., 90*:355–378, 1952.

820. Wesson, L. G., Jr., and Anslow, W. P., Jr.: Effect of osmotic and mercurial diuresis on simultaneous water diuresis. *Am. J. Physiol., 170*:255–269, 1952.

821. Wesson, L. G., Jr., Anslow, W. P., Jr., Raisz, L. G., Bolomey, A. A., and Ladd, M.: Effect of sustained expansion of extracellular fluid volume upon filtration rate, renal plasma flow and electrolyte and water excretion in the dog. *Am. J. Physiol., 162*:677–686, 1950.

822. Weston, R. E., Hanenson, I. B., Grossman, J., Horowitz, H. B., Berdasco, G. A., Wolfman, M., and Leiter, L.: Evidence for an homeostatic mechanism regulating body fluid volume in non-edematous human subjects. *Federation Proc., 13*:163, 1954.

823. Wettendorff, H.: Modifications du sang sous l'influence de la privation d'eau. Contribution a l'étude de la soif. Travaux du laboratoire de physiologie, *Instituts Solvay 4*:353–484, 1901.

824. Wherry, G.: Thirst at sea. *Brit. M. J., 1*:220, 1918.

825. Whillans, M. G., and Smith, G. F. M.: The ingestion of sea water as a means of attenuating fresh water rations. *Canad. J. Research,* (E) *26*:250–264, 1948.

826. White, A. G., Entmacher, P. S., Rubin, G., and Leiter, L.: Physiological and pharmacological regulation of human salivary electrolyte concentrations; with a discussion of electrolyte concentrations of some other exocrine secretions. *J. Clin. Investigation, 34*:246–255, 1955.

827. White House Conference on Child Health and Protection: *Growth and Development of the Child.* Part III. Nutrition, New York, Century, 1932, p. 316.

828. Whitehouse, A. G. R., Hancock, W., and Haldane, J. S.: The osmotic passage of water and gases through the human skin. *Proc. Roy. Soc., London, s. B., 111*:412–429, 1932.

829. Whitman, W. G.: Elimination of salt from sea-water ice. *Am. J. Science, 11* (Ser. 5):126–132, 1926.

830. Whitney, L. F.: *The Complete Book of Home Pet Care.* New York, Doubleday, 1950.

831. Whittaker, J. C.: *We Thought We Heard the Angels Sing.* New York, Dutton, 1943.

832. Whittingham, D. G. V.: Water deprivation during sea survival. *Gt. Britain Flying Personnel Research Committee,* FPRC Memo. 14, January 1951.

833. Widdowson, E. M.: Urea metabolism in protein deficiency. *Lancet, 2*:629, 1956.

834. Wigglesworth, V. B.: *The Principles of Insect Physiology.* New York, Dutton, 1950.

835. Wilkins, R. W., Tinsley, C. M., Culbertson, J. W., Burrows, B. A., Judson, W. E., and Burnett, C. H.: The effects of venous congestion of the limbs upon renal clearances and the excretion of water and salt. I. Studies in normal subjects and in hypertensive patients before and after splanchnicectomy. *J. Clin. Investigation, 32*:1101–1116, 1953.

836. Wilks, S.: Intense thirst a symptom of displacement of the stomach in diaphragmatic hernia. *Lancet, 2*:434–435, 1858.

837. Williams, D. R., and Teitelbaum, P.: Control of drinking behavior by means of an operant-conditioning technique. *Science, 124*:1294–1296, 1956.

838. Williams, T. F., Hollander, W., Jr., Strauss, M. B., Rossmeisl, E. C., and McLean, R.: Mechanism of increased renal sodium excretion following mannitol infusion in man. *J. Clin. Investigation, 34*:595–601, 1955.

839. Willis, W.: Loss of most of water supply fails to daunt raft voyager. *The Evening Star,* Washington, D. C., November 12, 1954, p. A-13. (North American Newspaper Alliance)

840. Willis, W.: *The Gods Were Kind:* an epic 6700 mile voyage alone across the Pacific. New York, Dutton, 1955.

841. Willis, W.: Personal communications, 1955, 1956.

842. Winkler, A. W., Danowski, T. S., Elkinton, J. R., and Peters, J. P.: Electrolyte and fluid studies during water deprivation and starvation in human subjects, and the effects of ingestion of fish, of carbohydrate, and of salt solutions. *J. Clin. Investigation, 23*:807–815, 1944.

843. Winkler, A. W., Elkinton, J. R., Hopper, J., Jr., and Hoff, H. E.: Experimental hypertonicity: alterations in the distribution of body water, and the cause of death. *J. Clin. Investigation, 23*:103–109, 1944.

844. Winsor, A. L.: The effect of dehydration on parotid secretion. *Am. J. Psychol., 42*:602–607, 1930.

845. Winton, F. R., and Bayliss, L. E.: *Human Physiology.* London, Churchill, 1935.

846. Wisotzki, C., and Eymüller, H.: Versuche mit neu-Cesol zur Bekämpfung von postoperativen Durstzuständen. *München. med. Wchnschr., 70*:301–302, 1923.

847. Witt, D. M., Keller, A. D., Batsel, H. L., and Lynch, J. R.: Absence of thirst and resultant syndrome associated with anterior hypothalamectomy in the dog. *Am. J. Physiol., 171*:780, 1952.

848. Wolf, A. V.: Studies on the behavior of *Lumbricus terrestris* L. to dehydration; and evidence for a dehydration tropism. *Ecology, 19*:233–242, 1938.

849. Wolf, A. V.: Weight changes of hydrated, normal, and dehydrated frog muscles in Ringer's solution. *J. Cell. & Comp. Physiol., 15*:355–361, 1940.

850. Wolf, A. V.: Paths of water exchange in the earthworm. *Physiol. Zoöl., 13*:294–308, 1940.

851. Wolf, A. V.: The relative retention of infused chloride, urea and water. *Am. J. Physiol., 138*:191–204, 1943.

852. Wolf, A. V.: The dehydrating effect of continuously administered water. *Am. J. Physiol., 143*:567–571, 1945.

853. Wolf, A. V.: The retention and excretion of continuously administered salt solutions. *Am. J. Physiol., 143*:572–578, 1945.

854. Wolf, A. V.: Renal regulation of water and some electrolytes in man, with special reference to their relative retention and excretion. *Am. J. Physiol., 148*:54–68, 1947.

855. Wolf, A. V.: Estimation of changes in plasma and extracellular fluid volume following changes in body content of water and certain solutes, by means of an osmometric equation. *Am. J. Physiol., 153*:499–502, 1948.

856. Wolf, A. V.: Osmometric analysis of thirst in man and dog. *Am. J. Physiol., 161*:75–86, 1950.

857. Wolf, A. V.: *The Urinary Function of the Kidney*. New York, Grune & Stratton, 1950.
858. Wolf, A. V.: The artificial kidney. *Science, 115*:193–199, 1952.
859. Wolf, A. V.: Demonstration concerning pressure-tension relations in various organs. *Science, 115*:243–244, 1952.
860. Wolf, A. V.: Correlatives of urinary salt excretion. *Federation Proc., 11*: 173–174, 1952.
861. Wolf, A. V.: Relative importance of load and distortion in renal excretion. *Federation Proc., 12*:158, 1953.
862. Wolf, A. V.: Some new perspectives in renal physiology. *J. Urol., 70*:1–8, 1953.
863. Wolf, A. V.: An algebraic inequality relating water and solute metabolism. *Federation Proc., 13*:166, 1954.
864. Wolf, A. V.: Circulation and metabolic exchange. Renal function in electrolyte and water balance. *Symposium on Circulation and Homeostasis*, 5–9 October, 1953. Medical Science Publication No. 3, pp. 79–89. Washington, Army Medical Service Graduate School, Walter Reed Army Medical Center.
865. Wolf, A. V.: Thirst. *Scient. Am., 194*:70–76, 1956.
866. Wolf, A. V.: Relative tonicity of cellular and extracellular fluid, in vivo. *J. Appl. Physiol., 8*:674–676, 1956.
867. Wolf, A. V.: The castaway at sea. *Nutrition Rev., 14*:161–164, 1956.
868. Wolf, A. V.: Body water. *Scient. Am., 199*:000–000, 1958. To be published.
869. Wolf, A. V.: Unpublished or new data.
870. Wolf, A. V., and Ball, S. M.: Effect of intravenous sodium sulfate on renal excretion in the dog. *Am. J. Physiol., 160*:353–360, 1950.
871. Wolf, A. V., and Eddy, H. A.: Effects of hydropenia and the ingestion of tap water and artificial sea waters in the fasting dog. Research Report WRAIR-90-57, June 1957, Walter Reed Army Institute of Research, Walter Reed Army Medical Center, Washington, D. C.
872. Wolf, A. V., and McDowell, M. E.: Sodium concentration deficit: nomogram for replacement. *J. Appl. Physiol., 6*:355–357, 1953.
873. Wolf, A. V., and McDowell, M. E.: Apparent and osmotic volumes of distribution of sodium, chloride, sulfate and urea. *Am. J. Physiol., 176*:207–212, 1954.
874. Wolf, A. V., and Meroney, F. C.: New data.
875. Wolf, A. V., Prentiss, P. G., Douglas, L. G., and Swett, R. J.: Potability of sea water with special reference to the cat. In preparation.
876. Wolf, A. V., Remp, D. G., Kiley, J. E., and Currie, G. D.: Artificial kidney function: kinetics of hemodialysis. *J. Clin. Investigation, 30*:1062–1070, 1951.
877. Wrong, O.: The volume control of body-fluids. *Brit. M. Bull., 13*:10–14, 1957.
878. Wynn, V., and Rob, C. G.: Water intoxication. *Lancet, 1*:587–594, 1954.
879. Wynn, V.: Water intoxication and serum hypotonicity. *Metabolism, 5*:490–499, 1956.
880. Yeates, N. T. M., Lee, D. H. K., and Hines, H. J. G.: Reactions of domestic fowls to hot atmospheres. *Proc. Roy. Soc. Queensland, 53*:105–128, 1941.
881. Yeressko, P., Jr.: Thirty-six days of starvation in the open sea. Abstracted in *J. A. M. A., 131*:549–550, 1946.

882. Young, I. E., Pearce, J. W., and Stevenson, J. A. F.: Renal responses to hypervolemia in the dog. *Canad. J. Biochem. & Physiol.*, 33:800–810, 1955.

883. Young, P. T.: Studies of food preference, appetite and dietary habit. V. Techniques for testing food preference and the significance of results obtained with different methods. *Compar. Psychol. Monographs 19* (No. 1): 1–58, 1945.

884. Young P. T.: Appetite, palatability and feeding habit: a critical review. *Psychol. Bull.*, 45:289–320, 1948.

885. Young, P. T.: Studies of food preference, appetite, and dietary habit. IX. Palatability versus appetite as determinants of the critical concentrations of sucrose and sodium chloride. *Compar. Psychol. Monographs 19* (No. 5): 1–44, 1949.

886. Young, P. T., and Chaplin, J. P.: Studies of food preference, appetite, and dietary habit. X. Preferences of adrenalectomized rats for salt solutions of different concentrations. *Compar. Psychol Monographs 19* (No. 5): 45–74, 1949.

887. Young, P. T., and Richey, H. W.: Diurnal drinking patterns in the rat. *J. Comp. & Physiol. Psychol.*, 45:80–89, 1952.

888. Young, W. F.: Discussion on water metabolism in sick and healthy infants. *Proc. Roy. Soc. Med.*, 36:219–220, 1943.

889. Zabaver, D.: La mort par la soif. Thèse, Univ. de Lyon, 1904.

890. Zak, G. A., Brun, C., and Smith, H. W.: The mechanism of formation of osmotically concentrated urine during the antidiuretic state. *J. Clin. Investigation*, 33:1064–1074, 1954.

891. Zaus, E. A.: Discussion of paper by Austin and Steggerda. *Illinois Med. J.*, 69:127, 1936.

892. Zotterman, Y.: The response of the frog's taste fibres to the application of pure water. *Acta physiol. Scandinav.*, 18:181–189, 1949.

893. Zuidema, G. D., Clarke, N. P., and Minton, M. F.: Osmotic regulation of body fluids. *Am. J. Physiol.*, 187:85–88, 1956.

INDEX

Authors are indexed only where referred to by name

511